Test Bank

Precalculus with Limits

THIRD EDITION

Ron Larson
The Pennsylvania State University,
The Behrend College

BROOKS/COLE
CENGAGE Learning·

Australia • Brazil • Japan • Korea • Mexico • Singapore • Spain • United Kingdom • United States

ISBN-13: 978-1-133-95461-3
ISBN-10: 1-133-95461-8

Brooks/Cole
20 Channel Center Street
Boston, MA 02210
USA

Cengage Learning is a leading provider of customized learning solutions with office locations around the globe, including Singapore, the United Kingdom, Australia, Mexico, Brazil, and Japan. Locate your local office at: **www.cengage.com/global**

Cengage Learning products are represented in Canada by Nelson Education, Ltd.

To learn more about Brooks/Cole, visit **www.cengage.com/brookscole**

Purchase any of our products at your local college store or at our preferred online store **www.cengagebrain.com**

For product information and technology assistance, contact us at **Cengage Learning Customer & Sales Support, 1-800-354-9706**

For permission to use material from this text or product, submit all requests online at **www.cengage.com/permissions** Further permissions questions can be emailed to **permissionrequest@cengage.com**

READ IMPORTANT LICENSE INFORMATION

Printed in the United States of America
1 2 3 4 5 6 7 16 15 14 13

Contents

Ch 1 Form A

_____ 1.   Approximate the coordinates of the points.

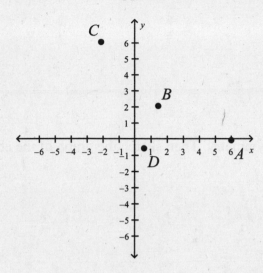

a.
$$A:\left(6,-\frac{1}{6}\right), B:\left(\frac{3}{2},2\right), C:(-2,6), D:\left(\frac{2}{3},-\frac{2}{3}\right)$$

b.
$$A:\left(6,-\frac{1}{6}\right), B:\left(\frac{3}{2},1\right), C:(-2,6), D:\left(\frac{2}{3},-\frac{2}{3}\right)$$

c.
$$A:\left(6,-\frac{1}{6}\right), B:\left(\frac{3}{2},0\right), C:(-2,6), D:\left(\frac{2}{3},-\frac{2}{3}\right)$$

d.
$$A:\left(6,-\frac{1}{6}\right), B:\left(\frac{3}{2},-1\right), C:(-2,6), D:\left(\frac{2}{3},-\frac{2}{3}\right)$$

e.
$$A:\left(6,-\frac{1}{6}\right), B:\left(\frac{3}{2},-2\right), C:(-2,6), D:\left(\frac{2}{3},-\frac{2}{3}\right)$$

_____ 2.   Find the distance between the points.

$(7.5,-3.3),(-5.5,9.5)$

(Round the answer upto two decimal places.)

a.   9.5
b.   7.5
c.   332.84
d.   5.5
e.   18.24

_____ 3.   Determine which of the following point lies on the graph of the equation.

$y = |x - 6| + 4$

a. $(2, 8)$
b. $(2, 10)$
c. $(2, 9)$
d. $(9, 8)$
e. $(3, 8)$

_____ 4.   Identify any intercepts and test for symmetry. Then sketch the graph of the equation.

$y = |x - 1|$

a. x- intercept: $(1, 0)$
       y- intercept: $(0, 1)$
       No symmetry

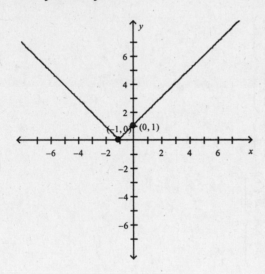

b.　　*x*- intercept: $(-1, 0)$
　　　 y- intercept: $(0, 1)$
　　　 No symmetry

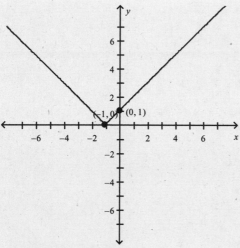

c.　　*x*- intercept: $(1, 0)$
　　　 y- intercept: $(1, 0)$
　　　 No symmetry

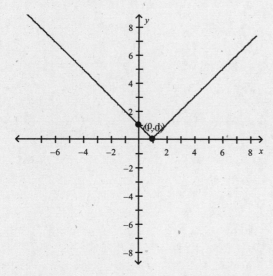

d. x- intercept: $(1,0)$
    y- intercept: $(0,1)$
    No symmetry

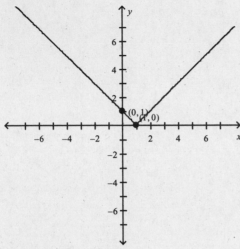

e. x- intercept: $(1,0)$
    y- intercept: $(1,0)$
    No symmetry

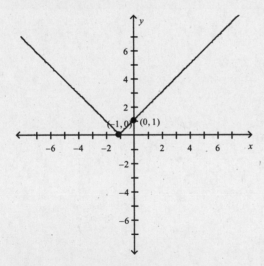

_____ 5.   Determine which point lies on the graph of the equation $y = 7x^2 - 3x + 2$.

a. $(1, 6)$
b. $(2, 6)$
c. $(1, 4)$
d. $(3, 5)$
e. $(2, 4)$

_____   6.   Plot the points and find the slope of the line passing through the pair of points.

(11, 0), (0, –9)

a.

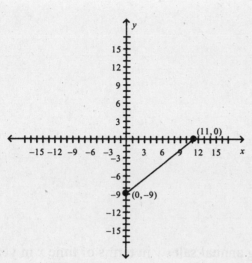

$$m = -\frac{11}{9}$$

d.

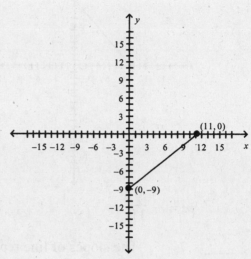

$$m = \frac{11}{9}$$

b.

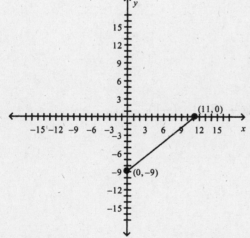

$$m = \frac{9}{11}$$

e.

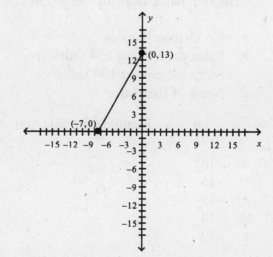

$$m = -\frac{7}{13}$$

5

c.

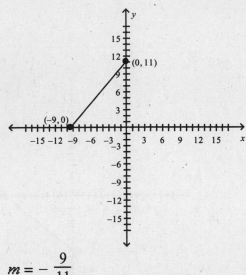

$$m = -\frac{9}{11}$$

_____ 7.   The slopes of line representing annual sales y in terms of time x in years. Use the slopes to interpret any change in annual sales for a one-year increase in time.

The line has a slope of $m = 134$.

a. No change in sales
b. Sales decreasing 134 units/yr
c. Sales increasing 134 units/yr
d. None of the above

_____ 8.   Evaluate the function $f(x) = 3x - 13$ at $f(-1)$.

a. −13
b. −16
c. −15
d. −14
e. −12

_____ 9.   Find all real values of x such that $f(x) = 0$.

$$f(x) = \frac{8x - 7}{7}$$

a. $\dfrac{5}{4}$

b. 1

c. $\dfrac{9}{8}$

d. $\dfrac{7}{8}$

e. $\dfrac{11}{8}$

_____ 10.   Which set of ordered pairs represents a function from P to Q?

$P = \{5, 10, 15, 20\}$ $\qquad\qquad$ $Q = \{-3, -1, 1\}$

a. $\{(5, 1), (15, -1), (5, -3), (15, 1)\}$

b. $\{(15, -3), (15, -1), (15, 1)\}$

c. $\{(5, -3), (10, -1), (10, 1), (15, -1), (20, -3)\}$

d. $\{(15, -1), (10, -3), (5, -1), (10, 1), (15, -3)\}$

e. $\{(10, -1), (15, 1), (20, -1)\}$

_____ 11.   Find the zeros of the function algebraically.

$$f(x) = \sqrt{8x} - 1$$

a. $0, \pm\sqrt{8}$

b. $\dfrac{1}{8}$

c. $0, \pm 8$

d. $0, \sqrt{8}$

e. $0, 8$

_____   12.   Find the coordinates of a second point on the graph of a function f if the given point is on the graph and the function is even and odd.

$\left(-x,y\right)$

a.   Even: $\left(x,y\right)$

    Odd: $\left(x,-y\right)$

b.   Even: $\left(x,-y\right)$

    Odd: $\left(-x,y\right)$

c.   Even: $\left(x,y\right)$

    Odd: $\left(-x,y\right)$

d.   Even: $\left(x,-y\right)$

    Odd: $\left(-x,-y\right)$

e.   Even: $\left(-x,-y\right)$

    Odd: $\left(-x,-y\right)$

_____   13.   Select the correct graph of the given function.

$$f(x) = -\frac{1}{6}x - \frac{5}{2}$$

a.

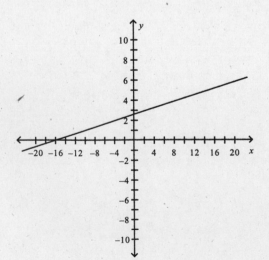

d.

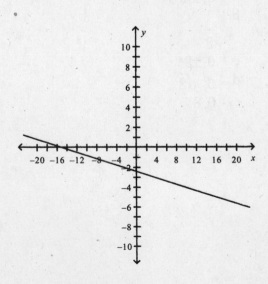

b.

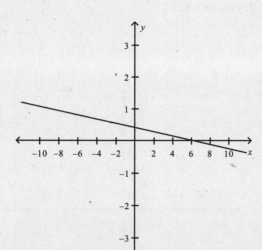

e.

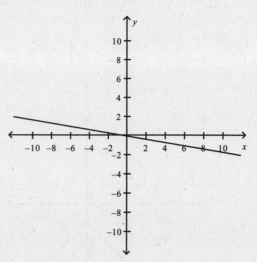

c.

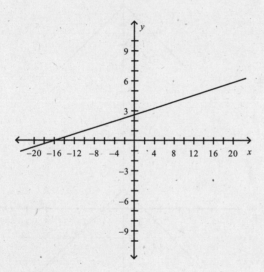

____   14.   Select the correct graph of the given function.

$f(x) = 1 - |x|$

a.

d.

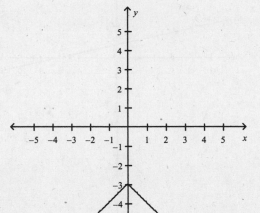

b.

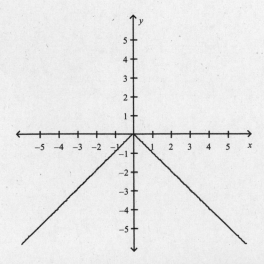

e.

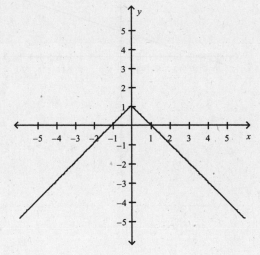

c.

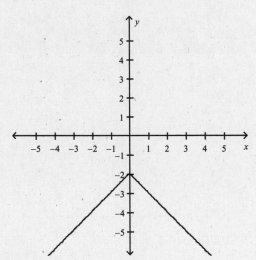

_____ 15.   Select the graph of the function.

$$f(x) = 5 - x^2 \qquad x < -2$$
$$= 3 + x \qquad -2 \leq x < 0$$
$$= x^2 + 2 \qquad x \geq 0$$

a.

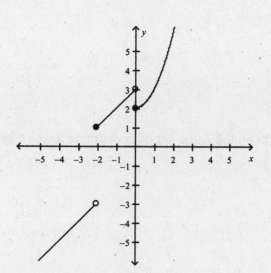

d.

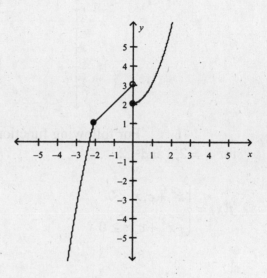

b.

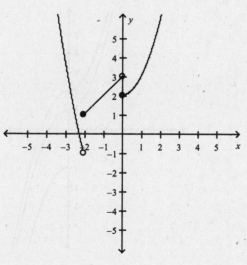

e.

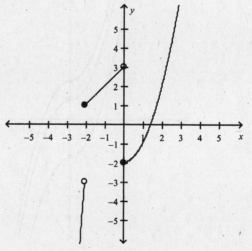

c.

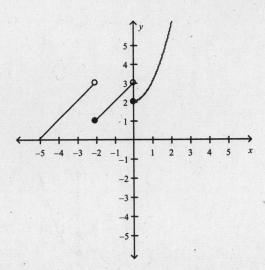

_____ 16.   For following function, select (on the same set of coordinate axes) a graph of function for $c = 2, 1$ and -2.

$$f(x) = \begin{cases} x^2 + c, & x < 0 \\ -x^2 + c, & x \geq 0 \end{cases}$$

a.

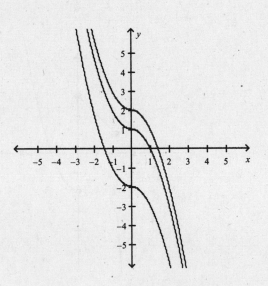

d.

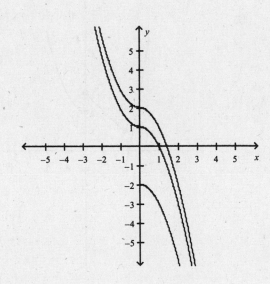

b.

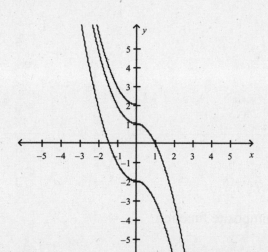

e.

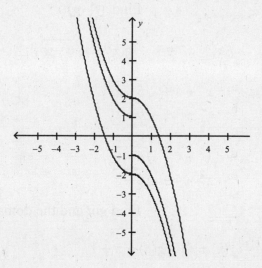

c.

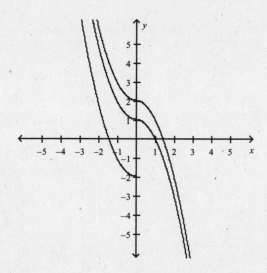

_____ 17. g is related to the parent function. Describe the sequence of transformations from f to g.

$g = -|x| - 6$

a. Vertical shift of the x-axis and vertical shift six units downward.
b. Reflection in the x-axis and vertical shift six units upward.
c. Reflection in the y-axis and vertical shift six units downward.
d. Reflection in the y-axis and vertical shift six units upward.
e. Reflection in the x-axis and vertical shift six units downward.

13

_____ 18. Find $(f-g)(x)$.

$f(x) = x^2 + 4, \quad g(x) = \sqrt{6-x}$

a. $x^2 + 4 + \sqrt{6-x}$

b. $x^2 - 4 + \sqrt{6-x}$

c. $x^2 - 4 + \sqrt{6+x}$

d. $x^2 + 4 - \sqrt{6-x}$

e. $x^2 - 4 - \sqrt{6-x}$

_____ 19. Find $g \circ f$ and the domain of composite function.

$f(x) = |x| , \ g(x) = x + 1$

a. $|x - 1|$

Domain of $g \circ f$: all real numbers x

b. $x - |1|$

Domain of $g \circ f$: all real numbers x

c. $|x| - 1$

Domain of $g \circ f$: all real numbers x

d. $|x| + 1$

Domain of $g \circ f$: all real numbers x

e. $|x + 1|$

Domain of $g \circ f$: all real numbers x

_____ 20. Find $(f+g)(x)$.

$f(x) = 2x^2 - 2x + 7$

$g(x) = 4x^2 - 2x + 9$

a. $(f+g)(x) = -2x^4 - 2$

b. $(f+g)(x) = -6x^2 + 4x - 16$

c. $(f+g)(x) = 6x^4 - 4x^2 + 16$

d. $(f+g)(x) = -2x^2 - 2$

e. $(f+g)(x) = 6x^2 - 4x + 16$

_____ 21.   Select the correct graph, showing f and g are inverse functions.

$$f(x) = 7x + 1, \quad g(x) = \frac{x-1}{7}$$

a.

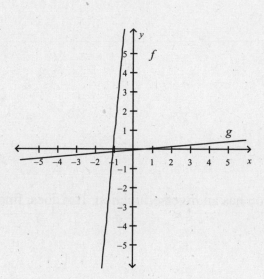

d.

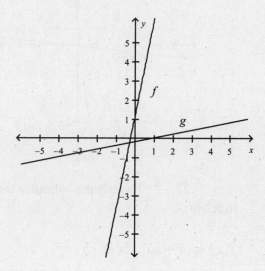

b.

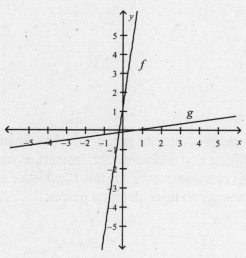

e.

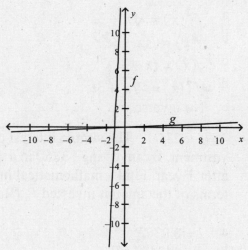

c.

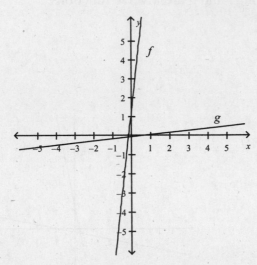

_____ 22.   Determine whether the function has an inverse function. If it does, find the inverse function.

$$f(x) = (x+3)^2, \quad x \geq -3$$

a. $f^{-1}(x) = \sqrt{x} - 3e$
b. $f(x) = -(x+3e)^2$
c. $f(x) = (x+3e)^{-2}$
d. $f^{-1}(x) = \sqrt{x} + 3e$
e. No inverse

_____ 23.   The simple interest on an investment is directly proportional to the amount of the investment. By investing $3850 in a certain bond issue, you obtained an interest payment of $116.75 after 1 year. Find a mathematical model that gives the interest I for this bond issue after 1 year in terms of the amount invested P. (Round your answer to three decimal places.)

a. $I = 0.030P$
b. $I = 449487.5P$
c. $I = 32.976P$
d. $I = 3850P$
e. $I = 116.75P$

_____ 24. Determine whether the variation model is of the form $y = kx$ or $y = \dfrac{k}{x}$ and find k. Then write a model that relates y and x.

x	7	14	21	28	35
y	2	4	6	8	10

a. $y = \dfrac{2}{7}x$

b. $y = \dfrac{7}{x}$

c. $y = \dfrac{2}{7x}$

d. $y = \dfrac{7}{2x}$

e. $y = \dfrac{7}{2}x$

_____ 25. An oceanographer took readings of the water temperatures C (in degrees Celsius) at several depths d (in meters). The data collected are shown in the table.

Depth, d	Temperature, C
1000	3.6°
2000	1.9°
3000	1.6°
4000	1.3°
5000	0.3°

Sketch a scatter plot of the data.

a.

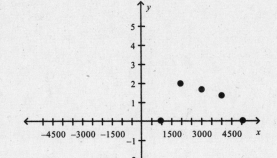

d.

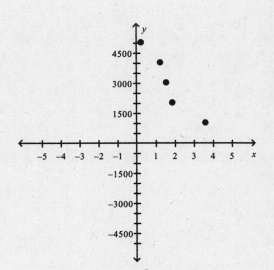

b.

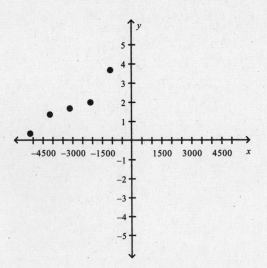

e.

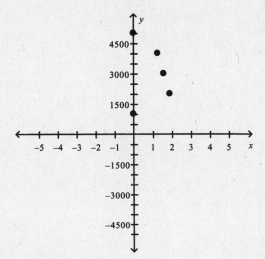

c.

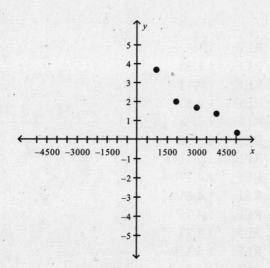

Ch 1 Form A
Answer Section

1.	ANS:	A	PTS:	1	REF:	1.1.6
2.	ANS:	E	PTS:	1	REF:	1.1.38
3.	ANS:	A	PTS:	1	REF:	1.2.11
4.	ANS:	D	PTS:	1	REF:	1.2.53
5.	ANS:	A	PTS:	1	REF:	1.2.9a
6.	ANS:	B	PTS:	1	REF:	1.3.30
7.	ANS:	C	PTS:	1	REF:	1.3.111a
8.	ANS:	B	PTS:	1	REF:	1.4.37b
9.	ANS:	D	PTS:	1	REF:	1.4.61
10.	ANS:	E	PTS:	1	REF:	1.4.15
11.	ANS:	B	PTS:	1	REF:	1.5.31
12.	ANS:	A	PTS:	1	REF:	1.5.129
13.	ANS:	D	PTS:	1	REF:	1.6.21
14.	ANS:	E	PTS:	1	REF:	1.6.40
15.	ANS:	D	PTS:	1	REF:	1.6.63
16.	ANS:	A	PTS:	1	REF:	1.7.10a
17.	ANS:	E	PTS:	1	REF:	1.7.41b
18.	ANS:	D	PTS:	1	REF:	1.8.13b
19.	ANS:	D	PTS:	1	REF:	1.8.45b
20.	ANS:	E	PTS:	1	REF:	1.8.11
21.	ANS:	B	PTS:	1	REF:	1.9.25b
22.	ANS:	A	PTS:	1	REF:	1.9.69
23.	ANS:	A	PTS:	1	REF:	1.10.39
24.	ANS:	A	PTS:	1	REF:	1.10.32
25.	ANS:	C	PTS:	1	REF:	1.10.83a

Ch 1 Form B

_____ 1.   Approximate the coordinates of the points.

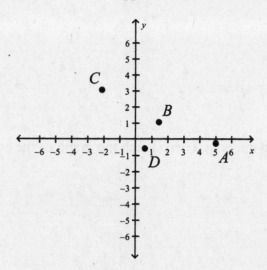

a.
$$A:\left(5,-\frac{1}{3}\right), B:\left(\frac{3}{2},-2\right), C:(-2,3), D:\left(\frac{2}{3},-\frac{2}{3}\right)$$

b.
$$A:\left(5,-\frac{1}{3}\right), B:\left(\frac{3}{2},0\right), C:(-2,3), D:\left(\frac{2}{3},-\frac{2}{3}\right)$$

c.
$$A:\left(5,-\frac{1}{3}\right), B:\left(\frac{3}{2},-1\right), C:(-2,3), D:\left(\frac{2}{3},-\frac{2}{3}\right)$$

d.
$$A:\left(5,-\frac{1}{3}\right), B:\left(\frac{3}{2},-3\right), C:(-2,3), D:\left(\frac{2}{3},-\frac{2}{3}\right)$$

e.
$$A:\left(5,-\frac{1}{3}\right), B:\left(\frac{3}{2},1\right), C:(-2,3), D:\left(\frac{2}{3},-\frac{2}{3}\right)$$

_____ 2.   Find the distance between the points.

$(6.5,-4.5),(-3.3,3.7)$

(Round the answer upto two decimal places.)

a. 3.7
b. 163.28
c. 6.5
d. 12.78
e. 3.3

_____ 3.   Determine which of the following point lies on the graph of the equation.

$y = |x - 1| + 2$

a. $(5,5)$
b. $(4,6)$
c. $(6,5)$
d. $(4,5)$
e. $(4,7)$

_____ 4.   Identify any intercepts and test for symmetry. Then sketch the graph of the equation.

$y = |x - 6|$

a. x- intercept: $(-6,0)$
     y- intercept: $(0,6)$
     No symmetry

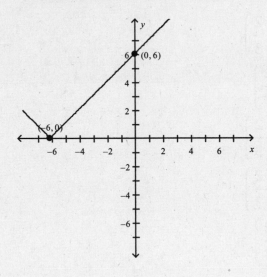

b. *x*- intercept: $(6, 0)$
    y- intercept: $(6, 0)$
    No symmetry

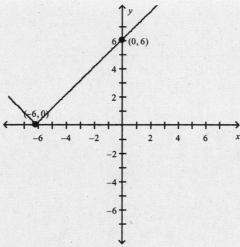

c. *x*- intercept: $(6, 0)$
    y- intercept: $(0, 6)$
    No symmetry

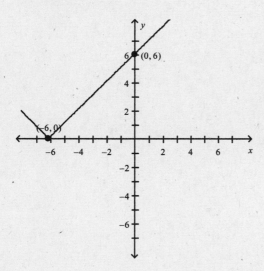

d. x- intercept: $(6,0)$
     y- intercept: $(0,6)$
     No symmetry

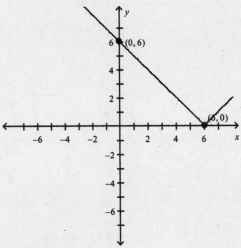

e. x- intercept: $(6,0)$
     y- intercept: $(6,0)$
     No symmetry

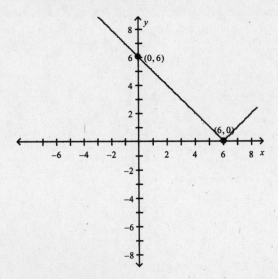

_____ 5.   Determine which point lies on the graph of the equation $y = 7x^2 - 10x - 5$.

a. $(1, -8)$
b. $(2, -10)$
c. $(1, -10)$
d. $(3, -9)$
e. $(2, -8)$

_____ 6.   Plot the points and find the slope of the line passing through the pair of points.

$(13, 0), (0, -3)$

a.

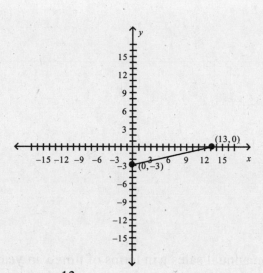

$$m = -\frac{13}{3}$$

d.

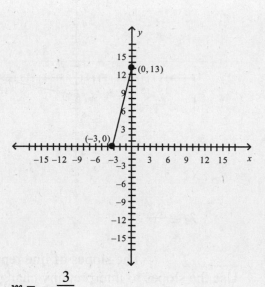

$$m = -\frac{3}{13}$$

b.

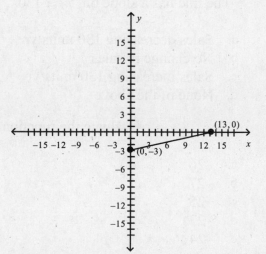

$$m = -\frac{1}{15}$$

e.

$$m = \frac{3}{13}$$

c.

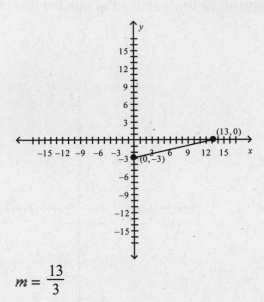

$$m = \frac{13}{3}$$

_____ 7.   The slopes of line representing annual sales y in terms of time x in years. Use the slopes to interpret any change in annual sales for a one-year increase in time.

The line has a slope of $m = 130$.

a. Sales decreasing 130 units/yr
b. No change in sales
c. Sales increasing 130 units/yr
d. None of the above

_____ 8.   Evaluate the function $f(x) = 3x - 12$ at $f(-5)$.

a. –26
b. –27
c. –25
d. –23
e. –24

_____ 9.   Find all real values of x such that $f(x) = 0$.

$$f(x) = \frac{2x - 4}{6}$$

a. $\frac{5}{2}$

b. $\frac{7}{2}$

c. 4

d. 3

e. 2

_____ 10.   Which set of ordered pairs represents a function from P to Q?

$P = \{5, 10, 15, 20\}$ $\qquad$ $Q = \{0, 2, 4\}$

a. $\{(15,0),(15,2),(15,4)\}$

b. $\{(5,4),(15,2),(5,0),(15,4)\}$

c. $\{(5,0),(10,2),(10,4),(15,2),(20,0)\}$

d. $\{(15,2),(10,0),(5,2),(10,4),(15,0)\}$

e. $\{(10,2),(15,4),(20,2)\}$

_____ 11.   Find the zeros of the function algebraically.

$$f(x) = \sqrt{4x} - 1$$

a. $0, \pm\sqrt{4}$

b. $0, \pm 4$

c. $\frac{1}{4}$

d. $0, \sqrt{4}$

e. $0, 4$

_____   12.   Find the coordinates of a second point on the graph of a function f if the given point is on the graph and the function is even and odd.

$(-x, y)$

a.   Even: $(x, -y)$

   Odd: $(-x, y)$

b.   Even: $(-x, -y)$

   Odd: $(-x, -y)$

c.   Even: $(x, -y)$

   Odd: $(-x, -y)$

d.   Even: (x, y)

   Odd: $(x, -y)$

e.   Even: (x, y)

   Odd: $(-x, y)$

_____   13.   Select the correct graph of the given function.

$$f(x) = -\frac{5}{6}x - \frac{9}{2}$$

a.   d.

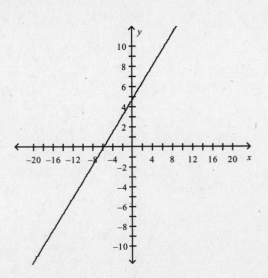   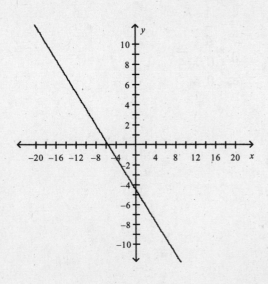

b.

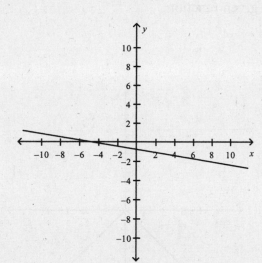

e.

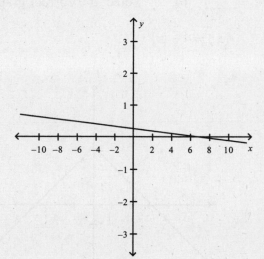

c.

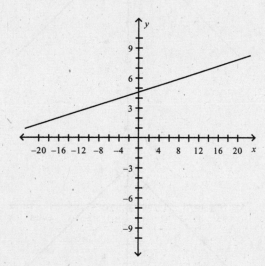

_____ 14.   Select the correct graph of the given function.

$f(x) = 4 - |x|$

a.

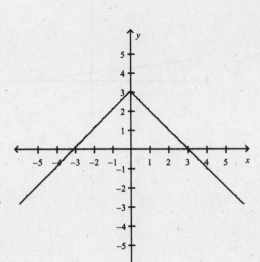

d.

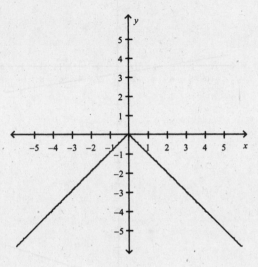

b.

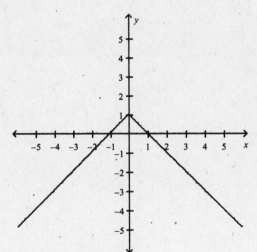

e.

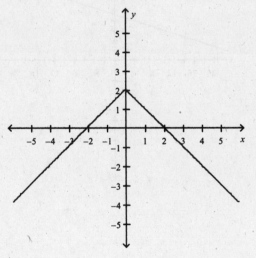

c.

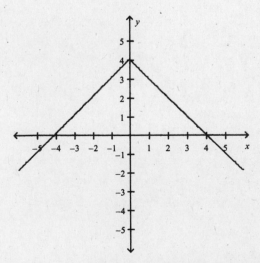

_____ 15.   Select the graph of the function.

$$f(x) = 1 - x^2 \qquad x < -2$$
$$= 3 + x \qquad -2 \leq x < 0$$
$$= x^2 + 3 \qquad x \geq 0$$

a.

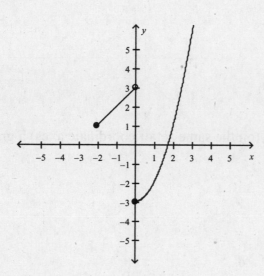

d.

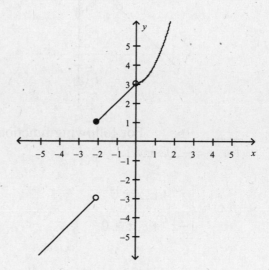

b.

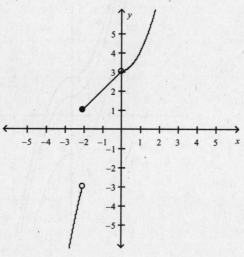

e.

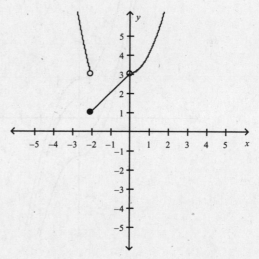

c.

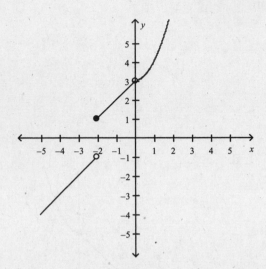

_____ 16.   For following function, select (on the same set of coordinate axes) a graph of function for $c = -2, 2$ and 1.

$$f(x) = \begin{cases} x^2 + c, & x < 0 \\ -x^2 + c, & x \geq 0 \end{cases}$$

a.

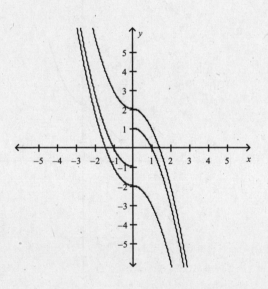

d.

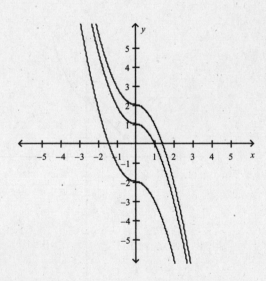

b.

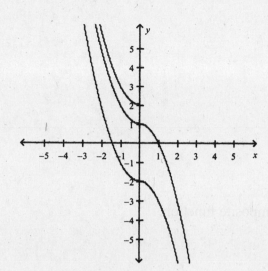

e.

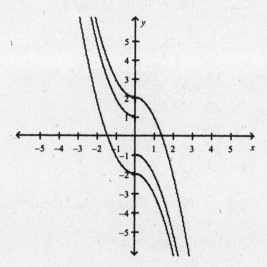

c.

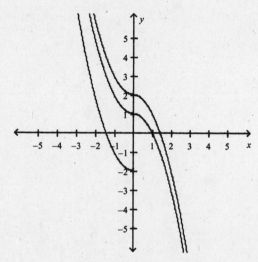

_____ 17. g is related to the parent function. Describe the sequence of transformations from f to g.

$g = -|x| - 4$

a. Reflection in the x-axis and vertical shift four units downward.
b. Vertical shift of the x-axis and vertical shift four units downward.
c. Reflection in the x-axis and vertical shift four units upward.
d. Reflection in the y-axis and vertical shift four units upward.
e. Reflection in the y-axis and vertical shift four units downward.

_____ 18.   Find $(f - g)(x)$.

$f(x) = x^2 + 3, \quad g(x) = \sqrt{5 - x}$

a. $x^2 + 3 - \sqrt{5 - x}$

b. $x^2 - 3 + \sqrt{5 - x}$

c. $x^2 + 3 + \sqrt{5 - x}$

d. $x^2 - 3 - \sqrt{5 - x}$

e. $x^2 - 3 + \sqrt{5 + x}$

_____ 19.   Find $g \circ f$ and the domain of composite function.

$f(x) = |x| \, , \; g(x) = x + 5$

a. $|x + 5|$
   Domain of $g \circ f$: all real numbers x

b. $|x - 5|$
   Domain of $g \circ f$: all real numbers x

c. $x - |5|$
   Domain of $g \circ f$: all real numbers x

d. $|x| + 5$
   Domain of $g \circ f$: all real numbers x

e. $|x| - 5$
   Domain of $g \circ f$: all real numbers x

_____ 20.   Find $(f + g)(x)$.

$f(x) = -3x^2 - 5x$

$g(x) = 7x^2 - 9x - 8$

a. $(f + g)(x) = -4x^2 + 14x + 8$

b. $(f + g)(x) = 4x^2 - 14x - 8$

c. $(f + g)(x) = -10x^2 + 4x + 8$

d. $(f + g)(x) = -10x^4 + 4x^2 + 8$

e. $(f + g)(x) = 4x^4 - 14x^2 - 8$

_____ 21.   Select the correct graph, showing *f* and *g* are inverse functions.

$$f(x) = 9x + 1, \ g(x) = \frac{x-1}{9}$$

a.

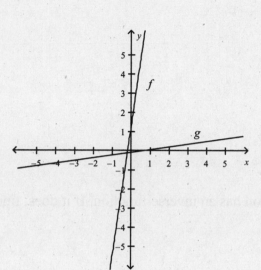

d.

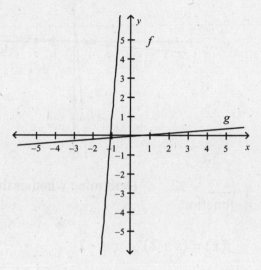

b.

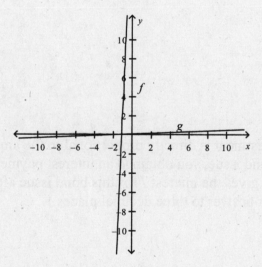

e.

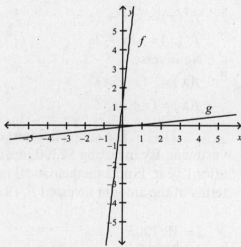

c.

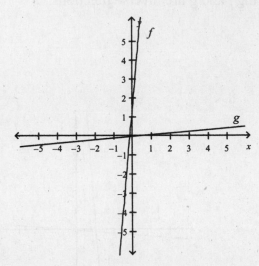

_____ 22. Determine whether the function has an inverse function. If it does, find the inverse function.

$$f(x) = (x+2)^2, \quad x \geq -2$$

a. $f^{-1}(x) = \sqrt{x} + 2e$

b. $f^{-1}(x) = \sqrt{x} - 2e$

c. No inverse

d. $f(x) = -(x+2e)^2$

e. $f(x) = (x+2e)^{-2}$

_____ 23. The simple interest on an investment is directly proportional to the amount of the investment. By investing $2300 in a certain bond issue, you obtained an interest payment of $116.75 after 1 year. Find a mathematical model that gives the interest I for this bond issue after 1 year in terms of the amount invested P. (Round your answer to three decimal places.)

a. $I = 19.700P$

b. $I = 2300P$

c. $I = 0.051P$

d. $I = 116.75P$

e. $I = 268525P$

_____ 24.   Determine whether the variation model is of the form $y = kx$ or $y = \dfrac{k}{x}$ and find k.

Then write a model that relates y and x.

x	7	14	21	28	35
y	2	4	6	8	10

a.
$$y = \frac{7}{2x}$$
b.
$$y = \frac{7}{2}x$$
c.
$$y = \frac{7}{x}$$
d.
$$y = \frac{2}{7x}$$
e.
$$y = \frac{2}{7}x$$

_____ 25.   An oceanographer took readings of the water temperatures C (in degrees Celsius) at several depths d (in meters). The data collected are shown in the table.

Depth, d	Temperature, C
1000	3.5°
2000	1.8°
3000	1.5°
4000	1.2°
5000	0.2°

Sketch a scatter plot of the data.

a.

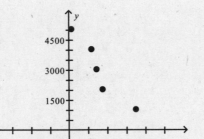

d.

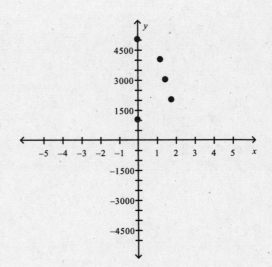

b.

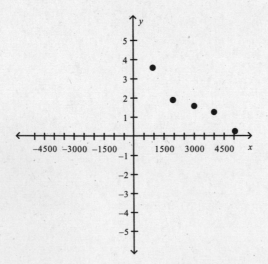

e.

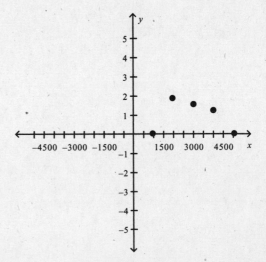

c.

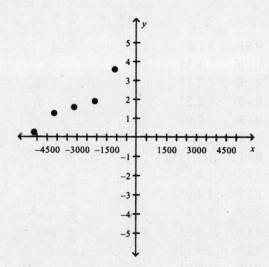

Ch 1 Form B
Answer Section

1.	ANS:	E	PTS:	1	REF:	1.1.6
2.	ANS:	D	PTS:	1	REF:	1.1.38
3.	ANS:	D	PTS:	1	REF:	1.2.11
4.	ANS:	D	PTS:	1	REF:	1.2.53
5.	ANS:	A	PTS:	1	REF:	1.2.9a
6.	ANS:	E	PTS:	1	REF:	1.3.30
7.	ANS:	C	PTS:	1	REF:	1.3.111a
8.	ANS:	B	PTS:	1	REF:	1.4.37b
9.	ANS:	E	PTS:	1	REF:	1.4.61
10.	ANS:	E	PTS:	1	REF:	1.4.15
11.	ANS:	C	PTS:	1	REF:	1.5.31
12.	ANS:	D	PTS:	1	REF:	1.5.129
13.	ANS:	D	PTS:	1	REF:	1.6.21
14.	ANS:	C	PTS:	1	REF:	1.6.40
15.	ANS:	B	PTS:	1	REF:	1.6.63
16.	ANS:	D	PTS:	1	REF:	1.7.10a
17.	ANS:	A	PTS:	1	REF:	1.7.41b
18.	ANS:	A	PTS:	1	REF:	1.8.13b
19.	ANS:	D	PTS:	1	REF:	1.8.45b
20.	ANS:	B	PTS:	1	REF:	1.8.11
21.	ANS:	E	PTS:	1	REF:	1.9.25b
22.	ANS:	B	PTS:	1	REF:	1.9.69
23.	ANS:	C	PTS:	1	REF:	1.10.39
24.	ANS:	E	PTS:	1	REF:	1.10.32
25.	ANS:	B	PTS:	1	REF:	1.10.83a

Ch 1 Form C

_____ 1.   Plot the points in the Cartesian plane.

$$\left(3, -\frac{1}{3}\right), \left(\frac{3}{4}, 1\right), (-2, 5), \left(\frac{4}{3}, -\frac{4}{3}\right)$$

a.

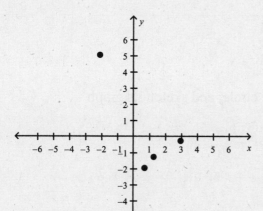

d.

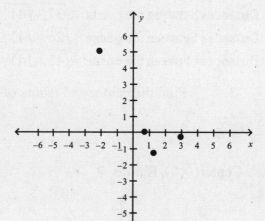

b.

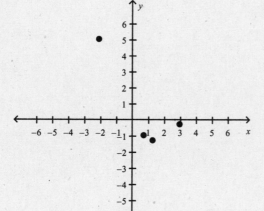

e.

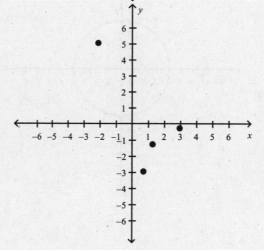

c.

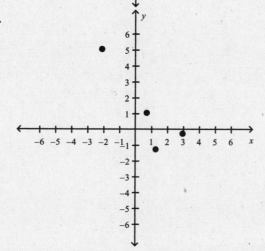

_____   2.   Show that the points form the vertices of the indicated polygon.

Isosceles triangle: $(5,9),(1,4),(6,8)$

a. Distances between the points: $\sqrt{19}, \sqrt{41}, \sqrt{2}$
b. Distances between the points: $\sqrt{41}, \sqrt{41}, \sqrt{2}$
c. Distances between the points: $\sqrt{37}, \sqrt{41}, \sqrt{2}$
d. Distances between the points: $\sqrt{26}, \sqrt{41}, \sqrt{2}$
e. Distances between the points: $\sqrt{43}, \sqrt{41}, \sqrt{2}$

_____   3.   Find the center and radius of the circle, and sketch its graph.

$x^2 + y^2 = 9$

a.   Center$(0,0)$, Radius 9

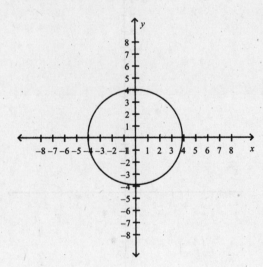

b.   Centre$(0, 0)$, Radius 3

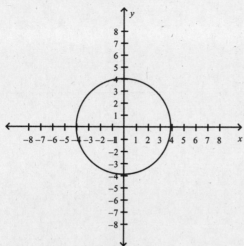

c.   Centre$(0, 0)$, Radius 3

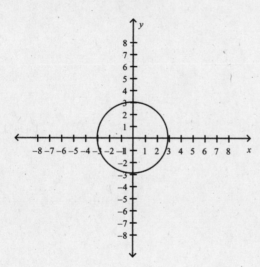

d.   Centre$(0, 0)$, Radius 9

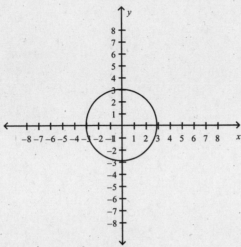

e.   Centre$(0, 0)$, Radius 3

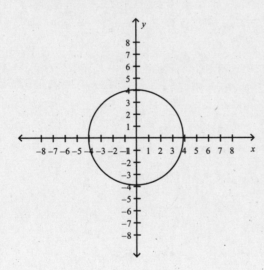

_____ 4.   Use a graphing utility to graph the equation. Use a standard setting. Approximate any intercepts.

$$y = 2 - \frac{1}{2}x$$

a.

Intercepts: $(4, 0), (0, 2)$

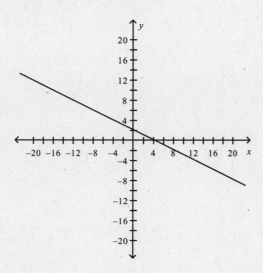

b.

Intercepts: $(0, 2), (4, 0)$

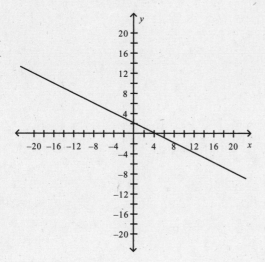

c.

Intercepts: $(4,0),(0,2)$

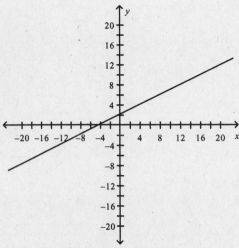

d.   Intercepts: $(-4,0),(0,-2)$

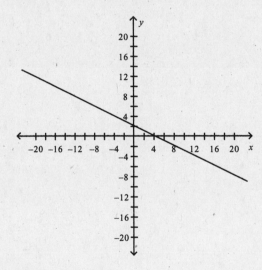

e.

Intercepts: $(0,2),(4,0)$

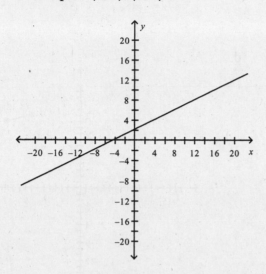

_____ 5.   Find the x- and y-intercepts of the graph of the equation $y = |-5x-4|$.

a.
x-intercept: $\left(-\dfrac{5}{4},\ 0\right)$

y-intercept: $(0,\ 4)$

b.
x-intercept: $\left(-\dfrac{4}{5},\ 0\right)$

y-intercept: $(0,\ -5)$

c.
x-intercept: $\left(-\dfrac{4}{5},\ 0\right)$

y-intercept: $(0,\ 4)$

d. x-intercept: $(4,\ 0)$
y-intercept: $(0,\ -5)$

e.
x-intercept: $\left(-\dfrac{5}{4},\ 0\right)$

y-intercept: none

_____ 6.   Plot the points and find the slope of the line passing through the pair of points.

(4, 8), (8,–8)

a.

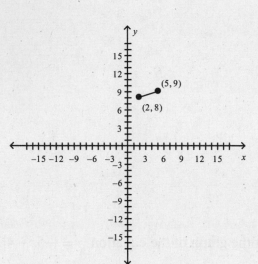

$m = -4$

b.

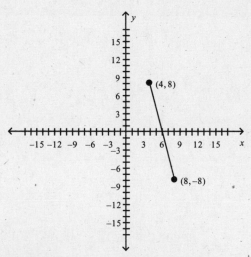

$m = -4$

d.

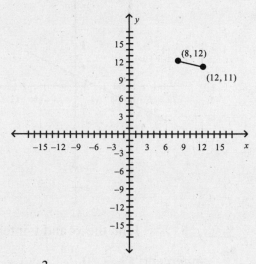

$m = 3$

e.

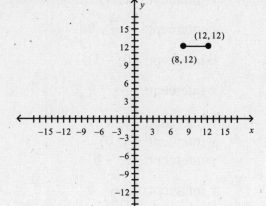

$m = 3$

c.

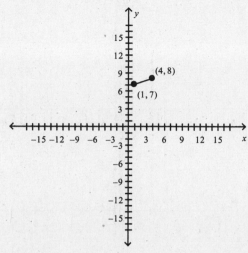

$m = 3$

_____   7.   The graph shows the average salaries for senior high school principals from 1996 through 2008.

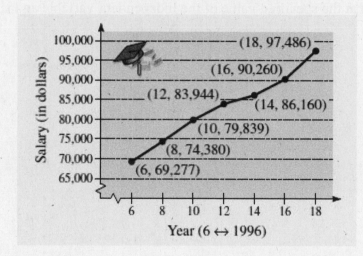

Find the slope of the line segment connecting the points for the years 1998 and 2002.

a.   2734.5
b.   −2732.5
c.   2729.5
d.   −2729.5
e.   2730.5

____ 8.   Evaluate the function $g(t) = 13t^2 - 10t + 11$ at $g(t) - g(8)$.

a. $13t^2 - 752 + 10t$
b. $10t^2 - 752t + 13$
c. $13t^2 - 752t - 10$
d. $10t^2 + 13t - 752$
e. $13t^2 - 10t - 752$

____ 9.   Find the domain of the function.

$f(x) = 4x^2 + 3x - 5$

a. All real numbers x such that $x > 0$
b. All real numbers x
c. All real numbers x such that $x < 0$
d. Non-negative real numbers x
e. Non-negative real numbers x such that $x \neq 0$

____ 10.   Evaluate the function at the specified value of the independent variable and simplify.
$q(y) = -6y - 5$
$q(0.2)$
a. 3.8
b. $-1.2y + 30$
c. $0.2y + 5$
d. $0.2y - 5$
e. –6.2

_____   11.   Select the graph of the function and find the zeros of the function and verify your result algebraically.

$$f(x) = \sqrt{2x + 9}$$

a.

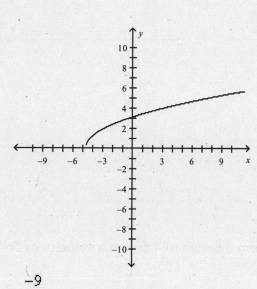

-9

d.

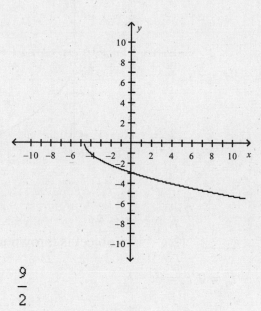

$\dfrac{9}{2}$

b.

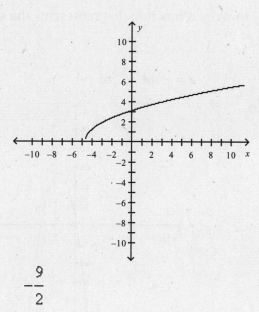

$-\dfrac{9}{2}$

e.

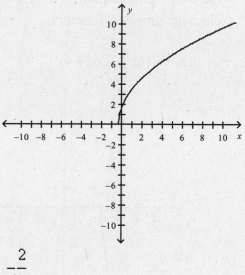

$-\dfrac{2}{9}$

c.

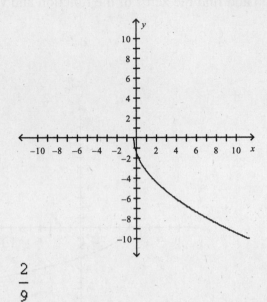

$$\frac{2}{9}$$

_____ 12.   An object is thrown upward from a height of 4 feet at a velocity of 56 feet per second.

$$t_1 = 0, t_2 = 3$$

Use the position equation $s = -16t^2 + v_0 t + s_0$ to write a function that represents the situation and select the graph of function.

a. $s = -16t^2 - 56t + 4$

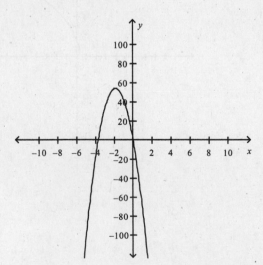

d. $s = -16t^2 + 56t + 4$

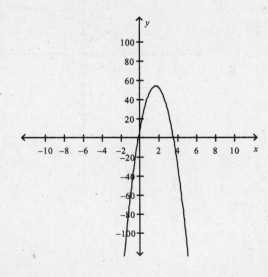

b. $s = -16t^2 + 56t - 4$

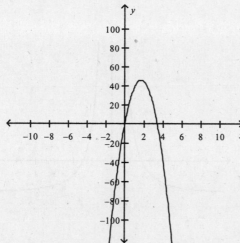

e. $s = -16t^2 + 56t$

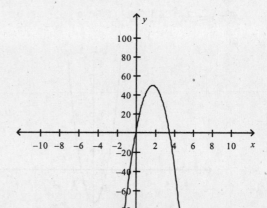

c. $s = -16t^2 - 56t - 4$

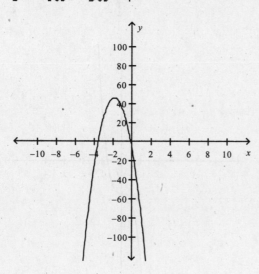

_____ 13. Select the correct graph of the given function.

$f(x) = 3x^2 - 1.75$

a.

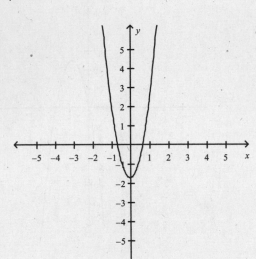

d.

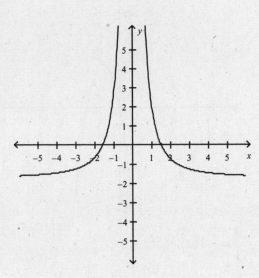

b.

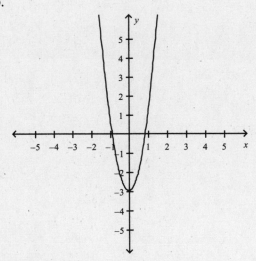

e.

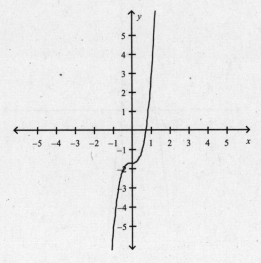

c.

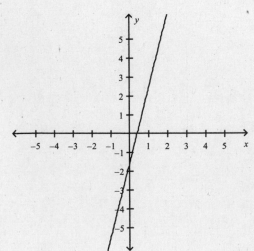

_____   14.   Evaluate the function $f(x) = \|x\|$ for $x = 1.4$.

a. 2
b. 5
c. 4
d. -1
e. 1

_____   15.   The cost of sending an overnight package from Los Angeles to Miami is $23.8 for a package weighing up to but not including 1 pound and $3 for each additional pound or portion of a pound. A model for the total cost C (in dollars) of sending the package is

$C = 23.8 + 3\|x\|, x > 0$ where, x is the weight in pounds.

Determine the cost of sending a package that weighs 5.25 pounds.

a. 39.8
b. 40.8
c. 42.8
d. 41.8
e. 38.8

____ 16.   Use the given graph of *f* to select the graph for following function. To print an enlarged copy of the graph, go to the website *www.mathgraphs.com*.

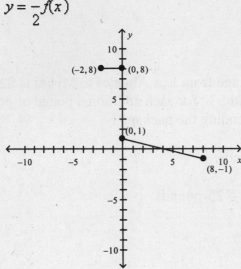

a.

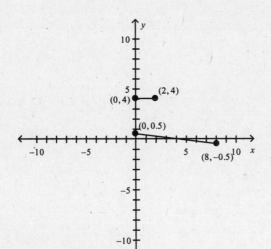

d.

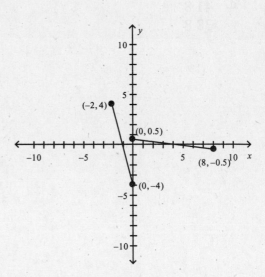

b.

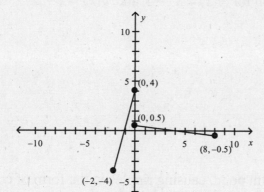

e.

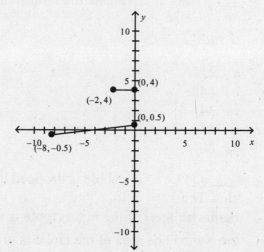

c.

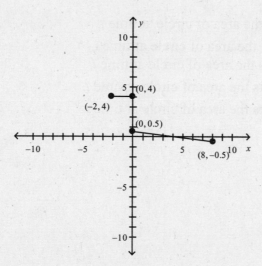

_____ 17.   *g* is related to the parent function. Identify the parent function *f*.

$$g(x) = 5 - \|x\|$$

a. $f(x) = -5 - \|x\|$
b. $f(x) = 5 + \|x\|$
c. $f(x) = |x|$
d. $f(x) = \|x\|$
e. $f(x) = 5 - \|x\|$

_____ 18.   Evaluate the indicated function for $f(x) = x^2 + 3$ and $g(x) = x - 5$.

$(f+g)(6)$

a. 42
b. −40
c. 34
d. 44
e. 40

_____ 19.   A pebble is dropped into a calm pond, causing ripples in the form of concentric circles. The
radius (in feet) of the outer ripple is $r(t) = 0.3t$, where t is the time in seconds after the pebble strikes
the water. The area of the circle is given by the function $A(r) = \pi r^2$. Find and interpret $(A \circ r)(t)$.

a. $(A \circ r)(t) = 0.3\pi t$; $(A \circ r)(t)$ represents the area of circle at time t.
b. $(A \circ r)(t) = 0.3\pi t^2$; $(A \circ r)(t)$ represents the area of circle at time t.
c. $(A \circ r)(t) = 0.09\pi t$; $(A \circ r)(t)$ represents the area of circle at time t.
d. $(A \circ r)(t) = 0.09\pi t^2$; $(A \circ r)(t)$ represents the area of circle at time t.
e. $(A \circ r)(t) = 0.09\pi t^3$; $(A \circ r)(t)$ represents the area of circle at time t.

_____ 20.   Find $(f - g)(x)$.

$$f(x) = -\frac{9x}{7x-2} \qquad g(x) = -\frac{4}{x}$$

a. $(f - g)(x) = \dfrac{-9x + 30}{7x - 2}$

b. $(f - g)(x) = \dfrac{-9x^2 + 28x + 8}{7x^2 - 2x}$

c. $(f - g)(x) = \dfrac{-9x + 4}{6x - 2}$

d. $(f - g)(x) = \dfrac{-9x^2 + 28x - 8}{7x^2 - 2x}$

e. $(f - g)(x) = \dfrac{-9x + 26}{7x - 2}$

_____ 21. Select the correct graph, showing f and g are inverse functions.

$f(x) = 6 - x^2$, $g(x) = \sqrt{6-x}$, $x \le 6$

a.

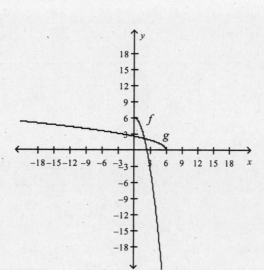

d.

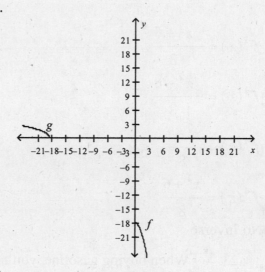

b.

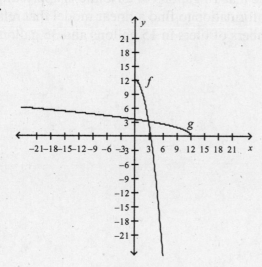

e.

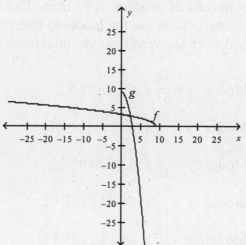

c.

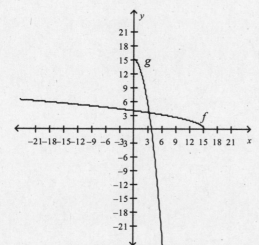

_____ 22.   Determine whether the function has an inverse function. If it does, find the inverse function.

$$f(x) = \sqrt{8x+6}$$

a.
$$f^{-1}(x) = -\frac{x^2+6}{8}$$

b.
$$f^{-1}(x) = -\frac{x^2-6}{8}$$

c.
$$f^{-1}(x) = \frac{x^2-6}{8}$$

d.
$$f^{-1}(x) = \frac{x^2+6}{8}$$

e.   No Inverse

_____ 23.   When buying gasoline, you notice that 18 gallons of gasoline is approximately the same amount of gasoline as 53 liters. Use this information to find a linear model that relates liters y to gallons x. Then use the model to find the numbers of liters in 15 gallons and 35 gallons. (Round your answer to one decimal place.)

a.
Model: $y = \frac{18}{53}x$; 5.1 L, 11.9 L

b.
Model: $y = \frac{53}{18}x$; 44.2 L, 11.9 L

c.
Model: $y = \frac{53}{18}x$; 5.1 L, 103.1 L

d.
Model: $y = \frac{53}{18}x$; 44.2 L, 103.1 L

e.
Model: $y = \frac{18}{53}x$; 44.2 L, 103.1 L

_____   24.   Use the given value of k to complete the table for the direct variation model

$y = kx^2$.

Plot the points on a rectangular coordinate system.

x	6	8	10	12	14
$y = kx^2$					

$k = 1$

a.

x	6	8	10	12	14
$y = kx^2$	6	61	10	12	14

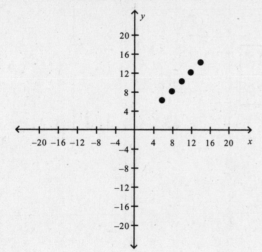

d.

x	6	8	10	12	14
$y = kx^2$	36	64	100	144	196

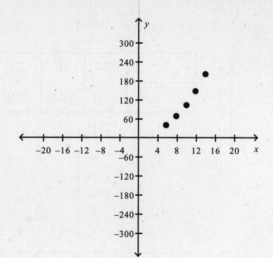

b.

x	6	8	10	12	14
$y = kx^2$	36	36	36	36	36

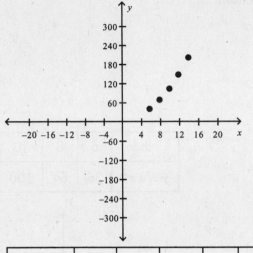

e.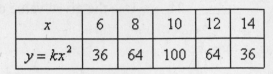

x	6	8	10	12	14
$y = kx^2$	36	64	100	64	36

c.

x	6	8	10	12	14
$y = kx^2$	196	144	100	64	36

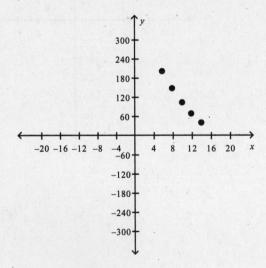

_____ 25. After determining whether the variation model below is of the form $y = kx$ or $y = \dfrac{k}{x}$, find the value of k.

x	4	8	12	16	20
y	$\dfrac{1}{6}$	$\dfrac{1}{12}$	$\dfrac{1}{18}$	$\dfrac{1}{24}$	$\dfrac{1}{30}$

a. $k = \dfrac{1}{4}$

b. $k = \dfrac{3}{2}$

c. $k = \dfrac{5}{4}$

d. $k = \dfrac{1}{2}$

e. $k = \dfrac{2}{3}$

Ch 1 Form C
Answer Section

1.	ANS:	C	PTS: 1	REF:	1.1.10
2.	ANS:	B	PTS: 1	REF:	1.1.46
3.	ANS:	C	PTS: 1	REF:	1.2.77
4.	ANS:	A	PTS: 1	REF:	1.2.57
5.	ANS:	C	PTS: 1	REF:	1.2.27
6.	ANS:	B	PTS: 1	REF:	1.3.32
7.	ANS:	C	PTS: 1	REF:	1.3.113b
8.	ANS:	E	PTS: 1	REF:	1.4.41c
9.	ANS:	B	PTS: 1	REF:	1.4.71
10.	ANS:	E	PTS: 1	REF:	1.4.38
11.	ANS:	B	PTS: 1	REF:	1.5.35
12.	ANS:	D	PTS: 1	REF:	1.5.115
13.	ANS:	A	PTS: 1	REF:	1.6.25
14.	ANS:	E	PTS: 1	REF:	1.6.43a
15.	ANS:	E	PTS: 1	REF:	1.6.69b
16.	ANS:	C	PTS: 1	REF:	1.7.14c
17.	ANS:	D	PTS: 1	REF:	1.7.47a
18.	ANS:	E	PTS: 1	REF:	1.8.17
19.	ANS:	D	PTS: 1	REF:	1.8.71
20.	ANS:	D	PTS: 1	REF:	1.8.16
21.	ANS:	A	PTS: 1	REF:	1.9.31b
22.	ANS:	C	PTS: 1	REF:	1.9.75
23.	ANS:	D	PTS: 1	REF:	1.10.42
24.	ANS:	D	PTS: 1	REF:	1.10.23
25.	ANS:	E	PTS: 1	REF:	1.10.33

Ch 1 Form D

_____   1.   Plot the points in the Cartesian plane.

$$\left(4, -\frac{1}{5}\right), \left(\frac{3}{2}, 5\right), (-2, 2), \left(\frac{2}{3}, -\frac{2}{3}\right)$$

a.
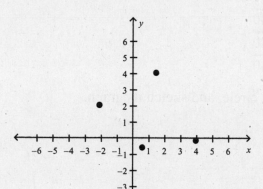

d.
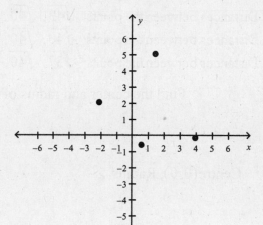

b.
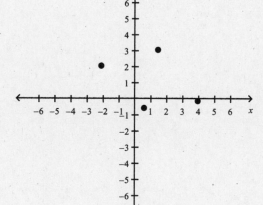

e.
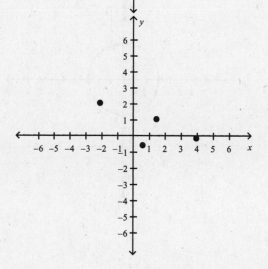

c.
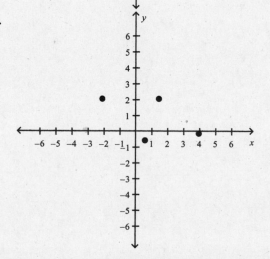

65

____ 2. Show that the points form the vertices of the indicated polygon.

Isosceles triangle: $(9,5),(3,3),(1,9)$

a. Distances between the points: $\sqrt{26}, \sqrt{40}, \sqrt{80}$
b. Distances between the points: $\sqrt{19}, \sqrt{40}, \sqrt{80}$
c. Distances between the points: $\sqrt{43}, \sqrt{40}, \sqrt{80}$
d. Distances between the points: $\sqrt{40}, \sqrt{40}, \sqrt{80}$
e. Distances between the points: $\sqrt{37}, \sqrt{40}, \sqrt{80}$

____ 3. Find the center and radius of the circle, and sketch its graph.

$x^2 + y^2 = 4$

a. Centre$(0,0)$, Radius 2

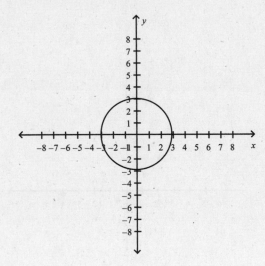

b.   Center$(0,0)$, Radius 4

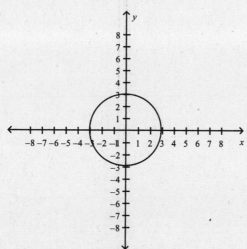

c.   Centre$(0,0)$, Radius 2

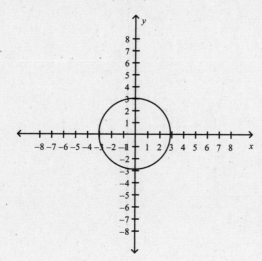

d.   Centre$(0,0)$, Radius 2

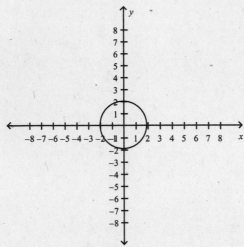

e.   Centre$(0,0)$, Radius 4

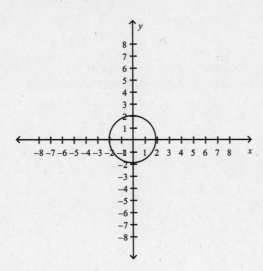

_____   4.   Use a graphing utility to graph the equation. Use a standard setting. Approximate any intercepts.

$$y = 6 - \frac{1}{2}x$$

a.

Intercepts: $(0,6), (12,0)$

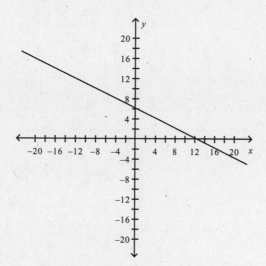

b.

Intercepts: $(0,6), (12,0)$

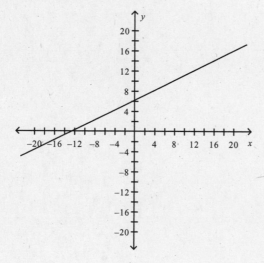

c.

Intercepts: $(12,0),(0,6)$

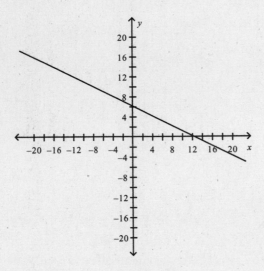

d.

Intercepts: $(12,0),(0,6)$

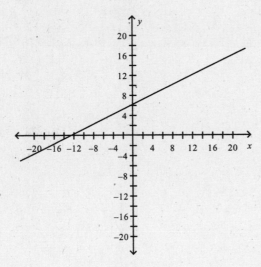

e.   Intercepts: $(-12, 0), (0, -6)$

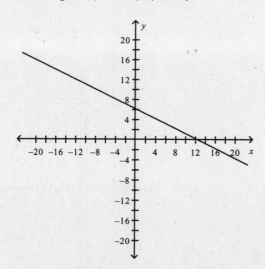

_____   5.   Find the x- and y-intercepts of the graph of the equation $y = |-3x - 4|$.

a. x-intercept: $\left(-\dfrac{3}{4}, 0\right)$

y-intercept: none

b. x-intercept: $\left(-\dfrac{3}{4}, 0\right)$

y-intercept: $(0, 4)$

c. x-intercept: $\left(-\dfrac{4}{3}, 0\right)$

y-intercept: $(0, -3)$

d. x-intercept: $\left(-\dfrac{4}{3}, 0\right)$

y-intercept: $(0, 4)$

e. x-intercept: $(4, 0)$

y-intercept: $(0, -3)$

_____ 6.   Plot the points and find the slope of the line passing through the pair of points.

(4, 8), (8,–8)

a.

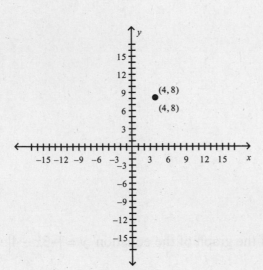

$m = 2$

d.

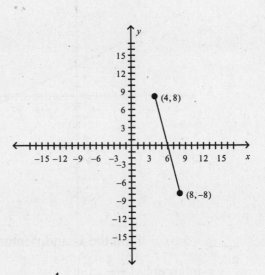

$m = -4$

b.

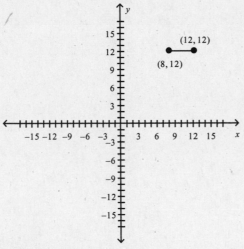

$m = 0$

e.

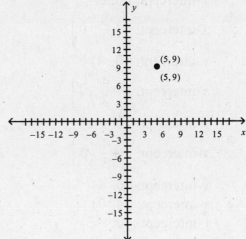

$m = -4$

c.

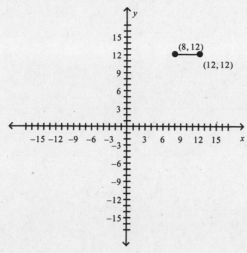

$m = 2$

_____ 7. The graph shows the average salaries for senior high school principals from 1996 through 2008.

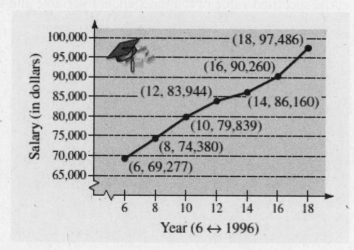

Find the slope of the line segment connecting the points for the years 1998 and 2002.

a. 2730.5
b. 2729.5
c. −2729.5
d. 2734.5
e. −2732.5

_____ 8. Evaluate the function $g(t) = 12t^2 - 3t + 9$ at $g(t) - g(2)$.

a. $12t^2 - 42 + 3t$
b. $12t^2 - 3t - 42$
c. $12t^2 - 42t - 3$
d. $3t^2 + 12t - 42$
e. $3t^2 - 42t + 12$

_____ 9. Find the domain of the function.

$f(x) = 2x^2 + 3x - 4$

a. Non-negative real numbers x such that $x \neq 0$
b. All real numbers x such that $x < 0$
c. Non-negative real numbers x
d. All real numbers x such that $x > 0$
e. All real numbers x

_____ 10. Evaluate the function at the specified value of the independent variable and simplify.
$g(y) = 2y - 6$
$g(-1.9)$
a. -9.8
b. $-1.9y + 6$
c. $-3.8y - 12$
d. 2.2
e. $-1.9y - 6$

_____   11.   Select the graph of the function and find the zeros of the function and verify your result algebraically.

$$f(x) = \sqrt{2x + 7}$$

a.

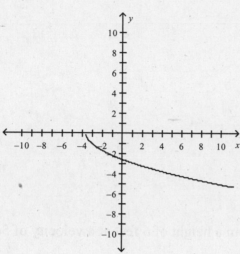

$$\frac{7}{2}$$

d.

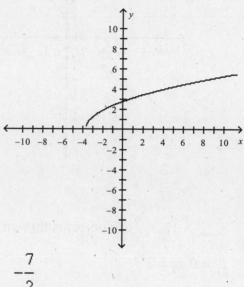

$$-\frac{7}{2}$$

b.

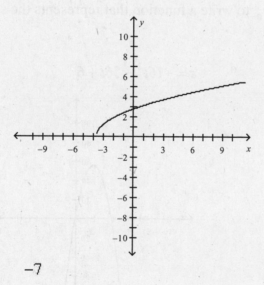

$$-7$$

e.

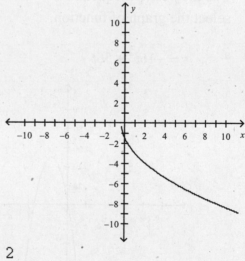

$$\frac{2}{7}$$

c.

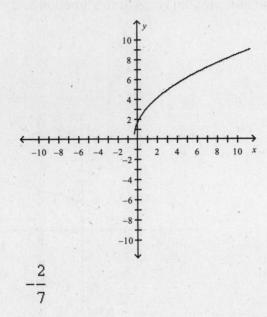

$$-\frac{2}{7}$$

_____ 12.   An object is thrown upward from a height of 6 feet at a velocity of 56 feet per second.

$$t_1 = 0, t_2 = 3$$

Use the position equation $s = -16t^2 + v_0 t + s_0$ to write a function that represents the situation and select the graph of function.

a. $s = -16t^2 + 56t$

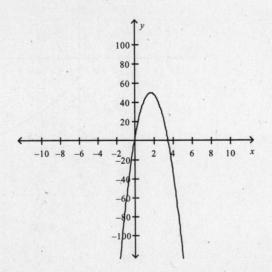

d. $s = -16t^2 - 56t + 6$

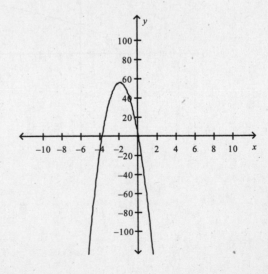

b. $s = -16t^2 + 56t + 6$

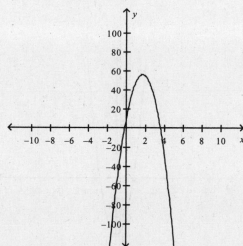

e. $s = -16t^2 - 56t - 6$

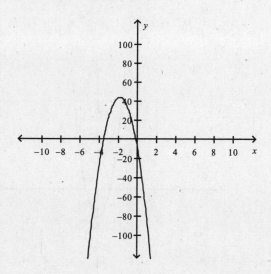

c. $s = -16t^2 + 56t - 6$

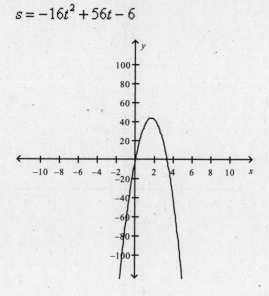

_____ 13.   Select the correct graph of the given function.

$f(x) = 3x^2 - 1.75$

a.

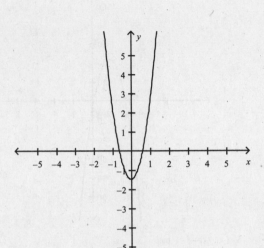

d.

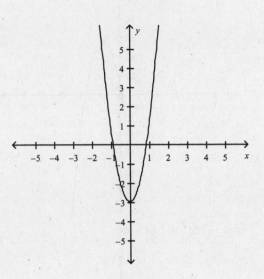

b.

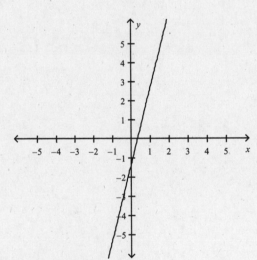

e.

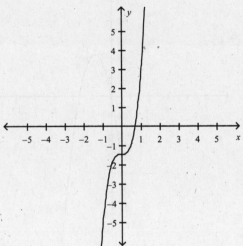

c.

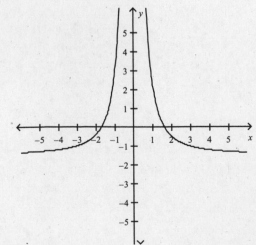

_____   14.   Evaluate the function $f(x) = \|x\|$ for $x = 1.4$.

a. 4
b. 2
c. 1
d. −1
e. 5

_____   15.   The cost of sending an overnight package from Los Angeles to Miami is \$27.5 for a package weighing up to but not including 1 pound and \$3.75 for each additional pound or portion of a pound. A model for the total cost C (in dollars) of sending the package is

$C = 27.5 + 3.75\|x\|$, $x > 0$ where, x is the weight in pounds.

Determine the cost of sending a package that weighs 7.25 pounds.

a. 56.75
b. 54.75
c. 57.75
d. 53.75
e. 55.75

_____ 16.   Use the given graph of *f* to select the graph for following function. To print an enlarged copy of the graph, go to the website *www.mathgraphs.com*.

$$y = \frac{1}{2}f(x)$$

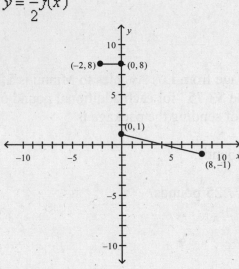

a.

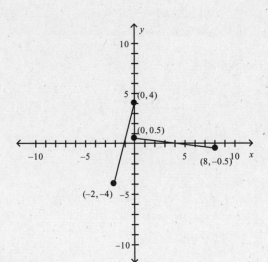

d.

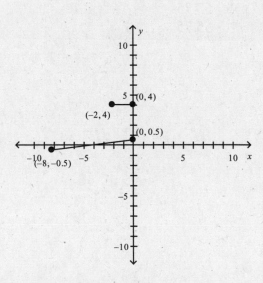

b.

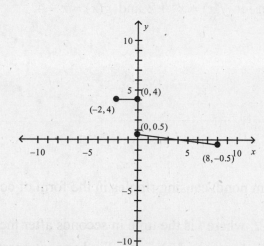

e.

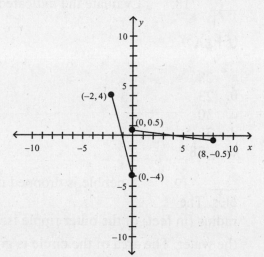

c.

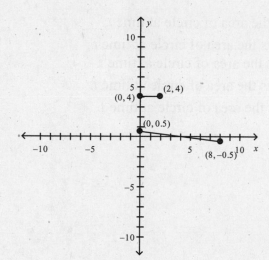

_____   17.   g is related to the parent function. Identify the parent function f.

$$g(x) = 2 - \|x\|$$

a. $f(x) = 2 - \|x\|$
b. $f(x) = -2 - \|x\|$
c. $f(x) = |x|$
d. $f(x) = \|x\|$
e. $f(x) = 2 + \|x\|$

81

_____   18.   Evaluate the indicated function for $f(x) = x^2 + 2$ and $g(x) = x - 4$.

$(f+g)(5)$

a. 28
b. 23
c. 30
d. 32
e. −28

_____   19.   A pebble is dropped into a calm pond, causing ripples in the form of concentric circles. The
radius (in feet) of the outer ripple is $r(t) = 0.2t$, where t is the time in seconds after the pebble strikes
the water. The area of the circle is given by the function $A(r) = \pi r^2$. Find and interpret $(A \circ r)(t)$.

a. $(A \circ r)(t) = 0.2\pi t$; $(A \circ r)(t)$ represents the area of circle at time t.
b. $(A \circ r)(t) = 0.04\pi t^2$; $(A \circ r)(t)$ represents the area of circle at time t.
c. $(A \circ r)(t) = 0.04\pi t$; $(A \circ r)(t)$ represents the area of circle at time t.
d. $(A \circ r)(t) = 0.04\pi t^3$; $(A \circ r)(t)$ represents the area of circle at time t.
e. $(A \circ r)(t) = 0.2\pi t^2$; $(A \circ r)(t)$ represents the area of circle at time t.

_____   20.   Find $(f - g)(x)$.

$$f(x) = \frac{7x}{8x - 2} \qquad\qquad g(x) = -\frac{5}{x}$$

a.
$$(f - g)(x) = \frac{7x^2 + 40x + 10}{8x^2 - 2x}$$

b.
$$(f - g)(x) = \frac{7x + 5}{7x - 2}$$

c.
$$(f - g)(x) = \frac{7x + 38}{8x - 2}$$

d.
$$(f - g)(x) = \frac{7x^2 + 40x - 10}{8x^2 - 2x}$$

e.
$$(f - g)(x) = \frac{7x + 42}{8x - 2}$$

_____ 21.   Select the correct graph, showing f and g are inverse functions.

$$f(x) = 12 - x^2, \ g(x) = \sqrt{12 - x}, \ x \le 12$$

a.

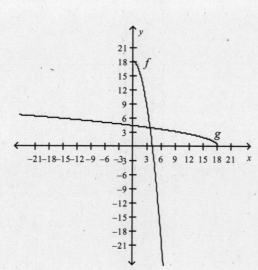

d.

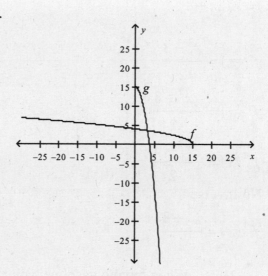

b.

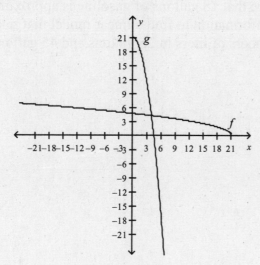

e.

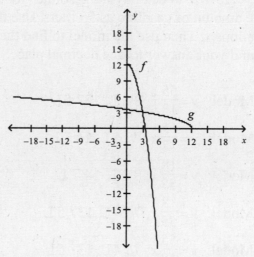

c.

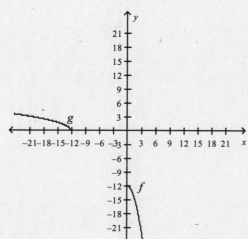

_____   22.   Determine whether the function has an inverse function. If it does, find the inverse function.

$$f(x) = \sqrt{2x + 8}$$

a.
$$f^{-1}(x) = \frac{x^2 - 8}{2}$$

b.
$$f^{-1}(x) = -\frac{x^2 + 8}{2}$$

c.
$$f^{-1}(x) = -\frac{x^2 - 8}{2}$$

d.   No Inverse

e.
$$f^{-1}(x) = \frac{x^2 + 8}{2}$$

_____   23.   When buying gasoline, you notice that 18 gallons of gasoline is approximately the same amount of gasoline as 55 liters. Use this information to find a linear model that relates liters y to gallons x. Then use the model to find the numbers of liters in 25 gallons and 45 gallons. (Round your answer to one decimal place.)

a.
Model: $y = \frac{55}{18}x$; 8.2 L, 137.5 L

b.
Model: $y = \frac{55}{18}x$; 76.4 L, 14.7 L

c.
Model: $y = \frac{18}{55}x$; 8.2 L, 14.7 L

d.
Model: $y = \frac{18}{55}x$; 76.4 L, 137.5 L

e.
Model: $y = \frac{55}{18}x$; 76.4 L, 137.5 L

_____   24.   Use the given value of k to complete the table for the direct variation model $y = kx^2$.

Plot the points on a rectangular coordinate system.

x	10	12	14	16	18
$y = kx^2$					

$k = 1$

a.

x	10	12	14	16	18
$y = kx^2$	100	100	100	100	100

d.

x	10	12	14	16	18
$y = kx^2$	10	101	14	16	18

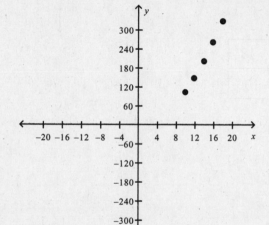

b.

x	10	12	14	16	18
$y = kx^2$	100	144	196	256	324

e.

x	10	12	14	16	18
$y = kx^2$	324	256	196	144	100

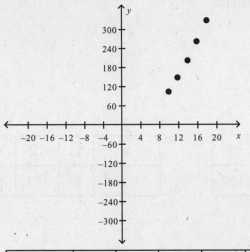

c.

x	10	12	14	16	18
$y = kx^2$	100	144	196	144	100

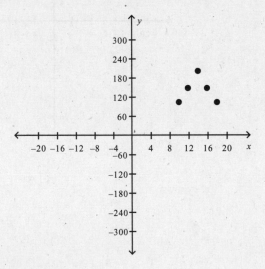

_____   25.   After determining whether the variation model below is of the form $y = kx$ or $y = \dfrac{k}{x}$, find the value of k.

x	24	48	72	96	120
y	$\dfrac{1}{36}$	$\dfrac{1}{72}$	$\dfrac{1}{108}$	$\dfrac{1}{144}$	$\dfrac{1}{180}$

a. $k = \dfrac{5}{4}$

b. $k = \dfrac{3}{2}$

c. $k = \dfrac{2}{3}$

d. $k = \dfrac{1}{24}$

e. $k = \dfrac{1}{12}$

Ch 1 Form D
Answer Section

1.	ANS:	D	PTS:	1	REF:	1.1.10
2.	ANS:	D	PTS:	1	REF:	1.1.46
3.	ANS:	D	PTS:	1	REF:	1.2.77
4.	ANS:	C	PTS:	1	REF:	1.2.57
5.	ANS:	D	PTS:	1	REF:	1.2.27
6.	ANS:	D	PTS:	1	REF:	1.3.32
7.	ANS:	B	PTS:	1	REF:	1.3.113b
8.	ANS:	B	PTS:	1	REF:	1.4.41c
9.	ANS:	E	PTS:	1	REF:	1.4.71
10.	ANS:	A	PTS:	1	REF:	1.4.38
11.	ANS:	D	PTS:	1	REF:	1.5.35
12.	ANS:	B	PTS:	1	REF:	1.5.115
13.	ANS:	A	PTS:	1	REF:	1.6.25
14.	ANS:	C	PTS:	1	REF:	1.6.43a
15.	ANS:	D	PTS:	1	REF:	1.6.69b
16.	ANS:	B	PTS:	1	REF:	1.7.14c
17.	ANS:	D	PTS:	1	REF:	1.7.47a
18.	ANS:	A	PTS:	1	REF:	1.8.17
19.	ANS:	B	PTS:	1	REF:	1.8.71
20.	ANS:	D	PTS:	1	REF:	1.8.16
21.	ANS:	E	PTS:	1	REF:	1.9.31b
22.	ANS:	A	PTS:	1	REF:	1.9.75
23.	ANS:	E	PTS:	1	REF:	1.10.42
24.	ANS:	B	PTS:	1	REF:	1.10.23
25.	ANS:	C	PTS:	1	REF:	1.10.33

Ch 1 Form E

_____   1.   The point is located five units below the *x*-axis and the coordinates of the point are equal. Find the coordinates of the point.

a. $(-5, 5)$
b. $(-5, 0)$
c. $(5, -5)$
d. $(-5, -5)$
e. $(5, 5)$

_____   2.   Plot the following points and find the distance between the points.

$(1, 3), (3, 1)$

a.

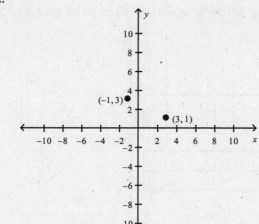

Distance: $2\sqrt{2}$

b.

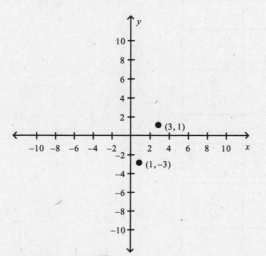

Distance: $2\sqrt{2}$

d.

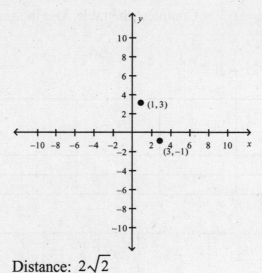

Distance: $2\sqrt{2}$

e.

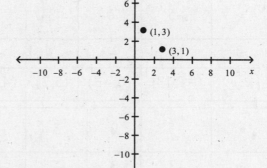

Distance: $2\sqrt{2}$

c.

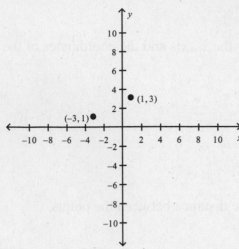

Distance: $2\sqrt{2}$

_____ 3.   Complete the table. Use the resulting solution points to sketch the graph of the equation.

$y = -2x + 3$

x	−5	0	3	4	$\frac{9}{2}$
y					
(x,y)					

a.

x	−5	0	3	4	$\frac{9}{2}$
y	13	3	−3	−5	−6
(x,y)	$(13,-5)$	$(3,0)$	$(3,-3)$	$(4,-5)$	$(9,-6)$

b.

x	−5	0	3	4	$\frac{9}{2}$
y	13	−3	3	−5	−6
(x,y)	$(-5,13)$	$(0,-3)$	$(3,3)$	$(4,-5)$	$(9,-6)$

c.

x	−5	0	3	4	$\frac{9}{2}$
y	13	3	−3	−5	−6
(x,y)	$(-5,13)$	$(0,3)$	$(-3,3)$	$(4,-5)$	$(-6,9)$

d.

x	-5	0	3	4	$\frac{9}{2}$
y	13	3	-3	-5	-6
(x,y)	$(-5,13)$	$(0,3)$	$(3,-3)$	$(4,-5)$	$(9,-6)$

e.

x	-5	0	3	4	$\frac{9}{2}$
y	13	3	-3	-5	-6
(x,y)	$(-5,13)$	$(3,0)$	$(-3,3)$	$(4,-5)$	$(9,-6)$

_____ 4.   Complete the table. Use the resulting solution points to sketch the graph of the equation.

$y = 5 - x^2$

x	3	5	-2	-3	0
y					
(x,y)					

a.

x	3	5	-2	-3	0
y	-4	-20	1	-4	5
(x,y)	$(3,-4)$	$(5,-20)$	$(1,-2)$	$(-3,-4)$	$(5,0)$

b.

x	3	5	-2	-3	0
y	-4	1	-20	-4	5
(x,y)	$(3,-4)$	$(5,1)$	$(-2,-20)$	$(-3,-4)$	$(0,5)$

c.

x	3	5	-2	-3	0
y	-4	-20	1	-4	5
(x,y)	$(3,-4)$	$(5,-20)$	$(-2,1)$	$(-3,-4)$	$(0,5)$

d.

x	3	5	-2	-3	0
y	-4	-20	1	-4	5
(x,y)	$(3,-4)$	$(-20,5)$	$(1,-2)$	$(-3,-4)$	$(0,5)$

e.

x	3	5	−2	−3	0
y	−4	−20	1	−4	5
(x,y)	$(-4,3)$	$(-20,5)$	$(-2,1)$	$(-3,-4)$	$(0,5)$

_____ 5.   Assume the graph has the indicated type of symmetry. Sketch the complete graph.

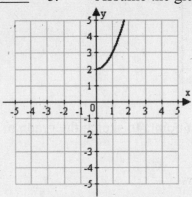

symmetric with respect to the *x*-axis

a.

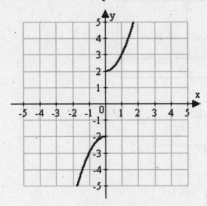

d.

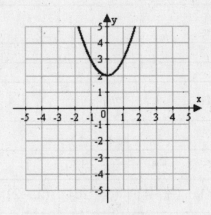

b.

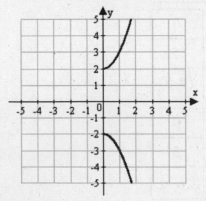

e.

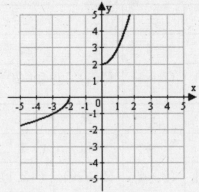

c.

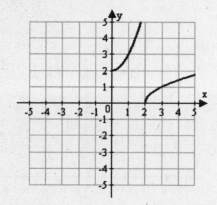

_____ 6.   Find the slope-intercept form of the equation of the line that passes through the given point and has the indicated slope m. Sketch the line.

$(-6, 6), \quad m = -2$

a.

$y = 6x + 6$

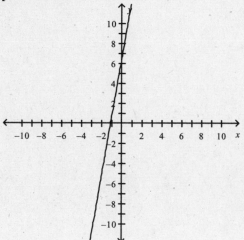

d.

$y = -2x - 6$

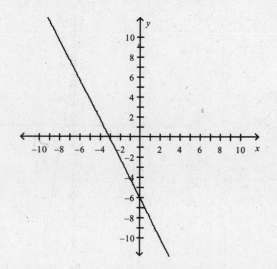

b.

$y = 6x + 6$

c.

$y = -6x - 6$

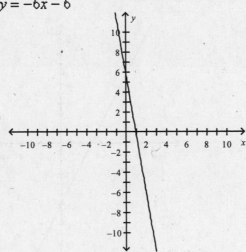

e.

$y = 6x - 6$

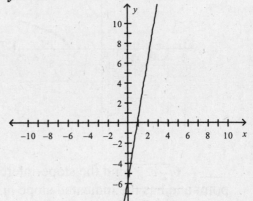

_____ 7.   A discount outlet is offering a 60% discount on all items. Write a linear equation giving the sale price S for an item with a list price L.

a. $L = 0.6S$
b. $S = 0.6L$
c. $L = 0.4S$
d. $S = 0.4L$
e. $S = 60L$

_____ 8.   Evaluate the function $f(x) = \begin{cases} 6x - 7, & x < -1 \\ 8, & -1 \leq x \leq 1 \\ x^2, & x > 1 \end{cases}$

94

at $f\left(-\dfrac{1}{3}\right)$.

a. −8
b. 25
c. 9
d. −25
e. 8

_____ 9.   Find the domain of the function.

$$f(x) = \dfrac{\sqrt{x+2}}{2+x}$$

a. All real numbers x such that $x < 2$
b. Non-negative real numbers x
c. All real numbers x
d. Non-negative real numbers x such that $x \ne 2$
e. All real numbers x such that $x > -2$

_____ 10.   Find all real values of x such that $f(x) = 0$.

$f(x) = 81x^2 - 49$

a. $\pm\dfrac{9}{7}$

b. $\pm\dfrac{7}{9}$

c. $-\dfrac{49}{81}$

d. $\dfrac{7}{9}$

e. $\pm\dfrac{49}{81}$

_____ 11.   Find the average rate of change of the function from $x_1 = 0$ to $x_2 = 3$.

$f(x) = 7x + 13$

a. The average rate of change from $x_1 = 0$ to $x_2 = 3$ is -7.
b. The average rate of change from $x_1 = 0$ to $x_2 = 3$ is 7.
c. The average rate of change from $x_1 = 0$ to $x_2 = 3$ is -13.
d. The average rate of change from $x_1 = 0$ to $x_2 = 3$ is 13.
e. The average rate of change from $x_1 = 0$ to $x_2 = 3$ is 19.

_____ 12.   An object is dropped from a height of 20 feet.

$t_1 = 1, t_2 = 2$

Use the position equation $s = -16t^2 + v_0 t + s_0$ to write a function that represents the situation and select the graph of function.

a. $s = -16t^2 + 20t$

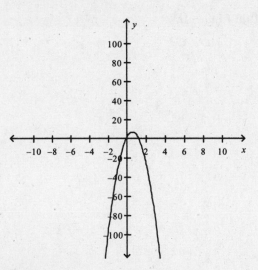

d. $s = -16t^2 + 20$

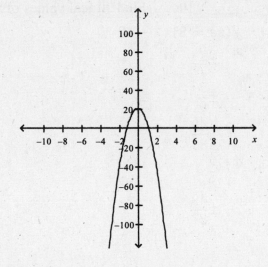

b. $s = 16t^2 - 20$

e. $s = -16t^2 - 20$

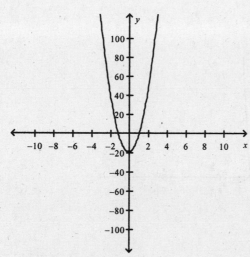

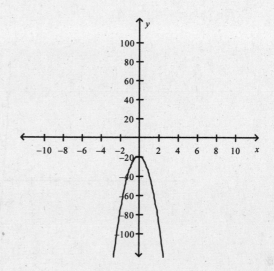

c. $s = 16t^2 + 20$

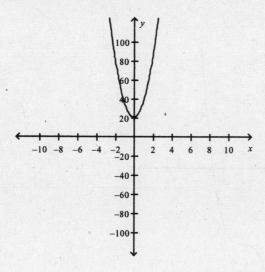

_____ 13.   Select the correct graph of the given function.

$f(x) = (x-4)^3 - 4$

a.

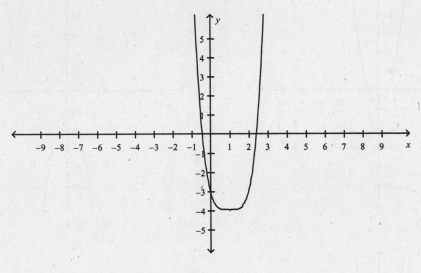

b.

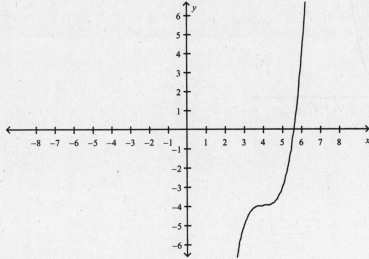

c.

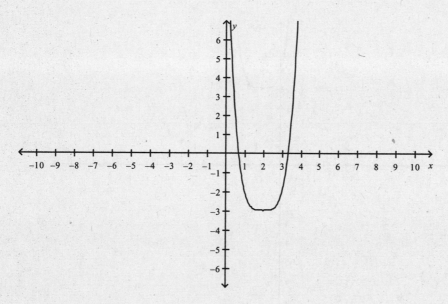

d.

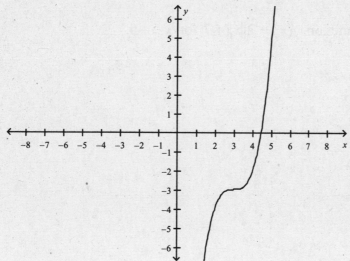

e.

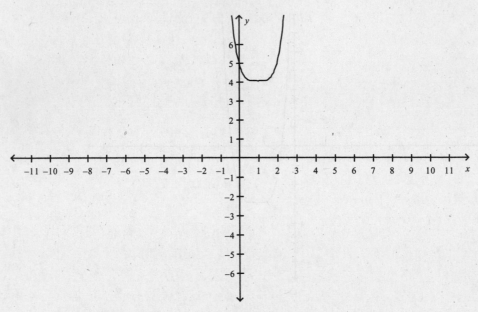

_____ 14.   Evaluate the function $f(x) = 2\|x\| + 7$ for $x = -5$.

a. -17
b. 0
c. -4
d. -3
e. 5

_____   15.   The table shows the monthly revenue y (in thousands of dollars) of a landscaping business for each month of the year 2008, with $x = 1$ representing January.

x	y
1	5.2
2	5.6
3	6.6
4	8.3
5	11.5
6	15.8
7	12.8
8	10.1
9	8.6
10	6.9
11	4.5
12	2.7

A mathematical model that represents these data is:

$$f(x) = -1.97x + 25.8 \qquad\qquad 1 \le x \le 6$$

$$ = 0.505x^2 - 1.47x + 6.8 \qquad 6 < x \le 12$$

Find $f(6)$ and $f(9)$.

a.   14.48, 34.975
b.   14.98, 35.475
c.   13.98, 35.225
d.   13.98, 34.475
e.   14.48, 34.725

_____ 16.   Use the graph of $f(x) = x^3$ to write an equation for the function whose graph is shown.

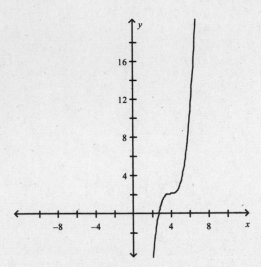

a. $y = (x - 4)^3 - 1$

b. $y = (x + 4)^3 + 2$

c. $y = (x + 4)^3 - 2$

d. $y = (x - 4)^3 + 2$

e. $y = (x - 4)^3 + 1$

_____ 17. g is related to the parent function. Use function notation to write g in terms of f.

$$g(x) = \sqrt{\frac{1}{3}x - 9}$$

a.
$$g(x) = f\left(\frac{1}{3}\right) + 9$$

b.
$$g(x) = f\left(\frac{1}{3}x\right) + 9$$

c.
$$g(x) = f\left(\frac{1}{3}\right) - 9$$

d.
$$f(x) = g\left(\frac{1}{3}x\right) - 9$$

e.
$$g(x) = f\left(\frac{1}{3}x\right) - 9$$

____   18.   Evaluate the indicated function for $f(x) = x^2 + 3$ and $g(x) = x - 2$.

$(fg)(2)$

a. 2
b. 0
c. 4
d. −1
e. 1

____   19.   The numbers of people playing tennis T (in millions) in the United States from 2000 through 2007 can be approximated by the function

$$T(t) = 0.0235t^4 - 0.3401t^3 + 2.556t^2 - 5.86t + 24.8$$

and the U.S. population P (in millions) from 2000 through 2007 can be approximated by the function $P(t) = 2.8t + 221.5$, where t represents the year, with $t = 0$ corresponding to 2000.

Evaluate the function $h(t) = \dfrac{0.0235t^4 - 0.3401t^3 + 2.556t^2 - 5.86t + 24.8}{2.8t + 221.5}$ for $t = 0$ and 3.

a. $h(0) = -\dfrac{221}{24},\ h(3) = -\dfrac{229}{22}$

b. $h(0) = -\dfrac{24}{221},\ h(3) = -\dfrac{22}{229}$

c. $h(0) = \dfrac{24}{229},\ h(3) = \dfrac{22}{221}$

d. $h(3) = \dfrac{221}{24},\ h(0) = \dfrac{229}{22}$

e. $h(0) = \dfrac{24}{221},\ h(3) = \dfrac{22}{229}$

____   20.   Find $f \circ g$.
$f(x) = -2x + 7 \qquad g(x) = x + 2$
a. $\left(f \circ g\right)(x) = -2x + 3$
b. $\left(f \circ g\right)(x) = -3x + 5$
c. $\left(f \circ g\right)(x) = -2x^2 + 3x + 14$
d. $\left(f \circ g\right)(x) = -3x + 9$
e. $\left(f \circ g\right)(x) = -2x + 9$

____ 21. Does the function have an inverse function?

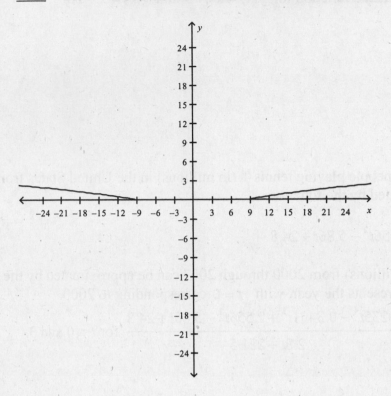

a. No
b. Yes

____ 22. Restrict the domain of the function f so that the function is one-to-one and has an inverse function. Then find the inverse function f^{-1}. State the domains and ranges of f and f^{-1}.

$f(x) = -10x^2 + 4$

a.

$$f^{-1}(x) = \frac{\sqrt{-10(x-4)}}{10}$$

The domain of f and the range of f^{-1} are all real numbers x such that $x \geq 0$.
The domain of f^{-1} and the range of f are all real numbers x such that $x \leq 4$.

b.

$$f^{-1}(x) = \frac{\sqrt{-4(x-10)}}{4}$$

The domain of f and the range of f^{-1} are all real numbers x such that $x \geq 0$.
The domain of f^{-1} and the range of f are all real numbers x such that $x \leq 4$.

c.

$$f^{-1}(x) = \frac{\sqrt{-10(x-4)}}{-10}$$

The domain of f and the range of f^{-1} are all real numbers x such that $x \geq 0$.

The domain of f^{-1} and the range of f are all real numbers x such that $x \leq 4$.

d.

$$f^{-1}(x) = \frac{\sqrt{-10(x-4)}}{10}$$

The domain of f and the range of f^{-1} are all real numbers x such that $x \geq 0$.

The domain of f^{-1} and the range of f are all real numbers x such that $x \leq -4$.

e.

$$f^{-1}(x) = \frac{\sqrt{-10(x+4)}}{10}$$

The domain of f and the range of f^{-1} are all real numbers x such that $x \geq 0$.

The domain of f^{-1} and the range of f are all real numbers x such that $x \leq 4$.

_____ 23.   A force of 260 newtons stretches a spring 0.13 meter. What force is required to stretch the spring 0.19 meter?

a.   390 N
b.   385 N
c.   380 N
d.   375 N
e.   260 N

_____ 24. Use the given value of k to complete the table for the direct variation model

$y = kx^2$.

Plot the points on a rectangular coordinate system.

x	4	6	8	10	12
$y = kx^2$					

$k = \dfrac{1}{4}$

a.

x	4	6	8	10	12
$y = kx^2$	36	25	16	9	4

d.

x	4	6	8	10	12
$y = kx^2$	4	9	16	25	36

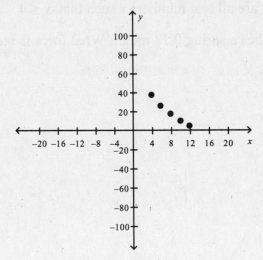

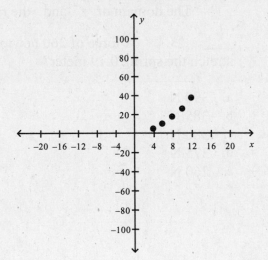

b.

x	4	6	8	10	12
$y = kx^2$	4	4	4	4	4

e.

x	4	6	8	10	12
$y = kx^2$	4	41	8	10	12

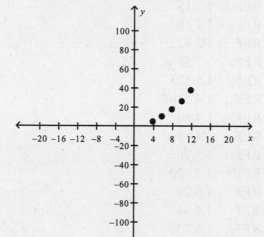

c.

x	4	6	8	10	12
$y = kx^2$	4	9	16	9	4

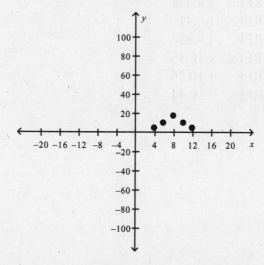

____ 25.   The sales tax on an item with a retail price of $972 is $77.76. Create a variational model that gives the retail price, *y*, in terms of the sales tax, *x*, and use it to determine the retail price of an item that has a sales tax of $92.34.

a. $1156.24
b. $1125.88
c. $1154.25
d. $1166.48
e. $1098.56

Ch 1 Form E
Answer Section

1.	ANS:	D	PTS:	1	REF:	1.1.13
2.	ANS:	E	PTS:	1	REF:	1.1.52
3.	ANS:	D	PTS:	1	REF:	1.2.15
4.	ANS:	C	PTS:	1	REF:	1.2.18
5.	ANS:	B	PTS:	1	REF:	1.2.42
6.	ANS:	D	PTS:	1	REF:	1.3.53
7.	ANS:	D	PTS:	1	REF:	1.3.123
8.	ANS:	E	PTS:	1	REF:	1.4.51b
9.	ANS:	E	PTS:	1	REF:	1.4.80
10.	ANS:	B	PTS:	1	REF:	1.4.63
11.	ANS:	B	PTS:	1	REF:	1.5.76
12.	ANS:	D	PTS:	1	REF:	1.5.120
13.	ANS:	B	PTS:	1	REF:	1.6.29
14.	ANS:	D	PTS:	1	REF:	1.6.46
15.	ANS:	D	PTS:	1	REF:	1.6.73b
16.	ANS:	D	PTS:	1	REF:	1.7.16b
17.	ANS:	E	PTS:	1	REF:	1.7.53d
18.	ANS:	B	PTS:	1	REF:	1.8.23
19.	ANS:	E	PTS:	1	REF:	1.8.66b
20.	ANS:	A	PTS:	1	REF:	1.8.43a
21.	ANS:	A	PTS:	1	REF:	1.9.41
22.	ANS:	A	PTS:	1	REF:	1.9.83
23.	ANS:	C	PTS:	1	REF:	1.10.46
24.	ANS:	D	PTS:	1	REF:	1.10.26
25.	ANS:	C	PTS:	1	REF:	1.10.44

Ch 1 Form F

_____   1.   The point is located two units below the *x*-axis and the coordinates of the point are equal. Find the coordinates of the point.

a. $(-2,-2)$
b. $(2,2)$
c. $(2,-2)$
d. $(-2,2)$
e. $(-2,0)$

_____   2.   Plot the following points and find the distance between the points.

$(5,9),(9,5)$

a.

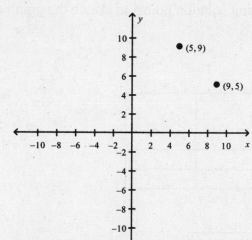

Distance: $4\sqrt{2}$

d.

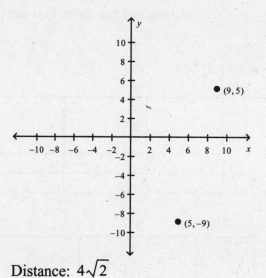

Distance: $4\sqrt{2}$

b.

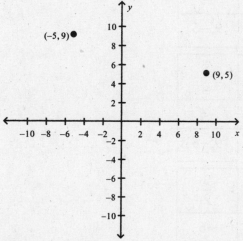

Distance: $4\sqrt{2}$

e.

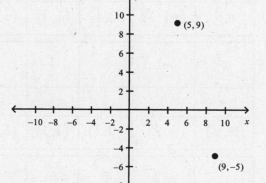

Distance: $4\sqrt{2}$

c.

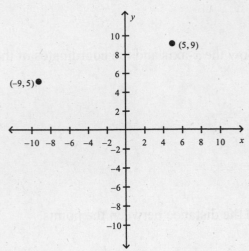

Distance: $4\sqrt{2}$

_____ 3. Complete the table. Use the resulting solution points to sketch the graph of the equation.

$y = -2x + 3$

x	−1	0	1	3	$\dfrac{9}{2}$
y					
(x,y)					

a.

x	−1	0	1	3	$\dfrac{9}{2}$
y	5	1	3	−3	−6
(x,y)	(−1,5)	(0,1)	(1,3)	(3,−3)	(9,−6)

b.

x	−1	0	1	3	$\dfrac{9}{2}$
y	5	3	1	−3	−6
(x,y)	(−1,5)	(0,3)	(1,1)	(3,−3)	(9,−6)

c.

x	−1	0	1	3	$\dfrac{9}{2}$
y	5	3	1	−3	−6
(x,y)	(5,−1)	(3,0)	(1,1)	(3,−3)	(9,−6)

d.

x	-1	0	1	3	$\dfrac{9}{2}$
y	5	3	1	-3	-6
(x,y)	$(-1,5)$	$(0,3)$	$(1,1)$	$(3,-3)$	$(-6,9)$

e.

x	-1	0	1	3	$\dfrac{9}{2}$
y	5	3	1	-3	-6
(x,y)	$(-1,5)$	$(3,0)$	$(1,1)$	$(3,-3)$	$(9,-6)$

_____ 4.   Complete the table. Use the resulting solution points to sketch the graph of the equation.

$y = 5 - x^2$

x	2	4	-3	0	-4
y					
(x,y)					

a.

x	2	4	-3	0	-4
y	1	-11	-4	5	-11
(x,y)	$(2,1)$	$(4,-11)$	$(-4,-3)$	$(0,5)$	$(-11,-4)$

b.

x	2	4	-3	0	-4
y	1	-4	-11	5	-11
(x,y)	$(2,1)$	$(4,-4)$	$(-3,-11)$	$(0,5)$	$(-4,-11)$

c.

x	2	4	-3	0	-4
y	1	-11	-4	5	-11
(x,y)	$(2,1)$	$(4,-11)$	$(-3,-4)$	$(0,5)$	$(-4,-11)$

d.

x	2	4	-3	0	-4
y	1	-11	-4	5	-11
(x,y)	$(1,2)$	$(-11,4)$	$(-3,-4)$	$(0,5)$	$(-4,-11)$

e.

x	2	4	−3	0	−4
y	1	−11	−4	5	−11
(x,y)	$(2,1)$	$(−11,4)$	$(−4,−3)$	$(0,5)$	$(−4,−11)$

_____ 5.　　　Assume the graph has the indicated type of symmetry. Sketch the complete graph.

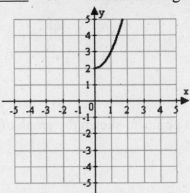

symmetric with respect to the x-axis

a.

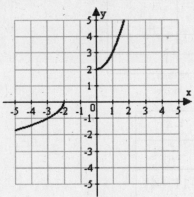

d.

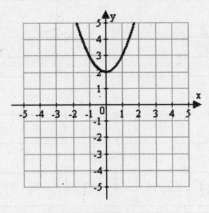

b.

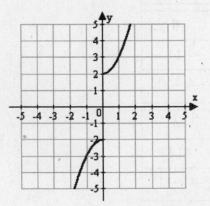

e.

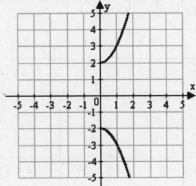

c.

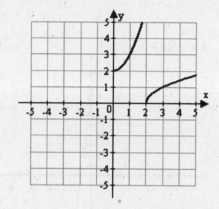

_____   6.   Find the slope-intercept form of the equation of the line that passes through the given point and has the indicated slope m. Sketch the line.

$(-8, 5)$, $m = -7$

a.

$y = 5x - 5$

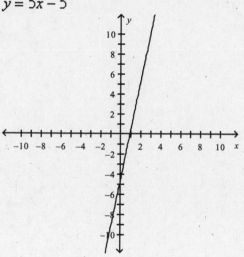

d.

$y = -7x - 51$

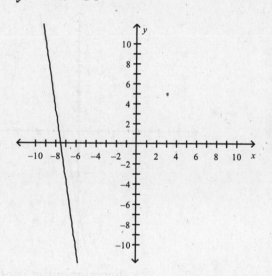

b.

$y = 5x + 5$

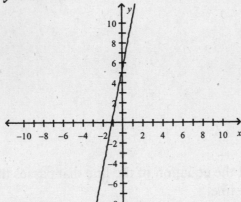

e.

$y = -8x - 8$

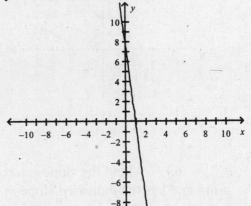

c.

$y = 5x + 5$

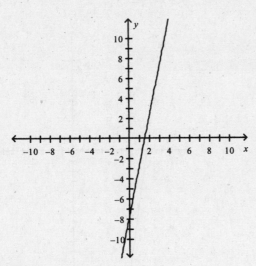

_____ 7.   A discount outlet is offering a 60% discount on all items. Write a linear equation giving the sale price S for an item with a list price L.

a. $L = 0.4S$
b. $S = 0.4L$
c. $L = 0.6S$
d. $S = 0.6L$
e. $S = 60L$

_____ 8.   Evaluate the function $f(x) = \begin{cases} 3x - 9, & x < -1 \\ 7, & -1 \leq x \leq 1 \\ x^2, & x > 1 \end{cases}$

at $f\left(-\dfrac{1}{7}\right)$.

a. -30
b. 7
c. 49
d. -7
e. 30

_____ 9. Find the domain of the function.

$$f(x) = \dfrac{\sqrt{x+3}}{3+x}$$

a. Non-negative real numbers x
b. All real numbers x
c. All real numbers x such that $x < 3$
d. Non-negative real numbers x such that $x \neq 3$
e. All real numbers x such that $x > -3$

_____ 10. Find all real values of x such that $f(x) = 0$.

$f(x) = 49x^2 - 64$

a. $\pm\dfrac{8}{7}$

b. $\dfrac{8}{7}$

c. $\pm\dfrac{7}{8}$

d. $-\dfrac{64}{49}$

e. $\pm\dfrac{64}{49}$

_____   11.   Find the average rate of change of the function from $x_1 = 0$ to $x_2 = 3$.

$f(x) = 6x + 9$

a.   The average rate of change from $x_1 = 0$ to $x_2 = 3$ is -9.
b.   The average rate of change from $x_1 = 0$ to $x_2 = 3$ is 19.
c.   The average rate of change from $x_1 = 0$ to $x_2 = 3$ is 6.
d.   The average rate of change from $x_1 = 0$ to $x_2 = 3$ is -6.
e.   The average rate of change from $x_1 = 0$ to $x_2 = 3$ is 9.

_____   12.   An object is dropped from a height of 15 feet.

$t_1 = 1, t_2 = 2$

Use the position equation $s = -16t^2 + v_0 t + s_0$ to write a function that represents the situation and select the graph of function.

a. $s = -16t^2 + 15$ d. $s = 16t^2 + 15$

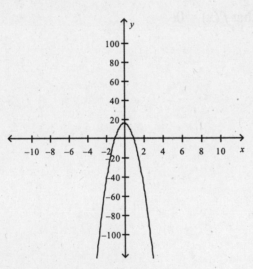 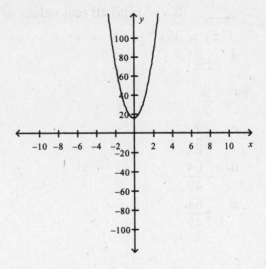

b. $s = 16t^2 - 15$

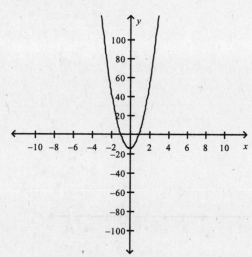

e. $s = -16t^2 - 15$

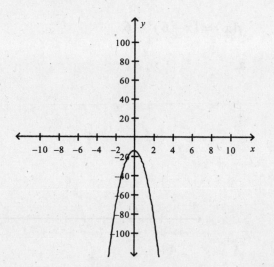

c. $s = -16t^2 + 15t$

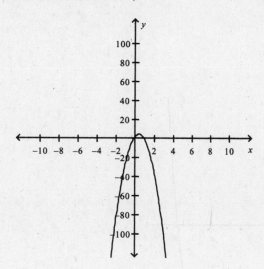

_____ 13. Select the correct graph of the given function.

$f(x) = (x - 6)^3 - 6$

a.

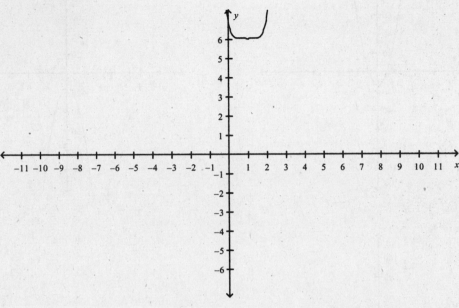

b.

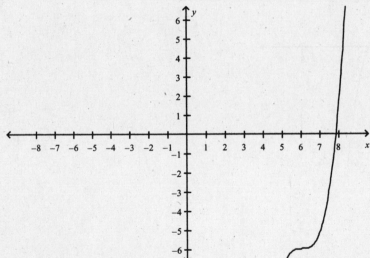

c.

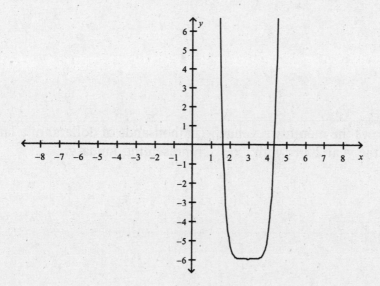

d.

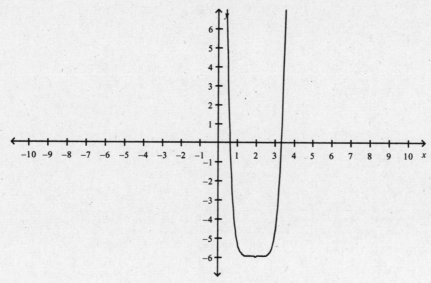

e.

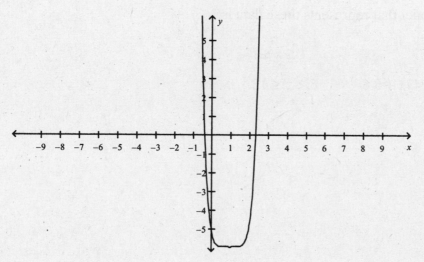

_____ 14.   Evaluate the function $f(x) = 2\|x\| + 7$ for $x = -7$.

a. -21
b. -7
c. 2
d. -2
e. 7

_____ 15.   The table shows the monthly revenue y (in thousands of dollars) of a landscaping business for each month of the year 2008, with $x = 1$ representing January.

x	y
1	5.2
2	5.6
3	6.6
4	8.3
5	11.5
6	15.8
7	12.8
8	10.1
9	8.6
10	6.9
11	4.5
12	2.7

A mathematical model that represents these data is:

$$f(x) = -1.97x + 25.9 \qquad 1 \le x \le 6$$
$$= 0.505x^2 - 1.47x + 6.6 \qquad 6 < x \le 12$$

Find $f(2)$ and $f(9)$.

a.   22.96, 35.275
b.   21.96, 35.025
c.   22.46, 34.525
d.   22.46, 34.775
e.   21.96, 34.275

_____ 16.   Use the graph of $f(x) = x^3$ to write an equation for the function whose graph is shown.

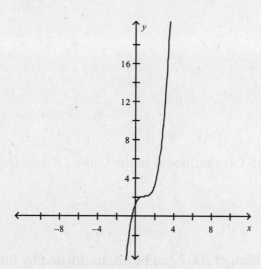

a. $y = (x - 1)^3 + 2$
b. $y = (x - 1)^3 - 1$
c. $y = (x - 1)^3 + 1$
d. $y = (x + 1)^3 - 2$
e. $y = (x + 1)^3 + 2$

_____ 17. g is related to the parent function. Use function notation to write g in terms of f.

$$g(x) = \sqrt{\frac{1}{5}x - 25}$$

a. $g(x) = f\left(\frac{1}{5}x\right) + 25$

b. $g(x) = f\left(\frac{1}{5}\right) - 25$

c. $f(x) = g\left(\frac{1}{5}x\right) - 25$

d. $g(x) = f\left(\frac{1}{5}\right) + 25$

e. $g(x) = f\left(\frac{1}{5}x\right) - 25$

_____ 18. Evaluate the indicated function for $f(x) = x^2 + 6$ and $g(x) = x - 4$.

$(fg)(2)$

a. -19
b. -20
c. 24
d. -18
e. -21

_____ 19. The numbers of people playing tennis T (in millions) in the United States from 2000 through 2007 can be approximated by the function

$$T(t) = 0.0232t^4 - 0.3401t^3 + 1.556t^2 - 7.86t + 27.8$$

and the U.S. population P (in millions) from 2000 through 2007 can be approximated by the function $P(t) = 7.8t + 223.5$, where t represents the year, with $t = 0$ corresponding to 2000.

Evaluate the function $h(t) = \dfrac{0.0232t^4 - 0.3401t^3 + 1.556t^2 - 7.86t + 27.8}{7.8t + 223.5}$ for $t = 0$ and 3.

a. $h(0) = -\dfrac{223}{27}$, $h(3) = -\dfrac{123}{5}$

b. $h(0) = -\dfrac{27}{223}$, $h(3) = -\dfrac{5}{123}$

c. $h(0) = \dfrac{27}{223}$, $h(3) = \dfrac{5}{123}$

d. $h(0) = \dfrac{9}{82}$, $h(3) = \dfrac{10}{223}$

e. $h(3) = \dfrac{223}{27}$, $h(0) = \dfrac{123}{5}$

_____ 20. Find $f \circ g$.
$f(x) = -4x + 3$ $g(x) = x - 5$

a. $(f \circ g)(x) = -4x^2 + 23x - 15$

b. $(f \circ g)(x) = -5x + 8$

c. $(f \circ g)(x) = -4x - 2$

d. $(f \circ g)(x) = -4x + 23$

e. $(f \circ g)(x) = -5x - 2$

_____   21.   Does the function have an inverse function?

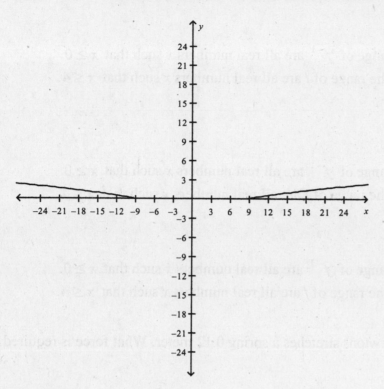

a. No
b. Yes

_____   22.   Restrict the domain of the function f so that the function is one-to-one and has an inverse function. Then find the inverse function f^{-1}. State the domains and ranges of f and f^{-1}.

$f(x) = -10x^2 + 4$

a.
$$f^{-1}(x) = \frac{\sqrt{-4(x-10)}}{4}$$

The domain of f and the range of f^{-1} are all real numbers x such that $x \geq 0$.
The domain of f^{-1} and the range of f are all real numbers x such that $x \leq 4$.

b.
$$f^{-1}(x) = \frac{\sqrt{-10(x-4)}}{10}$$

The domain of f and the range of f^{-1} are all real numbers x such that $x \geq 0$.
The domain of f^{-1} and the range of f are all real numbers x such that $x \leq -4$.

c.

$$f^{-1}(x) = \frac{\sqrt{-10(x-4)}}{10}$$

The domain of f and the range of f^{-1} are all real numbers x such that $x \geq 0$.

The domain of f^{-1} and the range of f are all real numbers x such that $x \leq 4$.

d.

$$f^{-1}(x) = \frac{\sqrt{-10(x+4)}}{10}$$

The domain of f and the range of f^{-1} are all real numbers x such that $x \geq 0$.

The domain of f^{-1} and the range of f are all real numbers x such that $x \leq 4$.

e.

$$f^{-1}(x) = \frac{\sqrt{-10(x-4)}}{-10}$$

The domain of f and the range of f^{-1} are all real numbers x such that $x \geq 0$.

The domain of f^{-1} and the range of f are all real numbers x such that $x \leq 4$.

____ 23. A force of 260 newtons stretches a spring 0.12 meter. What force is required to stretch the spring 0.18 meter?

a. 395 N
b. 400 N
c. 385 N
d. 390 N
e. 260 N

_____ 24.   Use the given value of k to complete the table for the direct variation model

$y = kx^2$.

Plot the points on a rectangular coordinate system.

x	6	8	10	12	14
$y = kx^2$					

$k = \dfrac{1}{4}$

a.

x	6	8	10	12	14
$y = kx^2$	6	61	10	12	14

d.

x	6	8	10	12	14
$y = kx^2$	9	9	9	9	9

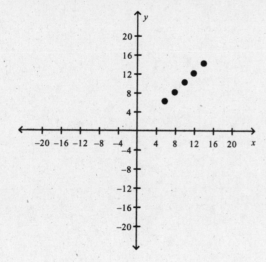

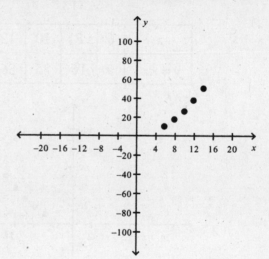

b.

x	6	8	10	12	14
$y = kx^2$	49	36	25	16	9

e.

x	6	8	10	12	14
$y = kx^2$	9	16	25	16	9

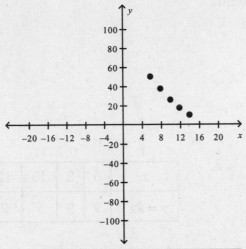

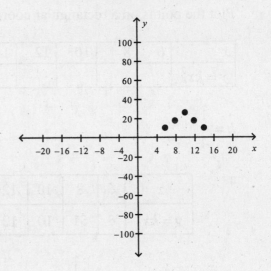

c.

x	6	8	10	12	14
$y = kx^2$	9	16	25	36	49

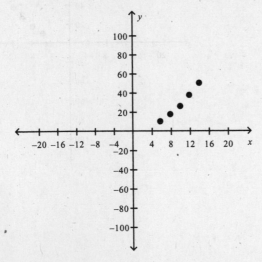

_____ 25. The sales tax on an item with a retail price of \$612 is \$55.08. Create a variational model that gives the retail price, y, in terms of the sales tax, x, and use it to determine the retail price of an item that has a sales tax of \$64.26.

a. \$714.00
b. \$726.23
c. \$658.31
d. \$715.99
e. \$685.63

Ch 1 Form F
Answer Section

1.	ANS:	A	PTS:	1	REF:	1.1.13
2.	ANS:	A	PTS:	1	REF:	1.1.52
3.	ANS:	B	PTS:	1	REF:	1.2.15
4.	ANS:	C	PTS:	1	REF:	1.2.18
5.	ANS:	E	PTS:	1	REF:	1.2.42
6.	ANS:	D	PTS:	1	REF:	1.3.53
7.	ANS:	B	PTS:	1	REF:	1.3.123
8.	ANS:	B	PTS:	1	REF:	1.4.51b
9.	ANS:	E	PTS:	1	REF:	1.4.80
10.	ANS:	A	PTS:	1	REF:	1.4.63
11.	ANS:	C	PTS:	1	REF:	1.5.76
12.	ANS:	A	PTS:	1	REF:	1.5.120
13.	ANS:	B	PTS:	1	REF:	1.6.29
14.	ANS:	B	PTS:	1	REF:	1.6.46
15.	ANS:	E	PTS:	1	REF:	1.6.73b
16.	ANS:	A	PTS:	1	REF:	1.7.16b
17.	ANS:	E	PTS:	1	REF:	1.7.53d
18.	ANS:	B	PTS:	1	REF:	1.8.23
19.	ANS:	C	PTS:	1	REF:	1.8.66b
20.	ANS:	D	PTS:	1	REF:	1.8.43a
21.	ANS:	A	PTS:	1	REF:	1.9.41
22.	ANS:	C	PTS:	1	REF:	1.9.83
23.	ANS:	D	PTS:	1	REF:	1.10.46
24.	ANS:	C	PTS:	1	REF:	1.10.26
25.	ANS:	A	PTS:	1	REF:	1.10.44

Ch 2 Form A

____ 1. Select the graph of the function $y = -3x^2$. Compare the graph of this function with the graph of $y = x^2$.

a.

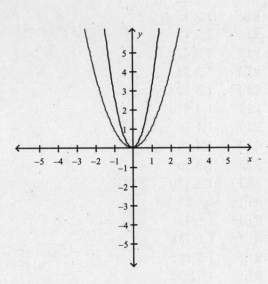

Vertical stretch

d.

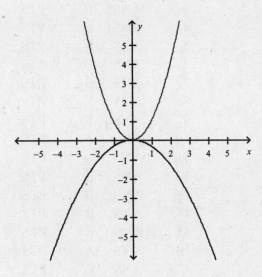

Vertical shrink and reflection in x-axis

b.

Vertical stretch and reflection in x-axis

e.

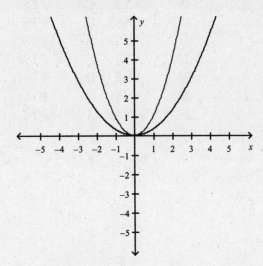

Vertical shrink

c.

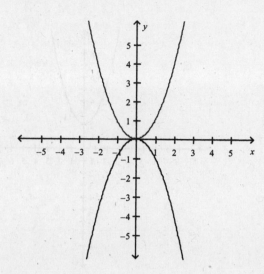

Reflection in x-axis

_____ 2.   Select the graph of the quadratic function $f(x) = x^2 + 3$. Identify the vertex and axis of symmetry.

a.

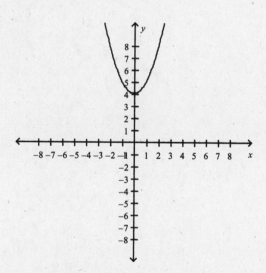

Vertex: $(0,4)$
Axis of symmetry: y-axis

d.

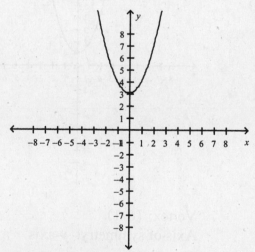

Vertex: $(0,3)$
Axis of symmetry: y-axis

129

b.

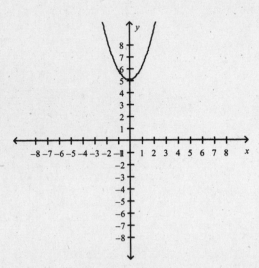

Vertex: $(0, 5)$
Axis of symmetry: y-axis

e.

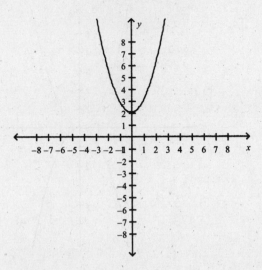

Vertex: $(0, 2)$
Axis of symmetry: y-axis

c.

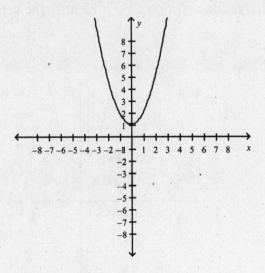

Vertex: $(0, 1)$
Axis of symmetry: y-axis

_____ 3.   The total revenue R earned (in thousands of dollars) from manufacturing handheld video games is given by

$$R(p) = -25p^2 + 1200p$$

where, p is the price per unit (in dollars).
Find the revenue when the price per unit is $35.

a. $11375100
b. $11375300
c. $11375000
d. $11375200
e. $11375400

_____ 4.   Find the standard form of the quadratic function shown below:

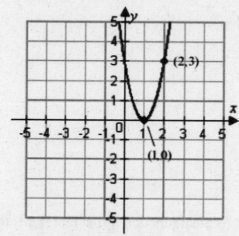

a. $f(x) = (x + 1)^2$
b. $f(x) = (x - 1)^2$
c. $f(x) = x^2 + 1$
d. $f(x) = 3(x - 1)^2$
e. $f(x) = 3(x + 1)^2$

_____ 5.   Select the correct description of right-hand and left-hand behavior of the graph of the polynomial function.

$$f(x) = \frac{1}{5}x^3 + 5x$$

a. Rises to the left, falls to the right
b. Rises to the right, rises to the left
c. Falls to the left, rises to the right
d. Falls to the right
e. Falls to the left, falls to the right

_____ 6.   Select from the following which is the polynomial function that has the given zeros.

$-4, -1, 0, 1, 4$

a. $f(x) = x^5 - 17x^3 + 16$
b. $f(x) = x^5 + 17x^3 + 16x$
c. $f(x) = x^5 - 17x^3 + 16x$
d. $f(x) = -x^5 - 17x^3 + 16x$
e. $f(x) = x^5 - 17x^3 - 16x$

_____ 7.   A roofing contractor is fabricating gutters from 20-inch aluminum sheeting. The contractor plans to use an aluminum siding folding press to create the gutter by creasing equal lengths for the sidewalls (see figure).

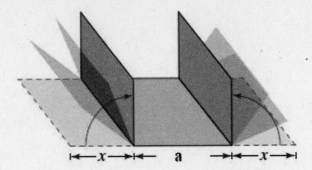

where $a = 20 - 2x$

Let x represent the height of the sidewall of the gutter. Write a function A that represents the cross-sectional area of the gutter.

a. $A = -2x^2 + 20x$
b. $A = 20x^2 - 2x$
c. $A = -20x - 2x^2$
d. $A = 2x^2 - 20x$
e. $A = 2x^2 + 20x$

_____ 8.   Use long division to divide.

$$\left(x^4 + 9x^3 + 20x^2 - x - 5 \right) \div (x + 5)$$

a. $x^3 + 4x^2 + 1$
b. $x^3 - 4x^2 - 1$
c. $x^3 + 4x^2 - 1$
d. $x^3 + 4x^2 + 1$
e. $x^3 - 4x^2 + 1$

_____ 9.   Use synthetic division to divide.

$$\left(4x^3 + x^2 - 11x + 6\right) \div (x+2)$$

a. $4x^2 - 5x - 6$

b. $4x^2 - 7x + 3$

c. $4x^2 - 2x - 2$

d. $4x^2 + 5x - 12$

e. $4x^2 + 7x - 4$

_____ 10.   Simplify the rational expression, $\dfrac{-3x^3 + x^2 + 40x - 48}{-3x + 4}$, by using long division or synthetic division.

a. $x^2 - 7x + 9$

b. $x^2 + 7x - 12$

c. $x^2 + 8x + 12$

d. $x^2 - 6x + 16$

e. $x^2 + x - 12$

_____ 11.   Use synthetic division to divide.

$$\frac{x^3 + 343}{x + 7}$$

a. $x^2 + 7x + 49, \; x \neq -7$

b. $x^2 - 7x - 49, \; x \neq -7$

c. $x^2 + 7x - 49, \; x \neq -7$

d. $x^2 - 7x + 49, \; x \neq -7$

e. $-x^2 + 7x - 49, \; x \neq -7$

_____ 12.   Write the complex number in standard form.

$-15i + i^2$

a. $-1 + 15i$

b. $-1 - 18i$

c. $1 + 15i$

d. $1 - 15i$

e. $-1 - 15i$

_____ 13.   Write the complex conjugate of the complex number. Then multiply the number by its complex conjugate.

$-7 + \sqrt{6}i$

a. $-7 - \sqrt{6}i, 55$
b. $7 - \sqrt{6}i, 55$
c. $-7 + \sqrt{6}i, 55$
d. $7 + \sqrt{6}i, 55$
e. $-6 - \sqrt{7}i, 55$

_____ 14.   Solve the equation and write complex solutions in standard form.

$x^2 + 6x + 16 = 0$

a. $x = -3 + \sqrt{7}i, -3 - \sqrt{7}i$
b. $x = 7 + \sqrt{10}i, 7 - \sqrt{10}i$
c. $x = -3 + \sqrt{10}i, -3 - \sqrt{10}i$
d. $x = 7 + \sqrt{7}i, 7 - \sqrt{7}i$
e. $x = 10 + \sqrt{7}i, 10 - \sqrt{7}i$

_____ 15.   Find all the rational zeros of the function.

$x^3 + 6x^2 + 9x + 4$

a. $-4, 1$
b. $4, 1$
c. $-4, -1$
d. $-4, -1, 1$
e. $4, -1$

_____ 16.   Find all the zeros of the function and write the polynomial as a product of linear factors.

$x^4 - 16$

a. $2, 2i; (x + 2)(x + 2)(x - 2i)(x - 2i)$
b. $\pm 2i; (x - 2i)(x + 2i)$
c. $\pm 2, \pm 2i; (x - 2)(x - 2)(x + 2i)(x + 2i)$
d. $\pm 2 (x - 2)(x + 2)$
e. $\pm 2, \pm 2i; (x - 2)(x + 2)(x - 2i)(x + 2i)$

_____   17.   Find all real solutions of the polynomial equation $x^4 - 4x^3 + 12x - 9 = 0$.

a. $x = 1, 3, \pm\sqrt{3}$

b. $x = 1, 9$

c. $x = 1, \pm\sqrt{3}$

d. $x = 1, -4, -3$

e. $x = 1, -9, 6$

_____   18.   Write $f(x) = x^3 - 4x^2 + 4x - 16$ as a product of linear factors.

a. $x = (x - 4)(x - 2)^2$

b. $x = (x - 4)(x + 2i)(x - 2i)$

c. $x = (x - 4)^2(x - 2i)$

d. $x = (x - 4)(x + 2)^2$

e. $x = (x + 4)(x - 4)(x + 2)$

_____   19.   Find the zeros of the rational function.

$$g(x) = \frac{x^2 - 16}{x + 4}$$

a. $x = 0$

b. $x = -16$

c. $x = 4$

d. $x = 16$

e. $x = -4$

_____   20.   Find all intercepts of the following function.

$$g(s) = \frac{6s}{s^2 + 6}$$

a.   intercept: $(0, 0)$

b. x-intercept: $(6, 0)$

c. x-intercept: $(-6, 0)$

d. y-intercept: $(0, -6)$

e. y-intercept: $(0, 6)$

_____ 21.   Which of the following is the graph of the given equation?

$f(x) = \dfrac{2}{x+1}$

a.

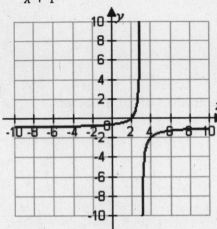

d.

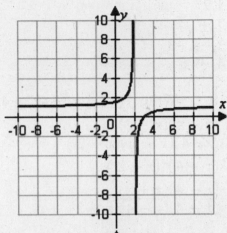

b.

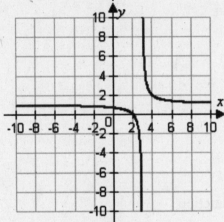

e.

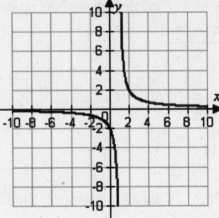

c.

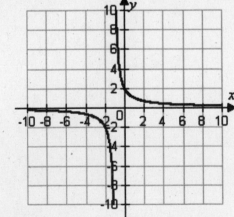

____ 22. Solve the inequality and graph the solution on the real number line.

$x^2 < 4$

a. $[-2, 2]$

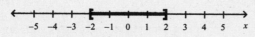

b. $[-2, 2]$

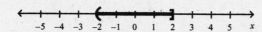

c. $(2, -2)$

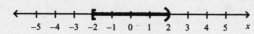

d. $(-2, 2)$

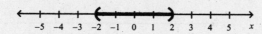

e. $(-2, 2)$

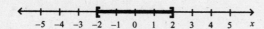

____ 23.   Use a graphing utility to graph the equation. Use the graph to approximate the values of x that satisfy the inequality.

Equation:

$$y = \frac{1}{4}x^2 - 4x + 1$$

Inequalities:
$y \le 0$

a.

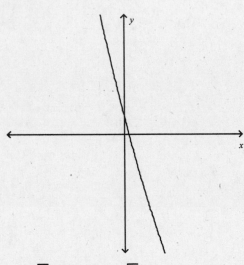

$$4 - \sqrt{4} \le x \le 4 + \sqrt{4}$$

d.

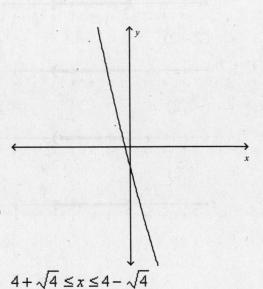

$$4 + \sqrt{4} \le x \le 4 - \sqrt{4}$$

b.

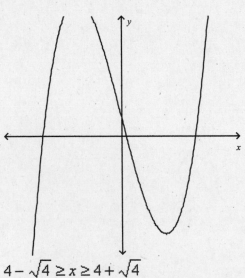

$$4 - \sqrt{4} \ge x \ge 4 + \sqrt{4}$$

e.

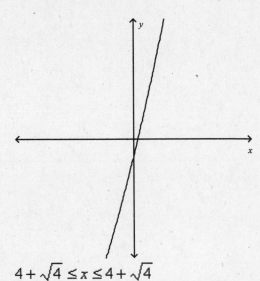

$$4 + \sqrt{4} \le x \le 4 + \sqrt{4}$$

c.

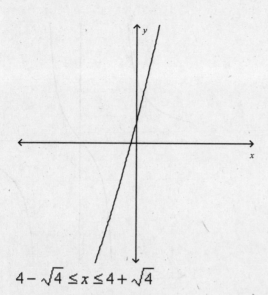

$$4 - \sqrt{4} \leq x \leq 4 + \sqrt{4}$$

_____ 24. Use a graphing utility to graph the equation. Use the graph to approximate the values of x that satisfy each inequality.

Equation:

$$y = \frac{5x}{x^2 + 4}$$

Inequality:
$y \geq 1$

a.

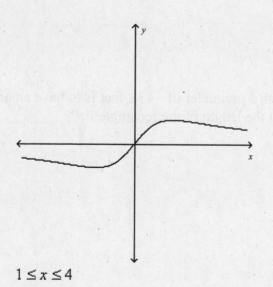

$$1 \leq x \leq 4$$

d.

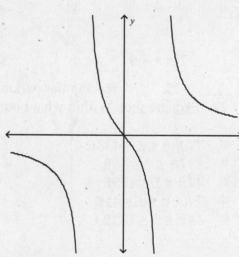

$$1 < x \leq 4$$

b.

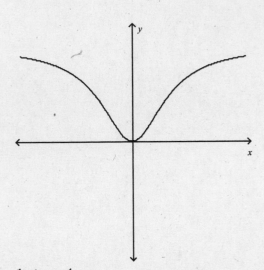

$1 \leq x < 4$

e.

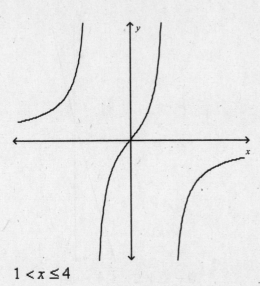

$1 < x \leq 4$

c.

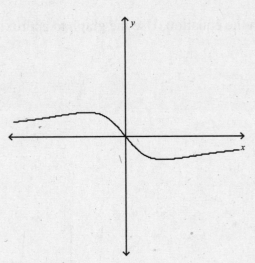

$1 < x < 4$

_____ 25.   A rectangular parking lot with a perimeter of 438 feet is to have an area of at least 7700 square feet. Within what bounds must the length of the rectangle lie?

a. $7700\,\text{ft} \leq L \leq 438\,\text{ft}$
b. $177\,\text{ft} \leq L \leq 46\,\text{ft}$
c. $47\,\text{ft} \leq L \leq 178\,\text{ft}$
d. $7700\,\text{ft} \leq L \leq 45\,\text{ft}$
e. $44\,\text{ft} \leq L \leq 175\,\text{ft}$

Ch 2 Form A
Answer Section

1.	ANS:	B	PTS:	1	REF:	2.1.13d
2.	ANS:	D	PTS:	1	REF:	2.1.19
3.	ANS:	C	PTS:	1	REF:	2.1.79a
4.	ANS:	D	PTS:	1	REF:	2.1.7
5.	ANS:	C	PTS:	1	REF:	2.2.21
6.	ANS:	C	PTS:	1	REF:	2.2.62
7.	ANS:	A	PTS:	1	REF:	2.2.99a
8.	ANS:	C	PTS:	1	REF:	2.3.15
9.	ANS:	B	PTS:	1	REF:	2.3.27
10.	ANS:	E	PTS:	1	REF:	2.3.81
11.	ANS:	D	PTS:	1	REF:	2.3.39
12.	ANS:	E	PTS:	1	REF:	2.4.17
13.	ANS:	A	PTS:	1	REF:	2.4.44
14.	ANS:	A	PTS:	1	REF:	2.4.70
15.	ANS:	C	PTS:	1	REF:	2.5.23
16.	ANS:	E	PTS:	1	REF:	2.5.67
17.	ANS:	A	PTS:	1	REF:	2.5.30
18.	ANS:	B	PTS:	1	REF:	2.5.74
19.	ANS:	C	PTS:	1	REF:	2.6.21
20.	ANS:	A	PTS:	1	REF:	2.6.39b
21.	ANS:	C	PTS:	1	REF:	2.6.17
22.	ANS:	D	PTS:	1	REF:	2.7.13
23.	ANS:	A	PTS:	1	REF:	2.7.38
24.	ANS:	A	PTS:	1	REF:	2.7.58a
25.	ANS:	E	PTS:	1	REF:	2.7.74

Ch 2 Form B

_____ 1.   Select the graph of the function $y = -5x^2$. Compare the graph of this function with the graph of $y = x^2$.

a.

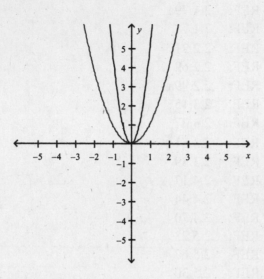

Vertical stretch

d.

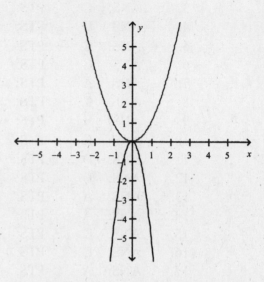

Vertical stretch and reflection in x-axis

b.

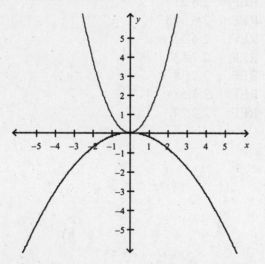

Vertical shrink and reflection in x-axis

e.

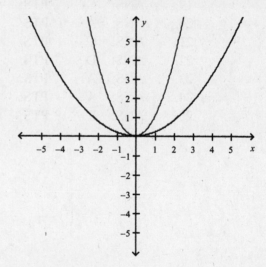

Vertical shrink

c.

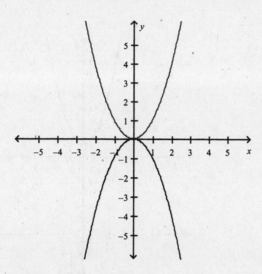

Reflection in x-axis

_____ 2.   Select the graph of the quadratic function $f(x) = x^2 + 3$. Identify the vertex and axis of symmetry.

a.

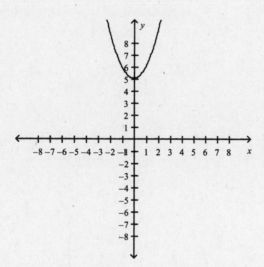

d.

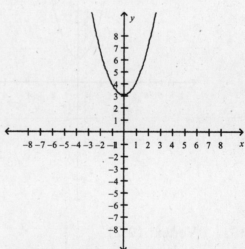

Vertex: $(0, 5)$
Axis of symmetry: y-axis

Vertex: $(0, 3)$
Axis of symmetry: y-axis

b.

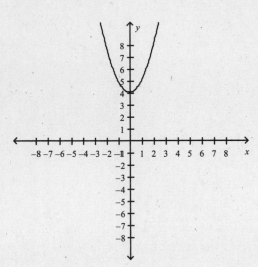

Vertex: $(0, 4)$
Axis of symmetry: y-axis

e.

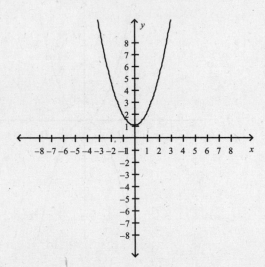

Vertex: $(0, 1)$
Axis of symmetry: y-axis

c.

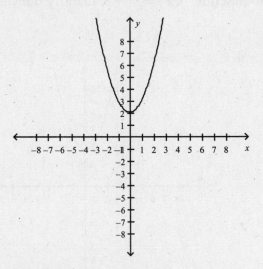

Vertex: $(0, 2)$
Axis of symmetry: y-axis

_____ 3.   The total revenue R earned (in thousands of dollars) from manufacturing handheld video games is given by

$$R(p) = -25p^2 + 1200p$$

where, p is the price per unit (in dollars).
Find the revenue when the price per unit is \$25.

a.   \$14375200
b.   \$14375000
c.   \$14375100
d.   \$14375400
e.   \$14375300

_____ 4.   Find the standard form of the quadratic function shown below:

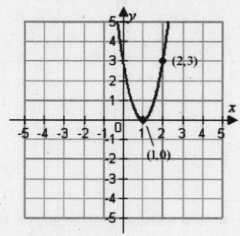

a. $f(x) = x^2 + 1$
b. $f(x) = 3(x + 1)^2$
c. $f(x) = (x - 1)^2$
d. $f(x) = (x + 1)^2$
e. $f(x) = 3(x - 1)^2$

_____ 5.   Select the correct description of right-hand and left-hand behavior of the graph of the polynomial function.

$$f(x) = \frac{1}{2}x^3 + 5x$$

a.   Falls to the right
b.   Rises to the left, falls to the right
c.   Rises to the right, rises to the left
d.   Falls to the left, rises to the right
e.   Falls to the left, falls to the right

_____ 6.   Select from the following which is the polynomial function that has the given zeros.

$-5,-2,0,2,5$

a. $f(x) = x^5 + 29x^3 + 100x$

b. $f(x) = x^5 - 29x^3 + 100$

c. $f(x) = -x^5 - 29x^3 + 100x$

d. $f(x) = x^5 - 29x^3 + 100x$

e. $f(x) = x^5 - 29x^3 - 100x$

_____ 7.   A roofing contractor is fabricating gutters from 10-inch aluminum sheeting. The contractor plans to use an aluminum siding folding press to create the gutter by creasing equal lengths for the sidewalls (see figure).

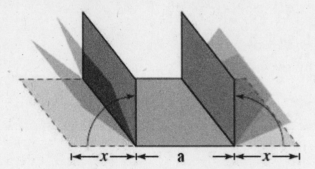

where $a = 10 - 2x$

Let x represent the height of the sidewall of the gutter. Write a function A that represents the cross-sectional area of the gutter.

a. $A = 10x^2 - 2x$

b. $A = -10x - 2x^2$

c. $A = -2x^2 + 10x$

d. $A = 2x^2 + 10x$

e. $A = 2x^2 - 10x$

_____ 8.   Use long division to divide.

$$\left(x^4 + 8x^3 + 15x^2 - x - 3 \right) \div (x+3)$$

a. $x^3 + 5x^2 + 1$

b. $x^3 + 5x^2 + 1$

c. $x^3 - 5x^2 + 1$

d. $x^3 - 5x^2 - 1$

e. $x^3 + 5x^2 - 1$

_____ 9.   Use synthetic division to divide.

$$\left(3x^3 - 8x^2 - 33x - 10\right) \div (x - 5)$$

a. $3x^2 - 9x - 5$

b. $3x^2 + x - 10$

c. $3x^2 + 7x + 2$

d. $3x^2 - 14x + 3$

e. $3x^2 + 5x + 6$

_____ 10.   Simplify the rational expression, $\dfrac{-4x^3 + 31x^2 - 35x - 100}{-4x - 5}$, by using long division or synthetic division.

a. $x^2 - 10x - 20$

b. $x^2 - 8x + 25$

c. $x^2 - x + 20$

d. $x^2 + x + 16$

e. $x^2 - 9x + 20$

_____ 11.   Use synthetic division to divide.

$$\frac{x^3 + 64}{x + 4}$$

a. $x^2 - 4x - 16, \; x \ne -4$

b. $-x^2 + 4x - 16, \; x \ne -4$

c. $x^2 + 4x + 16, \; x \ne -4$

d. $x^2 - 4x + 16, \; x \ne -4$

e. $x^2 + 4x - 16, \; x \ne -4$

_____ 12.   Write the complex number in standard form.

$$-13i + i^2$$

a. $1 - 13i$

b. $-1 + 13i$

c. $1 + 13i$

d. $-1 - 16i$

e. $-1 - 13i$

_____ 13. Write the complex conjugate of the complex number. Then multiply the number by its complex conjugate.

$-7+\sqrt{6}i$

a. $-7+\sqrt{6}i, 55$
b. $-6-\sqrt{7}i, 55$
c. $-7-\sqrt{6}i, 55$
d. $7+\sqrt{6}i, 55$
e. $7-\sqrt{6}i, 55$

_____ 14. Solve the equation and write complex solutions in standard form.
$x^2-12x+39=0$
a. $x=3+\sqrt{3}i, 3-\sqrt{3}i$
b. $x=3+\sqrt{5}i, 3-\sqrt{5}i$
c. $x=5+\sqrt{3}i, 5-\sqrt{3}i$
d. $x=6+\sqrt{5}i, 6-\sqrt{5}i$
e. $x=6+\sqrt{3}i, 6-\sqrt{3}i$

_____ 15. Find all the rational zeros of the function.

$x^3+12x^2+36x+32$

a. $-8, -2, 2$
b. $8, -2$
c. $-8, -2$
d. $-8, 2$
e. $8, 2$

_____ 16. Find all the zeros of the function and write the polynomial as a product of linear factors.

x^4-625

a. $\pm 5, \pm 5i; (x-5)(x-5)(x+5i)(x+5i)$
b. $\pm 5i; (x-5i)(x+5i)$
c. $5, 5i; (x+5)(x+5)(x-5i)(x-5i)$
d. $\pm 5 (x-5)(x+5)$
e. $\pm 5, \pm 5i; (x-5)(x+5)(x-5i)(x+5i)$

_____ 17.   Find all real solutions of the polynomial equation $x^4 - 3x^3 + 6x - 4 = 0$.

a. $x = 1, -4, 4$

b. $x = 1, -3, -2$

c. $x = 1, 4$

d. $x = 1, \pm\sqrt{2}$

e. $x = 1, 2, \pm\sqrt{2}$

_____ 18.   Write $f(x) = x^3 + 5x^2 + 9x + 45$ as a product of linear factors.

a. $x = (x + 5)(x - 5)(x + 3)$

b. $x = (x - 5)(x - 3)^2$

c. $x = (x - 5)(x + 3)^2$

d. $x = (x - 5)^2(x - 3i)$

e. $x = (x + 5)(x + 3i)(x - 3i)$

_____ 19.   Find the zeros of the rational function.

$$g(x) = \frac{x^2 - 16}{x + 4}$$

a. $x = -16$

b. $x = -4$

c. $x = 4$

d. $x = 0$

e. $x = 16$

_____ 20.   Find all intercepts of the following function.

$$g(s) = \frac{6s}{s^2 + 6}$$

a. y-intercept: $(0, 6)$

b. intercept: $(0, 0)$

c. y-intercept: $(0, -6)$

d. x-intercept: $(6, 0)$

e. x-intercept: $(-6, 0)$

_____ 21. Which of the following is the graph of the given equation?

$$f(x) = \frac{x-2}{x-3}$$

a.

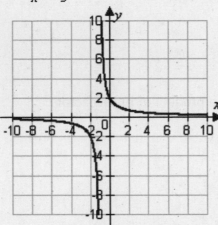

d.

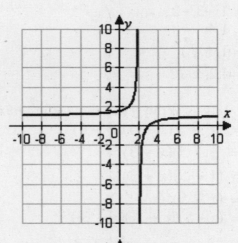

b.

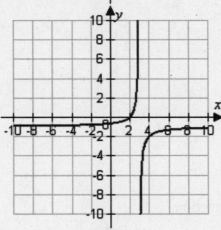

e.

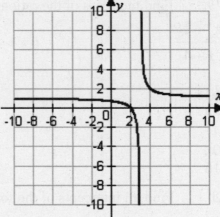

c.

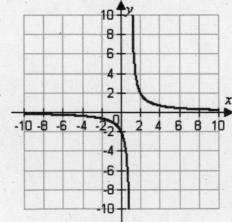

_____   22.   Solve the inequality and graph the solution on the real number line.

$x^2 < 4$

a. $(-2, 2)$

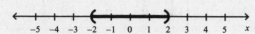

b. $(2, -2)$

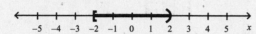

c. $[-2, 2]$

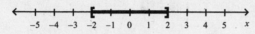

d. $(-2, 2)$

e. $[-2, 2]$

_____   23.   Use a graphing utility to graph the equation. Use the graph to approximate the values of x that satisfy the inequality.

Equation:

$$y = \frac{1}{2}x^2 - 2x + 1$$

Inequalities:
$$y \leq 0$$

a.

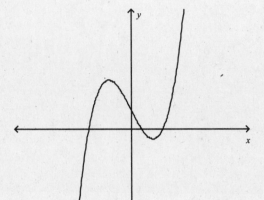

$$2 - \sqrt{2} \geq x \geq 2 + \sqrt{2}$$

d.

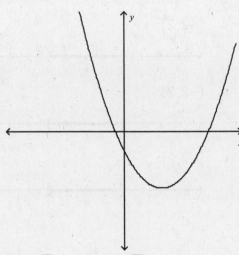

$$2 + \sqrt{2} \leq x \leq 2 - \sqrt{2}$$

b.

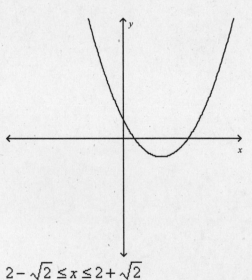

$$2 - \sqrt{2} \leq x \leq 2 + \sqrt{2}$$

e.

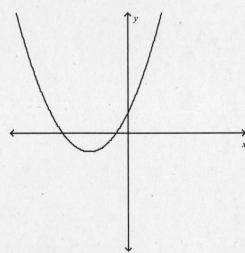

$$2 - \sqrt{2} \leq x \leq 2 + \sqrt{2}$$

c.

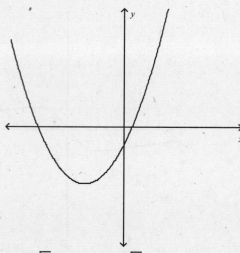

$$2 + \sqrt{2} \le x \le 2 + \sqrt{2}$$

_____ 24.   Use a graphing utility to graph the equation. Use the graph to approximate the values of x that satisfy each inequality.

Equation:

$$y = \frac{4x}{x^2 + 3}$$

Inequality:

$$y \ge 1$$

a.

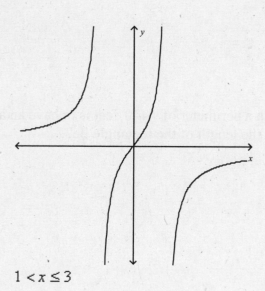

$$1 < x \le 3$$

d.

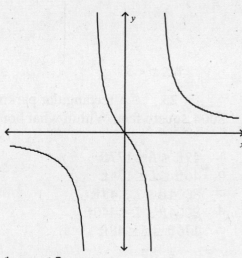

$$1 < x \le 3$$

b.

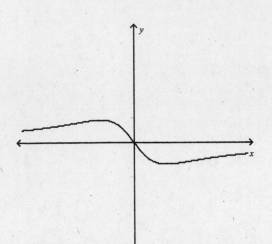

$1 < x < 3$

e.

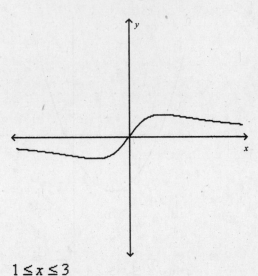

$1 \leq x \leq 3$

c.

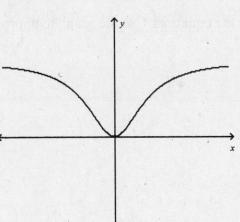

$1 \leq x < 3$

_____ 25. A rectangular parking lot with a perimeter of 440 feet is to have an area of at least 8004 square feet. Within what bounds must the length of the rectangle lie?

a. $49\,\text{ft} \leq L \leq 177\,\text{ft}$
b. $46\,\text{ft} \leq L \leq 174\,\text{ft}$
c. $8004\,\text{ft} \leq L \leq 47\,\text{ft}$
d. $8004\,\text{ft} \leq L \leq 440\,\text{ft}$
e. $176\,\text{ft} \leq L \leq 48\,\text{ft}$

Ch 2 Form B
Answer Section

1.	ANS:	D	PTS:	1	REF:	2.1.13d
2.	ANS:	D	PTS:	1	REF:	2.1.19
3.	ANS:	B	PTS:	1	REF:	2.1.79a
4.	ANS:	E	PTS:	1	REF:	2.1.7
5.	ANS:	D	PTS:	1	REF:	2.2.21
6.	ANS:	D	PTS:	1	REF:	2.2.62
7.	ANS:	C	PTS:	1	REF:	2.2.99a
8.	ANS:	E	PTS:	1	REF:	2.3.15
9.	ANS:	C	PTS:	1	REF:	2.3.27
10.	ANS:	E	PTS:	1	REF:	2.3.81
11.	ANS:	D	PTS:	1	REF:	2.3.39
12.	ANS:	E	PTS:	1	REF:	2.4.17
13.	ANS:	C	PTS:	1	REF:	2.4.44
14.	ANS:	E	PTS:	1	REF:	2.4.70
15.	ANS:	C	PTS:	1	REF:	2.5.23
16.	ANS:	E	PTS:	1	REF:	2.5.67
17.	ANS:	E	PTS:	1	REF:	2.5.30
18.	ANS:	E	PTS:	1	REF:	2.5.74
19.	ANS:	C	PTS:	1	REF:	2.6.21
20.	ANS:	B	PTS:	1	REF:	2.6.39b
21.	ANS:	E	PTS:	1	REF:	2.6.17
22.	ANS:	A	PTS:	1	REF:	2.7.13
23.	ANS:	B	PTS:	1	REF:	2.7.38
24.	ANS:	E	PTS:	1	REF:	2.7.58a
25.	ANS:	B	PTS:	1	REF:	2.7.74

Ch 2 Form C

_____ 1.   Select the graph of the function $y = x^2 - 1$. Compare the graph of this function with the graph of $y = x^2$.

a.

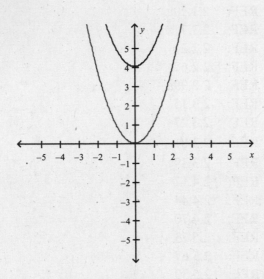

Horizontal stretch and vertical shift.

d.

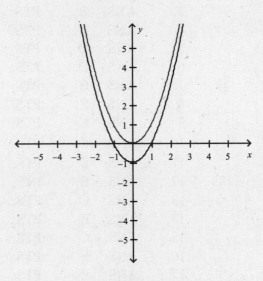

Horizontal stretch and vertical shift.

b.

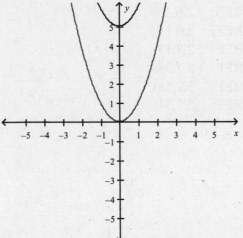

Horizontal stretch and vertical shift.

e.

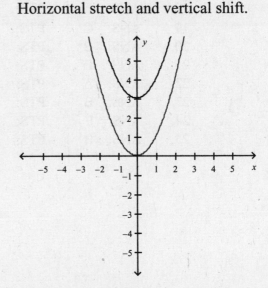

Horizontal stretch and vertical shift.

c.

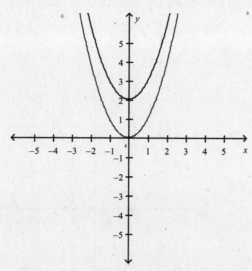

Horizontal stretch and vertical shift.

_____ 2.   Find two positive real numbers whose product is a maximum. The sum is 200.

a. 120,80
b. 130,70
c. 100, 100
d. 110,90
e. 10,190

_____ 3.   A small theater has a seating capacity of 2000. When the ticket price is $20, attend-
ance is 1500. For each $1 decrease in price, attendance increases by 105. Write the revenue R of the
theater as a function of ticket price x

a. $R(x) = -105x^2 - 350x,$ $15 \le x \le 20$
b. $R(x) = 105x^2 + 3500x,$ $15 \le x \le 20$
c. $R(x) = -105x^2 + 3500x,$ $15 \le x \le 20$
d. $R(x) = -105x^3 + 3500x,$ $15 \le x \le 20$
e. $R(x) = -105x^2 + 1500x,$ $15 \le x \le 20$

_____ 4.   Determine the x-intercept(s) of the quadratic function $f(x) = x^2 + 10x + 26$.
a. $(-3, 0), (-8, 0)$
b. $(-10, 0), (10, 0)$
c. no x-intercept(s)
d. $(-10, 0), (-8, 0)$
e. $(-5, 0), (16, 0)$

_____ 5.   Select the correct graph of the functions f and g in the same viewing window. Zoom out sufficiently far to show that the right-hand and left-hand behaviors of and appear identical.

$f(x) = 5x^3 - 6x + 1, \quad g(x) = 5x^3$

a.

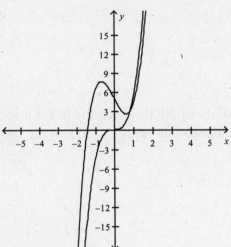

d.

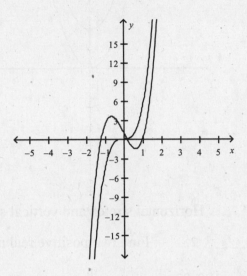

b.

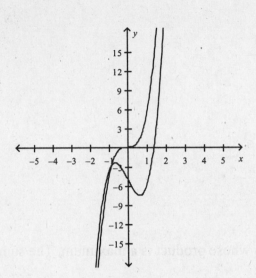

e.

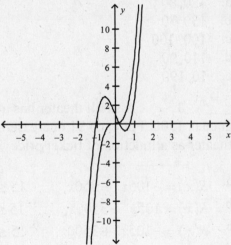

c.

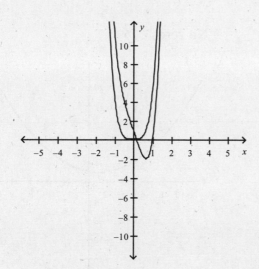

_____ 6.   Select the graph of the function and determine the zeros of the polynomial.

$$f(t) = \frac{1}{6}\left(t^2 - 2x + 12\right)$$

a.

No zeros

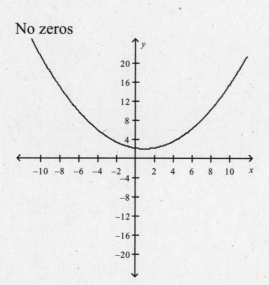

d.

$6, -6$

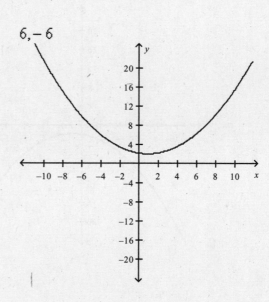

b.

$0, 6, -6$

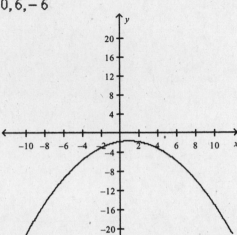

e.

No zeros

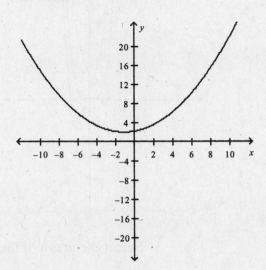

c.

No zeros

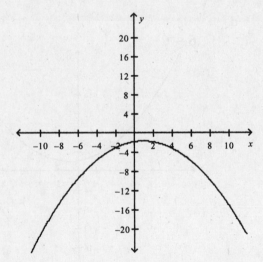

_____ 7.   Select the correct graph of the function given by $f(x) = x^4$. Explain how the graph of function g differs (if it does) from the graph of each function f.

$$g(x) = \frac{1}{6}f(x)$$

a.

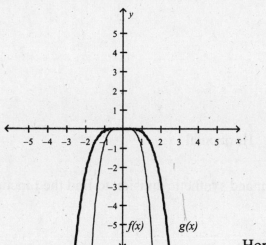

stretch   Horizontal

Horizontal
stretch

d.

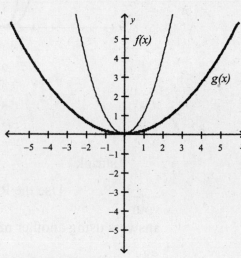

Vertical stretch

b.

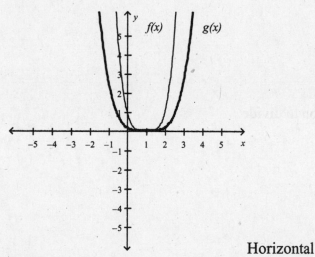

shrink   Horizontal
shrink

e.

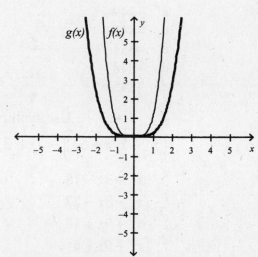

Vertical shrink

c.

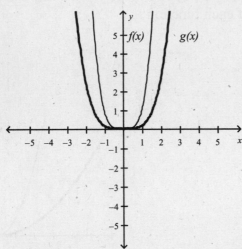

Horizontal

shrink

____   8.   Use the Remainder Theorem and synthetic division to find the function value. Verify your

answers using another method.

$$h(x) = x^3 - 6x^2 - 5x + 7, \qquad h(-8)$$

a. −849
b. −847
c. −851
d. −848
e. −845

____   9.   Use synthetic division to divide.
$$\left(x^3 - 27x + 54 \right) \div (x - 3)$$

a. $x^2 + 3x - 18$

b. $x^2 - 3x - 27$

c. $x^2 + 9x + 18$

d. $x^2 + 9x - 6$

e. $x^2 + 6x + 9$

____   10.   Use long division to divide.

$5x^2 + 8x + 4 \div x + 2$

a. $5x - 4,\ x \neq 2$
b. $5x - 4,\ x \neq -2$
c. $5x^2 - 4x,\ x \neq -2$
d. $5x + 4,\ x \neq -2$
e. $5x^2 + 4x,\ x \neq -2$

____   11.   Use synthetic division to divide.

$$\frac{4x^3 + 20x^2 - 27x - 18}{x + \dfrac{1}{2}}$$

a.
$\quad 4x^2 + 18x + 36,\ x \neq -\dfrac{1}{2}$

b.
$\quad 4x^2 + 18x - 36,\ x \neq -\dfrac{1}{2}$

c.
$\quad 4x^2 - 18x - 36,\ x \neq -\dfrac{1}{2}$

d.
$\quad -4x^2 + 18x - 36,\ x \neq -\dfrac{1}{2}$

e.
$\quad -x^2 - 18x - 36,\ x \neq -\dfrac{1}{2}$

____   12.   Perform the addition or subtraction and write the result in standard form.

$(5 - i) - (3 - i)$

a. 2
b. 4
c. 6
d. 5
e. 3

163

____   13.   Write the quotient in standard form.

$$-\frac{21}{3i}$$

a. $7i$

b. $\dfrac{7}{i}$

c. $-\dfrac{i}{7}$

d. $-7i$

e. $-\dfrac{7}{i}$

____   14.   Simplify the complex number and write it in standard form.

$$-35i^5$$

a. $-35i^3$

b. $35i^3$

c. $-35i$

d. -35

e. $35i$

____   15.   Select the graph of f.

$$f(x) = x^3 + x^2 - 4x - 4$$

a.

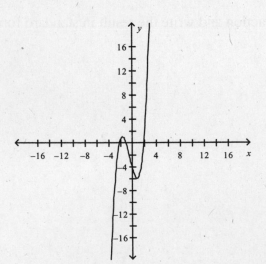

d.

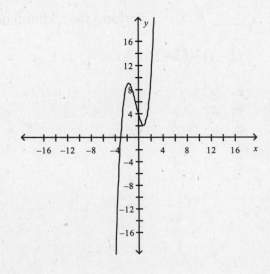

b.

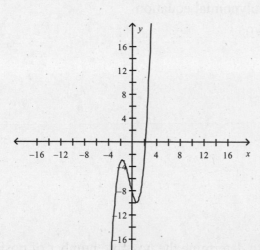

e.

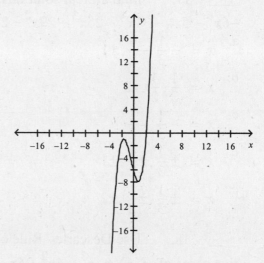

c.

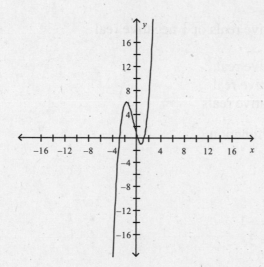

_____   16.   Find all the zeros of the function and write the polynomial as a product of linear factors.

$x^3 - 15x^2 + 73x - 111$

a. $6 \pm i, 3; (x - 6 + i)(x + 6 - i)(x - 3)$
b. $6 \pm i, 3; (x - 6 + i)(x - 6 + i)(x - 3)$
c. $-6 \pm i, 3; (x + 6 + i)(x + 6 - i)(x - 3)$
d. $6 \pm i, -3; (x - 6 + i)(x - 6 - i)(x + 3)$
e. $6 \pm i, 3; (x - 6 + i)(x - 6 - i)(x - 3)$

_____ 17.   Find all real solutions of the polynomial equation

$-6x^6 - 5x^5 - 31x^4 - 25x^3 - 29x^2 - 20x - 4 = 0.$

a. $x = -\dfrac{1}{3}, -\dfrac{1}{2}, \pm 1$

b. $x = \dfrac{1}{3}, \dfrac{1}{2}, \pm 2$

c. $x = -\dfrac{1}{3}, -\dfrac{1}{2}$

d. $x = \pm\dfrac{1}{3}, \pm\dfrac{1}{2}, \pm 1$

e. $x = \pm\dfrac{1}{3}, \pm\dfrac{1}{2}, \pm 2$

_____ 18.   Use Descartes' Rule of Signs to determine the possible number of positive and negative zeros of $f(x) = x^3 - 4x^2 + 6x - 5.$

a. 3 positive reals or 1 positive real; 3 negative reals or 1 negative real
b. no positive reals; no negative reals
c. 3 positive reals or 1 positive real; 1 negative real
d. 1 positive real; 3 negative reals or 1 negative real
e. 3 positive reals or 1 positive real; no negative reals

_____ 19.   Find domain of the following function.

$g(x) = \dfrac{x^2 - 9}{x^2 - 2x - 3}$

a. all real numbers x except $x = -9$ and $x = -1$
b. all real numbers x except $x = -2$ and $x = 3$
c. all real numbers x except $x = 2$ and $x = 9$
d. all real numbers x except $x = 3$ and $x = -1$
e. all real numbers x except $x = -3$ and $x = 1$

_____ 20.   Select the correct graph of the following function.

$$f(x) = \frac{x^2 - 9}{x}$$

a.

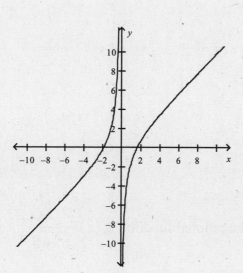

d.

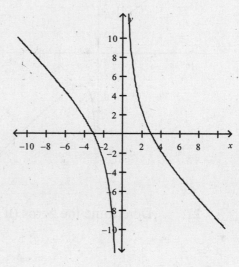

b.

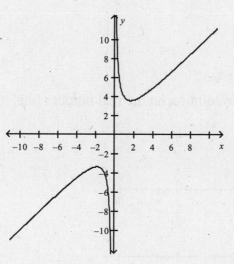

e.

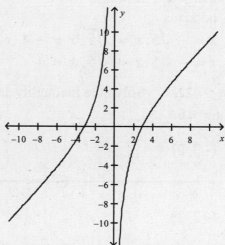

c.

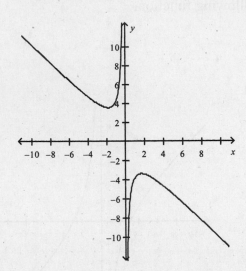

_____ 21.   Determine the zeros (if any) of the rational function $g(x)\dfrac{x^3-64}{x^2+5}$.

a. $x = 4$
b. $x = -4, x = 4$
c. no zeros
d. $x = -\sqrt{5}, x = \sqrt{5}, x = -4, x = 4$
e. $x = -\sqrt{5}, x = \sqrt{5}, x = 4$

_____ 22.   Solve the inequality and graph the solution on the real number line.
$x^2 + x < 6$

a. $(-3, 2)$

b. $(-3, 2)$

c. $(3, 2)$

d. $(-3, -2)$

e. $(-3, -2)$

_____ 23.   Solve the inequality and graph the solution on the real number line.

$$\frac{7x - 9}{x - 9} \geq 0$$

a. $\left(-\infty, \dfrac{9}{7}\right] \cup (9, \infty)$

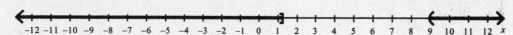

b. $\left(-\infty, \dfrac{9}{7}\right] \cup (-9, \infty)$

c. $\left(-\infty, -\dfrac{9}{7}\right] \cup (9, \infty)$

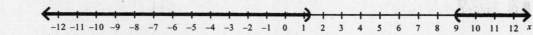

d. $\left(-\infty, -\dfrac{9}{7}\right] \cup (-9, \infty)$

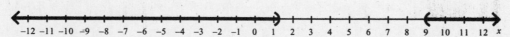

e. $\left(-\infty, \dfrac{9}{7}\right] \cap (9, \infty)$

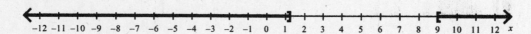

_____ 24.   Find the domain of x in the expression. Use a graphing utility to verify your result.

$$\sqrt{x^2 - 7x + 12}$$

a. $(-\infty, 3] \cup [4, \infty)$

b. $(-\infty, 3] \cap [4, \infty)$

c. $(\infty, -3] \cup [4, \infty)$

d. $(\infty, 3] \cap [4, \infty)$

e. $(\infty, -3] \cap [4, \infty)$

_____ 25.   Find the interval(s) for b such that the following equation has at least one real solution

$x^2 + bx + 5 = 0$.

a. $\left(-\infty, -5\right] \cup \left[-5, \infty\right)$

b. $\left(-\infty, -5\right] \cup \left[5, \infty\right)$

c. $\left(-\infty, -5\right] \cap \left[5, \infty\right]$

d. $\left(-\infty, 5\right] \cap \left[5, \infty\right]$

e. $\left(-\infty, 5\right] \cup \left[5, \infty\right]$

Ch 2 Form C
Answer Section

1.	ANS:	D	PTS:	1	REF:	2.1.14b
2.	ANS:	C	PTS:	1	REF:	2.1.71
3.	ANS:	C	PTS:	1	REF:	2.1.83a
4.	ANS:	C	PTS:	1	REF:	2.1.26
5.	ANS:	D	PTS:	1	REF:	2.2.31
6.	ANS:	A	PTS:	1	REF:	2.2.77b
7.	ANS:	E	PTS:	1	REF:	2.2.109f
8.	ANS:	A	PTS:	1	REF:	2.3.57c
9.	ANS:	A	PTS:	1	REF:	2.3.33
10.	ANS:	B	PTS:	1	REF:	2.3.12
11.	ANS:	B	PTS:	1	REF:	2.3.45
12.	ANS:	A	PTS:	1	REF:	2.4.23
13.	ANS:	A	PTS:	1	REF:	2.4.50
14.	ANS:	C	PTS:	1	REF:	2.4.81
15.	ANS:	A	PTS:	1	REF:	2.5.33b
16.	ANS:	E	PTS:	1	REF:	2.5.70
17.	ANS:	C	PTS:	1	REF:	2.5.32
18.	ANS:	E	PTS:	1	REF:	2.5.92
19.	ANS:	D	PTS:	1	REF:	2.6.27a
20.	ANS:	E	PTS:	1	REF:	2.6.55d
21.	ANS:	A	PTS:	1	REF:	2.6.24
22.	ANS:	A	PTS:	1	REF:	2.7.19
23.	ANS:	A	PTS:	1	REF:	2.7.43
24.	ANS:	A	PTS:	1	REF:	2.7.61
25.	ANS:	B	PTS:	1	REF:	2.7.83a

Ch 2 Form D

_____   1.   Select the graph of the function $y = x^2 - 2$. Compare the graph of this function with the graph of $y = x^2$.

a.

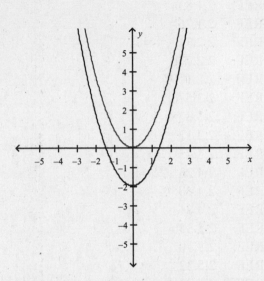

Horizontal stretch and vertical shift.

d.

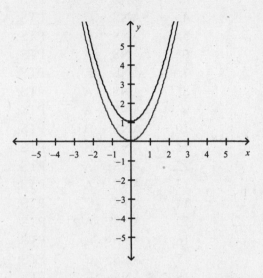

Horizontal stretch and vertical shift.

b.

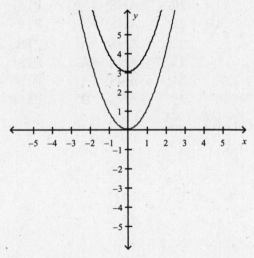

Horizontal stretch and vertical shift.

e.

Horizontal stretch and vertical shift.

c.

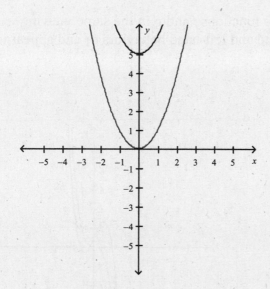

Horizontal stretch and vertical shift.

_____   2.   Find two positive real numbers whose product is a maximum. The sum is 140.

a.   100, 40
b.   10, 130
c.   70, 70
d.   80, 60
e.   90, 50

_____   3.   A small theater has a seating capacity of 2000. When the ticket price is $20, attendance is 1500. For each $1 decrease in price, attendance increases by 105. Write the revenue R of the theater as a function of ticket price x

a. $R(x) = -105x^3 + 3500x, \qquad 15 \le x \le 20$
b. $R(x) = -105x^2 - 350x, \qquad 15 \le x \le 20$
c. $R(x) = -105x^2 + 1500x, \qquad 15 \le x \le 20$
d. $R(x) = -105x^2 + 3500x, \qquad 15 \le x \le 20$
e. $R(x) = 105x^2 + 3500x, \qquad 15 \le x \le 20$

_____   4.   Determine the x-intercept(s) of the quadratic function $f(x) = x^2 - 8x + 17$.
a. $(4, 0), (6, 0)$
b. $(6, 0), (1, 0)$
c. $(-1, 0), (0, 0)$
d.   no x-intercept(s)
e. $(-1, 0), (1, 0)$

_____   5.   Select the correct graph of the functions *f* and *g* in the same viewing window. Zoom out sufficiently far to show that the right-hand and left-hand behaviors of and appear identical.

$$f(x) = 5x^3 - 7x + 1, \quad g(x) = 5x^3$$

a.

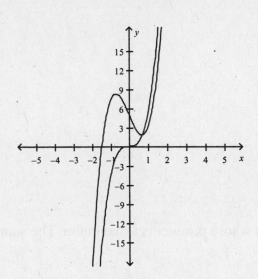

d.

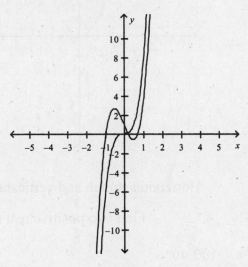

b.

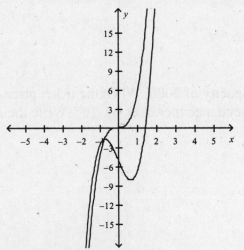

e.

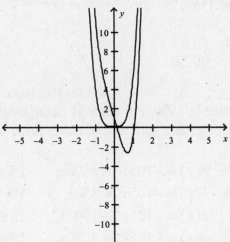

c.

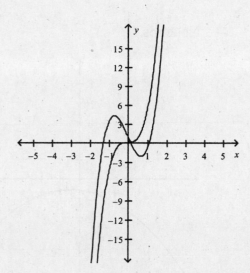

_____   6.   Select the graph of the function and determine the zeros of the polynomial.

$$f(t) = \frac{1}{8}\left(t^2 - 2x + 20\right)$$

a.

$0, 8, -8$

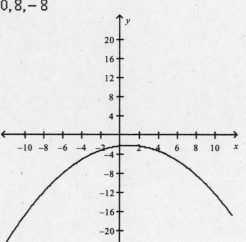

d.

No zeros

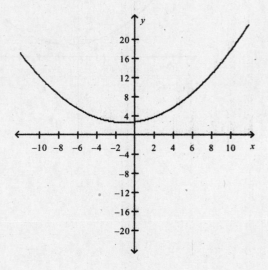

b.

8, −8

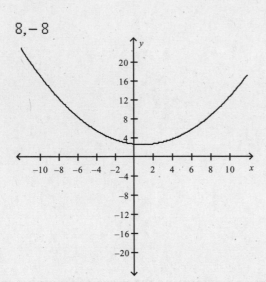

e.

No zeros

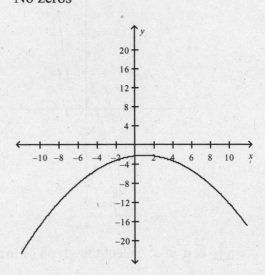

c.

No zeros

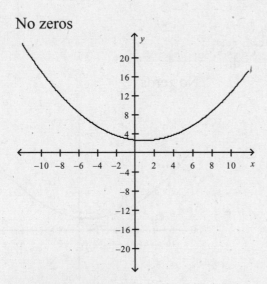

_____   7.   Select the correct graph of the function given by $f(x) = x^4$. Explain how the graph of function g differs (if it does) from the graph of each function f.

$$g(x) = \frac{1}{5}f(x)$$

a.

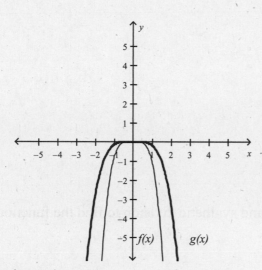

Horizontal stretch

d.

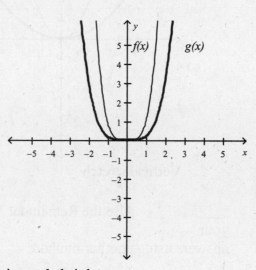

Horizontal shrink

b.

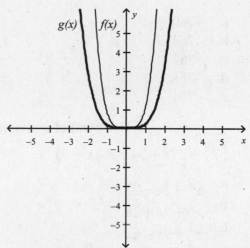

Horizontal shrink

e.

Vertical shrink

c.

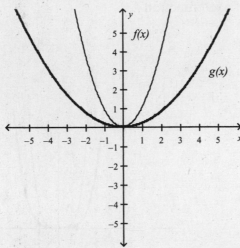

Vertical stretch

_____   8.   Use the Remainder Theorem and synthetic division to find the function value. Verify your
answers using another method.

$$h(x) = x^3 - 5x^2 - 8x + 6, \qquad h(-8)$$

a. -760
b. -764
c. -762
d. -758
e. -761

_____   9.   Use synthetic division to divide.
$$\left(x^3 - 27x + 54 \right) \div (x - 3)$$

a. $x^2 - 3x - 27$
b. $x^2 + 9x + 18$
c. $x^2 + 9x - 6$
d. $x^2 + 3x - 18$
e. $x^2 + 6x + 9$

_____ 10.   Use long division to divide.

$5x^2 + 12x + 9 \div x + 3$

a. $5x - 3, \ x \neq -3$
b. $5x^2 - 4x, \ x \neq -3$
c. $5x^2 + 4x, \ x \neq -3$
d. $5x - 4, \ x \neq 3$
e. $5x + 4, \ x \neq -3$

_____ 11.   Use synthetic division to divide.

$$\frac{4x^3 + 20x^2 - 25x - 17}{x + \dfrac{1}{2}}$$

a.
$-x^2 - 18x - 34, \ x \neq -\dfrac{1}{2}$

b.
$4x^2 - 18x - 34, \ x \neq -\dfrac{1}{2}$

c.
$-4x^2 + 18x - 34, \ x \neq -\dfrac{1}{2}$

d.
$4x^2 + 18x - 34, \ x \neq -\dfrac{1}{2}$

e.
$4x^2 + 18x + 34, \ x \neq -\dfrac{1}{2}$

_____ 12.   Perform the addition or subtraction and write the result in standard form.

$(11 - i) - (7 - i)$

a. 6
b. 7
c. 4
d. 5
e. 8

_____ 13. Write the quotient in standard form.

$$-\frac{15}{3i}$$

a. $5i$

b. $\dfrac{5}{i}$

c. $-\dfrac{5}{i}$

d. $-\dfrac{i}{5}$

e. $-5i$

_____ 14. Simplify the complex number and write it in standard form.

$$-26i^5$$

a. $-26i$

b. $26i^3$

c. -26

d. $26i$

e. $-26i^3$

_____ 15. Select the graph of f.

$$f(x) = x^3 + x^2 - 2x - 2$$

a.

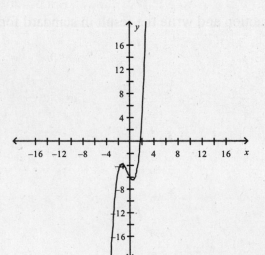

d.

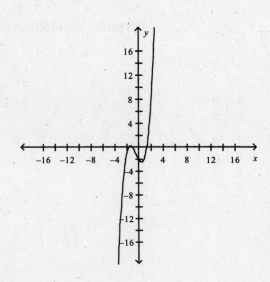

b.

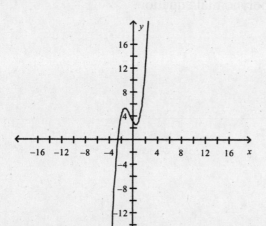

c.

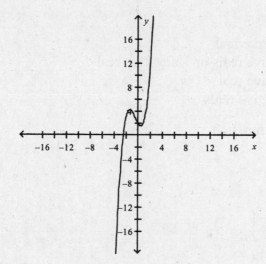

e.

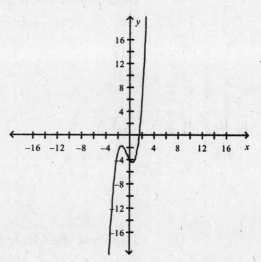

_____ 16.   Find all the zeros of the function and write the polynomial as a product of linear factors.

$x^3 - 12x^2 + 46x - 60$

a. $3 \pm i, 6; (x - 3 + i)(x - 3 + i)(x - 6)$
b. $-3 \pm i, 6; (x + 3 + i)(x + 3 - i)(x - 6)$
c. $3 \pm i, 6; (x - 3 + i)(x + 3 - i)(x - 6)$
d. $3 \pm i, 6; (x - 3 + i)(x - 3 - i)(x - 6)$
e. $3 \pm i, -6; (x - 3 + i)(x - 3 - i)(x + 6)$

_____ 17.   Find all real solutions of the polynomial equation

$6x^6 + x^5 + 29x^4 + 5x^3 + 19x^2 + 4x - 4 = 0.$

a. $x = \dfrac{1}{2}, -\dfrac{1}{3}, \pm 2$

b. $x = \pm\dfrac{1}{2}, \pm\dfrac{1}{3}, \pm 2$

c. $x = \pm\dfrac{1}{2}, \pm\dfrac{1}{3}, \pm 1$

d. $x = -\dfrac{1}{2}, \dfrac{1}{3}$

e. $x = -\dfrac{1}{2}, \dfrac{1}{3}, \pm 1$

_____ 18.   Use Descartes' Rule of Signs to determine the possible number of positive and negative zeros of $f(x) = 4x^3 - x^2 + 2x - 1$.

a.   no positive reals; no negative reals

b.   1 positive real; 3 negative reals or 1 negative real

c.   3 positive reals or 1 positive real; 3 negative reals or 1 negative real

d.   3 positive reals or 1 positive real; 1 negative real

e.   3 positive reals or 1 positive real; no negative reals

_____ 19.   Find domain of the following function.

$g(x) = \dfrac{x^2 - 49}{x^2 - 6x - 7}$

a.   all real numbers x except $x = 7$ and $x = -1$

b.   all real numbers x except $x = -7$ and $x = 1$

c.   all real numbers x except $x = 6$ and $x = 49$

d.   all real numbers x except $x = -6$ and $x = 7$

e.   all real numbers x except $x = -49$ and $x = -1$

_____   20.   Select the correct graph of the following function.

$$f(x) = \frac{x^2 - 16}{x}$$

a.

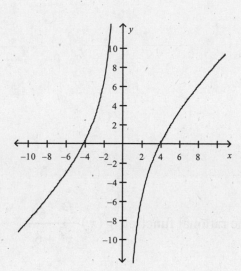

d.

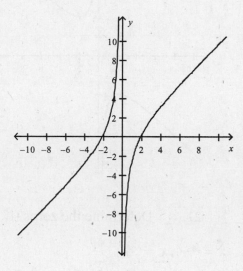

b.

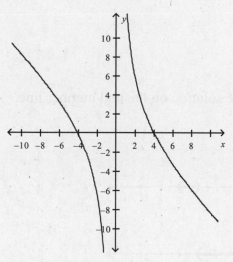

e.

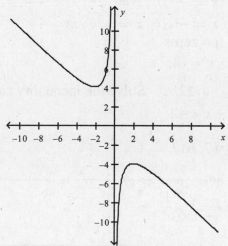

c.

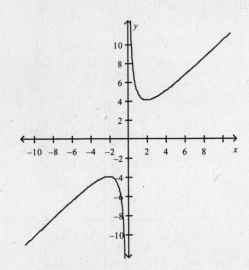

21. Determine the zeros (if any) of the rational function $g(x)\dfrac{x^3-64}{x^2+6}$.

a. $x = -4, x = 4$

b. $x = -\sqrt{6}, x = \sqrt{6}, x = -4, x = 4$

c. $x = -\sqrt{6}, x = \sqrt{6}, x = 4$

d. no zeros

e. $x = 4$

22. Solve the inequality and graph the solution on the real number line.
$x^2 + x < 42$

a. $(7, 6)$

b. $(-7, 6)$

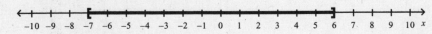

c. $(-7, 6)$

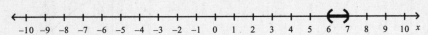

d. $(-7, -6)$

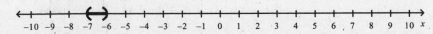

e. $(-7, -6)$

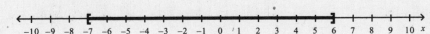

_____   23.   Solve the inequality and graph the solution on the real number line.

$$\frac{5x-7}{x-7} \geq 0$$

a. $\left(-\infty, \dfrac{7}{5}\right] \cup (7, \infty)$

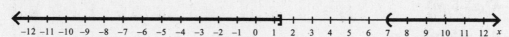

b. $\left(-\infty, -\dfrac{7}{5}\right] \cup (-7, \infty)$

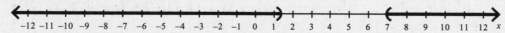

c. $\left(-\infty, \dfrac{7}{5}\right] \cap (7, \infty)$

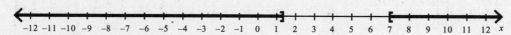

d. $\left(-\infty, -\dfrac{7}{5}\right] \cup (7, \infty)$

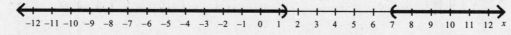

e. $\left(-\infty, \dfrac{7}{5}\right] \cup (-7, \infty)$

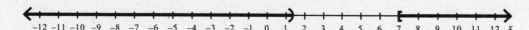

____   24.   Find the domain of x in the expression. Use a graphing utility to verify your result.

$$\sqrt{x^2 - 9x + 20}$$

a. $\left(-\infty, 4\right] \cup \left[5, \infty\right)$

b. $\left(\infty, 4\right] \cap \left[5, \infty\right)$

c. $\left(\infty, -4\right] \cap \left[5, \infty\right)$

d. $\left(\infty, -4\right] \cup \left[5, \infty\right)$

e. $\left(-\infty, 4\right] \cap \left[5, \infty\right)$

____   25.   Find the interval(s) for b such that the following equation has at least one real solution

$$x^2 + bx + 3 = 0.$$

a. $\left(-\infty, -3\right] \cap \left[3, \infty\right]$

b. $\left(-\infty, 3\right] \cap \left[3, \infty\right]$

c. $\left(-\infty, 3\right] \cup \left[3, \infty\right]$

d. $\left(-\infty, -3\right] \cup \left[-3, \infty\right)$

e. $\left(-\infty, -3\right] \cup \left[3, \infty\right)$

Ch 2 Form D
Answer Section

1.	ANS:	A	PTS:	1	REF:	2.1.14b
2.	ANS:	C	PTS:	1	REF:	2.1.71
3.	ANS:	D	PTS:	1	REF:	2.1.83a
4.	ANS:	D	PTS:	1	REF:	2.1.26
5.	ANS:	C	PTS:	1	REF:	2.2.31
6.	ANS:	C	PTS:	1	REF:	2.2.77b
7.	ANS:	E	PTS:	1	REF:	2.2.109f
8.	ANS:	C	PTS:	1	REF:	2.3.57c
9.	ANS:	D	PTS:	1	REF:	2.3.33
10.	ANS:	A	PTS:	1	REF:	2.3.12
11.	ANS:	D	PTS:	1	REF:	2.3.45
12.	ANS:	C	PTS:	1	REF:	2.4.23
13.	ANS:	A	PTS:	1	REF:	2.4.50
14.	ANS:	A	PTS:	1	REF:	2.4.81
15.	ANS:	D	PTS:	1	REF:	2.5.33b
16.	ANS:	D	PTS:	1	REF:	2.5.70
17.	ANS:	D	PTS:	1	REF:	2.5.32
18.	ANS:	E	PTS:	1	REF:	2.5.92
19.	ANS:	A	PTS:	1	REF:	2.6.27a
20.	ANS:	A	PTS:	1	REF:	2.6.55d
21.	ANS:	E	PTS:	1	REF:	2.6.24
22.	ANS:	B	PTS:	1	REF:	2.7.19
23.	ANS:	A	PTS:	1	REF:	2.7.43
24.	ANS:	A	PTS:	1	REF:	2.7.61
25.	ANS:	E	PTS:	1	REF:	2.7.83a

Ch 2 Form E

_____   1.   Use Descartes' Rule of Signs to determine the possible number of positive and negative zeros of $f(x) = 4x^3 - x^2 + 2x - 1$.
a.   no positive reals; no negative reals
b.   1 positive real; 3 negative reals or 1 negative real
c.   3 positive reals or 1 positive real; 3 negative reals or 1 negative real
d.   3 positive reals or 1 positive real; 1 negative real
e.   3 positive reals or 1 positive real; no negative reals

_____   2.   Select the graph of the function $y = (x-1)^2 + 1$. Compare the graph of this function
with the graph of $y = x^2$.

a.

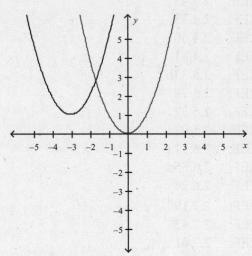

Horizontal shift

d.

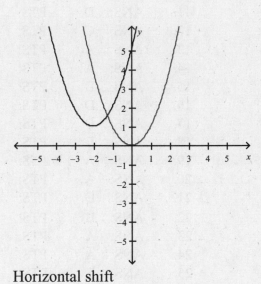

Horizontal shift

b.

Horizontal shift

e.

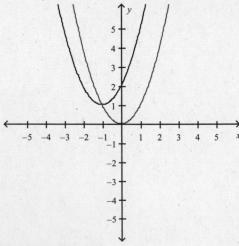

Horizontal shift

c.

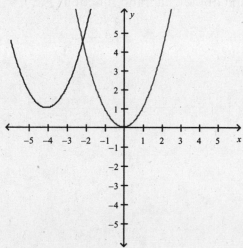

Horizontal shift

____   3.   The height y (in feet) of a punted football is given by

$$y = -\frac{16}{2025}x^2 + \frac{9}{5}x + 1.7$$

where x is the horizontal distance (in feet) from the point at which the ball is punted. What is the maximum height of the punt? (Round your answer to two decimal places.)

a.   144.22
b.   134.22
c.   124.22
d.   104.22
e.   114.22

____   4.   Determine whether the statement is true or false.

The function given by $f(x) = -17x^2 - 6$ has no x-intercepts.

a.   True
b.   False

_____ 5.   Determine the vertex of the graph of the quadratic function $f(x) = x^2 + x + \dfrac{5}{4}$.

a. $\left(\dfrac{1}{2}, \dfrac{5}{4}\right)$

b. $\left(\dfrac{1}{4}, -\dfrac{3}{4}\right)$

c. $\left(\dfrac{-1}{2}, 1\right)$

d. $\left(\dfrac{-1}{2}, \dfrac{3}{2}\right)$

e. $\left(1, \dfrac{5}{4}\right)$

_____ 6.   Determine the multiplicity of each zero and the number of turning points of the graph of the function.

$h(t) = t^2 - 10t + 25$

a. Odd   multiplicity; number of turning points: 1
b. Even multiplicity; number of turning points: 3
c. Even multiplicity; number of turning points: 1
d. Odd   multiplicity; number of turning points: 2
e. Even multiplicity; number of turning points: 2

_____ 7.   Select the graph of the function and determine the zeros of the polynomial.

$f(x) = x^2(x - 6)$

a.
$0, 6, -6$

d.
$0, 6$

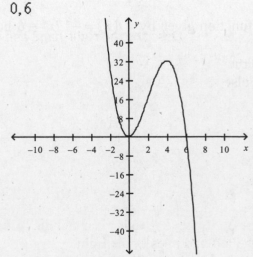

b.

0, 6

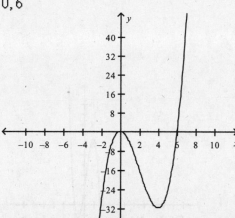

e.

0, − 6

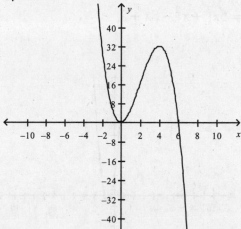

c.

0, − 6

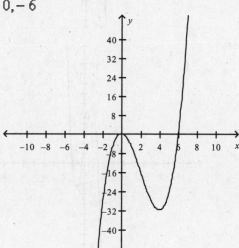

_____ 8.   Describe the right-hand and the left-hand behavior of the graph of
$t(x) = 4x^5 - 7x^3 - 13$.

a. Because the degree is odd and the leading coefficient is positive, the graph falls to the left and rises to the right.

b. Because the degree is odd and the leading coefficient is positive, the graph rises to the left and rises to the right.

c. Because the degree is odd and the leading coefficient is positive, the graph falls to the left and falls to the right.

d. Because the degree is odd and the leading coefficient is positive, the graph rises to the left and falls to the right.

e. Because the degree is even and the leading coefficient is positive, the graph rises to the left and rises to the right.

_____ 9.   Select the correct graph of the following function.

$$f(x) = 5x^3 + x^2 - 8x + 2$$

a.

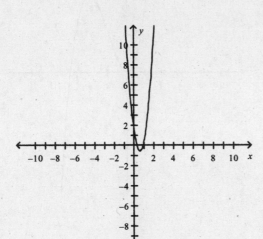

d.

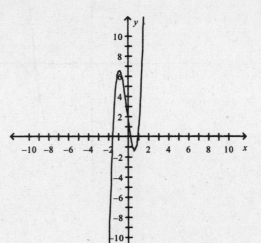

b.

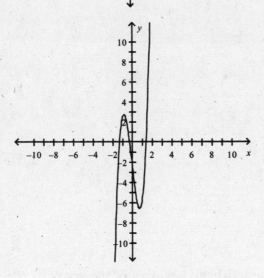

e.

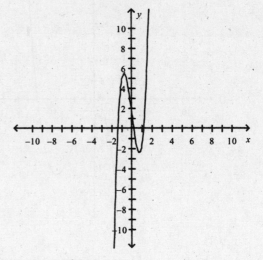

c.

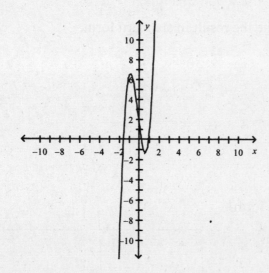

_____ 10.   If $f(x) = -3x^2 - 4x + 1$, use synthetic division to evaluate $f(4)$.
a. $f(4) = -63$
b. $f(4) = 33$
c. $f(4) = -31$
d. $f(4) = -27$
e. $f(4) = 31$

_____ 11.   Use the Remainder Theorem and synthetic division to find the function value. Verify your
answer using another method.

$$f(x) = 4x^3 - 9x + 4, \quad f\left(\frac{1}{2}\right)$$

a. 1
b. 2
c. 0
d. −3
e. −2

_____ 12.   Use long division to divide.

$$\left(x^3 - 125\right) \div (x - 5)$$

a. $x^2 + 5x + 25, \; x \neq 5$
b. $x^2 - 5x + 25, \; x \neq 5$
c. $x^2 + 5x - 25, \; x \neq 5$
d. $x^2 - 5x - 25, \; x \neq 5$

e. $-x^2 + 5x + 25,\ x \neq 5$

____ 13.   Perform the operation and write the result in standard form.

$(1 + i)(4 - 3i)$

a. $8 + i$
b. $7 + i$
c. $9 + i$
d. $11 + i$
e. $10 + i$

____ 14.   Write the quotient in standard form.

$$\frac{7 + 12i}{4i}$$

a. $3 - \dfrac{7}{4}i$

b. $3 - 3i$

c. $3 + \dfrac{7}{4}i$

d. $3i - \dfrac{7}{4}$

e. $3i + \dfrac{7}{4}$

____ 15.   Simplify the complex number and write it in standard form.

$$\frac{7}{i^3}$$

a. $7i^3$
b. $-7i^3$
c. 7
d. $-7i$
e. $7i$

____ 16.   Find a polynomial function with real coefficients that has the given zeros.

$4, -5i$

a. $x^3 - 4x^2 - 25x - 100$
b. $x^3 - 4x^2 + 25x + 100$
c. $x^3 + 4x^2 + 25x + 100$
d. $x^3 - 4x^2 + 25x - 100$

e. $x^3 + 4x^2 + 25x - 100$

_____   17.   Find all the zeros of the function and write the polynomial as a product of linear factors.

$x^4 + 29x^2 + 100$

a. $\pm 5i, \pm 2; (x + 5i)(x - 5i)(x + 2)(x - 2)$
b. $\pm 5i, \pm 2i; (x + 5i)(x - 5i)(x + 2i)(x - 2i)$
c. $-5i, -2i; (x - 5i)(x - 5i)(x - 2i)(x - 2i)$
d. $5i, 2i; (x + 5i)(x + 5i)(x + 2i)(x + 2i)$
e. $\pm 5, \pm 2i; (x + 5)(x - 5)(x + 2i)(x - 2i)$

_____   18.   Given $-5i$ is a root, determine all other roots of $f(x) = x^3 + 5x^2 + 25x + 125$.
a. $x = -5, \pm 5$
b. $x = -5, 5i$
c. $x = -5, \pm 5i$
d. $x = \pm 5, 5i$
e. $x = \pm 5, 5$

_____   19.   Find all intercepts of the following function.

$g(x) = \dfrac{1}{x - 4}$

a.
y-intercept: $\left(0, \dfrac{1}{4}\right)$

b.
x-intercept: $\left(-\dfrac{1}{4}, 0\right)$

c.
y-intercept: $\left(0, -\dfrac{1}{4}\right)$

d.
x-intercept: $\left(\dfrac{1}{4}, 0\right)$

e.
x-intercept: $\left(-\dfrac{1}{4}, 0\right)$ and y-intercept: $\left(0, -\dfrac{1}{4}\right)$

_____ 20. Select the correct graph of the following function.

$$f(x) = \frac{x^2}{2x+1}$$

a.

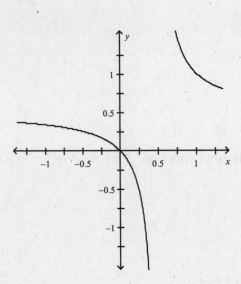

d.

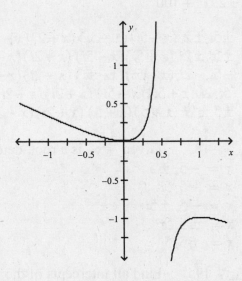

b.

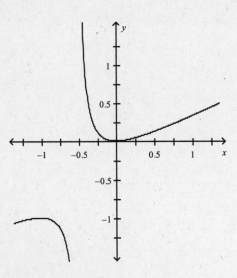

e.

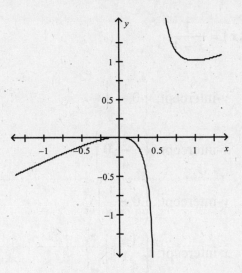

c.

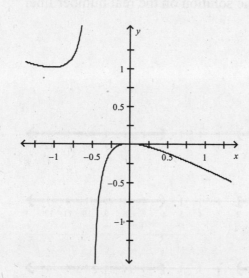

_____ 21.   Determine the equations of any horizontal and vertical asymptotes of

$f(x) = \dfrac{x+6}{x^2-36}$.

a.   horizontal: $y = 0$; vertical: $x = 6$
b.   horizontal: $y = 6$; vertical: $x = 0$
c.   horizontal: $y = -6$; vertical: $x = 6$
d.   horizontal: $y = 0$; vertical: $x = -6$
e.   horizontal: $y = 0$; vertical: none

_____ 22.   Solve the inequality and graph the solution on the real number line.

$x^2 > 2x + 24$

a. $(-\infty, -4) \cup (6, \infty)$

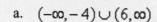

b. $(\infty, 4) \cup (6, \infty)$

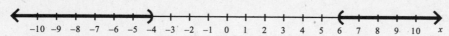

c. $(-\infty, -4) \cup (-6, -\infty)$

d. $(-\infty, -4) \cup (-6, \infty)$

e. $(-\infty, 4) \cup (6, \infty)$

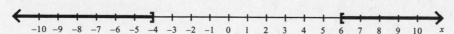

_____   23.   Solve the inequality and graph the solution on the real number line.

$$\frac{2}{x+2} > \frac{1}{x-2}$$

a. $(-2,2) \cup (6,\infty)$

b. $(-2,2) \cap (6,\infty)$

c. $(-2,-2) \cup (6,\infty)$

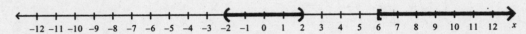

d. $(-2,2) \cap (-6,\infty)$

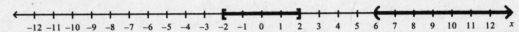

e. $(2,2) \cup (6,\infty)$

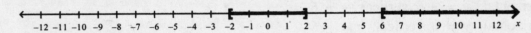

_____   24.   Find the domain of x in the expression. Use a graphing utility to verify your result.

$$\sqrt{\frac{x}{x^2-9}}$$

a. $(-9,0] \cup (9,\infty)$

b. $(-9,0] \cap (9,\infty)$

c. $(-9,0] \cap (3,\infty)$

d. $(-3,0] \cup (3,\infty)$

e. $(-9,0] \cap (-3,\infty)$

_____ 25.   Find the interval(s) for b such that the following equation has at least one real solution and write a conjecture about the interval(s) based on the values of the coefficients

$5x^2 + bx + 10 = 0$.

a. $\left(-\infty, -2\sqrt{50}\right] \cap \left[2\sqrt{50}, \infty\right)$

If $a < 0$ and $c < 0$, $b \leq 2\sqrt{ac}$ or $b \geq 2\sqrt{ac}$

b. $\left(-\infty, 2\sqrt{50}\right] \cup \left[2\sqrt{50}, \infty\right)$

If $a < 0$ and $c > 0$, $b \leq -2\sqrt{ac}$ or $b \geq 2\sqrt{ac}$

c. $\left(-\infty, -2\sqrt{50}\right] \cap \left[-2\sqrt{50}, \infty\right)$

If $a > 0$ and $c < 0$, $b \leq -2\sqrt{ac}$ or $b \geq 2\sqrt{ac}$

d. $\left(-\infty, 2\sqrt{50}\right] \cup \left[2\sqrt{50}, \infty\right)$

If $a > 0$ and $c > 0$, $-b \leq -2\sqrt{ac}$ or $b \leq 2\sqrt{ac}$

e. $\left(-\infty, -2\sqrt{50}\right] \cup \left[2\sqrt{50}, \infty\right)$

If $a > 0$ and $c > 0$, $b \leq -2\sqrt{ac}$ or $b \geq 2\sqrt{ac}$

Ch 2 Form E
Answer Section

1.	ANS:	E	PTS:	1	REF:	2.5.92
2.	ANS:	B	PTS:	1	REF:	2.1.16a
3.	ANS:	D	PTS:	1	REF:	2.1.76b
4.	ANS:	A	PTS:	1	REF:	2.1.87
5.	ANS:	C	PTS:	1	REF:	2.1.27
6.	ANS:	C	PTS:	1	REF:	2.2.37b
7.	ANS:	B	PTS:	1	REF:	2.2.85b
8.	ANS:	A	PTS:	1	REF:	2.2.26
9.	ANS:	D	PTS:	1	REF:	2.3.67e
10.	ANS:	A	PTS:	1	REF:	2.3.55
11.	ANS:	C	PTS:	1	REF:	2.3.55c
12.	ANS:	A	PTS:	1	REF:	2.3.17
13.	ANS:	B	PTS:	1	REF:	2.4.31
14.	ANS:	A	PTS:	1	REF:	2.4.56
15.	ANS:	E	PTS:	1	REF:	2.4.85
16.	ANS:	D	PTS:	1	REF:	2.5.46
17.	ANS:	B	PTS:	1	REF:	2.5.80
18.	ANS:	B	PTS:	1	REF:	2.5.55
19.	ANS:	C	PTS:	1	REF:	2.6.32b
20.	ANS:	B	PTS:	1	REF:	2.6.62d
21.	ANS:	A	PTS:	1	REF:	2.6.26
22.	ANS:	A	PTS:	1	REF:	2.7.22
23.	ANS:	A	PTS:	1	REF:	2.7.47
24.	ANS:	D	PTS:	1	REF:	2.7.64
25.	ANS:	E	PTS:	1	REF:	2.7.85

Ch 2 Form F

____ 1.   Use Descartes' Rule of Signs to determine the possible number of positive and negative zeros of $f(x) = 2x^3 - x^2 + x - 5$.

a.   3 positive reals or 1 positive real; 1 negative real
b.   3 positive reals or 1 positive real; no negative reals
c.   no positive reals; no negative reals
d.   3 positive reals or 1 positive real; 3 negative reals or 1 negative real
e.   1 positive real; 3 negative reals or 1 negative real

____ 2.   Select the graph of the function $y = (x - 1)^2 + 1$. Compare the graph of this function with the graph of $y = x^2$.

a.

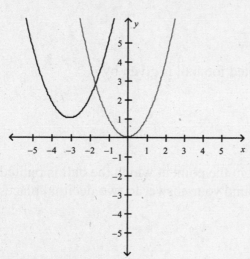

Horizontal shift

d.

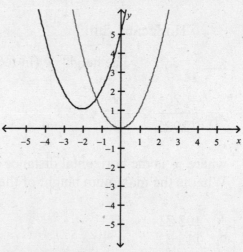

Horizontal shift

b.

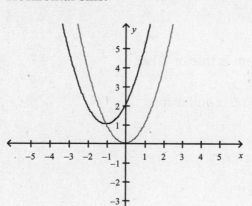

Horizontal shift

e.

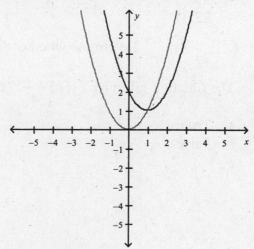

Horizontal shift

c.

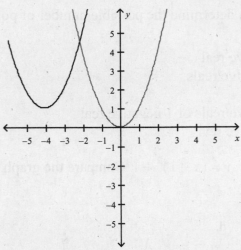

Horizontal shift

_____ 3.   The height y (in feet) of a punted football is given by

$$y = -\frac{20}{2025}x^2 + \frac{9}{5}x + 1.3$$

where x is the horizontal distance (in feet) from the point at which the ball is punted. What is the maximum height of the punt? (Round your answer to two decimal places.)

a. 103.31
b. 113.31
c. 123.31
d. 93.31
e. 83.31

_____ 4.   Determine whether the statement is true or false.

The function given by $f(x) = -17x^2 - 5$ has no x-intercepts.

a. True
b. False

_____ 5.   Determine the vertex of the graph of the quadratic function $f(x) = x^2 + 7x + \dfrac{53}{4}$.

a. $\left(7, \dfrac{53}{4}\right)$

b. $\left(\dfrac{7}{4}, \dfrac{45}{4}\right)$

c. $\left(\dfrac{7}{2}, \dfrac{53}{4}\right)$

d. $\left(\dfrac{-7}{2}, 1\right)$

e. $\left(\dfrac{-7}{2}, \dfrac{51}{2}\right)$

 6.   Determine the multiplicity of each zero and the number of turning points of the graph of the function.

$h(t) = t^2 - 10t + 25$

a. Odd   multiplicity; number of turning points: 1
b. Odd   multiplicity; number of turning points: 2
c. Even multiplicity; number of turning points: 1
d. Even multiplicity; number of turning points: 2
e. Even multiplicity; number of turning points: 3

_____ 7.   Select the graph of the function and determine the zeros of the polynomial.

$f(x) = x^2(x - 5)$

a.   d.

0, 5, -5   0, -5

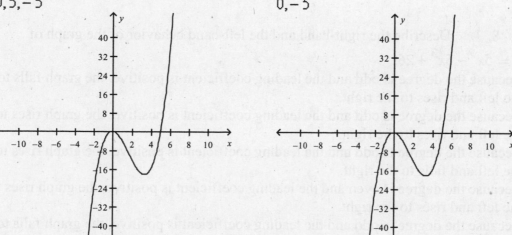

b.

0,− 5

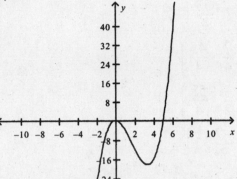

e.

0,5

c.

0,5

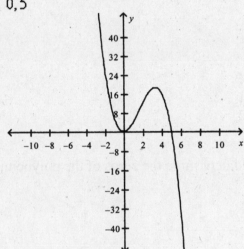

_____ 8.   Describe the right-hand and the left-hand behavior of the graph of
$p(x) = 5x^5 - 6x^3 + 26.$

a. Because the degree is odd and the leading coefficient is positive, the graph falls to the left and rises to the right.

b. Because the degree is odd and the leading coefficient is positive, the graph rises to the left and rises to the right.

c. Because the degree is odd and the leading coefficient is positive, the graph rises to the left and falls to the right.

d. Because the degree is even and the leading coefficient is positive, the graph rises to the left and rises to the right.

e. Because the degree is odd and the leading coefficient is positive, the graph falls to the left and falls to the right.

_____   9.   Select the correct graph of the following function.

$$f(x) = 5x^3 + x^2 - 5x + 5$$

a.

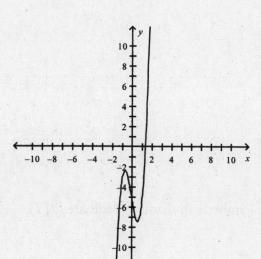

d.

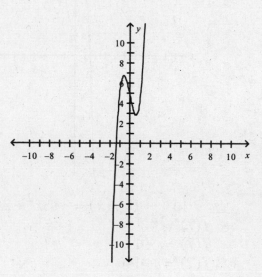

b.

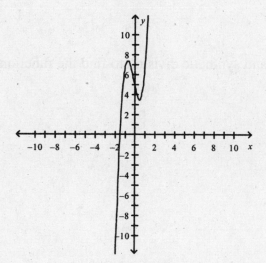

e.

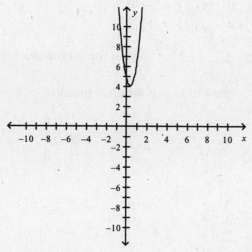

c.

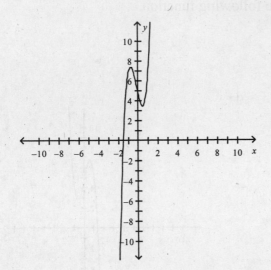

_____ 10. If $f(x) = -3x^2 + 2x - 7$, use synthetic division to evaluate $f(7)$.

a. $f(7) = 42$
b. $f(7) = -14$
c. $f(7) = -140$
d. $f(7) = -168$
e. $f(7) = 154$

_____ 11. Use the Remainder Theorem and synthetic division to find the function value. Verify your
answer using another method.

$$f(x) = 4x^3 - 3x + 4, \quad f\left(\frac{1}{2}\right)$$

a. 1
b. 4
c. 5
d. 3
e. 0

_____ 12. Use long division to divide.

$$\left(x^3 - 216\right) \div (x - 6)$$

a. $x^2 + 6x - 36, \ x \neq 6$
b. $-x^2 + 6x + 36, \ x \neq 6$
c. $x^2 - 6x + 36, \ x \neq 6$
d. $x^2 + 6x + 36, \ x \neq 6$

e. $x^2 - 6x - 36, \ x \neq 6$

_____ 13.   Perform the operation and write the result in standard form.

$(1+i)(6-5i)$

a. $15+i$
b. $11+i$
c. $12+i$
d. $13+i$
e. $14+i$

_____ 14.   Write the quotient in standard form.

$$\dfrac{7+14i}{3i}$$

a. $\dfrac{14}{3}i - \dfrac{7}{3}$

b. $\dfrac{14}{3}i + \dfrac{7}{3}$

c. $\dfrac{14}{3} + \dfrac{7}{3}i$

d. $\dfrac{14}{3} - \dfrac{7}{3}i$

e. $\dfrac{14}{3} - \dfrac{14}{3}i$

_____ 15.   Simplify the complex number and write it in standard form.

$$\dfrac{2}{i^3}$$

a. $2i^3$
b. $-2i$
c. $-2i^3$
d. 2
e. $2i$

_____ 16.   Find a polynomial function with real coefficients that has the given zeros.

$2, -3i$

a. $x^3 - 2x^2 + 9x + 18$
b. $x^3 + 2x^2 + 9x + 18$
c. $x^3 + 2x^2 + 9x - 18$
d. $x^3 - 2x^2 + 9x - 18$
e. $x^3 - 2x^2 - 9x - 18$

_____ 17.   Find all the zeros of the function and write the polynomial as a product of linear factors.

$x^4 + 13x^2 + 36$

a. $-3i, -2i; (x - 3i)(x - 3i)(x - 2i)(x - 2i)$
b. $\pm 3i, \pm 2i; (x + 3i)(x - 3i)(x + 2i)(x - 2i)$
c. $3i, 2i; (x + 3i)(x + 3i)(x + 2i)(x + 2i)$
d. $\pm 3i, \pm 2; (x + 3i)(x - 3i)(x + 2)(x - 2)$
e. $\pm 3, \pm 2i; (x + 3)(x - 3)(x + 2i)(x - 2i)$

_____ 18.   Given $-4i$ is a root, determine all other roots of $f(x) = x^3 - 5x^2 + 16x - 80$.
a. $x = 5, 4i$
b. $x = \pm 5, 4$
c. $x = \pm 5, 4i$
d. $x = -4, \pm 5i$
e. $x = 5, \pm 4$

_____ 19.   Find all intercepts of the following function.

$g(x) = \dfrac{1}{x - 4}$

a.
  y-intercept: $\left(0, -\dfrac{1}{4}\right)$

b.
  y-intercept: $\left(0, \dfrac{1}{4}\right)$

c.
  x-intercept: $\left(-\dfrac{1}{4}, 0\right)$ and y-intercept: $\left(0, -\dfrac{1}{4}\right)$

d.
  x-intercept: $\left(\dfrac{1}{4}, 0\right)$

e.

x-intercept: $\left(-\dfrac{1}{4}, 0\right)$

_____ 20.   Select the correct graph of the following function.

$f(x) = \dfrac{x^2}{6x+1}$

a.

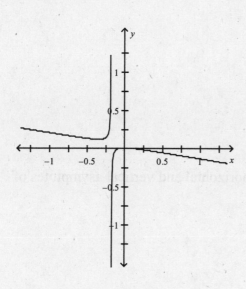

d.

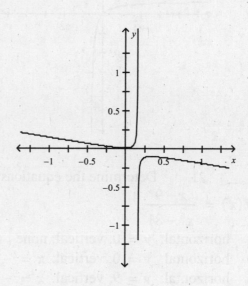

b.

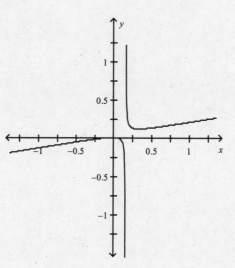

e.

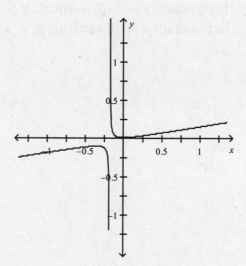

c.

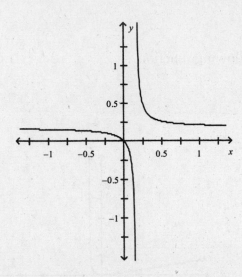

_____ 21. Determine the equations of any horizontal and vertical asymptotes of

$$f(x) = \frac{x-9}{x^2-81}.$$

a. horizontal: $y = 0$; vertical: none
b. horizontal: $y = 0$; vertical: $x = -9$
c. horizontal: $y = 9$; vertical: $x = -9$
d. horizontal: $y = -9$; vertical: $x = 0$
e. horizontal: $y = 0$; vertical: $x = 9$

_____   22.   Solve the inequality and graph the solution on the real number line.

$x^2 > 2x + 8$

a. $(-\infty, -2) \cup (4, \infty)$

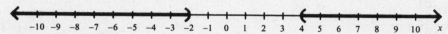

b. $(\infty, 2) \cup (4, \infty)$

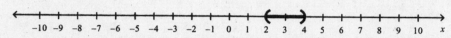

c. $(-\infty, -2) \cup (-4, -\infty)$

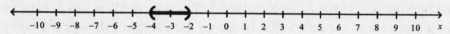

d. $(-\infty, 2) \cup (4, \infty)$

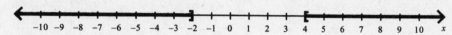

e. $(-\infty, -2) \cup (-4, \infty)$

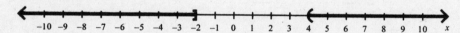

_____   23.   Solve the inequality and graph the solution on the real number line.

$\dfrac{2}{x+1} > \dfrac{1}{x-4}$

a. $(1, 4) \cup (9, \infty)$

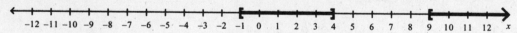

b. $(-1, -4) \cup (9, \infty)$

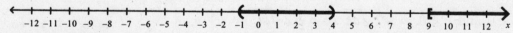

c. $(-1, 4) \cap (9, \infty)$

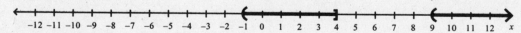

d. $(-1, 4) \cup (9, \infty)$

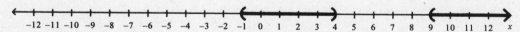

e. $(-1, 4) \cap (-9, \infty)$

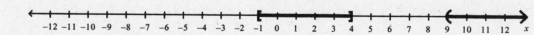

_____ 24.   Find the domain of x in the expression. Use a graphing utility to verify your result.

$$\sqrt{\dfrac{x}{x^2 - 36}}$$

a. $(-36, 0] \cap (-6, \infty)$

b. $(-36, 0] \cup (36, \infty)$

c. $(-6, 0] \cup (6, \infty)$

d. $(-36, 0] \cap (6, \infty)$

e. $(-36, 0] \cap (36, \infty)$

_____ 25.   Find the interval(s) for b such that the following equation has at least one real solution and write a conjecture about the interval(s) based on the values of the coefficients

$5x^2 + bx + 13 = 0.$

a. $\left(-\infty, 2\sqrt{65}\,\right] \cup \left[2\sqrt{65}, \infty\right)$

If $a < 0$ and $c > 0$, $b \leq -2\sqrt{ac}$ or $b \geq 2\sqrt{ac}$

b. $\left(-\infty, 2\sqrt{65}\,\right] \cup \left[2\sqrt{65}, \infty\right)$

If $a > 0$ and $c > 0$, $-b \leq -2\sqrt{ac}$ or $b \leq 2\sqrt{ac}$

c. $\left(-\infty, -2\sqrt{65}\,\right] \cap \left[-2\sqrt{65}, \infty\right)$

If $a > 0$ and $c < 0$, $b \leq -2\sqrt{ac}$ or $b \geq 2\sqrt{ac}$

d. $\left(-\infty, -2\sqrt{65}\,\right] \cup \left[2\sqrt{65}, \infty\right)$

If $a > 0$ and $c > 0$, $b \leq -2\sqrt{ac}$ or $b \geq 2\sqrt{ac}$

e. $\left(-\infty, -2\sqrt{65}\,\right] \cap \left[2\sqrt{65}, \infty\right)$

If $a < 0$ and $c < 0$, $b \leq 2\sqrt{ac}$ or $b \geq 2\sqrt{ac}$

Ch 2 Form F
Answer Section

1.	ANS: B	PTS: 1	REF: 2.5.92
2.	ANS: E	PTS: 1	REF: 2.1.16a
3.	ANS: E	PTS: 1	REF: 2.1.76b
4.	ANS: A	PTS: 1	REF: 2.1.87
5.	ANS: D	PTS: 1	REF: 2.1.27
6.	ANS: C	PTS: 1	REF: 2.2.37b
7.	ANS: E	PTS: 1	REF: 2.2.85b
8.	ANS: A	PTS: 1	REF: 2.2.26
9.	ANS: B	PTS: 1	REF: 2.3.67e
10.	ANS: C	PTS: 1	REF: 2.3.55
11.	ANS: D	PTS: 1	REF: 2.3.55c
12.	ANS: D	PTS: 1	REF: 2.3.17
13.	ANS: B	PTS: 1	REF: 2.4.31
14.	ANS: D	PTS: 1	REF: 2.4.56
15.	ANS: E	PTS: 1	REF: 2.4.85
16.	ANS: D	PTS: 1	REF: 2.5.46
17.	ANS: B	PTS: 1	REF: 2.5.80
18.	ANS: A	PTS: 1	REF: 2.5.55
19.	ANS: A	PTS: 1	REF: 2.6.32b
20.	ANS: E	PTS: 1	REF: 2.6.62d
21.	ANS: B	PTS: 1	REF: 2.6.26
22.	ANS: A	PTS: 1	REF: 2.7.22
23.	ANS: D	PTS: 1	REF: 2.7.47
24.	ANS: C	PTS: 1	REF: 2.7.64
25.	ANS: D	PTS: 1	REF: 2.7.85

Ch 3 Form A

_____ 1.   Evaluate the function at the indicated value of x. Round your result to three decimal places.

Function   _Value_
$f(x) = 0.5^x$ $x = 1.7$

a. -0.308
b. 1.7
c. 0.308
d. 0.5
e. -1.7

_____ 2.   Use a graphing utility to construct a table of values for the function. Round your answer to two decimal places.

$f(x) = 6^{-x}$

a.

x	-2	-1	0	1	2
$f(x)$	36	6	1	0.17	-0.03

b.

x	-2	-1	0	1	2
$f(x)$	-36	6	1	0.17	0.03

c.

x	-2	-1	0	1	2
$f(x)$	36	-6	1	0.17	0.03

d.

x	-2	-1	0	1	2
$f(x)$	36	6	1	-0.17	0.03

e.

x	-2	-1	0	1	2
$f(x)$	36	6	1	0.17	0.03

_____ 3.   Evaluate the function at the indicated value of x. Round your result to three decimal places.

Function

$h(x) = e^{-x}$

Value

$x = \dfrac{7}{8}$

a. 8.07
b. 0.875
c. 1.398
d. 7.5
e. 0.417

_____ 4.   Select the graph of the exponential function.

$s(t) = 2e^{0.13t}$

a.

d.

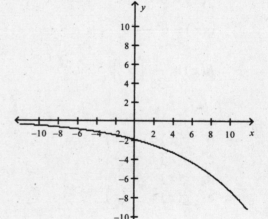

b.

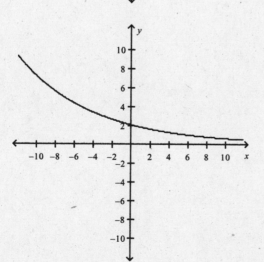

e.

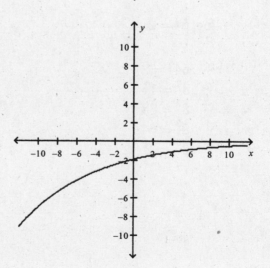

c.

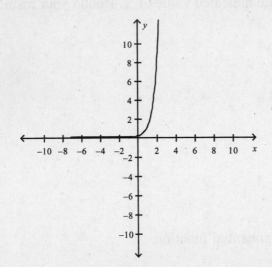

_____ 5.   Use properties of exponents to determine which functions (if any) are the same.

$$f(x) = 6^{x-2}$$

$$g(x) = 6^x - 36$$

$$h(x) = \frac{1}{36}\left(6^x\right)$$

a. $f(x) = h(x)$
b. $f(x) = -g(x)$
c. $f(x) = g(x)$
d. $g(x) = h(x)$
e. $g(x) = -h(x)$

_____ 6.   Write the logarithmic equation in exponential form.

$$\log_8 64 = 2$$

a. $64^8 = 2$
b. $8^2 = 16$
c. $8^2 = 88$
d. $8^2 = 64$
e. $8^{64} = 2$

_____ 7.   Write the exponential equation in logarithmic form.

$$4^{-2} = \frac{1}{16}$$

a. $\log_{16} \frac{1}{4} = -2$

b. $\log_4 \frac{1}{16} = 2$

c. $\log_4 16 = 2$

d. $\log_4 \frac{1}{16} = -2$

e. $\log_4 16 = -2$

_____ 8.   Evaluate the function at the indicated value of $x = a^2$.

$$g(x) = \log_a x$$

a. -2

b. $\frac{1}{2}$

c. $-\frac{1}{2}$

d. 2

e. 0

_____ 9.   Write the exponential equation in logarithmic form.

$$e^{4x} = 5$$

a. $\ln 5 = -4x$

b. $\ln 5 = -\frac{1}{4} x$

c. $\ln 5 = \frac{1}{4} x$

d. $\ln 5 = 4x$

e. $\ln 4 = 5x$

_____ 10. Use the One-to-One Property to solve the equation for *x*.

$$\log_2(8x+2) = \log_2 14$$

a. 8

b. $\dfrac{1}{6}$

c. $\dfrac{3}{2}$

d. $\dfrac{1}{14}$

e. $\dfrac{1}{8}$

_____ 11. Rewrite the logarithm as a ratio of common logarithms.

$$\log_5 17$$

a. $\dfrac{\log 5}{\log 17}$

b. $\log \dfrac{17}{5}$

c. $\dfrac{\log 17}{\log 5}$

d. $\log \dfrac{5}{17}$

e. None of these

_____ 12. Find the exact value of the logarithmic expression without using a calculator.

$$\log_9 \sqrt[3]{9}$$

a. 3

b. $\dfrac{1}{3}$

c. 9

d. 27

e. None of these

_____ 13. Condense the expression to the logarithm of a single quantity.

$\log x - 2\log y + 3\log z$

a. $\log \dfrac{z^3}{xy^2}$

b. $\log \dfrac{x}{y^2 z^3}$

c. $\log \dfrac{xy^2}{z^3}$

d. $\log \dfrac{y^2}{xz^3}$

e. $\log \dfrac{xz^3}{y^2}$

_____ 14. Evaluate the logarithm using the change-of-base formula. Round your result to three decimal places.

$\log_4 9$

a. 1.585
b. 5.585
c. 3.585
d. 4.585
e. 2.585

_____ 15.   Evaluate the logarithm $\log_{1/3} 1.877$ using the change of base formula. Round to 3 decimal places.

a. -1.745
b. -0.692
c. 0.630
d. 0.273
e. -0.573

_____ 16.   Determine whether the given x-value is a solution (or an approximate solution) of the equation.

$4^{5x-5} = 1024$

$x = 2$

a.   No

b.   Yes

____ 17. Solve for x. Approximate the result to three decimal places.

$$\log_5 x = \frac{1}{2}$$

a. $\sqrt{5} \approx 2.236$
b. $\sqrt{5} = 2.236$
c. $\sqrt{5} \approx -2.236$
d. $\dfrac{\sqrt{5}}{5} \approx 2.236$
e. $\sqrt{5} \approx 2.449$

____ 18. Solve the exponential equation algebraically. Approximate the result to three decimal places.

$$e^x - 8 = 12$$

a. $\ln 20 \approx 2.485$
b. $\ln 20 \approx 2.996$
c. $\ln 20 \approx -2.485$
d. $\ln 20 \approx 2.079$
e. $\ln 20 \approx -2.996$

____ 19. Solve the exponential equation algebraically. Approximate the result to three decimal places.

$$e^{2x} - 5e^x - 6 = 0$$

a. $\ln 6 \approx 3.792$
b. $\ln 6 \approx 2.792$
c. $\ln 6 \approx 0.792$
d. $\ln 6 \approx -0.208$
e. $\ln 6 \approx 1.792$

_____ 20.   Solve the logarithmic equation algebraically. Approximate the result to three decimal places.

$$6\log_3(0.5x) = 5$$

a. $2\left(3^{5/6}\right) \approx 3.996$

b. $2\left(3^{5/6}\right) \approx 6.996$

c. $2\left(3^{5/6}\right) \approx 4.996$

d. $2\left(3^{5/6}\right) \approx 5.996$

e. $2\left(3^{5/6}\right) \approx 2.996$

_____ 21.   Determine the principal that must be invested at rate r, compounded monthly, so that $\$1,500,000$ will be available for retirement in t years.

$r = 5\%, t = 10$

(Round the answer upto 2 decimal places.)

a. $\$1,110,741.56$
b. $\$1,010,741.56$
c. $\$710,741.56$
d. $\$810,741.56$
e. $\$910,741.56$

_____ 22.   Complete the table for a savings account in which interest is compounded continuously.

Initial investment	Annual % rate	Time to double	Amount after 10 years
$1000	$10\dfrac{1}{2}\%$	----	----

(Round the answer upto two decimal places.)

a. Time to double: $6.6\,yr$
   Amount after 10 years: $\$2857.65$
b. Time to double: $6.6\,yr$
   Amount after 10 years: $\$3107.65$
c. Time to double: $1.60\,yr$
   Amount after 10 years: $\$2857.65$
d. Time to double: $6.6\,yr$
   Amount after 10 years: $\$3357.65$
e. Time to double: $11.60\,yr$
   Amount after 10 years: $\$2857.65$

_____ 23.   Select a scatter plot of the given data.

r	2%	4%	6%	8%	10%	12%
t	55.48	28.01	18.85	14.27	11.53	9.69

a.

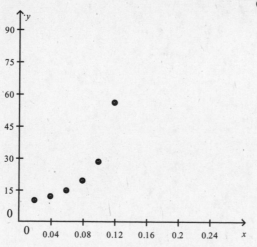

d.

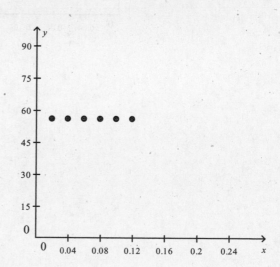

b.

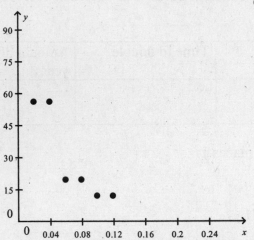

e.

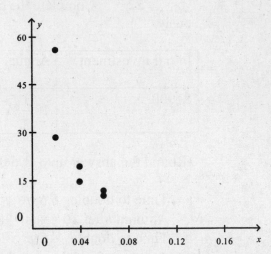

c.

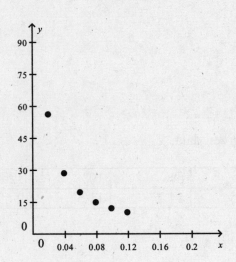

_____ 24.   Find the exponential model that $y = ae^{bx}$ fits the points shown in the table.

x	0	4
y	25	5

a. $y = 25e^{-0.4024x}$

b. $y = 25e^{0.5024x}$

c. $y = -\dfrac{1}{25}e^{0.4024x}$

d. $y = \dfrac{1}{25}e^{-0.6024x}$

e. $y = -\dfrac{1}{25}e^{-0.4024x}$

_____ 25.   Find the magnitude R of each earthquake of intensity I $\left(\text{let } I_0 = 1\right)$.

$I = 262300000$

a. 7.42

b. 6.42

c. 8.42

d. 10.42

e. 9.42

Ch 3 Form A
Answer Section

1.	ANS: C	PTS: 1	REF: 3.1.7
2.	ANS: E	PTS: 1	REF: 3.1.19a
3.	ANS: E	PTS: 1	REF: 3.1.33
4.	ANS: A	PTS: 1	REF: 3.1.47
5.	ANS: A	PTS: 1	REF: 3.1.79
6.	ANS: D	PTS: 1	REF: 3.2.7
7.	ANS: D	PTS: 1	REF: 3.2.19
8.	ANS: D	PTS: 1	REF: 3.2.27
9.	ANS: D	PTS: 1	REF: 3.2.66
10.	ANS: C	PTS: 1	REF: 3.2.88
11.	ANS: C	PTS: 1	REF: 3.3.7a
12.	ANS: B	PTS: 1	REF: 3.3.32
13.	ANS: E	PTS: 1	REF: 3.3.77
14.	ANS: A	PTS: 1	REF: 3.3.15
15.	ANS: E	PTS: 1	REF: 3.3.17
16.	ANS: B	PTS: 1	REF: 3.4.5a
17.	ANS: A	PTS: 1	REF: 3.4.24
18.	ANS: B	PTS: 1	REF: 3.4.37
19.	ANS: E	PTS: 1	REF: 3.4.59
20.	ANS: C	PTS: 1	REF: 3.4.97
21.	ANS: E	PTS: 1	REF: 3.5.23
22.	ANS: A	PTS: 1	REF: 3.5.16
23.	ANS: C	PTS: 1	REF: 3.5.30
24.	ANS: A	PTS: 1	REF: 3.5.41
25.	ANS: C	PTS: 1	REF: 3.5.64c

Ch 3 Form B

_____ 1.   Evaluate the function at the indicated value of x. Round your result to three decimal places.

Function   *Value*

$f(x) = 0.7^x$ $x = 1.2$

a. -1.2
b. -0.652
c. 1.2
d. 0.7
e. 0.652

_____ 2.   Use a graphing utility to construct a table of values for the function. Round your answer to two decimal places.

$f(x) = 2^{-x}$

a.

x	-2	-1	0	1	2
$f(x)$	4	-2	1	0.5	0.25

b.

x	-2	-1	0	1	2
$f(x)$	-4	2	1	0.5	0.25

c.

x	-2	-1	0	1	2
$f(x)$	4	2	1	0.5	0.25

d.

x	-2	-1	0	1	2
$f(x)$	4	2	1	-0.5	0.25

e.

x	-2	-1	0	1	2
$f(x)$	4	2	1	0.5	-0.25

_____   3.   Evaluate the function at the indicated value of x. Round your result to three decimal places.

Function   *Value*

$h(x) = e^{-x}$ $x = \dfrac{9}{8}$

a. 1.648
b. 0.325
c. 1.125
d. 9.5
e. 8.07

_____   4.   Select the graph of the exponential function.

$s(t) = 6e^{0.17t}$

a.

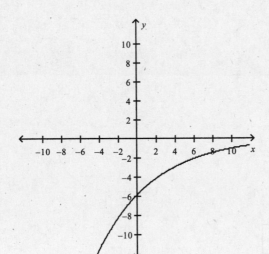

d.

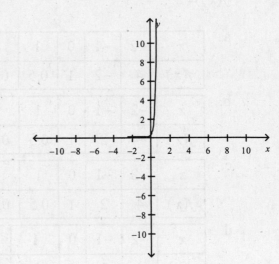

b.

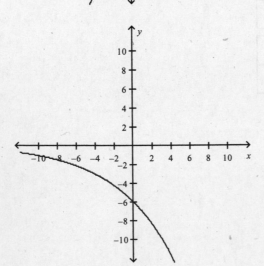

e.

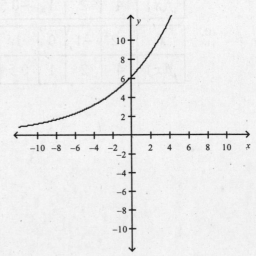

c.

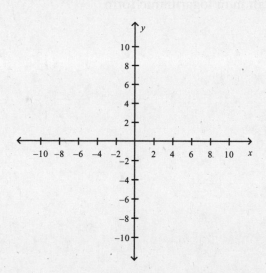

_____ 5.   Use properties of exponents to determine which functions (if any) are the same.

$f(x) = 3^{x-2}$

$g(x) = 3^x - 9$

$h(x) = \dfrac{1}{9}\left(3^x\right)$

a. $g(x) = h(x)$
b. $f(x) = h(x)$
c. $f(x) = -g(x)$
d. $f(x) = g(x)$
e. $g(x) = -h(x)$

_____ 6.   Write the logarithmic equation in exponential form.

$\log_7 49 = 2$

a. $49^7 = 2$
b. $7^2 = 49$
c. $7^2 = 77$
d. $7^{49} = 2$
e. $7^2 = 14$

229

_____ 7.   Write the exponential equation in logarithmic form.

$$9^{-2} = \frac{1}{81}$$

a. $\log_9 81 = -2$

b. $\log_9 \dfrac{1}{81} = -2$

c. $\log_9 81 = 2$

d. $\log_9 \dfrac{1}{81} = 2$

e. $\log_{81} \dfrac{1}{9} = -2$

_____ 8.   Evaluate the function at the indicated value of $x = a^8$.

$$g(x) = \log_a x$$

a. $-\dfrac{1}{8}$

b. -8

c. 0

d. 8

e. $\dfrac{1}{8}$

_____ 9.   Write the exponential equation in logarithmic form.

$$e^{9x} = 10$$

a. $\ln 10 = -9x$

b. $\ln 10 = 9x$

c. $\ln 10 = \dfrac{1}{9} x$

d. $\ln 10 = -\dfrac{1}{9} x$

e. $\ln 9 = 10x$

_____ 10.   Use the One-to-One Property to solve the equation for x.

$\log_4(6x+5) = \log_4 7$

a. $\dfrac{1}{6}$

b. $\dfrac{1}{7}$

c. $\dfrac{1}{3}$

d. 1

e. 6

_____ 11.   Rewrite the logarithm as a ratio of common logarithms.

$\log_5 19$

a. $\dfrac{\log 19}{\log 5}$

b. $\dfrac{19}{\log \dfrac{19}{5}}$

c. $\dfrac{5}{\log \dfrac{5}{19}}$

d. $\dfrac{\log 5}{\log 19}$

e. None of these

_____ 12.   Find the exact value of the logarithmic expression without using a calculator.

$\log_9 \sqrt[2]{9}$

a. 9

b. 18

c. $\dfrac{1}{2}$

d. 2

e. None of these

_____ 13.   Condense the expression to the logarithm of a single quantity.

$\log x - 4\log y + 5\log z$

a. $\log \dfrac{x}{y^4 z^5}$

b. $\log \dfrac{xz^5}{y^4}$

c. $\log \dfrac{y^4}{xz^5}$

d. $\log \dfrac{xy^4}{z^5}$

e. $\log \dfrac{z^5}{xy^4}$

_____ 14.   Evaluate the logarithm using the change-of-base formula. Round your result to three decimal places.

$\log_3 7$

a. 4.771
b. 3.771
c. 2.771
d. 5.771
e. 1.771

_____ 15.   Evaluate the logarithm $\log_{1/3} 1.289$ using the change of base formula. Round to 3 decimal places.

a. 0.254
b. −4.328
c. −0.231
d. 0.110
e. −0.279

_____ 16.   Determine whether the given x-value is a solution (or an approximate solution) of the equation.

$$4^{5x-5} = 1024$$

$$x = 2$$

a. Yes
b. No

_____ 17. Solve for x. Approximate the result to three decimal places.

$$\log_5 x = \frac{1}{2}$$

a. $\dfrac{\sqrt{5}}{5} \approx 2.236$

b. $\sqrt{5} \approx -2.236$

c. $\sqrt{5} \approx 2.236$

d. $\sqrt{5} \approx 2.449$

e. $\sqrt{5} = 2.236$

_____ 18. Solve the exponential equation algebraically. Approximate the result to three decimal places.

$$e^x - 9 = 15$$

a. $\ln 24 \approx 2.708$

b. $\ln 24 \approx 2.197$

c. $\ln 24 \approx -2.708$

d. $\ln 24 \approx -3.178$

e. $\ln 24 \approx 3.178$

_____ 19. Solve the exponential equation algebraically. Approximate the result to three decimal places.

$$e^{2x} - 7e^x - 8 = 0$$

a. $\ln 8 \approx 3.079$

b. $\ln 8 \approx 2.079$

c. $\ln 8 \approx 1.079$

d. $\ln 8 \approx 4.079$

e. $\ln 8 \approx 0.079$

_____ 20.   Solve the logarithmic equation algebraically. Approximate the result to three decimal places.

$6\log_4(0.5x) = 23$

a. $2\left(4^{23/6}\right) \approx 408.375$

b. $2\left(4^{23/6}\right) \approx 406.375$

c. $2\left(4^{23/6}\right) \approx 404.375$

d. $2\left(4^{23/6}\right) \approx 407.375$

e. $2\left(4^{23/6}\right) \approx 405.375$

_____ 21.   Determine the principal that must be invested at rate r, compounded monthly, so that $800,000$ will be available for retirement in t years.

$r = 5\%, t = 10$

(Round the answer upto 2 decimal places.)

a. $685,728.83
b. $285,728.83
c. $385,728.83
d. $485,728.83
e. $585,728.83

_____ 22.   Complete the table for a savings account in which interest is compounded continuously.

Initial investment	Annual % rate	Time to double	Amount after 10 years
$750	$7\frac{1}{2}\%$	----	----

(Round the answer upto two decimal places.)

a. Time to double: $9.24\,yr$
    Amount after 10 years: $1837.75
b. Time to double: $9.24\,yr$
    Amount after 10 years: $2087.75
c. Time to double: $9.24\,yr$
    Amount after 10 years: $1587.75
d. Time to double: $4.24\,yr$
    Amount after 10 years: $1587.75
e. Time to double: $14.24\,yr$
    Amount after 10 years: $1587.75

_____ 23.   Select a scatter plot of the given data.

r	4%	6%	8%	10%	12%	14%
t	28.01	18.85	14.27	11.53	9.69	8.38

a.

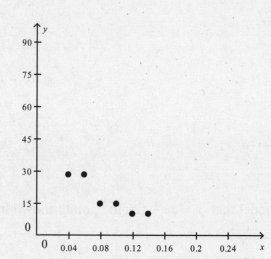

d.

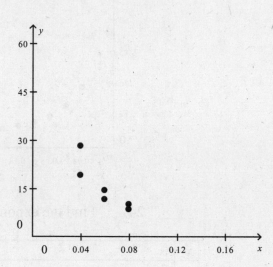

b.

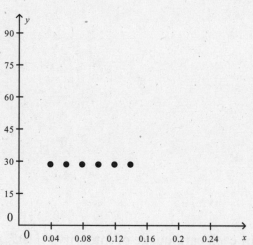

e.

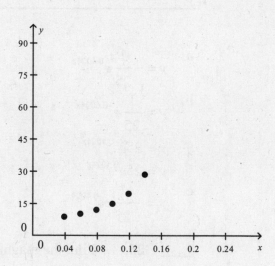

c.

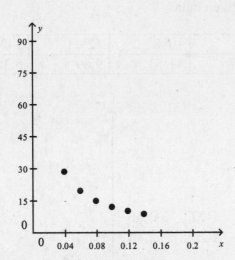

_____ 24. Find the exponential model that $y = ae^{bx}$ fits the points shown in the table.

x	0	4
y	25	5

a. $y = -\dfrac{1}{25}e^{0.4024x}$

b. $y = \dfrac{1}{25}e^{-0.6024x}$

c. $y = 25e^{-0.4024x}$

d. $y = 25e^{0.5024x}$

e. $y = -\dfrac{1}{25}e^{-0.4024x}$

_____ 25. Find the magnitude R of each earthquake of intensity I $\left(\text{let } I_0 = 1\right)$.

$I = 221300000$

a. 8.34

b. 9.34

c. 7.34

d. 6.34

e. 10.34

Ch 3 Form B
Answer Section

1.	ANS: E	PTS:	1	REF:	3.1.7
2.	ANS: C	PTS:	1	REF:	3.1.19a
3.	ANS: B	PTS:	1	REF:	3.1.33
4.	ANS: E	PTS:	1	REF:	3.1.47
5.	ANS: B	PTS:	1	REF:	3.1.79
6.	ANS: B	PTS:	1	REF:	3.2.7
7.	ANS: B	PTS:	1	REF:	3.2.19
8.	ANS: D	PTS:	1	REF:	3.2.27
9.	ANS: B	PTS:	1	REF:	3.2.66
10.	ANS: C	PTS:	1	REF:	3.2.88
11.	ANS: A	PTS:	1	REF:	3.3.7a
12.	ANS: C	PTS:	1	REF:	3.3.32
13.	ANS: B	PTS:	1	REF:	3.3.77
14.	ANS: E	PTS:	1	REF:	3.3.15
15.	ANS: C	PTS:	1	REF:	3.3.17
16.	ANS: A	PTS:	1	REF:	3.4.5a
17.	ANS: C	PTS:	1	REF:	3.4.24
18.	ANS: E	PTS:	1	REF:	3.4.37
19.	ANS: B	PTS:	1	REF:	3.4.59
20.	ANS: B	PTS:	1	REF:	3.4.97
21.	ANS: D	PTS:	1	REF:	3.5.23
22.	ANS: C	PTS:	1	REF:	3.5.16
23.	ANS: C	PTS:	1	REF:	3.5.30
24.	ANS: C	PTS:	1	REF:	3.5.41
25.	ANS: A	PTS:	1	REF:	3.5.64c

Ch 3 Form C

_____ 1. Evaluate the function at the indicated value of x. Round your result to three decimal places.

Function

$f(x) = 6000\left(6^x\right)$

Value

$x = -1.3$

a. 584.191
b. 784.191
c. −584.191
d. 684.191
e. −784.191

_____ 2. Use the graph of f to determine the transformation that yields the graph of g.

$f(x) = 3^x, g(x) = 3^x + 8$

a. Shift the graph of f eight units to the left.
b. Shift the graph of f eight units upward.
c. Shift the graph of f eight units to the right.
d. Shift the graph of f eight units downward.
e. Both the graphs f and g are same.

_____ 3. Use a graphing utility to construct a table of values for the function. Round your answer to three decimal places.

$f(x) = e^{3x}$

a.

x	−2	−1	0	1	2
$f(x)$	0.002	0.05	−1	20.086	403.429

b.

x	−2	−1	0	1	2
$f(x)$	0.002	0.05	1	−20.086	403.429

c.

x	−2	−1	0	1	2
$f(x)$	0.002	0.05	1	20.086	403.429

d.

x	−2	−1	0	1	2
$f(x)$	0.002	−0.05	1	20.086	403.429

e.

x	−2	−1	0	1	2
$f(x)$	0.002	−0.05	−1	−20.086	−403.429

_____ 4.   Use the One-to-One Property to solve the equation for x.

$$\left(\frac{1}{2}\right)^{x} = 16$$

a. $x = 5$
b. $x = -4$
c. $x = 4$
d. $x = -5$
e. $x = 6$

_____ 5.   Identify the graph of the function.

$$f(x) = \left(\frac{1}{2}\right)^{1-x}$$

a.

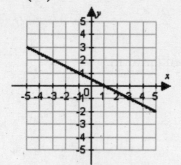

b.

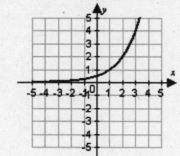

c.

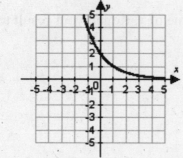

d.

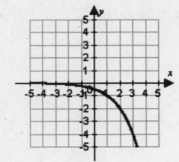

e.

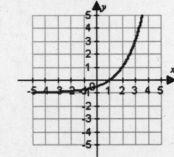

_____ 6. Write the logarithmic equation in exponential form.

$$\log \frac{1}{343} = -3$$

a. $7^{-3} = -343$

b. $343^{-3} = \frac{1}{7}$

c. $7^{-3} = -\frac{1}{343}$

d. $7^{-3} = 343$

e. $7^{-3} = \frac{1}{343}$

_____ 7. Evaluate $f(x) = \log x$ at the indicated value of x. Round your result to three decimal places.

$$x = \frac{3}{2}$$

a. 5.682

b. 1.5

c. −0.176

d. −5.682

e. 0.176

_____ 8.   Write the logarithmic equation in exponential form.

$$\ln\left(\frac{1}{6}\right) = -1.792\ldots$$

a. $e^{1.792\ldots} = -\dfrac{1}{6}$

b. $e^{1.792\ldots} = \dfrac{1}{6}$

c. $e^{-1.792\ldots} = 6$

d. $e^{-1.792\ldots} = \dfrac{1}{6}$

e. $e^{-1.792\ldots} = -\dfrac{1}{6}$

_____ 9.   Evaluate the function at the indicated value of $x = 0.57$. Round your result to three decimal places.

$$f(x) = 9\ln x$$

a. 5.059
b. −14.947
c. 0.57
d. −5.059
e. 14.947

_____ 10.   Identify the value of the function $f(x) = \log_{10} x$ at $x = 415$. Round to 3 decimal places.

a. 6.028
b. 3.618
c. 2.618
d. 4.118
e. 3.118

_____ 11.   Rewrite the logarithm as a ratio of common logarithms.

$\log_{1/7} x$

a. $\dfrac{\log x}{\log \dfrac{1}{7}}$

b. $\dfrac{\log \dfrac{1}{7}}{\log x}$

c. $\log \dfrac{x}{7}$

d. $\log 7x$

e. None of these

_____ 12.   Use the properties of logarithms to expand the expression as a sum, difference, and/or constant multiple of logarithms. (Assume all variables are positive.)

$\log_3 9x$

a. $\dfrac{\log_3 9}{\log_3 x}$

b. $\log_3 9 \times \log_3 x$

c. $\log_3 9 + \log_3 x$

d. $\log_3 9 - \log_3 x$

e. None of these

_____ 13. Condense the expression to the logarithm of a single quantity.

$$\frac{1}{2}\left[\log_7(x+8)+2\log_7(x-8)\right]-16\log_7 x$$

a. $\log_7 \dfrac{(x-8)\sqrt{x+8}}{x^{16}}$

b. $\log_7 \dfrac{x^8\sqrt{x-8}}{(x+8)}$

c. $\log_7 \dfrac{(x+8)\sqrt{x-8}}{x^8}$

d. $\log_7 \dfrac{x^{16}\sqrt{x+8}}{(x-8)}$

e. $\log_7 \dfrac{x^{16}\sqrt{x-8}}{(x+8)}$

_____ 14. Evaluate the logarithm using the change-of-base formula. Round your result to three decimal places.

$\log_{15} 1700$

a. 5.747
b. 3.747
c. 2.747
d. 6.747
e. 4.747

_____ 15. Simplify the expression $\log_3\left(\dfrac{1}{27}\right)^4$.

a. 4
b. The expression cannot be simplified.
c. −12
d. −108
e. 1

_____ 16.   Solve for x.

$6^x = 1,296$

a. 6
b. 10
c. 4
d. -6
e. -4

_____ 17.   Approximate the point of intersection of the graphs of f and g. Then solve the equation $f(x) = g(x)$ algebraically to verify your approximation.

$f(x) = \ln(x - 7)$

$g(x) = 0$

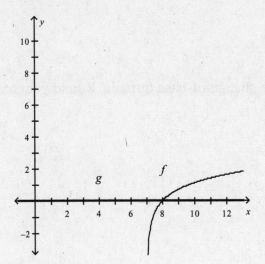

a. $(8, 0)$
b. $(8, 7)$
c. $(7, 0)$
d. $(8, -7)$
e. $(-8, 0)$

_____ 18.   Solve the exponential equation algebraically. Approximate the result to three decimal places.

$2^{-8x} = 0.60$

a. $-\dfrac{\ln(0.60)}{8\ln 2} \approx -0.092$

b. $-\dfrac{\ln(0.60)}{8\ln 2} \approx 0.092$

c. $\dfrac{\ln(0.60)}{8\ln 2} \approx 0.17$

d. $-\dfrac{\ln(0.60)}{8\ln 2} \approx 2.035$

e. $-\dfrac{\ln(0.60)}{8\ln 2} \approx 0.123$

_____ 19.   Solve the logarithmic equation algebraically. Approximate the result to three decimal places.

$\ln x - 4 = 0$

a. $e^4 \approx 55.598$

b. $e^4 \approx 52.598$

c. $e^4 \approx 56.598$

d. $e^4 \approx 57.598$

e. $e^4 \approx 54.598$

_____ 20. $7000 is invested in an account at interest rate r, compounded continuously. Find the time required for the amount to triple. (Approximate the result to two decimal places.)

$r = 0.04$

a.   25.47 yr

b.   28.47 yr

c.   29.47 yr

d.   27.47 yr

e.   26.47 yr

_____ 21. Select the correct graph for the given function

$y = 6 + \log(x + 2)$

a.

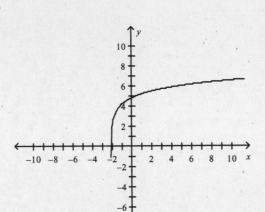

d.

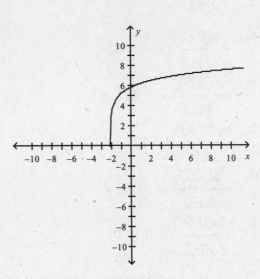

b.

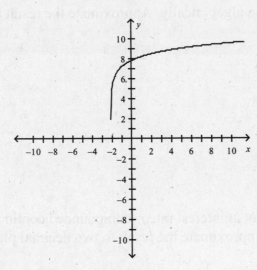

e.

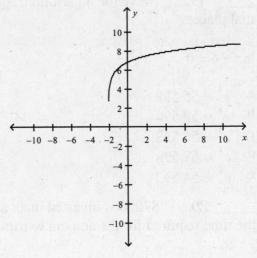

c.

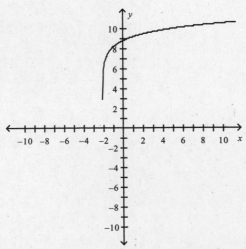

_____ 22.   Complete the table for a savings account in which interest is compounded continuously.

Initial investment	Annual rate	Time to double	Amount after 10 years
$14,000	---	---	$27995.88

(Round the answer upto two decimal places.)

a. Annual rate: 6.93%
    Time to double: 14 yr
b. Annual rate: 6.93%
    Time to double: 10 yr
c. Annual rate: 10.93%
    Time to double: 10 yr
d. Annual rate: 8.93%
    Time to double: 10 yr
e. Annual rate: 6.93%
    Time to double: 15 yr

_____ 23.   Complete the table for the radioactive isotope. Round your answer to two decimal places.

Isotope	Half-life (years)	Initial Quantity	Amount after 1000 years
^{14}C	5715	8g	----

a. Amount after 1000 years: 8.09g
b. Amount after 1000 years: 9.09g
c. Amount after 1000 years: 7.09g
d. Amount after 1000 years: 10.09g
e. Amount after 1000 years: 11.09g

_____ 24.   The number y of hits a new search-engine website receives each month can be modeled by $y = 4080e^{kt}$, where t represents the number of months the website has been operating. In the website's third month, there were 10,000 hits. find the value of k, and use this value to predict the number of hits the website will receive after 28 months.

a. $k = 0.2988$; About 1,110,523,084,335 hits
b. $k = 0.2988$; About 17,544,522 hits
c. $k = 0.2988$; About 137,137,823,414 hits
d. $k = 0.2988$; About 348,187,704 hits
e. $k = 0.2988$; About 6,910,116,039 hits

_____ 25.   An initial investment of $3000 doubles in value in 8.3 years. Assuming continuous compounding, what was the interest rate? Round to the nearest tenth of a percent.
a. 8.4%
b. 3.6%
c. 4.2%
d. 8.3%
e. 100%

Ch 3 Form C
Answer Section

1.	ANS: A	PTS: 1	REF: 3.1.11
2.	ANS: B	PTS: 1	REF: 3.1.23
3.	ANS: C	PTS: 1	REF: 3.1.39a
4.	ANS: B	PTS: 1	REF: 3.1.53
5.	ANS: B	PTS: 1	REF: 3.1.17
6.	ANS: E	PTS: 1	REF: 3.2.10
7.	ANS: E	PTS: 1	REF: 3.2.29
8.	ANS: D	PTS: 1	REF: 3.2.51
9.	ANS: D	PTS: 1	REF: 3.2.68
10.	ANS: C	PTS: 1	REF: 3.2.31
11.	ANS: A	PTS: 1	REF: 3.3.9a
12.	ANS: C	PTS: 1	REF: 3.3.46
13.	ANS: A	PTS: 1	REF: 3.3.84
14.	ANS: C	PTS: 1	REF: 3.3.21
15.	ANS: C	PTS: 1	REF: 3.3.26
16.	ANS: C	PTS: 1	REF: 3.4.14
17.	ANS: A	PTS: 1	REF: 3.4.28
18.	ANS: B	PTS: 1	REF: 3.4.42
19.	ANS: E	PTS: 1	REF: 3.4.83
20.	ANS: D	PTS: 1	REF: 3.4.117b
21.	ANS: E	PTS: 1	REF: 3.5.9
22.	ANS: B	PTS: 1	REF: 3.5.19
23.	ANS: C	PTS: 1	REF: 3.5.34
24.	ANS: B	PTS: 1	REF: 3.5.45
25.	ANS: A	PTS: 1	REF: 3.5.18

Ch 3 Form D

_____ 1.   Evaluate the function at the indicated value of x. Round your result to three decimal places.

Function   *Value*

$f(x) = 5000\left(6^x\right)$ $x = -1.2$

a. 582.356
b. 682.356
c. −782.356
d. 782.356
e. −582.356

_____ 2.   Use the graph of f to determine the transformation that yields the graph of g.

$f(x) = 2^x, g(x) = 2^x + 7$

a. Shift the graph of f seven units to the left.
b. Shift the graph of f seven units downward.
c. Shift the graph of f seven units upward.
d. Shift the graph of f seven units to the right.
e. Both the graphs f and g are same.

_____ 3.   Use a graphing utility to construct a table of values for the function. Round your answer to three decimal places.

$f(x) = e^{4x}$

a.

x	-2	-1	0	1	2
$f(x)$	0	0.018	-1	54.598	2,980.958

b.

x	-2	-1	0	1	2
$f(x)$	0	-0.018	-1	-54.598	$-2,980.958$

c.

x	-2	-1	0	1	2
$f(x)$	0	0.018	1	54.598	2,980.958

d.

x	-2	-1	0	1	2
$f(x)$	0	0.018	1	-54.598	2,980.958

e.

x	-2	-1	0	1	2
$f(x)$	0	-0.018	1	54.598	2,980.958

_____ 4.   Use the One-to-One Property to solve the equation for x.

$$\left(\frac{1}{3}\right)^x = 243$$

a. $x = -5$
b. $x = 6$
c. $x = -6$
d. $x = 5$
e. $x = 7$

_____ 5. Identify the graph of the function.

$$f(x) = \left(\frac{1}{2}\right)^{x^2}$$

a.

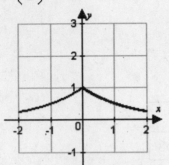

b.

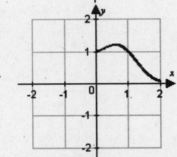

c.

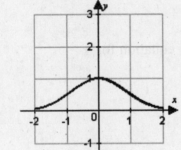

d.

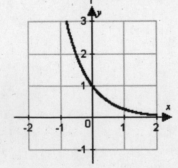

e.

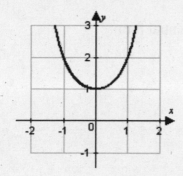

_____ 6.   Write the logarithmic equation in exponential form.

$$\log \frac{1}{3375} = -3$$

a. $15^{-3} = 3375$

b. $15^{-3} = -\dfrac{1}{3375}$

c. $3375^{-3} = \dfrac{1}{15}$

d. $15^{-3} = -3375$

e. $15^{-3} = \dfrac{1}{3375}$

_____ 7.   Evaluate $f(x) = \log x$ at the indicated value of x. Round your result to three decimal places.

$$x = \frac{9}{2}$$

a. -0.653

b. -1.531

c. 4.5

d. 0.653

e. 1.531

_____ 8.   Write the logarithmic equation in exponential form.

$$\ln\left(\frac{1}{6}\right) = -1.792\ldots$$

a. $e^{1.792\ldots} = \frac{1}{6}$

b. $e^{-1.792\ldots} = \frac{1}{6}$

c. $e^{1.792\ldots} = -\frac{1}{6}$

d. $e^{-1.792\ldots} = 6$

e. $e^{-1.792\ldots} = -\frac{1}{6}$

_____ 9.   Evaluate the function at the indicated value of $x = 0.51$. Round your result to three decimal places.

$$f(x) = 7\ln x$$

a.   −12.404
b.   4.713
c.   0.51
d.   12.404
e.   −4.713

_____ 10.   Identify the value of the function $f(x) = \log_{10} x$ at $x = 915$. Round to 3 decimal places.

a.   6.819
b.   2.961
c.   4.461
d.   3.961
e.   3.461

_____ 11.   Rewrite the logarithm as a ratio of common logarithms.

$\log_{1/2} x$

a. $\dfrac{\log x}{\log \dfrac{1}{2}}$

b. $\log 2x$

c. $\dfrac{\log \dfrac{1}{2}}{\log x}$

d. $\log \dfrac{x}{2}$

e. None of these

_____ 12.   Use the properties of logarithms to expand the expression as a sum, difference, and/or constant multiple of logarithms. (Assume all variables are positive.)

$\log_3 7x$

a. $\log_3 7 \times \log_3 x$

b. $\dfrac{\log_3 7}{\log_3 x}$

c. $\log_3 7 + \log_3 x$

d. $\log_3 7 - \log_3 x$

e. None of these

_____   13.   Condense the expression to the logarithm of a single quantity.

$$\frac{1}{2}\left[\log_5(x+2)+2\log_5(x-2)\right]-4\log_5 x$$

a. $\log_5 \dfrac{x^4\sqrt{x+2}}{(x-2)}$

b. $\log_5 \dfrac{x^2\sqrt{x-2}}{(x+2)}$

c. $\log_5 \dfrac{x^4\sqrt{x-2}}{(x+2)}$

d. $\log_5 \dfrac{(x-2)\sqrt{x+2}}{x^4}$

e. $\log_5 \dfrac{(x+2)\sqrt{x-2}}{x^2}$

_____   14.   Evaluate the logarithm using the change-of-base formula. Round your result to three decimal places.

$\log_{15} 1300$

a.   4.648
b.   6.648
c.   3.648
d.   5.648
e.   2.648

_____   15.   Simplify the expression $\log_3\left(\dfrac{1}{3}\right)^4$.

a.   3
b.   −12
c.   −4
d.   The expression cannot be simplified.
e.   4

_____   16.   Solve for x.

$7^x = 49$

a. 7
b. 2
c. 9
d. −7
e. −2

_____   17.   Approximate the point of intersection of the graphs of f and g. Then solve the equation $f(x) = g(x)$ algebraically to verify your approximation.

$f(x) = \ln(x - 5)$

$g(x) = 0$

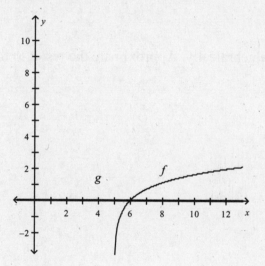

a. $(6, 5)$
b. $(6, -5)$
c. $(5, 0)$
d. $(6, 0)$
e. $(-6, 0)$

_____   18.   Solve the exponential equation algebraically. Approximate the result to three decimal places.

$7^{-5x} = 0.90$

a. $-\dfrac{\ln(0.90)}{5\ln 7} \approx 0.009$

b. $-\dfrac{\ln(0.90)}{5\ln 7} \approx 2.182$

c. $\dfrac{\ln(0.90)}{5\ln 7} \approx 3.694$

d. $-\dfrac{\ln(0.90)}{5\ln 7} \approx -0.011$

e. $-\dfrac{\ln(0.90)}{5\ln 7} \approx 0.011$

_____   19.   Solve the logarithmic equation algebraically. Approximate the result to three decimal places.

$\ln x - 7 = 0$

a. $e^7 \approx 1{,}094.633$

b. $e^7 \approx 1{,}099.633$

c. $e^7 \approx 1{,}098.633$

d. $e^7 \approx 1{,}096.633$

e. $e^7 \approx 1{,}097.633$

_____   20.   \$4000 is invested in an account at interest rate r, compounded continuously. Find the time required for the amount to triple. (Approximate the result to two decimal places.)

$r = 0.02$

a.   54.93 yr
b.   53.93 yr
c.   52.93 yr
d.   56.93 yr
e.   55.93 yr

_____ 21.   Select the correct graph for the given function

$y = 5 + \log(x + 2)$

a.

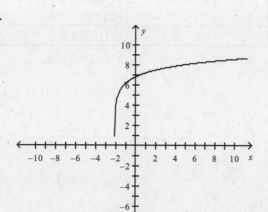

d.

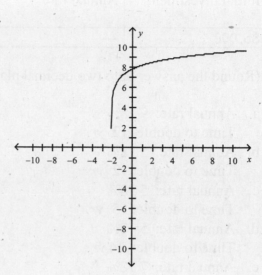

b.

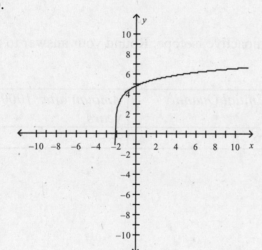

e.

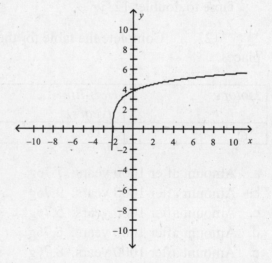

c.

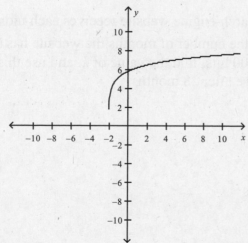

_____ 22. Complete the table for a savings account in which interest is compounded continuously.

Initial investment	Annual rate	Time to double	Amount after 10 years
$6,000	---	---	$10694.82

(Round the answer upto two decimal places.)

a. Annual rate: 9.78%
   Time to double: 12 yr
b. Annual rate: 5.78%
   Time to double: 12 yr
c. Annual rate: 5.78%
   Time to double: 15 yr
d. Annual rate: 5.78%
   Time to double: 14 yr
e. Annual rate: 7.78%
   Time to double: 12 yr

_____ 23. Complete the table for the radioactive isotope. Round your answer to two decimal places.

Isotope	Half-life (years)	Initial Quantity	Amount after 1000 years
^{14}C	5715	6.5g	----

a. Amount after 1000 years: 7.76g
b. Amount after 1000 years: 9.76g
c. Amount after 1000 years: 5.76g
d. Amount after 1000 years: 6.76g
e. Amount after 1000 years: 8.76g

_____ 24. The number y of hits a new search-engine website receives each month can be modeled by $y = 4080e^{kt}$, where t represents the number of months the website has been operating. In the website's third month, there were 10,000 hits. find the value of k, and use this value to predict the number of hits the website will receive after 28 months.

a. $k = 0.2988$; About 137,137,823,414 hits
b. $k = 0.2988$; About 6,910,116,039 hits
c. $k = 0.2988$; About 348,187,704 hits
d. $k = 0.2988$; About 17,544,522 hits
e. $k = 0.2988$; About 1,110,523,084,335 hits

_____   25.   An initial investment of $1000 doubles in value in 7.4 years. Assuming continuous compounding, what was the interest rate? Round to the nearest tenth of a percent.
a.   4.1%
b.   9.4%
c.   4.7%
d.   7.4%
e.   100%

Ch 3 Form D
Answer Section

1.	ANS: A	PTS: 1	REF: 3.1.11
2.	ANS: C	PTS: 1	REF: 3.1.23
3.	ANS: C	PTS: 1	REF: 3.1.39a
4.	ANS: A	PTS: 1	REF: 3.1.53
5.	ANS: C	PTS: 1	REF: 3.1.17
6.	ANS: E	PTS: 1	REF: 3.2.10
7.	ANS: D	PTS: 1	REF: 3.2.29
8.	ANS: B	PTS: 1	REF: 3.2.51
9.	ANS: E	PTS: 1	REF: 3.2.68
10.	ANS: B	PTS: 1	REF: 3.2.31
11.	ANS: A	PTS: 1	REF: 3.3.9a
12.	ANS: C	PTS: 1	REF: 3.3.46
13.	ANS: D	PTS: 1	REF: 3.3.84
14.	ANS: E	PTS: 1	REF: 3.3.21
15.	ANS: C	PTS: 1	REF: 3.3.26
16.	ANS: B	PTS: 1	REF: 3.4.14
17.	ANS: D	PTS: 1	REF: 3.4.28
18.	ANS: E	PTS: 1	REF: 3.4.42
19.	ANS: D	PTS: 1	REF: 3.4.83
20.	ANS: A	PTS: 1	REF: 3.4.117b
21.	ANS: C	PTS: 1	REF: 3.5.9
22.	ANS: B	PTS: 1	REF: 3.5.19
23.	ANS: C	PTS: 1	REF: 3.5.34
24.	ANS: D	PTS: 1	REF: 3.5.45
25.	ANS: B	PTS: 1	REF: 3.5.18

Ch 3 Form E

_____ 1.   Match the graph with its exponential function.

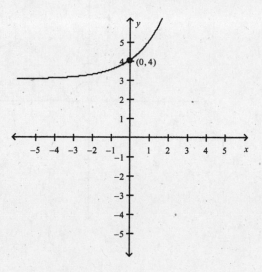

a. $y = 2^{-x} - 3$

b. $y = -2^{x} + 3$

c. $y = 2^{x} + 3$

d. $y = 2^{x} - 3$

e. $y = -2^{x} - 3$

_____ 2.   Select the graph of the exponential function.

$f(x) = 4^{-x^{2}}$

a.

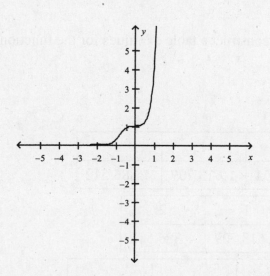

d.

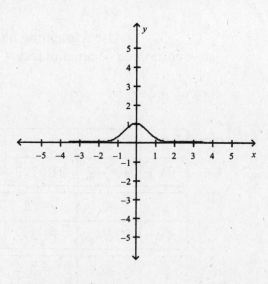

b.

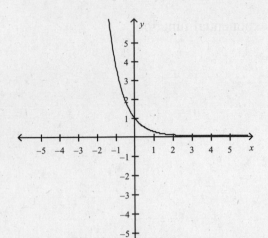

e.

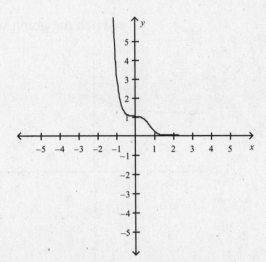

c.

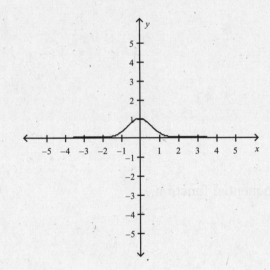

_____ 3. Use a graphing utility to construct a table of values for the function. Round your answer to three decimal places.

$f(x) = 4e^{x+5}$

a.

x	-2	-1	0	1	2
$f(x)$	80.342	218.392	593.651	1,613.709	4,386.512

b.

x	-2	-1	0	1	2
$f(x)$	80.342	218.392	0	1,613.709	4,386.512

c.

x	-2	-1	0	1	2
$f(x)$	80.342	-218.392	593.651	1,613.709	4,386.512

d.

x	−2	−1	0	1	2
$f(x)$	−80.342	218.392	593.651	1,613.709	4,386.512

e.

x	−2	−1	0	1	2
$f(x)$	−80.342	−218.392	593.651	1,613.709	4,386.512

_____   4.   Complete the table to determine the balance A for P dollars invested at rate r for t years and compounded n times per year.

$P = \$100;\ r = 2\%;\ t = 1\,\text{year}$

a.

n	1	2	4	12	365	continuous
A	$300	$102.02	$506.25	$635.86	$635.86	$102.02

b.

n	1	2	4	12	365	continuous
A	$400	$300	$506.25	$635.86	$635.86	$102.02

c.

n	1	2	4	12	365	continuous
A	$300	$400	$506.25	$102.02	$635.86	$635.86

d.

n	1	2	4	12	365	continuous
A	$300	$400	$300	$635.86	$635.86	$102.02

e.

n	1	2	4	12	365	continuous
A	$300	$400	$506.25	$635.86	$635.86	$102.02

_____   5.   What is the value of the function $f(x) = 25e^{.04x}$ at $x = 1.3$? Round to 3 decimal places.
a.   37.296
b.   26.492
c.   7.597
d.   42.051
e.   82.783

_____ 6.   Write the logarithmic equation in exponential form.

$$\log_{36} 6 = \frac{1}{2}$$

a. $36^{1/2} = -6$

b. $36^{1/2} = 6$

c. $6^{1/2} = 36$

d. $36^{1/2} = -\frac{1}{6}$

e. $36^{1/2} = \frac{1}{6}$

_____ 7.   Evaluate $f(x) = \log x$ at the indicated value of x. Round your result to three decimal places.

$x = 90.75$

a. 1.958

b. 0.511

c. 0.011

d. −0.511

e. −1.958

_____ 8.   Write the exponential equation in logarithmic form.

$e^7 = 1096.633\ldots$

a. $\ln 1096.633\ldots = -7$

b. $\ln 1096.633\ldots = -\frac{1}{7}$

c. $\ln 1096.633\ldots = 7$

d. $\ln 1096.633\ldots = \frac{1}{7}$

e. $\ln 7 = 1096.633\ldots$

_____ 9. Evaluate $g(x) = \ln x$ at the indicated value of x.

$x = e^{-6}$

a. 6
b. $-\dfrac{1}{6}$
c. -6
d. $\dfrac{1}{6}$
e. e^{-6}

_____ 10. Evaluate the function $f(x) = \dfrac{1}{4} \ln x$ at $x = 1.803$. Round to 3 decimal places. (You may use your calculator.)
a. undefined
b. 0.876
c. 0.147
d. 0.339
e. -0.347

_____ 11. Rewrite the logarithm as a ratio of natural logarithms.

$\ln_x \dfrac{4}{11}$

a. $\dfrac{\ln \dfrac{4}{11}}{\ln x}$

b. $\ln \dfrac{11}{4x}$

c. $\ln \dfrac{4}{11} x$

d. $\dfrac{\ln x}{\ln \dfrac{4}{11}}$

e. None of these

_____ 12.   Use the properties of logarithms to expand the expression as a sum, difference, and/or constant multiple of logarithms. (Assume all variables are positive.)

$$\log_7 \frac{x^2}{y^2 z^3}$$

a. $2\log_7 x + 2\log_7 y + 3\log_7 z$

b. $2\log_7 x + 2\log_7 y - 3\log_7 z$

c. $\dfrac{2\log_7 x}{2\log_7 y \times 3\log_7 z}$

d. $2\log_7 x - 2\log_7 y - 3\log_7 z$

e. $2\log_7 x - 2\log_7 y + 3\log_7 z$

_____ 13.   Determine whether the statement is true or false given that $f(x) = \ln x$.

$$f(x-9) = f(x) - f(9), \quad x > 0$$

a. True

b. False; $\ln(x-9) \neq \ln(x) - \ln(9), \quad x > 0$

_____ 14.   Use the properties of logarithms to rewrite and simplify the logarithmic expression.

$$\ln\left(\frac{5}{e^6}\right)$$

a. $\ln 5$

b. $\ln 11$

c. $\ln 5 - 6$

d. $\ln 6 - 5$

e. $\ln 6$

_____ 15.   Condense the expression $3\left(\log x - \log y\right)$ to the logarithm of a single term.

a. $\log\left(\dfrac{x}{y}\right)^3$

b. $\log\dfrac{x^3\left(\sqrt[3]{y}\right)}{y}$

c. $\log\dfrac{3x}{3y}$

d. $\log\dfrac{x^3}{y}$

e. $3\left(\log x - \log y\right)$

_____ 16.   Solve for x. Approximate the result to three decimal places.

$e^x = 4$

a. $\ln 4 \approx 1.466$
b. $\ln 4 \approx 1.436$
c. $\ln 4 \approx 1.476$
d. $\ln 4 \approx 1.386$
e. $\ln 4 \approx 1.456$

_____ 17.   Solve the exponential equation algebraically. Approximate the result to three decimal places.

$2\left(3^x\right) = 36$

a. $\dfrac{\ln 3}{\ln 18} \approx 2.631$

b. $\dfrac{\ln 18}{\ln 3} \approx -0.38$

c. $\dfrac{\ln 18}{\ln 3} \approx -2.631$

d. $\dfrac{\ln 18}{\ln 3} \approx 2.631$

e. $\dfrac{\ln 18}{\ln 3} \approx 0.38$

_____ 18.   Solve the exponential equation algebraically. Approximate the result to three decimal places.

$4\left(3^{4-x}\right) = 16$

a. $4 - \dfrac{\ln 4}{\ln 3} \approx 5.738$

b. $4 - \dfrac{\ln 4}{\ln 3} \approx 6.738$

c. $4 - \dfrac{\ln 4}{\ln 3} \approx 3.738$

d. $4 - \dfrac{\ln 4}{\ln 3} \approx 4.738$

e. $4 - \dfrac{\ln 4}{\ln 3} \approx 2.738$

_____ 19.   Solve the logarithmic equation algebraically. Approximate the result to three decimal places.

$2\ln x = 19$

a. $e^{19/2} \approx 13,359.727$

b. $e^{19/2} \approx 13,358.727$

c. $e^{19/2} \approx 13,357.727$

d. $e^{19/2} \approx 13,360.727$

e. $e^{19/2} \approx 13,361.727$

_____ 20.   \$7000 is invested in an account at interest rate r, compounded continuously. Find the time required for the amount to triple. (Approximate the result to two decimal places.)

$r = 0.0555$

a. 14.49 yr
b. 13.49 yr
c. 11.49 yr
d. 19.79 yr
e. 10.49 yr

_____ 21.   Select the correct graph for the given function

$y = \ln(x+3)$

a.

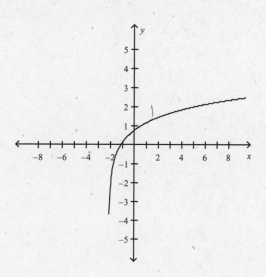

d.

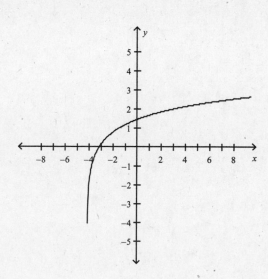

b.

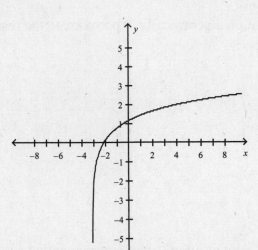

e.

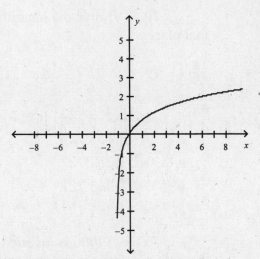

c.

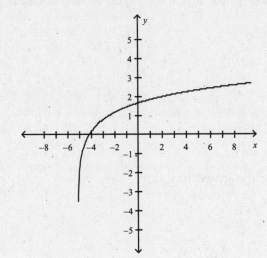

_____ 22.   Complete the table for a savings account in which interest is compounded continuously.

Initial investment	Annual rate	Time to double	Amount after 10 years
---	5.33%	---	$1,758

(Round the answer upto two decimal places.)

a. Initial investment:$3757.5
    Time to double: $10\,yr$
b. Initial investment:$4757.5
    Time to double: $12\,yr$
c. Initial investment:$2757.5
    Time to double: $11\,yr$
d. Initial investment:$1,758
    Time to double: $13\,yr$
e. Initial investment:$5757.5
    Time to double: $8\,yr$

_____ 23.   Complete the table for the radioactive isotope.

Isotope	Half-life (years)	Initial Quantity	Amount after 1000 years
^{226}Ra	1599	---	1g

a. *Initial Quantity*: 3.54g
b. *Initial Quantity*: 5.54g
c. *Initial Quantity*: 1.54g
d. *Initial Quantity*: 4.54g
e. *Initial Quantity*: 2.54g

_____ 24.   The populations P (in thousands) of Orlando, Florida from 2000 through 2007 can be modeled by $P = 1553.1e^{kt}$, where t represents the year, with $t = 0$ corresponding to 2000. In 2005, the population of Orlando, Florida was about 1,902,000. Find the value of k.

a. $k = 0.03183$
b. $k = 0.02863$
c. $k = 0.02163$
d. $k = 0.04053$
e. $k = 0.03063$

_____ 25. An initial investment of $9000 grows at an annual interest rate of 5% compounded continuously. How long will it take to double the investment?
a. 1 year
b. 14.40 years
c. 13.86 years
d. 14.86 years
e. 13.40 years

Ch 3 Form E
Answer Section

1.	ANS: C	PTS: 1	REF: 3.1.14
2.	ANS: D	PTS: 1	REF: 3.1.29
3.	ANS: A	PTS: 1	REF: 3.1.41a
4.	ANS: E	PTS: 1	REF: 3.1.59
5.	ANS: D	PTS: 1	REF: 3.1.36
6.	ANS: B	PTS: 1	REF: 3.2.13
7.	ANS: A	PTS: 1	REF: 3.2.32
8.	ANS: C	PTS: 1	REF: 3.2.59
9.	ANS: C	PTS: 1	REF: 3.2.72
10.	ANS: C	PTS: 1	REF: 3.2.68
11.	ANS: A	PTS: 1	REF: 3.3.11b
12.	ANS: D	PTS: 1	REF: 3.3.63
13.	ANS: B	PTS: 1	REF: 3.3.103
14.	ANS: C	PTS: 1	REF: 3.3.28
15.	ANS: A	PTS: 1	REF: 3.3.72
16.	ANS: D	PTS: 1	REF: 3.4.19
17.	ANS: D	PTS: 1	REF: 3.4.33
18.	ANS: E	PTS: 1	REF: 3.4.50
19.	ANS: A	PTS: 1	REF: 3.4.90
20.	ANS: D	PTS: 1	REF: 3.4.120b
21.	ANS: B	PTS: 1	REF: 3.5.11
22.	ANS: D	PTS: 1	REF: 3.5.22
23.	ANS: C	PTS: 1	REF: 3.5.36
24.	ANS: D	PTS: 1	REF: 3.5.48a
25.	ANS: C	PTS: 1	REF: 3.5.15

Ch 3 Form F

_____ 1.   Match the graph with its exponential function.

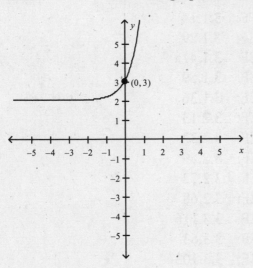

a. $y = 6^x + 2$

b. $y = -6^x - 2$

c. $y = 6^x - 2$

d. $y = -6^x + 2$

e. $y = 6^{-x} - 2$

_____ 2.   Select the graph of the exponential function.

$$f(x) = 3^{-x^2}$$

a.

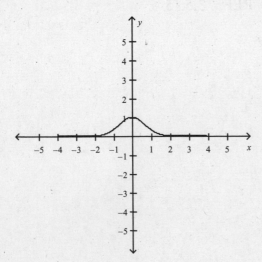

d.

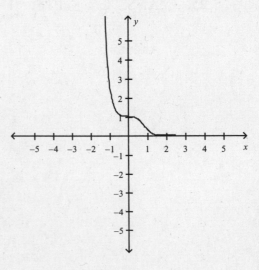

b.

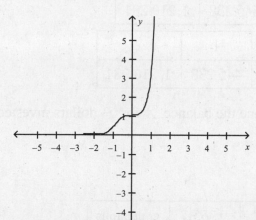

e.

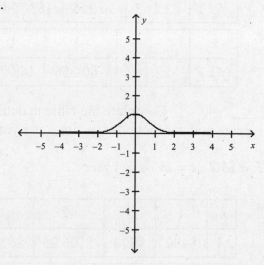

c.

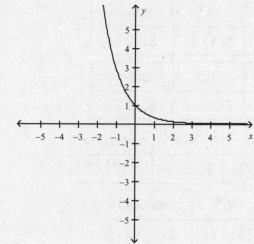

_____   3.   Use a graphing utility to construct a table of values for the function. Round your answer to three decimal places.

$$f(x) = 3e^{x+4}$$

a.

x	−2	−1	0	1	2
$f(x)$	22.167	−60.256	163.794	445.238	1,210.281

b.

x	−2	−1	0	1	2
$f(x)$	−22.167	60.256	163.794	445.238	1,210.281

c.

x	−2	−1	0	1	2
$f(x)$	22.167	60.256	0	445.238	1,210.281

d.

x	-2	-1	0	1	2
$f(x)$	22.167	60.256	163.794	445.238	1,210.281

e.

x	-2	-1	0	1	2
$f(x)$	-22.167	-60.256	163.794	445.238	1,210.281

_____ 4.   Complete the table to determine the balance A for P dollars invested at rate r for t years and compounded n times per year.

$P = \$100; r = 2\%; t = 1\,\text{year}$

a.

n	1	2	4	12	365	continuous
A	\$400	\$300	\$506.25	\$635.86	\$635.86	\$102.02

b.

n	1	2	4	12	365	continuous
A	\$300	\$400	\$506.25	\$635.86	\$635.86	\$102.02

c.

n	1	2	4	12	365	continuous
A	\$300	\$400	\$506.25	\$102.02	\$635.86	\$635.86

d.

n	1	2	4	12	365	continuous
A	\$300	\$102.02	\$506.25	\$635.86	\$635.86	\$102.02

e.

n	1	2	4	12	365	continuous
A	\$300	\$400	\$300	\$635.86	\$635.86	\$102.02

_____ 5.   What is the value of the function $f(x) = 25e^{0.4x}$ at $x = 1.3$? Round to 3 decimal places.
a. 37.296
b. 26.492
c. 7.597
d. 42.051
e. 82.783

____　6.　Write the logarithmic equation in exponential form.

$$\log_{36} 6 = \frac{1}{2}$$

a.　$36^{1/2} = 6$
b.　$6^{1/2} = 36$
c.　$36^{1/2} = -\dfrac{1}{6}$
d.　$36^{1/2} = \dfrac{1}{6}$
e.　$36^{1/2} = -6$

____　7.　Evaluate $f(x) = \log x$ at the indicated value of x. Round your result to three decimal places.

$x = 94.75$

a.　0.011
b.　1.977
c.　−0.506
d.　0.506
e.　−1.977

____　8.　Write the exponential equation in logarithmic form.

$e^8 = 2980.958\ldots$

a.　$\ln 2980.958\ldots = \dfrac{1}{8}$
b.　$\ln 8 = 2980.958\ldots$
c.　$\ln 2980.958\ldots = -8$
d.　$\ln 2980.958\ldots = -\dfrac{1}{8}$
e.　$\ln 2980.958\ldots = 8$

_____ 9.   Evaluate $g(x) = \ln x$ at the indicated value of x.

$x = e^{-6}$

a. $-\dfrac{1}{6}$

b. -6

c. 6

d. $\dfrac{1}{6}$

e. e^{-6}

_____ 10.   Evaluate the function $f(x) = \dfrac{1}{3}\ln x$ at $x = 1.803$. Round to 3 decimal places. (You may use your calculator.)

a. -0.366

b. 0.453

c. 0.838

d. 0.196

e.   undefined

_____ 11.   Rewrite the logarithm as a ratio of natural logarithms.

$\ln_x \dfrac{6}{11}$

a. $\ln\dfrac{6}{11}x$

b. $\dfrac{\ln\dfrac{6}{11}}{\ln x}$

c. $\dfrac{\ln x}{\ln\dfrac{6}{11}}$

d. $\ln\dfrac{11}{6x}$

e.   None of these

_____ 12.   Use the properties of logarithms to expand the expression as a sum, difference, and/or constant multiple of logarithms. (Assume all variables are positive.)

$$\log_9 \frac{x^4}{y^4 z^3}$$

a. $\dfrac{4\log_9 x}{4\log_9 y \times 3\log_9 z}$

b. $4\log_9 x + 4\log_9 y - 3\log_9 z$

c. $4\log_9 x - 4\log_9 y + 3\log_9 z$

d. $4\log_9 x + 4\log_9 y + 3\log_9 z$

e. $4\log_9 x - 4\log_9 y - 3\log_9 z$

_____ 13.   Determine whether the statement is true or false given that $f(x) = \ln x$.

$f(x-4) = f(x) - f(4), \ x > 0$

a.   False; $\ln(x-4) \neq \ln(x) - \ln(4), \ x > 0$

b.   True

_____ 14.   Use the properties of logarithms to rewrite and simplify the logarithmic expression.

$$\ln\left(\frac{2}{e^3}\right)$$

a. $\ln 2 - 3$

b. $\ln 5$

c. $\ln 3$

d. $\ln 2$

e. $\ln 3 - 2$

_____ 15.   Condense the expression $7(\log x - \log y)$ to the logarithm of a single term.

a. $\log\left(\dfrac{x}{y}\right)^7$

b. $\log \dfrac{x^7}{y}$

c. $\log \dfrac{x^7\left(\sqrt[7]{y}\right)}{y}$

d. $\log \dfrac{7x}{7y}$

e. $7(\log x - \log y)$

_____ 16.   Solve for x. Approximate the result to three decimal places.

$e^x = 4$

a. $\ln 4 \approx 1.456$
b. $\ln 4 \approx 1.476$
c. $\ln 4 \approx 1.466$
d. $\ln 4 \approx 1.386$
e. $\ln 4 \approx 1.436$

_____ 17.   Solve the exponential equation algebraically. Approximate the result to three decimal places.

$4\left(3^x\right) = 56$

a. $\dfrac{\ln 14}{\ln 3} \approx 2.402$

b. $\dfrac{\ln 14}{\ln 3} \approx 0.416$

c. $\dfrac{\ln 14}{\ln 3} \approx -2.402$

d. $\dfrac{\ln 3}{\ln 14} \approx 2.402$

e. $\dfrac{\ln 14}{\ln 3} \approx -0.416$

_____ 18.   Solve the exponential equation algebraically. Approximate the result to three decimal places.

$5\left(3^{5-x}\right) = 30$

a. $5 - \dfrac{\ln 6}{\ln 3} \approx 6.369$

b. $5 - \dfrac{\ln 6}{\ln 3} \approx 7.369$

c. $5 - \dfrac{\ln 6}{\ln 3} \approx 4.369$

d. $5 - \dfrac{\ln 6}{\ln 3} \approx 3.369$

e. $5 - \dfrac{\ln 6}{\ln 3} \approx 5.369$

_____ 19.   Solve the logarithmic equation algebraically. Approximate the result to three decimal places.

$6 \ln x = 13$

a. $e^{13/6} \approx 10.729$
b. $e^{13/6} \approx 9.729$
c. $e^{13/6} \approx 7.729$
d. $e^{13/6} \approx 6.729$
e. $e^{13/6} \approx 8.729$

_____ 20.   \$7000 is invested in an account at interest rate r, compounded continuously. Find the time required for the amount to triple. (Approximate the result to two decimal places.)

$r = 0.0240$

a. 27.88 yr
b. 26.88 yr
c. 29.88 yr
d. 45.78 yr
e. 30.88 yr

_____ 21.   Select the correct graph for the given function

$y = \ln(x+4)$

a.

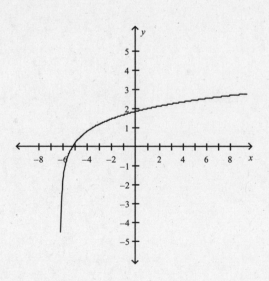

d.

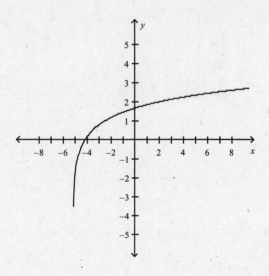

b.

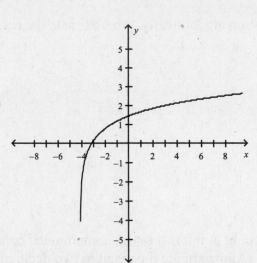

e.

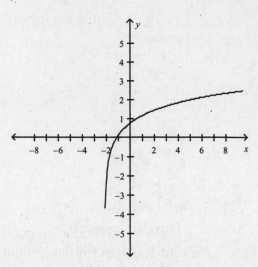

c.

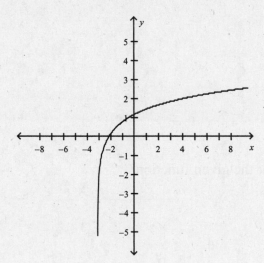

_____ 22.   Complete the table for a savings account in which interest is compounded continuously.

Initial investment	Annual rate	Time to double	Amount after 10 years
---	8.66%	---	$1,101

(Round the answer upto two decimal places.)

a. Initial investment:$5101
    Time to double: 11 yr
b. Initial investment:$2101
    Time to double: 9 yr
c. Initial investment:$3101
    Time to double: 10 yr
d. Initial investment:$4101
    Time to double: 13 yr
e. Initial investment:$1,101
    Time to double: 8 yr

_____ 23.   Complete the table for the radioactive isotope.

Isotope	Half-life (years)	Initial Quantity	Amount after 1000 years
^{226}Ra	1599	---	4 g

a. *Initial Quantity*: 7.17g
b. *Initial Quantity*: 6.17g
c. *Initial Quantity*: 8.17g
d. *Initial Quantity*: 10.17g
e. *Initial Quantity*: 9.17g

_____ 24.   The populations P (in thousands) of Orlando, Florida from 2000 through 2007 can be modeled by $P = 1727.6e^{kt}$, where t represents the year, with $t = 0$ corresponding to 2000. In 2002, the population of Orlando, Florida was about 1,850,000. Find the value of k.

a. $k = 0.03423$
b. $k = 0.02863$
c. $k = 0.03063$
d. $k = 0.03183$
e. $k = 0.02163$

_____   25.   An initial investment of $4000 grows at an annual interest rate of 5% compounded
continuously. How long will it take to double the investment?
a.   13.86 years
b.   13.40 years
c.   14.86 years
d.   14.40 years
e.   1 year

Ch 3 Form F
Answer Section

1.	ANS: A	PTS: 1	REF:	3.1.14
2.	ANS: E	PTS: 1	REF:	3.1.29
3.	ANS: D	PTS: 1	REF:	3.1.41a
4.	ANS: B	PTS: 1	REF:	3.1.59
5.	ANS: D	PTS: 1	REF:	3.1.36
6.	ANS: A	PTS: 1	REF:	3.2.13
7.	ANS: B	PTS: 1	REF:	3.2.32
8.	ANS: E	PTS: 1	REF:	3.2.59
9.	ANS: B	PTS: 1	REF:	3.2.72
10.	ANS: D	PTS: 1	REF:	3.2.68
11.	ANS: B	PTS: 1	REF:	3.3.11b
12.	ANS: E	PTS: 1	REF:	3.3.63
13.	ANS: A	PTS: 1	REF:	3.3.103
14.	ANS: A	PTS: 1	REF:	3.3.28
15.	ANS: A	PTS: 1	REF:	3.3.72
16.	ANS: D	PTS: 1	REF:	3.4.19
17.	ANS: A	PTS: 1	REF:	3.4.33
18.	ANS: D	PTS: 1	REF:	3.4.50
19.	ANS: E	PTS: 1	REF:	3.4.90
20.	ANS: D	PTS: 1	REF:	3.4.120b
21.	ANS: B	PTS: 1	REF:	3.5.11
22.	ANS: E	PTS: 1	REF:	3.5.22
23.	ANS: B	PTS: 1	REF:	3.5.36
24.	ANS: A	PTS: 1	REF:	3.5.48a
25.	ANS: A	PTS: 1	REF:	3.5.15

Ch 4 Form A

_____ 1. Find (if possible) the complement of the following angle.

$\dfrac{\pi}{4}$

a. Complement: π

b. Complement: $-\dfrac{\pi}{4}$

c. Complement: $\dfrac{\pi}{4}$

d. Complement: $\dfrac{\pi}{2}$

e. Complement: $\dfrac{2}{\pi}$

_____ 2. Convert the angle measure from degrees to radians. Round to three decimal places.

$-0.63°$

a. $-0.63° \approx -0.311$ radian

b. $-0.63° \approx -0.089$ radian

c. $-0.63° \approx -0.011$ radian

d. $-0.63° \approx -1.311$ radians

e. $-0.63° \approx -1.011$ radians

_____ 3. Determine two coterminal angles (one positive and one negative) for $\theta = -489°$.

a. $141°, -219°$

b. $321°, -399°$

c. $231°, -309°$

d. $141°, -309°$

e. $231°, -129°$

_____   4.   Find the point (x,y) on the unit circle that corresponds to the real number t. (Round your answer to one decimal place.)

$$t = \frac{\pi}{5}$$

a. $t = \dfrac{\pi}{5}$ corresponds to the point $(0.8, -0.6)$.

b. $t = \dfrac{\pi}{5}$ corresponds to the point $(-0.8, -0.6)$.

c. $t = \dfrac{\pi}{5}$ corresponds to the point $(0.8, 0.6)$.

d. $t = \dfrac{\pi}{5}$ corresponds to the point $(0.6, -0.8)$.

e. $t = \dfrac{\pi}{5}$ corresponds to the point $(0.6, 0.8)$.

_____   5.   Use the value of the trigonometric function to find the $\sin(-t)$.

$$\sin t = \frac{1}{4}$$

a. $\sin(-t) = -\dfrac{1}{4}$

b. $\sin(-t) = -4$

c. $\sin(-t) = 4$

d. $\sin(-t) = \infty$

e. $\sin(-t) = \dfrac{1}{4}$

_____   6.   Find the value of given trigonometric function. Round your answer to four decimal places.

$\cos(-1.7)$

a. $\cos(-1.7) \approx 0.0712$

b. $\cos(-1.7) \approx -0.0288$

c. $\cos(-1.7) \approx 0.1288$

d. $\cos(-1.7) \approx -0.1288$

e. $\cos(-1.7) \approx -0.2288$

7. Find the exact values of the three trignometric functions of the angle θ ($\sin\theta$, $\cos\theta$, $\tan\theta$) of the two triangles shown below. Is the function values are the same? Explain.

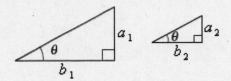

$a_1 = 3, b_1 = 4$ $a_2 = 1.5, b_2 = 2$

a.
$$\sin\theta_1 = \frac{3}{5}, \quad \cos\theta_1 = \frac{4}{5}, \quad \tan\theta_1 = \frac{3}{4}$$
$$\sin\theta = \frac{2.5}{1.5} = \frac{5}{3}, \quad \cos\theta = \frac{2.5}{2} = \frac{5}{4}, \quad \tan\theta = \frac{2}{1.5} = \frac{4}{3}$$
The function values are different   because the triangles are not similar and corresponding sides are not proportional.

b.
$$\sin\theta = \frac{5}{3}, \quad \cos\theta = \frac{5}{4}, \quad \tan\theta_1 = \frac{3}{4}$$
$$\sin\theta = \frac{2.5}{1.5} = \frac{5}{3}, \quad \cos\theta = \frac{2.5}{2} = \frac{5}{4}, \quad \tan\theta = \frac{1.5}{2} = \frac{3}{4}$$
The function values are the same because the triangles are similar and corresponding sides are proportional.

c.
$$\sin\theta = \frac{4}{5}, \quad \cos\theta = \frac{3}{5}, \quad \tan\theta = \frac{3}{4}$$
$$\sin\theta = \frac{2}{2.5} = \frac{4}{5}, \quad \cos\theta = \frac{1.5}{2.5} = \frac{3}{5}, \quad \tan\theta = \frac{1.5}{2.5} = \frac{3}{4}$$
The function values are the same because the triangles are similar and corresponding sides are proportional.

d.
$$\sin\theta = \frac{5}{3}, \quad \cos\theta = \frac{5}{4}, \quad \tan\theta = \frac{3}{4}$$
$$\sin\theta = \frac{2.5}{3} = \frac{5}{1.5}, \quad \cos\theta = \frac{2.5}{4} = \frac{5}{2}, \quad \tan\theta = \frac{1.5}{4} = \frac{3}{2}$$
The function values are different   because the triangles are not similar and corresponding sides are not proportional.

e.
$$\sin\theta = \frac{3}{5}, \quad \cos\theta = \frac{4}{5}, \quad \tan\theta = \frac{3}{4}$$
$$\sin\theta = \frac{1.5}{2.5} = \frac{3}{5}, \quad \cos\theta = \frac{2}{2.5} = \frac{4}{5}, \quad \tan\theta = \frac{1.5}{2} = \frac{3}{4}$$
The function values are the same because the triangles are similar and corresponding sides are proportional.

_____   8.   Use a calculator to evaluate function given below. Round your answer to four decimal places. (Be sure the calculator is in the correct angle mode.)

$\tan 34.5°$

a. $\tan 34.5° \approx 2.6051$
b. $\tan 34.5° \approx 1.4550$
c. $\tan 34.5° \approx 0.6873$
d. $\tan 34.5° \approx 0.0576$
e. $\tan 34.5° \approx 0.3839$

_____   9.   Find the values of θ in degrees $(0° < \theta < 90°)$ and radians $(0 < \theta < \pi/2)$ without the aid of a calculator.

$$\sec \theta = \frac{2\sqrt{3}}{3}$$

a.
$$\theta = 30° = \frac{\pi}{6}$$
b.
$$\theta = 60° = \frac{\pi}{3}$$
c. $\theta = 0° = 0$
d.
$$\theta = 90° = \frac{\pi}{2}$$
e.
$$\theta = 45° = \frac{\pi}{4}$$

_____   10.   Find the reference angle θ', and select θ and θ' in standard position.

$\theta = 305°$

a. $\theta' = -65°$ d. $\theta' = 45°$

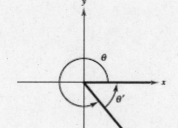   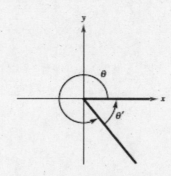

b. $\theta' = 65°$ e. $\theta' = -55°$

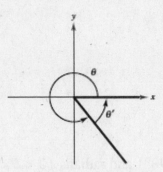   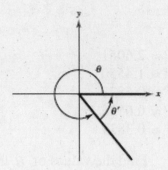

c. $\theta' = 55°$

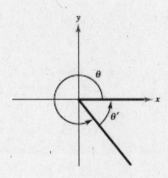

_____   11.   Use a calculator to evaluate the trigonometric function. Round your answer to four decimal

places. (Be sure the calculator is set in the correct angle mode.)

cot 1.35

a.   cot $1.35 \approx -2.3500$
b.   cot $1.35 \approx 0.2245$
c.   cot $1.35 \approx 2.3500$
d.   cot $1.35 \approx -0.7755$
e.   cot $1.35 \approx 1.2245$

_____   12.   A company that produces snowboards, which are seasonal products, forecasts monthly sales over the next 2 years to be $S = 23.1 + 0.442t + 4.3\cos(\pi t / 6)$, where S is measured in thousands of units and t is the time in months, with $t = 1$ representing January 2010. Predict sales for following month. Round your answer to three decimal places.

February 2011

a. $S \approx 30.438$

   30,438 units

b. $S \approx 32.438$

   32,438 units

c. $S \approx 33.438$

   33,438 units

d. $S \approx 31.438$

   31,438 units

e. $S \approx 29.438$

   29,438 units

_____   13.   The point $(-5, -12)$ is on the terminal side of an angle in standard position. Determine the exact value of $\sec\theta$.

a. $\sec\theta = \dfrac{12}{5}$

b. $\sec\theta = \dfrac{5}{12}$

c. $\sec\theta = \dfrac{17}{12}$

d. $\sec\theta = -\dfrac{13}{5}$

e. $\sec\theta = \dfrac{8}{13}$

_____   14.   Find the period and amplitude.

$$y = \frac{6}{9} \cos \frac{4x}{9}$$

a. Period: π; Amplitude: 9

b. Period: $\dfrac{\pi}{2}$; Amplitude: $\dfrac{1}{9}$

c. Period: 2π; Amplitude: 1

d. Period: $\dfrac{9\pi}{2}$; Amplitude: $\dfrac{2}{3}$

e. Period: π; Amplitude: $\dfrac{3}{2}$

_____   15. g is related to a parent function $f(x) = \sin(x)$ or $f(x) = \cos(x)$.

$$g(x) = \cos(4x - \pi) + 3$$

Describe the sequence of transformations from f to g.

a. One cycle of $g(x)$ corresponds to the interval $\left[\dfrac{\pi}{4}, \dfrac{3\pi}{4} \right]$ and $g(x)$ is obtained by shifting $f(x)$ downward 3 units.

b. One cycle of $f(x)$ corresponds to the interval $\left[\dfrac{\pi}{4}, \dfrac{3\pi}{4} \right]$ and $f(x)$ is obtained by shifting $g(x)$ upward 3 units.

c. One cycle of $g(x)$ corresponds to the interval $[\pi, 3\pi]$ and $g(x)$ is obtained by shifting $f(x)$ downward 3 units.

d. One cycle of $g(x)$ corresponds to the interval $\left[\dfrac{\pi}{4}, \dfrac{3\pi}{4} \right]$ and $g(x)$ is obtained by shifting $f(x)$ upward 3 units.

e. One cycle of $g(x)$ corresponds to the interval $[\pi, 3\pi]$ and $g(x)$ is obtained by shifting $f(x)$ upward 3 units.

_____   16.   After exercising for a few minutes, a person has a respiratory cycle for which the velocity of airflow is approximated by

$$v = 1.75 \sin\left(\frac{\pi t}{5}\right),$$

where t is the time (in seconds).
(Inhalation occurs when $v > 0$ and exhalation occurs when $v < 0$.)

Find the number of cycles per minute.

a.   8 cycles/min
b.   9 cycles/min
c.   11 cycles/min
d.   7 cycles/min
e.   6 cycles/min

_____   17.   A plane flying at an altitude of 9 miles above a radar antenna will pass directly over the radar antenna (see figure). Let d be the ground distance from the antenna to the point directly under the plane and let x be the angle of elevation to the plane from the antenna.
(d is positive as the plane approaches the antenna.)
Write d as a function of x.

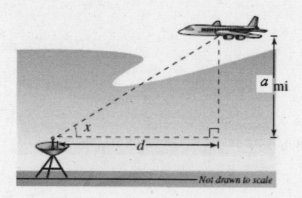

a. $d = 9\sin x$
b. $d = 9\cos x$
c. $d = 9\tan x$
d. $d = 9\cot x$
e. $d = 9\csc x$

_____ 18.   Determine whether the function is even, odd, or neither.

$f(x) = 5\sec x$

a.   Neither
b.   Even
c.   Odd

_____ 19.   A television camera is on a reviewing platform a meters from the street on which a parade will be passing from left to right (see figure). Write the distance d from the camera to a particular unit in the parade as a function of the angle x.

$a = 29$

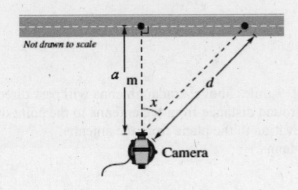

a. $d = 29\cos x$
b. $d = 29\sec x$
c. $d = 29\sin x$
d. $d = 29\tan x$
e. $d = 29\cot x$

_____ 20.   Evaluate the expression. Round your result to two decimal places.

$\arctan 25$

a.   3.53
b.   0.53
c.   1.53
d.   2.53
e.   −0.47

_____ 21.   Find an algebraic expression that is equivalent to the expression..

$\cos(\arcsin 5x)$

a. $\sqrt{1+25x^2}$

b. $\dfrac{\sqrt{1-25x^2}}{1-25x^2}$

c. $\dfrac{\sqrt{1+25x^2}}{1+25x^2}$

d. $\sqrt{1-25x^2}$

e. $\sqrt{25x^2-1}$

_____ 22.   Use the properties of inverse trigonometric functions to evaluate $\tan\left[\arctan(0.31)\right]$.

a. -0.13
b. 0.54
c. 0.01
d. 0.31
e. 0.35

_____ 23.   The height of an outdoor basketball backboard is $12\dfrac{1}{2}$ feet, and the backboard casts a

shadow $17\dfrac{1}{4}$ feet long.

Find the angle of elevation of the sun. Round your answer to one decimal place.

a. $36.9°$
b. $37.9°$
c. $35.9°$
d. $39.9°$
e. $38.9°$

_____ 24.   Determine the angle between the diagonal of a cube and its edge, as shown in the figure, where $a = 18$. Round your answer to one decimal place.

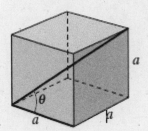

a. 56.7°
b. 57.7°
c. 55.7°
d. 54.7°
e. 58.7°

_____ 25.   A ball that is bobbing up and down on the end of a spring has a maximum displacement of 3 inches. Its motion (in ideal conditions) is modeled by

$$y = \frac{1}{5} \cos 12t \ (t > 0),$$

where y is measured in feet and t is the time in seconds.
What is the period of the oscillations?

a. $\dfrac{\pi}{5}$

b. $\dfrac{\pi}{6}$

c. $\dfrac{\pi}{12}$

d. $\dfrac{12}{\pi}$

e. $\dfrac{6}{\pi}$

Ch 4 Form A
Answer Section

1.	ANS:	C	PTS:	1	REF:	4.1.31a
2.	ANS:	C	PTS:	1	REF:	4.1.71
3.	ANS:	E	PTS:	1	REF:	4.1.51b
4.	ANS:	C	PTS:	1	REF:	4.2.9
5.	ANS:	A	PTS:	1	REF:	4.2.43a
6.	ANS:	D	PTS:	1	REF:	4.2.53
7.	ANS:	E	PTS:	1	REF:	4.3.9
8.	ANS:	C	PTS:	1	REF:	4.3.48a
9.	ANS:	A	PTS:	1	REF:	4.3.59a
10.	ANS:	C	PTS:	1	REF:	4.4.46
11.	ANS:	B	PTS:	1	REF:	4.4.84
12.	ANS:	D	PTS:	1	REF:	4.4.100b
13.	ANS:	D	PTS:	1	REF:	4.4.15
14.	ANS:	D	PTS:	1	REF:	4.5.15
15.	ANS:	D	PTS:	1	REF:	4.5.63a
16.	ANS:	E	PTS:	1	REF:	4.5.88b
17.	ANS:	D	PTS:	1	REF:	4.6.91
18.	ANS:	B	PTS:	1	REF:	4.6.57
19.	ANS:	A	PTS:	1	REF:	4.6.92
20.	ANS:	C	PTS:	1	REF:	4.7.28
21.	ANS:	D	PTS:	1	REF:	4.7.69
22.	ANS:	D	PTS:	1	REF:	4.7.50
23.	ANS:	C	PTS:	1	REF:	4.8.28c
24.	ANS:	D	PTS:	1	REF:	4.8.46
25.	ANS:	B	PTS:	1	REF:	4.8.63b

Ch 4 Form B

_____ 1.   Find (if possible) the complement of the following angle.

$$\frac{\pi}{3}$$

a. Complement: π

b. Complement: $\dfrac{\pi}{3}$

c. Complement: $\dfrac{3}{\pi}$

d. Complement: $\dfrac{\pi}{6}$

e. Complement: $-\dfrac{\pi}{3}$

_____ 2.   Convert the angle measure from degrees to radians. Round to three decimal places.

$-0.45°$

a. $-0.45° \approx -0.008$ radian

b. $-0.45° \approx -0.308$ radian

c. $-0.45° \approx -1.308$ radians

d. $-0.45° \approx -0.092$ radian

e. $-0.45° \approx -1.008$ radians

_____ 3.   Determine two coterminal angles (one positive and one negative) for $\theta = -468°$.

a. $252°, -108°$

b. $342°, -378°$

c. $162°, -198°$

d. $252°, -288°$

e. $162°, -288°$

_____ 4.   Find the point (x,y) on the unit circle that corresponds to the real number t. (Round your answer to one decimal place.)

$$t = \frac{\pi}{7}$$

a. $t = \dfrac{\pi}{7}$ corresponds to the point $(0.9,-0.4)$.

b. $t = \dfrac{\pi}{7}$ corresponds to the point $(-0.9,-0.4)$.

c. $t = \dfrac{\pi}{7}$ corresponds to the point $(0.4,-0.9)$.

d. $t = \dfrac{\pi}{7}$ corresponds to the point $(0.4,0.9)$.

e. $t = \dfrac{\pi}{7}$ corresponds to the point $(0.9,0.4)$.

_____ 5.   Use the value of the trigonometric function to find the $\sin(-t)$.

$$\sin t = \frac{1}{4}$$

a. $\sin(-t) = -4$
b. $\sin(-t) = \dfrac{1}{4}$
c. $\sin(-t) = \infty$
d. $\sin(-t) = -\dfrac{1}{4}$
e. $\sin(-t) = 4$

_____ 6.   Find the value of given trigonometric function. Round your answer to four decimal places.

$\cos(-1.6)$

a. $\cos(-1.6) \approx -0.1292$
b. $\cos(-1.6) \approx 0.0292$
c. $\cos(-1.6) \approx 0.0708$
d. $\cos(-1.6) \approx -0.0292$
e. $\cos(-1.6) \approx 0.1708$

_____ 7.   Find the exact values of the three trignometric functions of the angle θ ($\sin\theta$, $\cos\theta$, $\tan\theta$) of the two triangles shown below. Is the function values are the same? Explain.

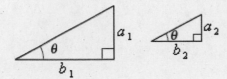

$a_1 = 7$, $b_1 = 24$ $a_2 = 3.5$, $b_2 = 12$

a.
$$\sin\theta = \frac{25}{7},\ \cos\theta = \frac{25}{24},\ \tan\theta_1 = \frac{7}{24}$$
$$\sin\theta = \frac{12.5}{3.5} = \frac{25}{7},\ \cos\theta = \frac{12.5}{12} = \frac{25}{24},\ \tan\theta = \frac{3.5}{12} = \frac{7}{24}$$
The function values are the same because the triangles are similar and corresponding sides are proportional.

b.
$$\sin\theta_1 = \frac{7}{25},\ \cos\theta_1 = \frac{24}{25},\ \tan\theta_1 = \frac{7}{24}$$
$$\sin\theta = \frac{12.5}{3.5} = \frac{25}{7},\ \cos\theta = \frac{12.5}{12} = \frac{25}{24},\ \tan\theta = \frac{12}{3.5} = \frac{24}{7}$$
The function values are different   because the triangles are not similar and corresponding sides are not proportional.

c.
$$\sin\theta = \frac{7}{25},\ \cos\theta = \frac{24}{25},\ \tan\theta = \frac{7}{24}$$
$$\sin\theta = \frac{3.5}{12.5} = \frac{7}{25},\ \cos\theta = \frac{12}{12.5} = \frac{24}{25},\ \tan\theta = \frac{3.5}{12} = \frac{7}{24}$$
The function values are the same because the triangles are similar and corresponding sides are proportional.

d.
$$\sin\theta = \frac{24}{25},\ \cos\theta = \frac{7}{25},\ \tan\theta = \frac{7}{24}$$
$$\sin\theta = \frac{12}{12.5} = \frac{24}{25},\ \cos\theta = \frac{3.5}{12.5} = \frac{7}{25},\ \tan\theta = \frac{3.5}{12.5} = \frac{7}{24}$$
The function values are the same because the triangles are similar and corresponding sides are proportional.

e.
$$\sin\theta = \frac{25}{7},\ \cos\theta = \frac{25}{24},\ \tan\theta = \frac{7}{24}$$
$$\sin\theta = \frac{12.5}{7} = \frac{25}{3.5},\ \cos\theta = \frac{12.5}{24} = \frac{25}{12},\ \tan\theta = \frac{3.5}{24} = \frac{7}{12}$$
The function values are different   because the triangles are not similar and corresponding sides are not proportional.

_____ 8.   Use a calculator to evaluate function given below. Round your answer to four decimal places. (Be sure the calculator is in the correct angle mode.)

$\tan 34.5°$

a. $\tan 34.5° \approx 0.6873$
b. $\tan 34.5° \approx 0.3839$
c. $\tan 34.5° \approx 1.4550$
d. $\tan 34.5° \approx 2.6051$
e. $\tan 34.5° \approx 0.0576$

_____ 9.   Find the values of θ in degrees $(0° < \theta < 90°)$ and radians $(0 < \theta < \pi/2)$ without the aid of a calculator.

$\sec \theta =$ Undefined

a.
$$\theta = 60° = \frac{\pi}{3}$$

b. $\theta = 0° = 0$

c.
$$\theta = 90° = \frac{\pi}{2}$$

d.
$$\theta = 30° = \frac{\pi}{6}$$

e.
$$\theta = 45° = \frac{\pi}{4}$$

_____ 10.   Find the reference angle θ', and select θ and θ' in standard position.

$\theta = 300°$

a. $\theta' = 60°$ d. $\theta' = -70°$

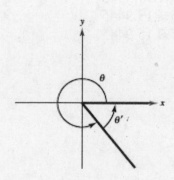

b. $\theta' = 70°$

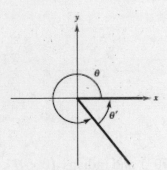

e. $\theta' = 50°$

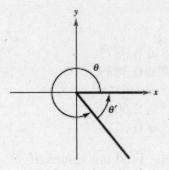

c. $\theta' = -60°$

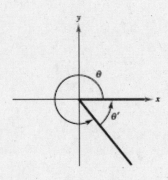

_____ 11.   Use a calculator to evaluate the trigonometric function. Round your answer to four decimal

places. (Be sure the calculator is set in the correct angle mode.)

cot 6.35

a.   cot 6.35 ≈ 7.3500
b.   cot 6.35 ≈ −7.3500
c.   cot 6.35 ≈ 14.9445
d.   cot 6.35 ≈ 13.9445
e.   cot 6.35 ≈ 15.9445

____   12.   A company that produces snowboards, which are seasonal products, forecasts monthly sales over the next 2 years to be $S = 23.1 + 0.442t + 4.3\cos(\pi t / 6)$, where S is measured in thousands of units and t is the time in months, with $t = 5$ representing January 2010. Predict sales for   following month. Round your answer to three decimal places.

February 2011

a. $S \approx 24.756$

   24,756 units

b. $S \approx 25.756$

   25,756 units

c. $S \approx 28.756$

   28,756 units

d. $S \approx 27.756$

   27,756 units

e. $S \approx 26.756$

   26,756 units

____   13.   The point $(-8, -15)$ is on the terminal side of an angle in standard position. Determine the exact value of $\sec\theta$.

a. $\sec\theta = \dfrac{9}{17}$

b. $\sec\theta = \dfrac{15}{8}$

c. $\sec\theta = \dfrac{23}{15}$

d. $\sec\theta = \dfrac{8}{15}$

e. $\sec\theta = -\dfrac{17}{8}$

_____ 14.   Find the period and amplitude.

$$y = \frac{4}{7}\cos\frac{4x}{7}$$

a. Period: 2π; Amplitude: 1

b.
Period: $\dfrac{\pi}{2}$; Amplitude: $\dfrac{1}{7}$

c. Period: π; Amplitude: 7

d.
Period: $\dfrac{7\pi}{2}$; Amplitude: $\dfrac{4}{7}$

e.
Period: π; Amplitude: $\dfrac{7}{4}$

_____ 15. g is related to a parent function $f(x) = \sin(x)$ or $f(x) = \cos(x)$.

$$g(x) = \cos(4x - \pi) + 2$$

Describe the sequence of transformations from f to g.

a.
One cycle of $f(x)$ corresponds to the interval $\left[\dfrac{\pi}{4}, \dfrac{3\pi}{4}\right]$ and $f(x)$ is obtained by

shifting $g(x)$ upward 2 units.

b. One cycle of $g(x)$ corresponds to the interval $[\pi, 3\pi]$ and $g(x)$ is obtained by
shifting $f(x)$ upward 2 units.

c. One cycle of $g(x)$ corresponds to the interval $[\pi, 3\pi]$ and $g(x)$ is obtained by
shifting $f(x)$ downward 2 units.

d.
One cycle of $g(x)$ corresponds to the interval $\left[\dfrac{\pi}{4}, \dfrac{3\pi}{4}\right]$ and $g(x)$ is obtained by

shifting $f(x)$ downward 2 units.

e.
One cycle of $g(x)$ corresponds to the interval $\left[\dfrac{\pi}{4}, \dfrac{3\pi}{4}\right]$ and $g(x)$ is obtained by

shifting $f(x)$ upward 2 units.

_____   16.   After exercising for a few minutes, a person has a respiratory cycle for which the velocity of airflow is approximated by

$$v = 1.75 \sin\left(\frac{\pi t}{2}\right),$$

where t is the time (in seconds).
(Inhalation occurs when $v > 0$ and exhalation occurs when $v < 0$.)

Find the number of cycles per minute.

a.   18 cycles/min
b.   17 cycles/min
c.   20 cycles/min
d.   15 cycles/min
e.   16 cycles/min

_____   17.   A plane flying at an altitude of 9 miles above a radar antenna will pass directly over the radar antenna (see figure). Let d be the ground distance from the antenna to the point directly under the plane and let x be the angle of elevation to the plane from the antenna.
 (d is positive as the plane approaches the antenna.)
Write d as a function of x.

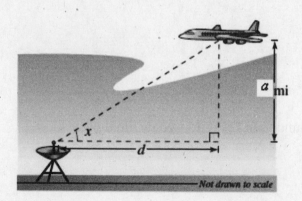

a. $d = 9\cos x$
b. $d = 9\tan x$
c. $d = 9\sin x$
d. $d = 9\cot x$
e. $d = 9\csc x$

____ 18. Determine whether the function is even, odd, or neither.

$f(x) = 6 \sec x$

a. Neither
b. Even
c. Odd

____ 19. A television camera is on a reviewing platform a meters from the street on which a parade will be passing from left to right (see figure). Write the distance d from the camera to a particular unit in the parade as a function of the angle x.

$a = 27$

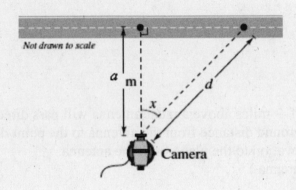

Not drawn to scale

Camera

a. $d = 27 \sec x$
b. $d = 27 \sin x$
c. $d = 27 \cot x$
d. $d = 27 \tan x$
e. $d = 27 \cos x$

____ 20. Evaluate the expression. Round your result to two decimal places.

$\arctan 40$

a. 1.55
b. 2.55
c. 0.55
d. 3.55
e. −0.45

_____ 21.   Find an algebraic expression that is equivalent to the expression..

$\cos(\arcsin 5x)$

a. $\sqrt{1+25x^2}$

b. $\dfrac{\sqrt{1-25x^2}}{1-25x^2}$

c. $\dfrac{\sqrt{1+25x^2}}{1+25x^2}$

d. $\sqrt{25x^2-1}$

e. $\sqrt{1-25x^2}$

_____ 22.   Use the properties of inverse trigonometric functions to evaluate $\tan\left[\arctan(-0.68)\right]$.

a. -0.64

b. -1.12

c. -0.98

d. -0.45

e. -0.68

_____ 23.   The height of an outdoor basketball backboard is $12\frac{1}{3}$ feet, and the backboard casts a shadow $17\frac{1}{9}$ feet long.

Find the angle of elevation of the sun. Round your answer to one decimal place.

a.   38.8°

b.   37.8°

c.   39.8°

d.   35.8°

e.   36.8°

_____ 24.   Determine the angle between the diagonal of a cube and its edge, as shown in the figure, where $a = 16$. Round your answer to one decimal place.

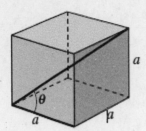

a. 58.7°
b. 57.7°
c. 54.7°
d. 55.7°
e. 56.7°

_____ 25.   A ball that is bobbing up and down on the end of a spring has a maximum displacement of 3 inches. Its motion (in ideal conditions) is modeled by

$$y = \frac{1}{5} \cos 16t \ (t > 0),$$

where y is measured in feet and t is the time in seconds.
What is the period of the oscillations?

a. $\dfrac{\pi}{5}$

b. $\dfrac{\pi}{16}$

c. $\dfrac{\pi}{8}$

d. $\dfrac{8}{\pi}$

e. $\dfrac{16}{\pi}$

Ch 4 Form B
Answer Section

1.	ANS:	D	PTS:	1	REF:	4.1.31a
2.	ANS:	A	PTS:	1	REF:	4.1.71
3.	ANS:	A	PTS:	1	REF:	4.1.51b
4.	ANS:	E	PTS:	1	REF:	4.2.9
5.	ANS:	D	PTS:	1	REF:	4.2.43a
6.	ANS:	D	PTS:	1	REF:	4.2.53
7.	ANS:	C	PTS:	1	REF:	4.3.9
8.	ANS:	A	PTS:	1	REF:	4.3.48a
9.	ANS:	C	PTS:	1	REF:	4.3.59a
10.	ANS:	A	PTS:	1	REF:	4.4.46
11.	ANS:	C	PTS:	1	REF:	4.4.84
12.	ANS:	E	PTS:	1	REF:	4.4.100b
13.	ANS:	E	PTS:	1	REF:	4.4.15
14.	ANS:	D	PTS:	1	REF:	4.5.15
15.	ANS:	E	PTS:	1	REF:	4.5.63a
16.	ANS:	D	PTS:	1	REF:	4.5.88b
17.	ANS:	D	PTS:	1	REF:	4.6.91
18.	ANS:	B	PTS:	1	REF:	4.6.57
19.	ANS:	E	PTS:	1	REF:	4.6.92
20.	ANS:	A	PTS:	1	REF:	4.7.28
21.	ANS:	E	PTS:	1	REF:	4.7.69
22.	ANS:	E	PTS:	1	REF:	4.7.50
23.	ANS:	D	PTS:	1	REF:	4.8.28c
24.	ANS:	C	PTS:	1	REF:	4.8.46
25.	ANS:	C	PTS:	1	REF:	4.8.63b

Ch 4 Form C

_____ 1. Find the quadrant in which the given angle lies.

$-168°\,50'$

a. Quadrant III
b. Quadrant I
c. Quadrant IV
d. Quadrant II
e. None of the above

_____ 2. Convert angle measure to decimal degree form. Round your answer to three decimal places.

$52°27'29''$

a. $52°27'29'' \approx 52.458°$
b. $52°27'29'' \approx 52.273°$
c. $52°27'29'' \approx 62.458°$
d. $52°27'29'' \approx 108°$
e. $52°27'29'' \approx 42.458°$

_____ 3. Rewrite $-\dfrac{7\pi}{18}$ in degree measure.

a. $-70°$
b. $-105°$
c. $-140°$
d. $-35°$
e. $-47°$

_____   4.   Find the point (x, y) on the unit circle that corresponds to the real number t.

$$t = \frac{17\pi}{6}$$

a.
$t = \dfrac{17\pi}{6}$ corresponds to the point $\left(\dfrac{1}{2}, -\dfrac{\sqrt{3}}{2}\right)$.

b.
$t = \dfrac{17\pi}{6}$ corresponds to the point $\left(-\dfrac{\sqrt{3}}{2}, \dfrac{1}{2}\right)$.

c.
$t = \dfrac{17\pi}{6}$ corresponds to the point $\left(-\dfrac{\sqrt{3}}{2}, -\dfrac{1}{2}\right)$.

d.
$t = \dfrac{17\pi}{6}$ corresponds to the point $\left(\dfrac{\sqrt{3}}{2}, -\dfrac{1}{2}\right)$.

e.
$t = \dfrac{17\pi}{6}$ corresponds to the point $\left(\dfrac{\sqrt{3}}{2}, \dfrac{1}{2}\right)$.

_____   5.   Use the value of the trigonometric function to find $\csc t$.

$$\sin(-t) = \frac{3}{4}$$

a. $\csc t = \dfrac{3}{4}$

b. $\csc t = -\dfrac{3}{4}$

c. $\csc t = \infty$

d. $\csc t = \dfrac{4}{3}$

e. $\csc t = -\dfrac{4}{3}$

_____ 6. Find the value of given trigonometric function. Round your answer to four decimal places.

$\sec 1.5$

a. $\sec 1.5 \approx 14.2368$
b. $\sec 1.5 \approx 14.3368$
c. $\sec 1.5 \approx 14.1368$
d. $\sec 1.5 \approx 14.0368$
e. $\sec 1.5 \approx -14.1368$

_____ 7. Use the Pythagorean Theorem to determine the third side and then find the three trignometric functions of θ: $\sin \theta$, $\cot \theta$, and $\csc \theta$

$$\cos \theta = \frac{24}{25}$$

a. $\sin \theta = \dfrac{7}{25}$, $\cot \theta = \dfrac{24}{7}$, $\csc \theta = \dfrac{25}{7}$

b. $\sin \theta = \dfrac{24}{25}$, $\cot \theta = \dfrac{24}{7}$, $\csc \theta = \dfrac{25}{24}$

c. $\sin \theta = \dfrac{7}{24}$, $\cot \theta = \dfrac{24}{25}$, $\csc \theta = \dfrac{24}{7}$

d. $\sin \theta = \dfrac{7}{25}$, $\cot \theta = \dfrac{7}{24}$, $\csc \theta = \dfrac{25}{7}$

e. $\sin \theta = \dfrac{25}{7}$, $\cot \theta = \dfrac{24}{7}$, $\csc \theta = \dfrac{7}{25}$

_____ 8. Use a calculator to evaluate function given below. Round your answer to four decimal places. (Be sure the calculator is in the correct angle mode.)

$\sec 47.37°$

a. $\sec 47.37° \approx -1.4142$
b. $\sec 47.37° \approx 1.4765$
c. $\sec 47.37° \approx 1.3592$
d. $\sec 47.37° \approx 1.4142$
e. $\sec 47.37° \approx 1.0307$

_____ 9.   Solve for x as indicated.

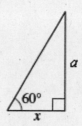

$a = 4$

a. $x = 3\sqrt{3}$

b. $x = 4\sqrt{3}$

c. $x = \dfrac{4}{3}$

d. $x = \dfrac{4\sqrt{3}}{3}$

e. $x = \sqrt{3}$

_____ 10.   Find the reference angle θ', and select θ and θ' in standard position.

$\theta = 11.8$

a. $\theta' = 4\pi - 12.8$ d. $\theta' = 4\pi - 11.8$

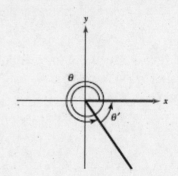

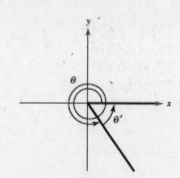

b. $\theta' = -4\pi - 11.8$ e. $\theta' = 4\pi + 11.8$

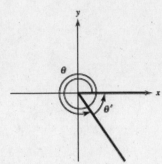   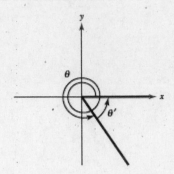

c. $\theta' = 4\pi + 12.8$

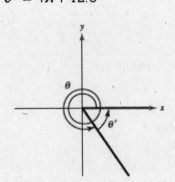

_____   11.   Use a calculator to evaluate the trigonometric function. Round your answer to four decimal

places. (Be sure the calculator is set in the correct angle mode.)

sin (−0.75)

a. $\sin(-0.75) \approx -2.6816$
b. $\sin(-0.75) \approx 2.6816$
c. $\sin(-0.75) \approx -0.6816$
d. $\sin(-0.75) \approx 1.6816$
e. $\sin(-0.75) \approx 0.6816$

_____ 12.   Find the indicated trigonometric value in the specified quadrant.

Function	Quadrant	Trignometric value
$\csc \theta = -4$	IV	$\cot \theta$

a. $\cot \theta = -\sqrt{14}$

b. $\cot \theta = \sqrt{17}$

c. $\cot \theta = \sqrt{14}$

d. $\cot \theta = -\sqrt{15}$

e. $\cot \theta = \sqrt{15}$

_____ 13.   Use a calculator to evaluate $\tan 335°$. Round your answer to four decimal places.

a.   −1.2232

b.   −0.9663

c.   −2.2370

d.   −2.9870

e.   −0.4663

_____ 14.   Find the relationship between the graphs of f and g. Consider amplitude, period, and shifts.

$f(x) = \cos 2x$

$g(x) = -\cos 2x$

a. f is a reflection of g in the y-axis.

b. f is a reflection of g in the x-axis.

c. g is a reflection of f in the y-axis.

d. g is a shift of f π units to the right.

e. g is a reflection of f in the x-axis.

_____ 15. g is related to a parent function $f(x) = \sin(x)$ or $g(x) = \cos(x)$.

$g(x) = 2\sin(2x - \pi) - 5$

Describe the sequence of transformations from f to g.

a.
One cycle of $g(x)$ is $\left[\dfrac{\pi}{2}, \dfrac{3\pi}{2}\right]$. $g(x)$ is also shifted down 5 units and has an amplitude of 2.

b. One cycle of $g(x)$ is $[\pi, 3\pi]$. $g(x)$ is also shifted down 5 units and has an amplitude of 5.

c.
One cycle of $g(x)$ is $\left[\dfrac{\pi}{2}, \dfrac{3\pi}{2}\right]$. $g(x)$ is also shifted down 2 units and has an amplitude of 2.

d.
One cycle of $g(x)$ is $\left[\dfrac{\pi}{2}, \dfrac{3\pi}{2}\right]$. $g(x)$ is also shifted up 5 units and has an amplitude of 2.

e.
One cycle of $f(x)$ is $\left[\dfrac{\pi}{2}, \dfrac{3\pi}{2}\right]$. $f(x)$ is also shifted down 5 units and has an amplitude of 2.

_____ 16.   When tuning a piano, a technician strikes a tuning fork for the A above middle C and sets
up a wave motion that can be approximated by

$y = 0.001\sin 880t,$

where t is the time (in seconds).
The frequency is given by $f = 1/p$. What is the frequency of the note?

a. 88 cycles/sec
b. 440 cycles/sec
c. 880 cycles/sec
d. $\dfrac{1}{880}$ cycles/sec
e. $\dfrac{1}{440}$ cycles/sec

_____ 17.　　State the period of the function.

$$y = \frac{1}{8} \cot \pi x$$

a. 7π
b. $\dfrac{\pi}{2}$
c. 5π
d. 6π
e. 1

_____ 18.　　Determine whether the function is even, odd, or neither.

$$f(x) = 5 \csc \frac{x}{5}$$

a. Even
b. Odd
c. Neither

_____ 19.　　Determine whether the statement is true or false. Justify your answer.

The graph of $y = 3\csc x$ can be obtained on a calculator by graphing the reciprocal of $y = 3\sin x$.

a. True
b. False

_____ 20.　　Evaluate the expression. Round your result to two decimal places.

arctan 1.1

a. 1.83
b. −0.17
c. 2.83
d. −1.17
e. 0.83

_____ 21.   A boat is pulled in by means of a winch located on a dock $a = 9$ feet above the deck of the boat (see figure). Let θ be the angle of elevation from the boat to the winch and let s be the length of the rope from the winch to the boat. Write θ as a function of s.

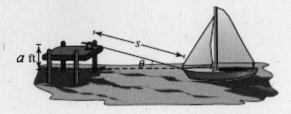

a. $\theta = \text{arccsc}\ \dfrac{9}{s}$

b. $\theta = \text{arcsec}\ \dfrac{9}{s}$

c. $\theta = \text{arccos}\ \dfrac{9}{s}$

d. $\theta = \text{arctan}\ \dfrac{9}{s}$

e. $\theta = \text{arcsin}\ \dfrac{9}{s}$

_____ 22.   Find the exact value of $\csc\left(\sin^{-1}\dfrac{11}{61}\right)$.

a. $\dfrac{61}{11}$

b. $\dfrac{72}{11}$

c. $\dfrac{11}{61}$

d. $\dfrac{61}{11}$

e. $\dfrac{61}{72}$

_____ 23.   For the simple harmonic motion described by the trigonometric function, find the least positive value of t for which $d = 0$.

$$d = \frac{1}{64} \sin 796\pi t$$

a. 64

b. $\dfrac{1}{796}$

c. 796

d. $\dfrac{1}{64}$

e. $\dfrac{1}{1588}$

_____ 24.   Find the lengths of all the unknown members of the truss. Round your answer to two decimal places.

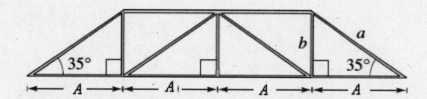

$A = 10$

a. $b \approx 9,\ a \approx 14.2$

b. $b \approx 12.2,\ a \approx 7$

c. $b \approx 8,\ a \approx 13.2$

d. $b \approx 10,\ a \approx 15.2$

e. $b \approx 7,\ a \approx 12.2$

_____ 25.   If $B = 20°$ and $a = 8$, determine the value of b. Round to two decimal places.

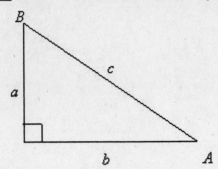

a. 7.52

b. 2.74

c. 2.91

d. 8.51

e. 21.98

Ch 4 Form C
Answer Section

1.	ANS: A	PTS: 1	REF: 4.1.43a
2.	ANS: A	PTS: 1	REF: 4.1.83a
3.	ANS: A	PTS: 1	REF: 4.1.62a
4.	ANS: B	PTS: 1	REF: 4.2.13
5.	ANS: E	PTS: 1	REF: 4.2.44b
6.	ANS: C	PTS: 1	REF: 4.2.56
7.	ANS: A	PTS: 1	REF: 4.3.14
8.	ANS: B	PTS: 1	REF: 4.3.50b
9.	ANS: D	PTS: 1	REF: 4.3.65
10.	ANS: D	PTS: 1	REF: 4.4.52
11.	ANS: C	PTS: 1	REF: 4.4.87
12.	ANS: D	PTS: 1	REF: 4.4.72
13.	ANS: E	PTS: 1	REF: 4.4.53
14.	ANS: E	PTS: 1	REF: 4.5.21
15.	ANS: A	PTS: 1	REF: 4.5.65a
16.	ANS: B	PTS: 1	REF: 4.5.91b
17.	ANS: E	PTS: 1	REF: 4.6.11
18.	ANS: B	PTS: 1	REF: 4.6.60
19.	ANS: B	PTS: 1	REF: 4.6..96
20.	ANS: E	PTS: 1	REF: 4.7.34
21.	ANS: E	PTS: 1	REF: 4.7.105a
22.	ANS: D	PTS: 1	REF: 4.7.65
23.	ANS: B	PTS: 1	REF: 4.8.60d
24.	ANS: E	PTS: 1	REF: 4.8.51
25.	ANS: C	PTS: 1	REF: 4.8.7

Ch 4 Form D

____   1.   Find the quadrant in which the given angle lies.

$-151° 50'$

a. Quadrant I
b. Quadrant III
c. Quadrant IV
d. Quadrant II
e. None of the above

____   2.   Convert angle measure to decimal degree form. Round your answer to three decimal places.

$76°24'31''$

a. $76°24'31'' \approx 86.409°$
b. $76°24'31'' \approx 131°$
c. $76°24'31'' \approx 66.409°$
d. $76°24'31'' \approx 76.409°$
e. $76°24'31'' \approx 76.243°$

____   3.   Rewrite $-\dfrac{13\pi}{9}$ in degree measure.

a. $-173°$
b. $-130°$
c. $-260°$
d. $-390°$
e. $-520°$

____   4.   Find the point (x, y) on the unit circle that corresponds to the real number t.

$$t = \frac{5\pi}{6}$$

a. $t = \dfrac{5\pi}{6}$ corresponds to the point $\left(-\dfrac{\sqrt{3}}{2}, \dfrac{1}{2} \right)$.

b. $t = \dfrac{5\pi}{6}$ corresponds to the point $\left(-\dfrac{\sqrt{3}}{2}, -\dfrac{1}{2} \right)$.

c. $t = \dfrac{5\pi}{6}$ corresponds to the point $\left(\dfrac{\sqrt{3}}{2}, -\dfrac{1}{2} \right)$.

d. $t = \dfrac{5\pi}{6}$ corresponds to the point $\left(\dfrac{\sqrt{3}}{2}, \dfrac{1}{2} \right)$.

e. $t = \dfrac{5\pi}{6}$ corresponds to the point $\left(\dfrac{1}{2}, -\dfrac{\sqrt{3}}{2} \right)$.

____   5.   Use the value of the trigonometric function to find $\csc t$.

$$\sin(-t) = \frac{3}{10}$$

a. $\csc t = -\dfrac{10}{3}$

b. $\csc t = \dfrac{10}{3}$

c. $\csc t = \infty$

d. $\csc t = \dfrac{3}{10}$

e. $\csc t = -\dfrac{3}{10}$

____ 6.   Find the value of given trigonometric function. Round your answer to four decimal places.

$\sec 1.7$

a. $\sec 1.7 \approx -7.6613$
b. $\sec 1.7 \approx -7.7613$
c. $\sec 1.7 \approx -7.5613$
d. $\sec 1.7 \approx 7.7613$
e. $\sec 1.7 \approx -7.8613$

____ 7.   Use the Pythagorean Theorem to determine the third side and then find the three trignometric functions of θ: $\sin\theta$, $\cot\theta$, and $\csc\theta$

$$\cos\theta = \frac{24}{25}$$

a.
$$\sin\theta = \frac{7}{25}, \cot\theta = \frac{24}{7}, \csc\theta = \frac{25}{7}$$

b.
$$\sin\theta = \frac{24}{25}, \cot\theta = \frac{24}{7}, \csc\theta = \frac{25}{24}$$

c.
$$\sin\theta = \frac{7}{25}, \cot\theta = \frac{7}{24}, \csc\theta = \frac{25}{7}$$

d.
$$\sin\theta = \frac{25}{7}, \cot\theta = \frac{24}{7}, \csc\theta = \frac{7}{25}$$

e.
$$\sin\theta = \frac{7}{24}, \cot\theta = \frac{24}{25}, \csc\theta = \frac{24}{7}$$

____ 8.   Use a calculator to evaluate function given below. Round your answer to four decimal places. (Be sure the calculator is in the correct angle mode.)

$\sec 46.67°$

a. $\sec 46.67° \approx 1.1145$
b. $\sec 46.67° \approx -1.4663$
c. $\sec 46.67° \approx 1.3748$
d. $\sec 46.67° \approx 1.4572$
e. $\sec 46.67° \approx 1.3673$

_____ 9.   Solve for x as indicated.

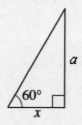

$a = 4$

a. $x = \sqrt{3}$

b. $x = \dfrac{4}{3}$

c. $x = 3\sqrt{3}$

d. $x = \dfrac{4\sqrt{3}}{3}$

e. $x = 4\sqrt{3}$

_____ 10.   Find the reference angle θ', and select θ and θ' in standard position.

$\theta = 11.1$

a. $\theta' = 4\pi + 11.1$ d. $\theta' = -4\pi - 11.1$

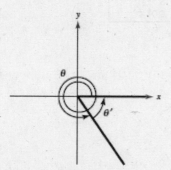 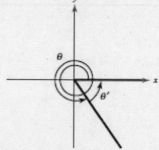

b. $\theta' = 4\pi - 12.1$ e. $\theta' = 4\pi + 12.1$

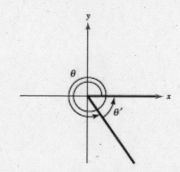 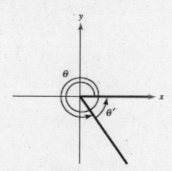

c. $\theta' = 4\pi - 11.1$

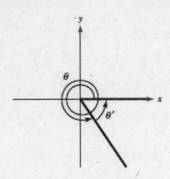

_____ 11.   Use a calculator to evaluate the trigonometric function. Round your answer to four decimal

places. (Be sure the calculator is set in the correct angle mode.)

$\sin(-0.80)$

a. $\sin(-0.80) \approx -2.7174$
b. $\sin(-0.80) \approx 1.7174$
c. $\sin(-0.80) \approx 0.7174$
d. $\sin(-0.80) \approx -0.7174$
e. $\sin(-0.80) \approx 2.7174$

_____ 12.   Find the indicated trigonometric value in the specified quadrant.

Function	Quadrant	Trignometric value
$\csc \theta = -4$	IV	$\cot \theta$

a. $\cot \theta = -\sqrt{14}$
b. $\cot \theta = \sqrt{17}$
c. $\cot \theta = \sqrt{15}$
d. $\cot \theta = -\sqrt{15}$
e. $\cot \theta = \sqrt{14}$

_____ 13.   Use a calculator to evaluate $\cos 305°$. Round your answer to four decimal places.
a. 0.0736
b. 0.5736
c. -1.7150
d. -0.1059
e. -0.9650

____ 14. Find the relationship between the graphs of f and g. Consider amplitude, period, and shifts.

$f(x) = \cos 5x$

$g(x) = -\cos 5x$

a. f is a reflection of g in the y-axis.
b. g is a reflection of f in the x-axis.
c. g is a shift of f π units to the right.
d. f is a reflection of g in the x-axis.
e. g is a reflection of f in the y-axis.

____ 15. g is related to a parent function $f(x) = \sin(x)$ or $g(x) = \cos(x)$.

$g(x) = 6\sin(6x - \pi) - 9$

Describe the sequence of transformations from f to g.

a. One cycle of $g(x)$ is $\left[\dfrac{\pi}{6}, \dfrac{3\pi}{6}\right]$. $g(x)$ is also shifted down 6 units and has an amplitude of 6.

b. One cycle of $g(x)$ is $\left[\dfrac{\pi}{6}, \dfrac{3\pi}{6}\right]$. $g(x)$ is also shifted up 9 units and has an amplitude of 6.

c. One cycle of $g(x)$ is $\left[\dfrac{\pi}{6}, \dfrac{3\pi}{6}\right]$. $g(x)$ is also shifted down 9 units and has an amplitude of 6.

d. One cycle of $f(x)$ is $\left[\dfrac{\pi}{6}, \dfrac{3\pi}{6}\right]$. $f(x)$ is also shifted down 9 units and has an amplitude of 6.

e. One cycle of $g(x)$ is $[\pi, 3\pi]$. $g(x)$ is also shifted down 9 units and has an amplitude of 9.

_____ 16.   When tuning a piano, a technician strikes a tuning fork for the A above middle C and sets
up a wave motion that can be approximated by

$y = 0.001 \sin 880t,$

where t is the time (in seconds).
The frequency is given by $f = 1/p$. What is the frequency of the note?

a. 440 cycles/sec
b. 880 cycles/sec
c. $\dfrac{1}{440}$ cycles/sec
d. $\dfrac{1}{880}$ cycles/sec
e. 88 cycles/sec

_____ 17.   State the period of the function.

$y = \dfrac{1}{2}\cot \pi x$

a. 4π
b. $\dfrac{\pi}{2}$
c. 3π
d. 2π
e. 1

_____ 18.   Determine whether the function is even, odd, or neither.

$f(x) = 2\csc \dfrac{x}{2}$

a. Even
b. Neither
c. Odd

_____ 19.   Determine whether the statement is true or false. Justify your answer.

The graph of $y = 5\csc x$ can be obtained on a calculator by graphing the reciprocal of $y = 5\sin x$.

a. True
b. False

_____ 20.   Evaluate the expression. Round your result to two decimal places.

arctan 1.7

a.   1.04
b.   2.04
c. −0.96
d.   0.04
e.   3.04

_____ 21.   A boat is pulled in by means of a winch located on a dock $a = 7$ feet above the deck of the boat (see figure). Let θ be the angle of elevation from the boat to the winch and let s be the length of the rope from the winch to the boat. Write θ as a function of s.

a.
$$\theta = \operatorname{arcsec} \frac{7}{s}$$
b.
$$\theta = \arctan \frac{7}{s}$$
c.
$$\theta = \operatorname{arccsc} \frac{7}{s}$$
d.
$$\theta = \arccos \frac{7}{s}$$
e.
$$\theta = \arcsin \frac{7}{s}$$

_____ 22.   Find the exact value of $\cos\left(\sin^{-1} \frac{3}{5} \right)$.

a. $\dfrac{4}{9}$

b. $\dfrac{9}{5}$

c. $\dfrac{4}{5}$

d. $\dfrac{5}{3}$

e. $\dfrac{3}{5}$

____ 23.   For the simple harmonic motion described by the trigonometric function, find the least positive value of t for which $d = 0$.

$$d = \frac{1}{64} \sin 793\pi t$$

a. $\dfrac{1}{64}$

b. $\dfrac{1}{793}$

c. 793

d. 64

e. $\dfrac{1}{1582}$

____ 24.   Find the lengths of all the unknown members of the truss. Round your answer to two decimal places.

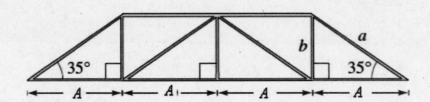

$A = 20$

a. $b \approx 17,\ a \approx 27.4$
b. $b \approx 14,\ a \approx 24.4$
c. $b \approx 16,\ a \approx 26.4$
d. $b \approx 24.4,\ a \approx 14$
e. $b \approx 15,\ a \approx 25.4$

_____   25.   If $B = 43°$ and $a = 6$, determine the value of b. Round to two decimal places.

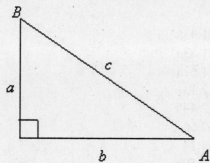

a.   6.43
b.   4.09
c.   5.60
d.   8.20
e.   4.39

Ch 4 Form D
Answer Section

1.	ANS:	B	PTS:	1	REF:	4.1.43a
2.	ANS:	D	PTS:	1	REF:	4.1.83a
3.	ANS:	C	PTS:	1	REF:	4.1.62a
4.	ANS:	A	PTS:	1	REF:	4.2.13
5.	ANS:	A	PTS:	1	REF:	4.2.44b
6.	ANS:	B	PTS:	1	REF:	4.2.56
7.	ANS:	A	PTS:	1	REF:	4.3.14
8.	ANS:	D	PTS:	1	REF:	4.3.50b
9.	ANS:	D	PTS:	1	REF:	4.3.65
10.	ANS:	C	PTS:	1	REF:	4.4.52
11.	ANS:	D	PTS:	1	REF:	4.4.87
12.	ANS:	D	PTS:	1	REF:	4.4.72
13.	ANS:	B	PTS:	1	REF:	4.4.53
14.	ANS:	B	PTS:	1	REF:	4.5.21
15.	ANS:	C	PTS:	1	REF:	4.5.65a
16.	ANS:	A	PTS:	1	REF:	4.5.91b
17.	ANS:	E	PTS:	1	REF:	4.6.11
18.	ANS:	C	PTS:	1	REF:	4.6.60
19.	ANS:	B	PTS:	1	REF:	4.6..96
20.	ANS:	A	PTS:	1	REF:	4.7.34
21.	ANS:	E	PTS:	1	REF:	4.7.105a
22.	ANS:	C	PTS:	1	REF:	4.7.65
23.	ANS:	B	PTS:	1	REF:	4.8.60d
24.	ANS:	B	PTS:	1	REF:	4.8.51
25.	ANS:	C	PTS:	1	REF:	4.8.7

Ch 4

_____   1.   Find the supplement of the following angle.

$92°$

a. Supplement: $268°$
b. Supplement: $92°$
c. Supplement: $88°$
d. Supplement: $2°$
e. Supplement: $89°$

_____   2.   Find the length of the arc on a circle of radius r intercepted by a central angle θ. Round to two decimal places.

Radius r	Central Angle θ
21 centimeters	$40°$

a. $s \approx 16.66$ centimeters
b. $s \approx 21.22$ centimeters
c. $s \approx 14.66$ centimeters
d. $s \approx 4.67$ centimeters
e. $s \approx 12.66$ centimeters

_____   3.   Find the angle, in radians, in the figure below if $S = 10$ and $r = 7$.

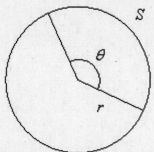

a. $\dfrac{10\pi}{7}$

b. $\dfrac{7}{10}$

c. $\dfrac{10}{7}$

d. $\dfrac{7\pi}{10}$

e. $\dfrac{17\pi}{7}$

_____ 4. Evaluate (if possible) the sine, cosine, and tangent of the real number.

$$t = -\frac{7\pi}{2}$$

a. $t = -\frac{7\pi}{2}$ corresponds to the point $(x, y) = (0, 0)$.

$$\sin\left(-\frac{7\pi}{2}\right) = 0$$

$$\cos\left(-\frac{7\pi}{2}\right) = 0$$

$$\tan\left(-\frac{7\pi}{2}\right) = 0$$

b. $t = -\frac{7\pi}{2}$ corresponds to the point $(x, y) = (1, 0)$.

$$\sin\left(-\frac{7\pi}{2}\right) = 1$$

$$\cos\left(-\frac{7\pi}{2}\right) = 0$$

$$\tan\left(-\frac{7\pi}{2}\right) = 0$$

c. $t = -\frac{7\pi}{2}$ corresponds to the point $(x, y) = (0, 1)$.

$$\sin\left(-\frac{7\pi}{2}\right) = 1$$

$$\cos\left(-\frac{7\pi}{2}\right) = 0$$

$$\tan\left(-\frac{7\pi}{2}\right)$$ is undefined.

d.
$$t = -\frac{7\pi}{2}$$ corresponds to the point $(x, y) = (1, 0)$.

$$\sin\left(-\frac{7\pi}{2}\right) = 0$$

$$\cos\left(-\frac{7\pi}{2}\right) = 1$$

$$\tan\left(-\frac{7\pi}{2}\right) = 0$$

e. Not possible

____ 5.   Use the value of the trigonometric function to find $\sec(-t)$.

$$\cos t = -\frac{3}{4}$$

a.
$$\sec(-t) = \frac{4}{3}$$

b.
$$\sec(-t) = -\frac{3}{4}$$

c.
$$\sec(-t) = -\frac{4}{3}$$

d. $\sec(-t) = \infty$

e.
$$\sec(-t) = \frac{3}{4}$$

_____ 6. The displacement from equilibrium of an oscillating weight suspended by a spring is given by

$$y(t) = \frac{1}{4}\cos 6t,$$ where y is the displacement (in feet) and t is the time (in seconds). Find the displacements when $t = \frac{1}{5}$.

a. $y\left(\frac{1}{5}\right) \approx 0.19$ foot

b. $y\left(\frac{1}{5}\right) \approx 0.49$ foot

c. $y\left(\frac{1}{5}\right) \approx 0.29$ foot

d. $y\left(\frac{1}{5}\right) \approx 0.39$ foot

e. $y\left(\frac{1}{5}\right) \approx 0.09$ foot

_____ 7. Use the Pythagorean Theorem to determine the third side and then find the two trignometric functions of θ: $\sin\theta$ and $\cot\theta$

$\csc\theta = 6$

a. $\sin\theta = \frac{1}{6}$, $\cot\theta = \sqrt{35}$

b. $\sin\theta = \sqrt{35}$, $\cot\theta = \frac{1}{6}$

c. $\sin\theta = 1$, $\cot\theta = \frac{1}{6}$

d. $\sin\theta = 1$, $\cot\theta = \sqrt{35}$

e. $\sin\theta = \frac{1}{6}$, $\cot\theta = 1$

_____ 8.   Use a calculator to evaluate function given below. Round your answer to four decimal places. (Be sure the calculator is in the correct angle mode.)

$\csc 45°2'$

a. $\csc 45°2' \approx 0.7075$
b. $\csc 45°2' \approx 0.7067$
c. $\csc 45°2' \approx 1.0012$
d. $\csc 45°2' \approx 1.4134$
e. $\csc 45°2' \approx 1.4150$

_____ 9.   Given $\sin 30° = \dfrac{1}{2}$ and $\cos 30° = \dfrac{\sqrt{3}}{2}$, determine the following:

$\tan 30°$

a.
   $\tan 30° = \dfrac{\sqrt{2}}{2}$
b. $\tan 30° = \sqrt{3}$
c. $\tan 30° = 1$
d.   undefined
e.
   $\tan 30° = \dfrac{\sqrt{3}}{3}$

_____ 10.   Use a calculator to evaluate the trigonometric function. Round your answer to four decimal

places. (Be sure the calculator is set in the correct angle mode.)

$\sec 230°$

a. $\sec 230° \approx -0.0222$
b. $\sec 230° \approx 0.9778$
c. $\sec 230° \approx -0.9778$
d. $\sec 230° \approx -1.5557$
e. $\sec 230° \approx -0.5557$

_____   11.   An airplane, flying at an altitude of $a = 6$ miles, is on a flight path that passes directly over an observer (see figure). If θ is the angle of elevation from the observer to the plane, find the distance d from the observer to the plane when $\theta = 30°$.

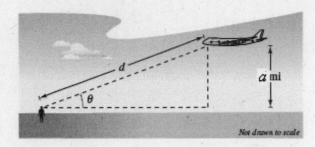

a. $d = 12$ miles
b. $d = 6$ miles
c. $d \approx 6.9$ miles
d. $d = 13$ miles
e. $d = 7$ miles

_____   12.   Find the indicated trigonometric value in the specified quadrant.

Function	Quad-rant	Trignometric value
$\cos \theta = \dfrac{6}{13}$	I	$\sec \theta$

a. $\sec \theta = -\dfrac{1}{2}$

b. $\sec \theta = \dfrac{1}{2}$

c. $\sec \theta = \dfrac{13}{6}$

d. $\sec \theta = \dfrac{14}{13}$

e. $\sec \theta = -\dfrac{13}{6}$

_____   13.   Given the equation below, determine two solutions such that $0° \leq \theta < 360°$.

$\cos \theta = -\dfrac{\sqrt{3}}{2}$

a. $\theta = 150°, 210°$
b. $\theta = 135°, 225°$
c. $\theta = 240°, 300°$
d. $\theta = 225°, 315°$
e. $\theta = 120°, 240°$

_____   14.   Find the relationship between the graphs of f and g. Consider amplitude, period, and shifts.

$f(x) = \cos 7x$

$g(x) = -3 + \cos 7x$

a. g is a shift of f 7 units downwards.
b. g is a shift of f 3 units upwards.
c. f is a reflection of g in the x-axis.
d. g is a shift of f 3 units downwards.
e.   The period of g is 3 times the period of f.

_____   15.   Use a graphing utility to select the graph of the function. Include two full periods.

$y = -2 \sin\left(\dfrac{8}{3} x - \dfrac{\pi}{3} \right)$

a.

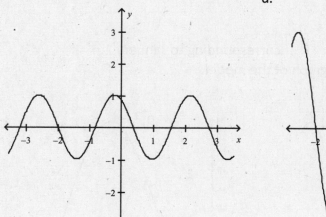

d.

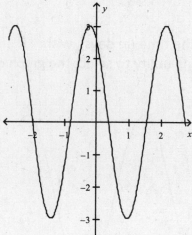

b.

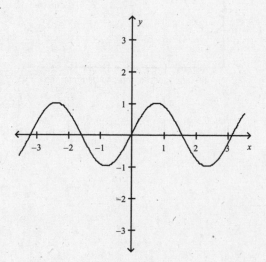

e.

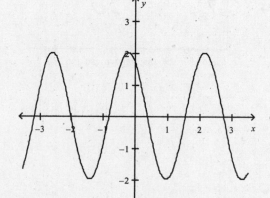

c.

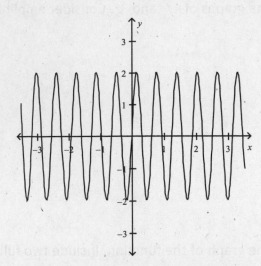

16. The daily consumption C (in gallons) of diesel fuel on a farm is modeled by

$$C = 30.6 + 21.6 \sin\left(\frac{2\pi t}{365} + 10.5\right)$$

where t is the time (in days), with $t = 1$ corresponding to January 1.
Use a graphing utility to select the graph of the model.

a.

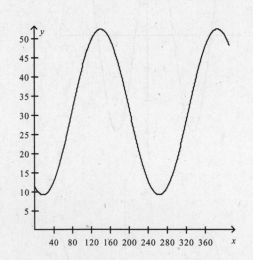

d.

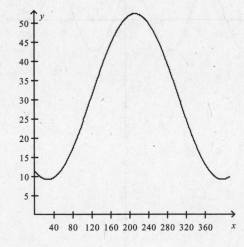

b.

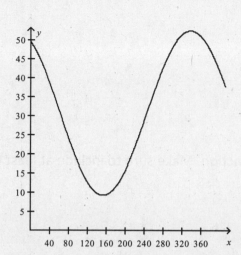

e.

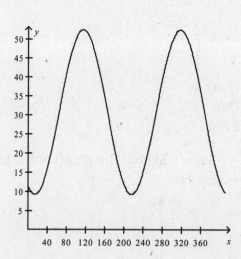

c.

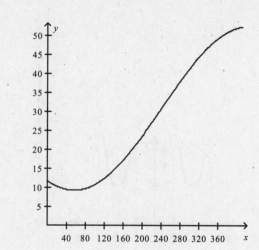

_____ 17.   State the period of the function.

$$y = -2\sec\frac{\pi x}{2}$$

a. $\dfrac{\pi}{2}$

b. 4

c. 4π

d. 6

e. 10

_____   18.   Determine whether the function is even, odd, or neither.

$$f(x) = x^6 \cot \frac{x}{3}$$

a. Neither
b. Odd
c. Even

_____   19.   Sketch the graph of the given function. Make sure to include at least two periods.

$$y = -2 \csc 2x$$

a.

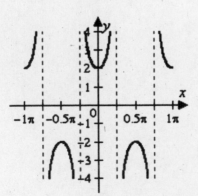

d.

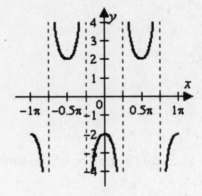

b.

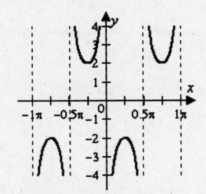

e.

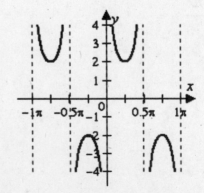

c.

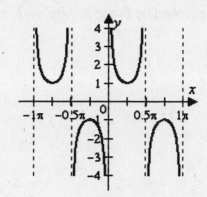

_____ 20.   Evaluate the expression. Round your result to two decimal places.

$$\tan^{-1}\left(-\frac{83}{6}\right)$$

a. −3.50

b. 0.50

c. −0.50

d. −1.50

e. −2.50

_____ 21.   Find the value of the expression. Round your result to two decimal places.

arcsec 2.14

a. −1.08

b. 1.08

c. 2.06

d. 2.14

e. −2.14

_____   22.   Which of the following functions is represented by the graph below?

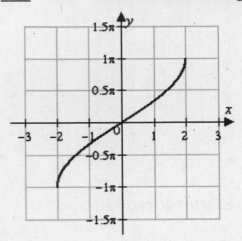

a. $\arccos \dfrac{x}{2}$

b. $\arcsin 2x$

c. $2\arccos x$

d. $2\arcsin \dfrac{x}{2}$

e. $\arccos(x+1)$

_____   23.   An observer in a lighthouse $a = 350$ feet above sea level observes two ships directly offshore.
The angles of depression to the ships are $4°$ and $6.5°$ (see figure). How far apart are the ships?
Round your answer to one decimal place.

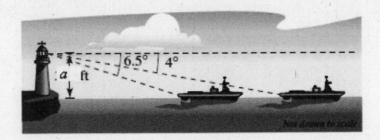

a.   1933.3 ft
b.   1935.3 ft
c.   1936.3 ft
d.   1934.3 ft
e.   1937.3 ft

_____   24.   For the simple harmonic motion described by the trigonometric function, find the maximum displacement.

$$d = 8\cos\frac{6\pi}{5}t$$

a. 5
b. $\dfrac{6}{5}$

c. 8
d. $\dfrac{1}{8}$

e. $\dfrac{5}{6}$

_____   25.   The angle of elevation of the sun is $34°$. Find the length, l, of a shadow cast by a tree that is 53 feet tall. Round answer to two decimal places.
a. $l = 79.09$ feet
b. $l = 94.78$ feet
c. $l = 63.93$ feet
d. $l = 59.45$ feet
e. $l = 78.58$ feet

Ch 4 Form E
Answer Section

1.	ANS:	C	PTS:	1	REF:	4.1.54b
2.	ANS:	C	PTS:	1	REF:	4.1.92
3.	ANS:	C	PTS:	1	REF:	4.1.98
4.	ANS:	C	PTS:	1	REF:	4.2.25
5.	ANS:	C	PTS:	1	REF:	4.2.46b
6.	ANS:	E	PTS:	1	REF:	4.2.59b
7.	ANS:	A	PTS:	1	REF:	4.3.20
8.	ANS:	D	PTS:	1	REF:	4.3.52b
9.	ANS:	E	PTS:	1	REF:	4.3.31c
10.	ANS:	D	PTS:	1	REF:	4.4.76
11.	ANS:	A	PTS:	1	REF:	4.4.97a
12.	ANS:	C	PTS:	1	REF:	4.4.73
13.	ANS:	A	PTS:	1	REF:	4.4.92b
14.	ANS:	D	PTS:	1	REF:	4.5.26
15.	ANS:	E	PTS:	1	REF:	4.5.68
16.	ANS:	D	PTS:	1	REF:	4.5.93c
17.	ANS:	B	PTS:	1	REF:	4.6.14
18.	ANS:	B	PTS:	1	REF:	4.6.64
19.	ANS:	A	PTS:	1	REF:	4.6.23
20.	ANS:	D	PTS:	1	REF:	4.7.38
21.	ANS:	B	PTS:	1	REF:	4.7.127
22.	ANS:	D	PTS:	1	REF:	4.7.86
23.	ANS:	A	PTS:	1	REF:	4.8.24
24.	ANS:	C	PTS:	1	REF:	4.8.57a
25.	ANS:	E	PTS:	1	REF:	4.8.19

Ch 4 Form F

_____ 1.   Given the equation below, determine two solutions such that $0° \le \theta < 360°$.

$$\cos \theta = -\frac{\sqrt{3}}{2}$$

a. $\theta = 225°, 315°$
b. $\theta = 135°, 225°$
c. $\theta = 120°, 240°$
d. $\theta = 150°, 210°$
e. $\theta = 240°, 300°$

_____ 2.   After leaving the runway, a plane's angle of ascent is $15°$ and its speed is 265 feet per second. How many minutes will it take for the airplane to climb to a height of 11,000 feet? Round answer to two decimal places.

a.   2.07 minutes
b.   1.48 minutes
c.   2.67 minutes
d.   0.69 minutes
e.   1.06 minutes

_____ 3.   For the simple harmonic motion described by the trigonometric function, find the value of when $t = 7$.

$$d = 9\cos\frac{6\pi}{7}t$$

Round your answer to nearest whole number.

a.   0
b.   7
c.   1
d.   2
e.   9

____   4.   A passenger in an airplane at an altitude of $a = 40$ kilometers sees two towns directly to the east of the plane. The angles of depression to the towns are $28°$ and $55°$ (see figure). How far apart are the towns? How far apart are the ships? Round your answer to one decimal place.

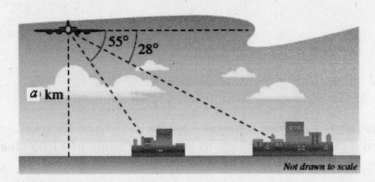

Not drawn to scale

a. 47.2 km
b. 48.2 km
c. 51.2 km
d. 50.2 km
e. 49.2 km

____   5.   Find angle $75°$ in radian measure as a multiple of π.

a. $\dfrac{4\pi}{3}$

b. $\dfrac{\sqrt{2}}{\pi}$

c. 12π

d. $\dfrac{5\pi}{12}$

e. $\dfrac{\pi\sqrt{2}}{2}$

_____ 6.   Find the radian measure of the central angle of a circle of radius r that intercepts an arc of length s.

Radius r ArcLength s

  6 inches   25 inches

a. $\theta = 150$ radians

b. $\theta = \dfrac{6}{25}$ radians

c. $\theta = \dfrac{6}{31}$ radians

d. $\theta = \dfrac{25}{6}$ radians

e. $\theta = 31$ radians

_____ 7.   Convert $38° 51' 37''$ to degree-decimal form. Round answer to three decimal places.

a. $38.855°$

b. $38.860°$

c. $39.741°$

d. $38.428°$

e. $38.430°$

_____ 8.   Evaluate (if possible) the sine, cosine, and tangent of the real number.

$t = \dfrac{19\pi}{3}$

a.
$t = \dfrac{19\pi}{3}$ corresponds to the point $(x,y) = \left(\dfrac{1}{2}, \dfrac{\sqrt{3}}{2} \right)$.

$\sin\left(\dfrac{19\pi}{3} \right) = -\dfrac{1}{2}$

$\cos\left(\dfrac{19\pi}{3} \right) = \dfrac{\sqrt{3}}{2}$

$\tan\left(\dfrac{19\pi}{3} \right) = -\sqrt{3}$

b. $t = \dfrac{19\pi}{4}$ corresponds to the point $(x,y) = \left(\dfrac{1}{2}, \dfrac{\sqrt{3}}{2} \right)$.

$$\sin\left(\dfrac{19\pi}{3} \right) = \dfrac{\sqrt{3}}{2}$$

$$\cos\left(\dfrac{19\pi}{3} \right) = \dfrac{1}{2}$$

$$\tan\left(\dfrac{19\pi}{3} \right) = \sqrt{3}$$

c. $t = \dfrac{19\pi}{3}$ corresponds to the point $(x,y) = \left(-\dfrac{1}{2}, -\dfrac{\sqrt{3}}{2} \right)$.

$$\sin\left(\dfrac{19\pi}{3} \right) = -\dfrac{1}{2}$$

$$\cos\left(\dfrac{19\pi}{3} \right) = -\dfrac{\sqrt{3}}{2}$$

$$\tan\left(\dfrac{19\pi}{3} \right) = \dfrac{\sqrt{3}}{3}$$

d. $t = \dfrac{19\pi}{3}$ corresponds to the point $(x,y) = \left(\dfrac{1}{2}, -\dfrac{\sqrt{3}}{2} \right)$.

$$\sin\left(\dfrac{19\pi}{3} \right) = -\dfrac{1}{2}$$

$$\cos\left(\dfrac{19\pi}{3} \right) = \dfrac{\sqrt{3}}{2}$$

$$\tan\left(\dfrac{19\pi}{3} \right) = -\dfrac{\sqrt{3}}{3}$$

e.   Not possible

_____ 9.   Use the value of the trigonometric function to find $\sin(\pi - t)$.

$$\sin t = \frac{5}{6}$$

a. $\sin(\pi - t) = \frac{5}{6}$

b. $\sin(\pi - t) = -\frac{5}{6}$

c. $\sin(\pi - t) = -\frac{6}{5}$

d. $\sin(\pi - t) = \infty$

e. $\sin(\pi - t) = \frac{6}{5}$

_____ 10.   The displacement from equilibrium of an oscillating weight suspended by a spring and subject to the damping effect of friction is given by $y(t) = \frac{1}{4} e^{-t} \cos 6t$, where y is the displacement (in feet) and t is the time (in seconds). Complete the following table.(Round your answer to four decimal places.)

t	0	$\frac{1}{6}$	$\frac{1}{5}$	$\frac{3}{4}$	4
y					

a.

t	0	$\frac{1}{6}$	$\frac{1}{5}$	$\frac{3}{4}$	4
y	0.2500	0.1143	0.2742	−0.0249	0.0019

b.

t	0	$\frac{1}{6}$	$\frac{1}{5}$	$\frac{3}{4}$	4
y	0.2500	0.1143	0.0742	−0.0249	0.0019

c.

t	0	$\frac{1}{6}$	$\frac{1}{5}$	$\frac{3}{4}$	4
y	0.3500	0.1143	0.0742	−0.0249	0.2500

d.

t	0	$\dfrac{1}{6}$	$\dfrac{1}{5}$	$\dfrac{3}{4}$	4
y	0.3500	0.3143	0.0742	-0.0249	0.2500

e.

t	0	$\dfrac{1}{6}$	$\dfrac{1}{5}$	$\dfrac{3}{4}$	4
y	0.2500	0.1143	0.0742	0.1751	0.2019

____ 11.   Select an appropriate triangle to complete the table. $(0° \le \theta \le 90°, 0 \le \theta \le \pi/2)$

Function	θ (deg)	θ (rad)	Function Value
sin	60°		

a.

Function	$\theta\,(deg)$	$\theta(rad)$	Function Value
sin	60°	0	0

b.

Function	$\theta\,(deg)$	$\theta(rad)$	Function Value
sin	60°	$\dfrac{\pi}{3}$	$\dfrac{\sqrt{3}}{2}$

c.

Function	$\theta\,(deg)$	$\theta(rad)$	Function Value
sin	60°	$\dfrac{\pi}{4}$	$\dfrac{\sqrt{2}}{2}$

d.

Function	$\theta\,(deg)$	$\theta(rad)$	Function Value
sin	60°	$\dfrac{\pi}{2}$	1

e.

Function	$\theta\,(deg)$	$\theta(rad)$	Function Value
sin	60°	$\dfrac{\pi}{6}$	$\dfrac{1}{2}$

_____ 12.   Use a calculator to evaluate function given below. Round your answer to four decimal places. (Be sure the calculator is in the correct angle mode.)

$\cot 16°16'$

a. $\cot 16°16' \approx 0.2918$
b. $\cot 16°16' \approx 1.0417$
c. $\cot 16°16' \approx 3.4271$
d. $\cot 16°16' \approx 3.5700$
e. $\cot 16°16' \approx 0.9600$

_____ 13.   Given $\sec \theta = \sqrt{10}$ and $\tan \theta = 3$, determine the following.
$\cot(90° - \theta)$

a. $\cot(90° - \theta) = \sqrt{10}$
b. $\cot(90° - \theta) = \dfrac{1}{3}$
c. $\cot(90° - \theta) = 3$
d.   undefined
e. $\cot(90° - \theta) = \dfrac{\sqrt{10}}{3}$

_____ 14.   Use a calculator to evaluate the trigonometric function. Round your answer to four decimal
places. (Be sure the calculator is set in the correct angle mode.)

$\cos(-135°)$

a. $\cos(-135°) \approx -0.9826$
b. $\cos(-135°) \approx 0.2929$
c. $\cos(-135°) \approx 0.9826$
d. $\cos(-135°) \approx -0.7071$
e. $\cos(-135°) \approx -0.0174$

____ 15.   The displacement from equilibrium of an oscillating weight suspended by a spring is given by
$y(t) = 2\cos 6t$, where y is the displacement (in centimeters) and t is the time (in seconds). Find the displacement when $t = \dfrac{1}{11}$. Round your answer to two decimal places.

a.
$$y\left(\frac{1}{11}\right) \approx 1.57 \text{ centimeters}$$

b.
$$y\left(\frac{1}{11}\right) \approx 2.71 \text{ centimeters}$$

c.
$$y\left(\frac{1}{11}\right) \approx 1.71 \text{ centimeters}$$

d.
$$y\left(\frac{1}{11}\right) = 3 \text{ centimeters}$$

e.
$$y\left(\frac{1}{11}\right) = 2 \text{ centimeters}$$

____ 16.   The displacement from equilibrium of an oscillating weight suspended by a spring is given by
$y(t) = 2\cos 6t$, where y is the displacement (in centimeters) and t is the time (in seconds). Find the displacement when $t = \dfrac{1}{4}$. Round your answer to two decimal places.

a.
$$y\left(\frac{1}{4}\right) \approx 1.14 \text{ centimeters}$$

b.
$$y\left(\frac{1}{4}\right) \approx 1.08 \text{ centimeters}$$

c.
$$y\left(\frac{1}{4}\right) = 3 \text{ centimeters}$$

d.
$$y\left(\frac{1}{4}\right) \approx 0.14 \text{ centimeter}$$

e.
$$y\left(\frac{1}{4}\right) = 2 \text{ centimeters}$$

_____   17.   Find the relationship between the graphs of f and g. Consider amplitude, period, and shifts.

$f(x) = \sin x$

$g(x) = \sin 4x$

a. f is a reflection of g in the x-axis.
b. g is a shift of f π units to the right.
c. g is a reflection of f in the y-axis.
d.   The period of f is 4 times the period of g.
e.   The period of g is 4 times the period of f.

_____   18.   Use a graphing utility to select the graph of the function. Include two full periods.

$$y = \frac{1}{100} \sin 100 \pi t$$

a.

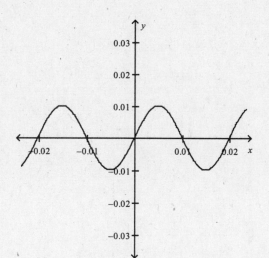

d.

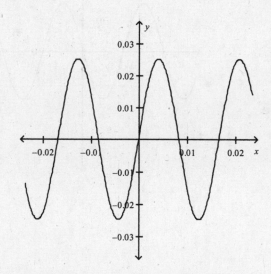

b.

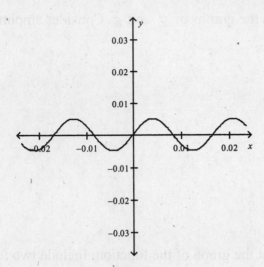

e.

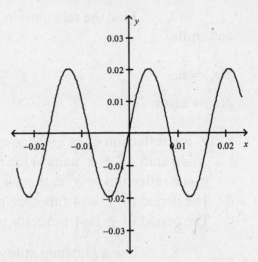

c.

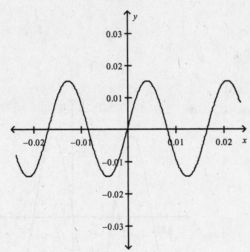

_____ 19.   Determine the period and amplitude of the following function.

$$y = 4\cos\left(\frac{3x}{4} + \frac{\pi}{4}\right)$$

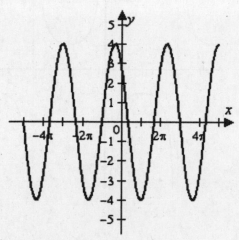

a.   period: $\dfrac{8\pi}{3}$; amplitude: 4

b.   period: 2π, amplitude: 2

c.   period: 10π, amplitude: 2

d.   period: 5π, amplitude: 4

e.   period: 3π, amplitude: 4

_____ 20.   Select the graph of the function. Include two full periods.

$$y = 0.5\csc \pi x$$

a.   d.

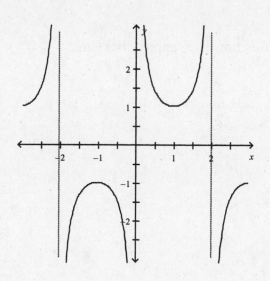 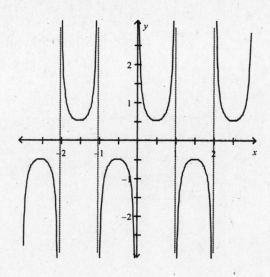

b.

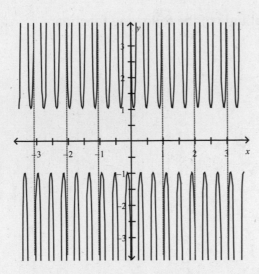

e.

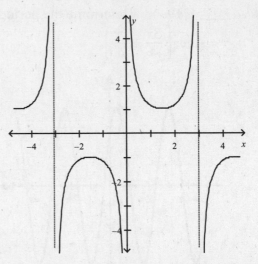

c.

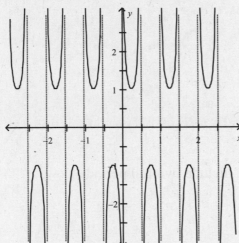

_____   21.   Describe the behavior of the function as x approaches zero.

$f(x) = |4x \cos x|$

a. $f \to +\infty$ as $x \to 0$.
b. $f \to 1$ as $x \to 0$.
c. $f \to 0$ as $x \to 0$.
d. $f \to -1$ as $x \to 0$.
e. $f \to -\infty$ as $x \to 0$.

_____   22.   Use a graphing utility to graph the function below, making sure to show at least two periods.

$\tan \dfrac{x}{4}$

a.

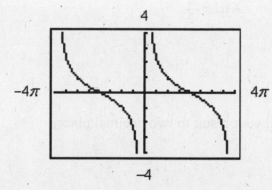

$\text{Xscl} = \dfrac{\pi}{2}$

b.

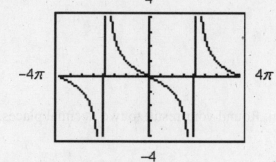

$\text{Xscl} = \dfrac{\pi}{2}$

c.

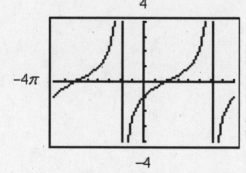

$\text{Xscl} = \dfrac{\pi}{2}$

d.

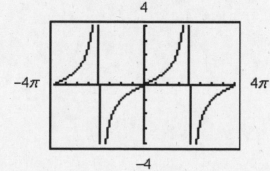

$\text{Xscl} = \dfrac{\pi}{2}$

e.

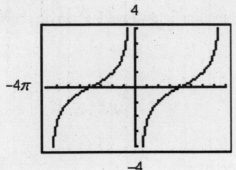

$$X scl = \frac{\pi}{2}$$

_____   23.   Evaluate the expression. Round your result to two decimal places.

$$\tan^{-1}\left(-\sqrt{300}\right)$$

a.   −0.51
b.   −1.51
c.   0.49
d.   −3.51
e.   −2.51

_____   24.   Find the value of the expression. Round your result to two decimal places.

$$\text{arccot}\, \frac{17}{3}$$

a.   0.17
b.   1.17
c.   1.40
d.   −1.40
e.   −0.17

_____ 25.   Use a graphing utility to graph the function below.

$y = 2 \sin^{-1}(3x)$

a.

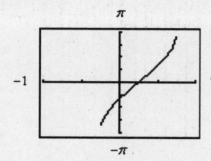

$Y scl = \dfrac{\pi}{4}$

b.

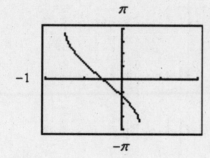

$Y scl = \dfrac{\pi}{4}$

c.

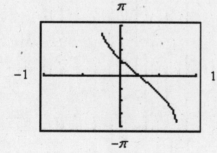

$Y scl = \dfrac{\pi}{4}$

d.

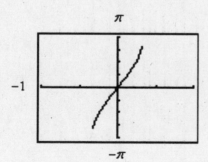

$Y scl = \dfrac{\pi}{4}$

e.

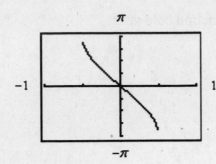

$Y \text{scl} = \dfrac{\pi}{4}$

Ch 4 Form F
Answer Section

1.	ANS:	D	PTS:	1	REF:	4.4.92b
2.	ANS:	C	PTS:	1	REF:	4.8.34b
3.	ANS:	E	PTS:	1	REF:	4.8.57c
4.	ANS:	A	PTS:	1	REF:	4.8.25
5.	ANS:	D	PTS:	1	REF:	4.1.57a
6.	ANS:	D	PTS:	1	REF:	4.1.93
7.	ANS:	B	PTS:	1	REF:	4.1.83a
8.	ANS:	B	PTS:	1	REF:	4.2.27
9.	ANS:	A	PTS:	1	REF:	4.2.47a
10.	ANS:	B	PTS:	1	REF:	4.2.60b
11.	ANS:	B	PTS:	1	REF:	4.3.21
12.	ANS:	C	PTS:	1	REF:	4.3.53a
13.	ANS:	C	PTS:	1	REF:	4.3.34c
14.	ANS:	D	PTS:	1	REF:	4.4.77
15.	ANS:	C	PTS:	1	REF:	4.4.98b
16.	ANS:	D	PTS:	1	REF:	4.4.98c
17.	ANS:	D	PTS:	1	REF:	4.5.24
18.	ANS:	A	PTS:	1	REF:	4.5.72
19.	ANS:	A	PTS:	1	REF:	4.5.6
20.	ANS:	D	PTS:	1	REF:	4.6.21
21.	ANS:	C	PTS:	1	REF:	4.6.73
22.	ANS:	D	PTS:	1	REF:	4.6.39
23.	ANS:	B	PTS:	1	REF:	4.7.39
24.	ANS:	A	PTS:	1	REF:	4.7.131
25.	ANS:	D	PTS:	1	REF:	4.7.94

Ch 5 Form A

_____   1.   Use the given values to evaluate (if possible) three trigonometric functions $\cos x$, $\csc x$, $\tan x$.

$\sin x = \dfrac{1}{5}$

a.
$\cos x = -\dfrac{2\sqrt{6}}{5}$

$\csc x = 5$

$\tan x = \dfrac{2\sqrt{6}}{24}$

b.
$\cos x = -\dfrac{2\sqrt{6}}{5}$

$\csc x = -5$

$\tan x = -\dfrac{2\sqrt{6}}{24}$

c.
$\cos x = \dfrac{2\sqrt{6}}{5}$

$\csc x = 5$

$\tan x = -\dfrac{2\sqrt{6}}{24}$

d.
$\cos x = \dfrac{2\sqrt{6}}{5}$

$\csc x = 5$

$\tan x = \dfrac{2\sqrt{6}}{24}$

e.
$\cos x = \dfrac{2\sqrt{6}}{5}$

$\csc x = \dfrac{1}{5}$

$\tan x = \dfrac{2\sqrt{6}}{24}$

_____ 2. Use the given values to evaluate (if possible) three trigonometric functions $\csc \theta$, $\tan \theta$, $\cos \theta$.

$$\sin \theta = -5, \quad \cot \theta = 0$$

a.
$$\csc \theta = -\frac{1}{5}$$
$\tan \theta$ is undefined.
$$\cos \theta = -2\sqrt{6}$$

b.
$$\csc \theta = \frac{1}{5}$$
$\tan \theta$ is undefined.
$$\cos \theta = 2\sqrt{6}$$

c.
$$\csc \theta = -\frac{1}{5}$$
$\tan \theta$ is undefined.
$$\cos \theta = 0$$

d.
$$\csc \theta = \frac{1}{5}$$
$\tan \theta$ is undefined.
$$\cos \theta = -2\sqrt{6}$$

e. $\csc \theta$ is undefined.
$$\tan \theta = \frac{1}{5}$$
$$\cos \theta = -2\sqrt{6}$$

_____ 3. Use the trigonometric substitution to select the algebraic expression as a trigonometric function of θ, where $0 < \theta < \dfrac{\pi}{2}$.

$$\sqrt{4 - x^2}, \ x = 2 \sin \theta$$

a. $4 \sin \theta$
b. $4 \cos \theta$
c. $-2 \cos \theta$
d. $2 \cos \theta$
e. $2 \sin \theta$

_____ 4. Rewrite the expression as a single logarithm and simplify the result.

$\ln|\sin x| + \ln|\cot x|$

a. $\ln|\csc x|$
b. $\ln|\cos x|$
c. $\ln|\tan x|$
d. $\ln|\sin x|$

e. $\ln|\cot x|$

_____ 5. Use fundamental identities to simplify the expression below and then determine which of the following is *not* equivalent.

$\sin \alpha(\csc \alpha - \sin \alpha)$

a. $\cos^2 \alpha$

b. $\dfrac{\csc^2 \alpha - 1}{\csc^2 \alpha}$

c. $1 - \sin^2 \alpha$

d. $1 - \cot^2 \alpha$

e. $\dfrac{\csc^2 \alpha - \sec^2 \alpha + \tan^2 \alpha}{\csc^2 \alpha}$

_____ 6. Evaluate the following expression.

$2 \tan t \cot t$

a. 0

b. 4

c. 1

d. 2

e. 3

_____ 7. Which of the following expression is equivalent to

$\dfrac{3 \cot^2 t}{\csc t}$

a. $\dfrac{-1 - \sin^2 t}{3 \sin t}$

b. $\dfrac{3 + 3 \cos^2 t}{\cos t}$

c. $\dfrac{3 + 3 \sin^2 t}{\sin t}$

d. $\dfrac{3 - 3 \sin^2 t}{\sin t}$

e. $\dfrac{3 - 3 \cos^2 t}{\cos t}$

_____ 8.   Which of the following expression is equivalent to

$$1 - 2\cos^2 x + 2\cos^4 x$$

a. $\sin^4 x - \cos x$
b. $\sin x + \cos x$
c. $\sin x + \cos^4 x$
d. $\sin^4 x + \cos^4 x$
e. $\sin^4 x - \cos^4 x$

_____ 9.   Evaluate the following expression.

$$5\cos 5x - \frac{5\cos 5x}{1 - \tan 5x}$$

a. $\dfrac{-5\sin 5x \cos 5x}{\sin 5x + \cos 5x}$

b. $\dfrac{10\sin 5x \cos 5x}{\sin 5x - \cos 5x}$

c. $\dfrac{5\sin 5x \cos 5x}{\sin 5x + \cos 5x}$

d. $\dfrac{-5\sin 5x \cos 5x}{\sin 5x - \cos 5x}$

e. $\dfrac{5\sin 5x \cos 5x}{\sin 5x - \cos 5x}$

_____   10.   Which of the following expression is equivalent to given expression.

$$\sqrt{\frac{9-9\cos\theta}{1+\cos\theta}}$$

a. $\dfrac{3-3\sin\theta}{|\cos\theta|}$

b. $\dfrac{3-3\cos\theta}{|\sin\theta|}$

c. $\dfrac{1-\cos\theta}{|\sin\theta|}$

d. $\dfrac{3+3\cos\theta}{|\sin\theta|}$

e. $\dfrac{3+3\sin\theta}{|\cos\theta|}$

_____   11.   Solve the following equation.

$4\cos x + 2 = 0$

a. $\dfrac{4\pi}{3}+n\pi,\ \dfrac{2\pi}{3}+n\pi$

b. $\dfrac{7\pi}{6}+2n\pi,\ \dfrac{11\pi}{6}+2n\pi$

c. $\dfrac{\pi}{3}+n\pi,\ \dfrac{\pi}{3}+n\pi$

d. $\dfrac{2\pi}{3}+2n\pi,\ \dfrac{4\pi}{3}+2n\pi$

e. $\dfrac{\pi}{2}+n\pi,\ \dfrac{2\pi}{5}+n\pi$

_____ 12.   Solve the following equation.

$2\tan^2 3x = 6$

a. $\dfrac{\pi}{3} + n\pi, \dfrac{\pi}{3} + n\pi$

b. $\dfrac{\pi}{2} + n\pi, \dfrac{2\pi}{5} + n\pi$

c. $\dfrac{\pi}{9} + \dfrac{n\pi}{3}, \dfrac{2\pi}{9} + \dfrac{n\pi}{3}$

d. $\dfrac{2\pi}{3} + n\pi, \dfrac{2\pi}{3} + n\pi$

e. $\dfrac{4\pi}{3} + n\pi, \dfrac{2\pi}{3} + n\pi$

_____ 13.   Find all solutions of the following equation in the interval $[0, 2\pi)$.

$\sin x - 2 = \cos x - 2$

a. $\dfrac{\pi}{4}, \dfrac{5\pi}{4}$

b. $\dfrac{\pi}{2}, \dfrac{5\pi}{2}$

c. $\dfrac{3\pi}{4}, \dfrac{5\pi}{4}$

d. $\dfrac{3\pi}{4}, \dfrac{7\pi}{4}$

e. $\dfrac{\pi}{2}, \dfrac{5\pi}{2}$

_____ 14. Use a graphing utility to graph the function.

Functions   *Trigonometic functions*

$f(x) = \cos x + \sin x$ $\cos x - \sin x = 0$

a.

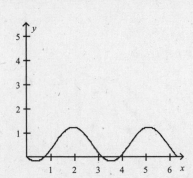

d.

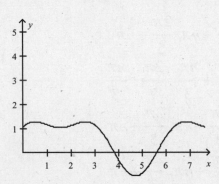

b.

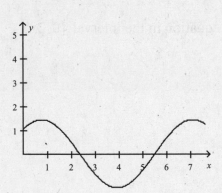

e.

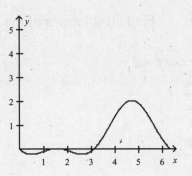

c.

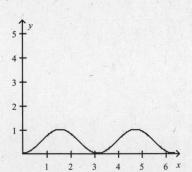

_____   15.   Solve the following equation.

$4\tan^4 x - 1 = 0$

a. $x = \dfrac{\pi}{2} + n\pi$, where n is an integer

b. $x = n\pi$ and $x = \dfrac{3\pi}{2} + 2n\pi$, where n is an integer

c. $x = n\pi$ and $x = \dfrac{\pi}{2} + n\pi$, where n is an integer

d. $x = n\pi$ and $x = \dfrac{3\pi}{4} + n\pi$, where n is an integer

e. $x = \dfrac{\pi}{4} + \dfrac{n\pi}{2}$, where n is an integer

_____   16.   Find the expression as the sine of an angle.

$\sin 5 \cos 1.1 - \cos 5 \sin 1.1$

a. $\sin 3.9$

b. $\sin 4.3$

c. $\sin 4$

d. $\sin 4.2$

e. $\sin 4.1$

_____   17.   Simplify the expression algebraically.

$8\sin\left(\dfrac{\pi}{2} + x\right)$

a. $-8\cos x$

b. $\dfrac{1}{8}\cos x$

c. $8\cos x$

d. $8\sin x$

e. $-\dfrac{1}{8}\cos x$

____ 18. A weight is attached to a spring suspended vertically from a ceiling. When a driving force is applied to the system, the weight moves vertically from its equilibrium position, and this motion is modeled by

$$y = \frac{1}{3} \sin 2t + \frac{1}{4} \cos 2t$$

where y is the distance from equilibrium (in feet) and t is the time (in seconds).
Find the amplitude of the oscillations of the weight.

a. $\dfrac{12}{5}$ ft

b. $\dfrac{1}{5}$ ft

c. $\dfrac{5}{12}$ ft

d. $\dfrac{1}{10}$ ft

e. $\dfrac{1}{12}$ ft

____ 19. Use the formula $a \sin B\theta + b \cos B\theta = \sqrt{a^2 + b^2} \cos(B\theta - C)$, where $C = \arctan(a/b), a > 0$, to find the trigonometric expression in the form $a \sin B\theta + b \cos B\theta$

$$5 \cos\left(\theta - \frac{\pi}{4}\right)$$

a. $\dfrac{5\sqrt{2}}{2} \cos\theta$

b. $-\dfrac{5\sqrt{2}}{2} \sin\theta + \dfrac{5\sqrt{2}}{2} \cos\theta$

c. $\dfrac{5\sqrt{2}}{2} \sin\theta - \dfrac{5\sqrt{2}}{2} \cos\theta$

d. $\dfrac{5\sqrt{2}}{2} \sin\theta + \dfrac{5\sqrt{2}}{2} \cos\theta$

e. $-\dfrac{5\sqrt{2}}{2} \sin\theta - \dfrac{5\sqrt{2}}{2} \cos\theta$

_____ 20.   Find the exact value of the given expression using a sum or difference formula.
$\sin 285°$

a. $\dfrac{\left(\sqrt{3}+1\right)\left(2\sqrt{2}\right)}{8}$

b. $\dfrac{\left(-\sqrt{3}-1\right)\left(2\sqrt{2}\right)}{8}$

c. $\dfrac{\left(\sqrt{3}-1\right)\left(2\sqrt{2}\right)}{8}$

d. $\dfrac{\left(-\sqrt{3}+1\right)\left(2\sqrt{2}\right)}{8}$

_____ 21.   Use the figure to find the exact value of the trigonometric function.

$\cos 2\theta$

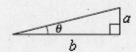

$a = 1, b = 4$

a. $\dfrac{16}{17}$

b. $\dfrac{17}{15}$

c. $\dfrac{15}{16}$

d. $\dfrac{15}{17}$

e. $\dfrac{17}{16}$

_____ 22.   Use a double-angle formula to rewrite the expression.

$6 \sin^2 x - 3$

a. $-3 \cos 2x$
b. $3 \cos 2x$
c. $-6 \cos x$
d. $3 \cos x$
e. $6 \cos 2x$

_____ 23.   Use the sum-to-product formulas to select the sum or difference as a product.

$\sin 5\theta - \sin 3\theta$

a. $2 \sin 4\theta \cos \theta$
b. $2 \cos 4\theta \sin \theta$
c. $2 \cos 4\theta \cos \theta$
d. $2 \sin 5\theta \cos 3\theta$
e. $2 \sin 4\theta \sin \theta$

_____ 24.   Evaluate the expression.

$\cos 8\alpha$

a. $\cos^4 4\alpha + \sin^4 4\alpha$
b. $\cos^2 4\alpha - \sin^2 4\alpha$
c. $\cos^2 4\alpha + \sin^2 4\alpha$
d. $\cos^4 4\alpha - \sin^2 4\alpha$
e. $\cos^4 4\alpha - \sin^4 4\alpha$

_____ 25.   Use a double-angle formula to find the exact value of $\cos 2u$ when $\sin u = \dfrac{7}{25}$, where $\dfrac{\pi}{2} < u < \pi$.

a. $\cos 2u = \dfrac{527}{625}$

b. $\cos 2u = -\dfrac{1152}{625}$

c. $\cos 2u = -\dfrac{478}{625}$

d. $\cos 2u = \dfrac{336}{625}$

e. $\cos 2u = \dfrac{168}{625}$

Ch 5 Form A
Answer Section

1.	ANS:	D	PTS:	1	REF:	5.1.11a
2.	ANS:	C	PTS:	1	REF:	5.1.23
3.	ANS:	D	PTS:	1	REF:	5.1.95
4.	ANS:	B	PTS:	1	REF:	5.1.114
5.	ANS:	D	PTS:	1	REF:	5.1.41
6.	ANS:	D	PTS:	1	REF:	5.2.9
7.	ANS:	D	PTS:	1	REF:	5.2.19
8.	ANS:	D	PTS:	1	REF:	5.2.64
9.	ANS:	E	PTS:	1	REF:	5.2.32
10.	ANS:	B	PTS:	1	REF:	5.2.42
11.	ANS:	D	PTS:	1	REF:	5.3.11
12.	ANS:	C	PTS:	1	REF:	5.3.22
13.	ANS:	A	PTS:	1	REF:	5.3.38
14.	ANS:	B	PTS:	1	REF:	5.3.81
15.	ANS:	D	PTS:	1	REF:	5.3.22
16.	ANS:	A	PTS:	1	REF:	5.4.29
17.	ANS:	C	PTS:	1	REF:	5.4.62
18.	ANS:	C	PTS:	1	REF:	5.4.89b
19.	ANS:	D	PTS:	1	REF:	5.4.104
20.	ANS:	B	PTS:	1	REF:	5.4.25
21.	ANS:	D	PTS:	1	REF:	5.5.11
22.	ANS:	A	PTS:	1	REF:	5.5.34
23.	ANS:	B	PTS:	1	REF:	5.5.92
24.	ANS:	B	PTS:	1	REF:	5.5.117
25.	ANS:	A	PTS:	1	REF:	5.5.37

Ch 5 Form B

_____ 1.   Use the given values to evaluate (if possible) three trigonometric functions $\cos x$, $\csc x$, $\tan x$.

$$\sin x = \frac{1}{4}$$

a.
$$\cos x = \frac{\sqrt{15}}{4}$$
$$\csc x = 4$$
$$\tan x = \frac{\sqrt{15}}{15}$$

b.
$$\cos x = \frac{\sqrt{15}}{4}$$
$$\csc x = 4$$
$$\tan x = -\frac{\sqrt{15}}{15}$$

c.
$$\cos x = \frac{\sqrt{15}}{4}$$
$$\csc x = \frac{1}{4}$$
$$\tan x = \frac{\sqrt{15}}{15}$$

d.
$$\cos x = -\frac{\sqrt{15}}{4}$$
$$\csc x = 4$$
$$\tan x = \frac{\sqrt{15}}{15}$$

e.
$$\cos x = -\frac{\sqrt{15}}{4}$$
$$\csc x = -4$$
$$\tan x = -\frac{\sqrt{15}}{15}$$

_____   2.   Use the given values to evaluate (if possible) three trigonometric functions $\csc \theta$, $\tan \theta$, $\cos \theta$.

$\sin \theta = -2$, $\cot \theta = 0$

a. $\csc \theta$ is undefined.

$\tan \theta = \dfrac{1}{2}$

$\cos \theta = -\sqrt{3}$

b. $\csc \theta = \dfrac{1}{2}$

$\tan \theta$ is undefined.

$\cos \theta = \sqrt{3}$

c. $\csc \theta = -\dfrac{1}{2}$

$\tan \theta$ is undefined.

$\cos \theta = -\sqrt{3}$

d. $\csc \theta = -\dfrac{1}{2}$

$\tan \theta$ is undefined.

$\cos \theta = 0$

e. $\csc \theta = \dfrac{1}{2}$

$\tan \theta$ is undefined.

$\cos \theta = -\sqrt{3}$

_____   3.   Use the trigonometric substitution to select the algebraic expression as a trigonometric function of θ, where $0 < \theta < \dfrac{\pi}{2}$.

$\sqrt{4 - x^2}$, $x = 2 \sin \theta$

a. $2 \sin \theta$
b. $4 \cos \theta$
c. $2 \cos \theta$
d. $4 \sin \theta$
e. $-2 \cos \theta$

_____   4.   Rewrite the expression as a single logarithm and simplify the result.

$\ln|\csc x| + \ln|\cos x|$

a. $\ln|\csc x|$
b. $\ln|\cos x|$
c. $\ln|\tan x|$
d. $\ln|\cot x|$

e. $\ln|\sin x|$

_____   5.   Use fundamental identities to simplify the expression below and then determine which of the following is *not* equivalent.

$\sin \alpha(\csc \alpha - \sin \alpha)$

a. $1 - \sin^2 \alpha$

b. $\cos^2 \alpha$

c. $\dfrac{\csc^2 \alpha - 1}{\csc^2 \alpha}$

d. $\dfrac{\csc^2 \alpha - \sec^2 \alpha + \tan^2 \alpha}{\csc^2 \alpha}$

e. $1 - \cot^2 \alpha$

_____   6.   Evaluate the following expression.

$3 \tan t \cot t$

a.   5

b.   1

c.   3

d.   2

e.   4

_____   7.   Which of the following expression is equivalent to

$\dfrac{7 \cot^2 t}{\csc t}$

a. $\dfrac{7 - 7\cos^2 t}{\cos t}$

b. $\dfrac{7 + 7\sin^2 t}{\sin t}$

c. $\dfrac{7 - 7\sin^2 t}{\sin t}$

d. $\dfrac{-1 - \sin^2 t}{7 \sin t}$

e. $\dfrac{7 + 7\cos^2 t}{\cos t}$

____   8.   Which of the following expression is equivalent to

$$5 - 10\cos^2 x + 10\cos^4 x$$

a. $5\sin^4 x - 5\cos^5 x$
b. $5\sin^4 x + 5\cos^4 x$
c. $5\sin^4 x - 5\cos^4 x$
d. $5\sin^5 x + 5\cos^4 x$
e. $5\sin^5 x + 5\cos^5 x$

____   9.   Evaluate the following expression.

$$5\cos 2x - \frac{5\cos 2x}{1 - \tan 2x}$$

a. $\dfrac{-5\sin 2x \cos 2x}{\sin 2x - \cos 2x}$

b. $\dfrac{5\sin 2x \cos 2x}{\sin 2x + \cos 2x}$

c. $\dfrac{-5\sin 2x \cos 2x}{\sin 2x + \cos 2x}$

d. $\dfrac{10\sin 2x \cos 2x}{\sin 2x - \cos 2x}$

e. $\dfrac{5\sin 2x \cos 2x}{\sin 2x - \cos 2x}$

_____ 10.   Which of the following expression is equivalent to given expression.

$$\sqrt{\frac{9 - 9\cos\theta}{1 + \cos\theta}}$$

a. $\dfrac{3 - 3\sin\theta}{|\cos\theta|}$

b. $\dfrac{1 - \cos\theta}{|\sin\theta|}$

c. $\dfrac{3 - 3\cos\theta}{|\sin\theta|}$

d. $\dfrac{3 + 3\cos\theta}{|\sin\theta|}$

e. $\dfrac{3 + 3\sin\theta}{|\cos\theta|}$

_____ 11.   Solve the following equation.

$$10\cos x + 5 = 0$$

a. $\dfrac{\pi}{2} + n\pi,\ \dfrac{2\pi}{5} + n\pi$

b. $\dfrac{4\pi}{3} + n\pi,\ \dfrac{2\pi}{3} + n\pi$

c. $\dfrac{7\pi}{6} + 2n\pi,\ \dfrac{11\pi}{6} + 2n\pi$

d. $\dfrac{\pi}{3} + n\pi,\ \dfrac{\pi}{3} + n\pi$

e. $\dfrac{2\pi}{3} + 2n\pi,\ \dfrac{4\pi}{3} + 2n\pi$

_____ 12. Solve the following equation.

$3\tan^2 3x = 9$

a. $\dfrac{\pi}{9} + \dfrac{n\pi}{3}, \dfrac{2\pi}{9} + \dfrac{n\pi}{3}$

b. $\dfrac{4\pi}{3} + n\pi, \dfrac{2\pi}{3} + n\pi$

c. $\dfrac{\pi}{3} + n\pi, \dfrac{\pi}{3} + n\pi$

d. $\dfrac{2\pi}{3} + n\pi, \dfrac{2\pi}{3} + n\pi$

e. $\dfrac{\pi}{2} + n\pi, \dfrac{2\pi}{5} + n\pi$

_____ 13. Find all solutions of the following equation in the interval $[0, 2\pi)$.

$\sin x - 4 = \cos x - 4$

a. $\dfrac{\pi}{2}, \dfrac{5\pi}{2}$

b. $\dfrac{3\pi}{4}, \dfrac{7\pi}{4}$

c. $\dfrac{\pi}{4}, \dfrac{5\pi}{4}$

d. $\dfrac{\pi}{2}, \dfrac{5\pi}{2}$

e. $\dfrac{3\pi}{4}, \dfrac{5\pi}{4}$

_____ 14.   Use a graphing utility to graph the function.

Functions   *Trigonometic functions*

$f(x) = \sin x + \cos x$ $\cos x - \sin x = 0$

a.

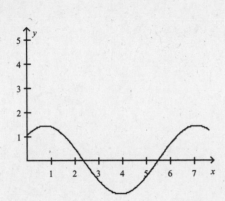

d.

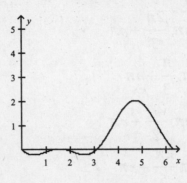

b.

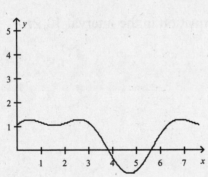

e.

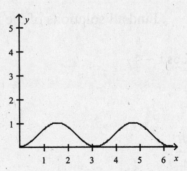

c.

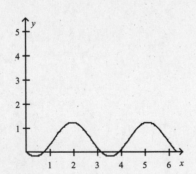

_____ 15. Solve the following equation.

$4\sin^4 x - 1 = 0$

a. $x = n\pi$ and $x = \dfrac{3\pi}{4} + n\pi$, where n is an integer

b. $x = \dfrac{\pi}{2} + n\pi$, where n is an integer

c. $x = n\pi$ and $x = \dfrac{\pi}{2} + n\pi$, where n is an integer

d. $x = \dfrac{\pi}{4} + \dfrac{n\pi}{2}$, where n is an integer

e. $x = n\pi$ and $x = \dfrac{3\pi}{2} + 2n\pi$, where n is an integer

_____ 16. Find the expression as the sine of an angle.

$\sin 3 \cos 1.7 - \cos 3 \sin 1.7$

a. $\sin 1.5$
b. $\sin 1.6$
c. $\sin 1.7$
d. $\sin 1.3$
e. $\sin 1.4$

_____ 17. Simplify the expression algebraically.

$6\sin\left(\dfrac{\pi}{2} + x\right)$

a. $\dfrac{1}{6}\cos x$

b. $-6\cos x$

c. $-\dfrac{1}{6}\cos x$

d. $6\sin x$

e. $6\cos x$

____ 18.   A weight is attached to a spring suspended vertically from a ceiling. When a driving force is applied to the system, the weight moves vertically from its equilibrium position, and this motion is modeled by

$$y = \frac{1}{3} \sin 2t + \frac{1}{4} \cos 2t$$

where y is the distance from equilibrium (in feet) and t is the time (in seconds).
Find the amplitude of the oscillations of the weight.

a. $\frac{1}{10}$ ft

b. $\frac{5}{12}$ ft

c. $\frac{12}{5}$ ft

d. $\frac{1}{5}$ ft

e. $\frac{1}{12}$ ft

____ 19.   Use the formula $a \sin B\theta + b \cos B\theta = \sqrt{a^2 + b^2} \cos(B\theta - C)$, where $C = \arctan(a/b), a > 0$, to find the trigonometric expression in the form $a \sin B\theta + b \cos B\theta$

$$13 \cos\left(\theta - \frac{\pi}{4}\right)$$

a. $-\frac{13\sqrt{2}}{2} \sin \theta - \frac{13\sqrt{2}}{2} \cos \theta$

b. $-\frac{13\sqrt{2}}{2} \sin \theta + \frac{13\sqrt{2}}{2} \cos \theta$

c. $\frac{13\sqrt{2}}{2} \sin \theta - \frac{13\sqrt{2}}{2} \cos \theta$

d. $\frac{13\sqrt{2}}{2} \cos \theta$

e. $\frac{13\sqrt{2}}{2} \sin \theta + \frac{13\sqrt{2}}{2} \cos \theta$

_____ 20.   Find the exact value of the given expression using a sum or difference formula.

$\sin 255°$

a. $\dfrac{\left(\sqrt{3}+1\right)\left(2\sqrt{2}\right)}{8}$

b. $\dfrac{\left(-\sqrt{3}-1\right)\left(2\sqrt{2}\right)}{8}$

c. $\dfrac{\left(-\sqrt{3}+1\right)\left(2\sqrt{2}\right)}{8}$

d. $\dfrac{\left(\sqrt{3}-1\right)\left(2\sqrt{2}\right)}{8}$

_____ 21.   Use the figure to find the exact value of the trigonometric function.

$\cos 2\theta$

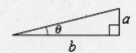

$a = 1, b = 2$

a. $\dfrac{3}{4}$

b. $\dfrac{3}{5}$

c. $\dfrac{5}{3}$

d. $\dfrac{5}{4}$

e. $\dfrac{4}{5}$

____ 22.   Use a double-angle formula to rewrite the expression.

$10 \sin^2 x - 5$

a. $5 \cos x$
b. $5 \cos 2x$
c. $10 \cos 2x$
d. $-5 \cos 2x$
e. $-10 \cos x$

____ 23.   Use the sum-to-product formulas to select the sum or difference as a product.

$\sin 9\theta - \sin 7\theta$

a. $2 \sin 8\theta \cos \theta$
b. $2 \sin 8\theta \sin \theta$
c. $2 \cos 8\theta \sin \theta$
d. $2 \sin 9\theta \cos 7\theta$
e. $2 \cos 8\theta \cos \theta$

____ 24.   Evaluate the expression.

$\cos 6\alpha$

a. $\cos^4 3\alpha - \sin^2 3\alpha$
b. $\cos^2 3\alpha + \sin^2 3\alpha$
c. $\cos^4 3\alpha + \sin^4 3\alpha$
d. $\cos^2 3\alpha - \sin^2 3\alpha$
e. $\cos^4 3\alpha - \sin^4 3\alpha$

____ 25.   Use a double-angle formula to find the exact value of $\cos 2u$ when
$\sin u = \dfrac{3}{5}$, where $\dfrac{\pi}{2} < u < \pi$.

a. $\cos 2u = \dfrac{2}{25}$

b. $\cos 2u = \dfrac{7}{25}$

c. $\cos 2u = \dfrac{12}{25}$

d. $\cos 2u = -\dfrac{32}{25}$

e. $\cos 2u = \dfrac{24}{25}$

Ch 5 Form B
Answer Section

1.	ANS:	A	PTS:	1	REF:	5.1.11a
2.	ANS:	D	PTS:	1	REF:	5.1.23
3.	ANS:	C	PTS:	1	REF:	5.1.95
4.	ANS:	D	PTS:	1	REF:	5.1.114
5.	ANS:	E	PTS:	1	REF:	5.1.41
6.	ANS:	C	PTS:	1	REF:	5.2.9
7.	ANS:	C	PTS:	1	REF:	5.2.19
8.	ANS:	B	PTS:	1	REF:	5.2.64
9.	ANS:	E	PTS:	1	REF:	5.2.32
10.	ANS:	C	PTS:	1	REF:	5.2.42
11.	ANS:	E	PTS:	1	REF:	5.3.11
12.	ANS:	A	PTS:	1	REF:	5.3.22
13.	ANS:	C	PTS:	1	REF:	5.3.38
14.	ANS:	A	PTS:	1	REF:	5.3.81
15.	ANS:	A	PTS:	1	REF:	5.3.22
16.	ANS:	D	PTS:	1	REF:	5.4.29
17.	ANS:	E	PTS:	1	REF:	5.4.62
18.	ANS:	B	PTS:	1	REF:	5.4.89b
19.	ANS:	E	PTS:	1	REF:	5.4.104
20.	ANS:	B	PTS:	1	REF:	5.4.25
21.	ANS:	B	PTS:	1	REF:	5.5.11
22.	ANS:	D	PTS:	1	REF:	5.5.34
23.	ANS:	C	PTS:	1	REF:	5.5.92
24.	ANS:	D	PTS:	1	REF:	5.5.117
25.	ANS:	B	PTS:	1	REF:	5.5.37

Ch 5 Form C

_____ 1. Use the given values to evaluate (if possible) three trigonometric functions $\cos x, \sin x,$ $\cot x$.

$$\tan x = \frac{8}{15}, \sec x = -\frac{19}{15}$$

a. $\cos x = \frac{15}{19}$

$\sin x = -\frac{8}{19}$

$\cot x = \frac{15}{8}$

b. $\cos x = -\frac{15}{19}$

$\sin x = -\frac{8}{19}$

$\cot x = -\frac{15}{8}$

c. $\cos x = -\frac{15}{19}$

$\sin x = \frac{8}{19}$

$\cot x = \frac{15}{8}$

d. $\cos x = \frac{15}{19}$

$\sin x = \frac{8}{19}$

$\cot x = \frac{15}{8}$

e. $\cos x = -\frac{15}{19}$

$\sin x = -\frac{8}{19}$

$\cot x = \frac{15}{8}$

_____ 2.   Perform the multiplication and use the fundamental identities to simplify.

$(\cos x + \sin x)^2$

a. $1 + \sin x + \cos x$
b. $2 + 2\sin x \cos x$
c. $1 + 2\sin x + \cos x$
d. $1 + \sin x \cos x$
e. $1 + 2\sin x \cos x$

_____ 3.   Use the trigonometric substitution to select the algebraic expression as a trigonometric function of θ, where $0 < \theta < \dfrac{\pi}{2}$.

$\sqrt{4x^2 + 9}$, $2x = 3\tan \theta$

a. $4\sec \theta$
b. $2\tan \theta$
c. $4\tan \theta$
d. $-2\sec \theta$
e. $3\sec \theta$

_____ 4.   The forces acting on an object weighing W units on an inclined plane positioned at an angle of θ with the horizontal (see figure) are modeled by

$\mu W \cos \theta = W \sin \theta$

where μ is the coefficient of friction. Solve the equation for μ and simplify the result.

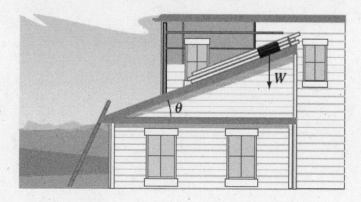

a. $\mu = \cos \theta$
b. $\mu = \csc \theta$
c. $\mu = \cot \theta$
d. $\mu = \sin \theta$
e. $\mu = \tan \theta$

_____ 5.   Factor; then use fundamental identities to simplify the expression below and determine which of the following is *not* equivalent.

$\cot^2 \alpha \tan^2 \alpha + \cot^2 \alpha$

a. $\sec^2 \alpha$

b. $\csc^2 \alpha$

c. $\dfrac{1}{1 - \cos^2 \alpha}$

d. $\dfrac{1}{\sin^2 \alpha}$

e. $1 + \cot^2 \alpha$

_____ 6.   Evaluate the following expression.

$2 \sec y \cos y$

a. 2

b. 3

c. 5

d. 4

e. 1

_____ 7.   Evaluate the following expression.

$\sec^7 x (\sec x \tan x) - \sec^5 x (\sec x \tan x)$

a. $6 \sec x \tan^6 x$

b. $\sec^5 x \tan^7 x$

c. $\sec^5 x \tan^3 x$

d. $\sec^6 x \tan x$

e. $\sec^6 x \tan^3 x$

_____ 8.   Evaluate the following expression.

$\dfrac{\sec \theta - 5}{1 - 5\cos \theta}$

a. $\cos \theta$

b. $\sec \theta$

c. $\sec \theta - \cos \theta$

d. $-\sec \theta$

e. $-\cos \theta$

_____   9.   Evaluate the following expression.

$$\dfrac{\cos\left[\left(\dfrac{\pi}{2}\right)-x\right]}{\sin\left[\left(\dfrac{\pi}{2}\right)-x\right]}$$

a. $\cot x$
b. $-\tan x$
c. $\tan x$
d. $2\tan x$
e. $-\cot x$

_____   10.   Evaluate the following expression.

$$4\sec^2 y - 4\cot^2\left(\dfrac{\pi}{2}-y\right)$$

a. 0
b. -4
c. -5
d. 4
e. 5

_____   11.   Solve the following equation.

$$2\sqrt{3}\csc x - 4 = 0$$

a. $\dfrac{\pi}{4}+2n\pi,\ \dfrac{2\pi}{4}+2n\pi$

b. $\dfrac{\pi}{3}+2n\pi,\ \dfrac{2\pi}{3}+\pi$

c. $\dfrac{\pi}{3}+\pi,\ \dfrac{2\pi}{3}+2n\pi$

d. $\dfrac{\pi}{3}+2n\pi,\ \dfrac{2\pi}{3}+2n\pi$

e. $\dfrac{\pi}{2}+2n\pi,\ \dfrac{2\pi}{3}+2n\pi$

____   12.   Solve the following equation.

$\cos 2x (8 \cos x + 4) = 0$

a. $\dfrac{2\pi}{3} + n\pi, \dfrac{2\pi}{3} + n\pi$

b. $\dfrac{\pi}{3} + n\pi, \dfrac{\pi}{3} + n\pi$

c. $\dfrac{\pi}{2} + n\pi, \dfrac{2\pi}{5} + n\pi$

d. $\dfrac{4\pi}{3} + n\pi, \dfrac{2\pi}{3} + n\pi, \dfrac{4\pi}{3} + 2n\pi$

e. $\dfrac{\pi}{4} + \dfrac{n\pi}{2}, \dfrac{2\pi}{3} + 2n\pi, \dfrac{4\pi}{3} + 2n\pi$

____   13.   Solve the multiple-angle equation.

$5 \sec 4x = 10$

a. $\dfrac{5\pi}{12} + \dfrac{n\pi}{3}, \dfrac{\pi}{12} + \dfrac{n\pi}{2}$

b. $\dfrac{\pi}{2} + \dfrac{n\pi}{3}, \dfrac{\pi}{12} + \dfrac{n\pi}{2}$

c. $\dfrac{3\pi}{4} + \dfrac{n\pi}{3}, \dfrac{\pi}{12} + \dfrac{n\pi}{2}$

d. $\dfrac{\pi}{12} - \dfrac{n\pi}{3}, \dfrac{5\pi}{12} + \dfrac{n\pi}{2}$

e. $\dfrac{\pi}{12} + \dfrac{n\pi}{2}, \dfrac{5\pi}{12} + \dfrac{n\pi}{2}$

_____ 14.   Use a graphing utility to select the correct graph the function.

Functions   *Trigonometic functions*

$$f(x) = 2(\sin x \cos x) \qquad 2\left(-\sin^2 x - \cos^2 x\right) = 0$$

a.

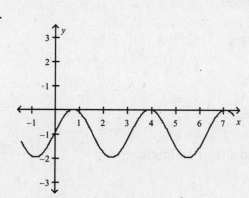

d.

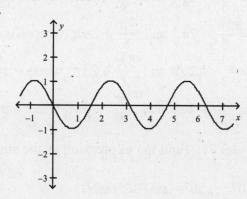

b.

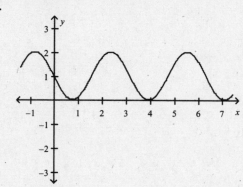

e.

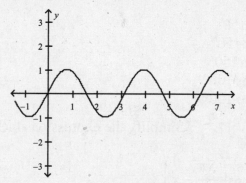

c.

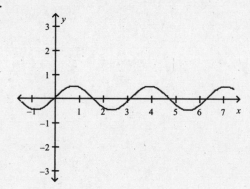

_____ 15.   Solve the multiple-angle equation.

$$\cos \frac{x}{2} = -\frac{\sqrt{3}}{2}$$

a. $x = \dfrac{5\pi}{3} + 2n\pi$ and $\dfrac{8\pi}{3} + 2n\pi$, where n is an integer

b. $x = \dfrac{7\pi}{6} + 2n\pi$ and $\dfrac{11\pi}{6} + 2n\pi$, where n is an integer

c. $x = \dfrac{5\pi}{6} + 2n\pi$ and $\dfrac{7\pi}{6} + 2n\pi$, where n is an integer

d. $x = \dfrac{2\pi}{3} + 2n\pi$ and $\dfrac{5\pi}{3} + 2n\pi$, where n is an integer

e. $x = \dfrac{5\pi}{3} + 4n\pi$ and $\dfrac{7\pi}{3} + 4n\pi$, where n is an integer

_____ 16.   Find the expression as the sine or cosine of an angle.

$$\cos 100° \cos 50° - \sin 100° \sin 50°$$

a. $\sin 50°$
b. $\cos 50°$
c. $\sin 150°$
d. $\cos 100°$
e. $\cos 150°$

_____ 17.   Simplify the expression algebraically.

$$\frac{7}{\sqrt{2}} \cos\left(\frac{5\pi}{4} - x\right)$$

a. $\dfrac{7}{2}(\cos x - \sin x)$

b. $\dfrac{7}{2}(\sin x - \cos x)$

c. $-\dfrac{7}{2}(\cos x + \sin x)$

d. $\dfrac{7}{2}\left(\cos \dfrac{5x}{4} + \sin \dfrac{5x}{4}\right)$

e. $\dfrac{7}{2}\left(\cos \dfrac{5x}{4} - \sin \dfrac{5x}{4}\right)$

_____ 18.   Use the formula $a \sin B\theta + b \cos B\theta = \sqrt{a^2 + b^2}\ \sin(B\theta + C)$, where $C = \arctan(b/a), a > 0$, to find the trigonometric expression in the following forms.

$$y = \sqrt{a^2 + b^2}\ \sin(B\theta + C)$$

$$5\sin 2\theta + 3\cos 2\theta$$

a. $\sqrt{34}\ \sin(2\theta - 0.5404)$
b. $\sqrt{34}\ \sin(2\theta + 0.5404)$
c. $\sqrt{34}\ \sin(\theta - 0.5404)$
d. $\sin(2\theta + 0.5404)$
e. $\sqrt{34}\ \sin(\theta + 0.5404)$

_____ 19.   Use a graphing utility to select correct graph y_1 and y_2 in the same viewing window. Use the graphs to determine whether $y_1 = y_2$. Explain your reasoning.

$$y_1 = \sin(x + 2), y_2 = \sin x + \sin 2$$

a.

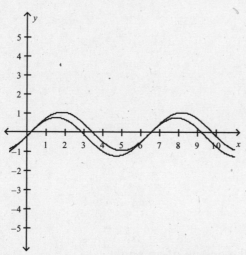

No, $y_1 = y_2$ because their graphs are different.

d.

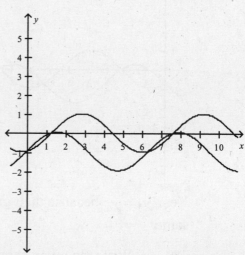

No, $y_1 \neq y_2$ because their graphs are Same.

b.

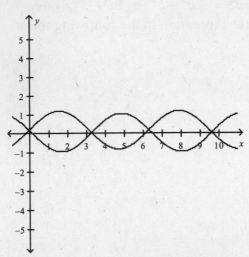

Yes, $y_1 = y_2$ because their graphs are different.

e.

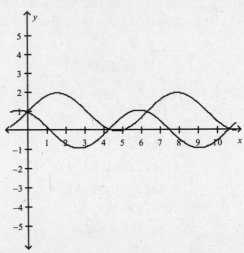

No, $y_1 \neq y_2$ because their graphs are different.

c.

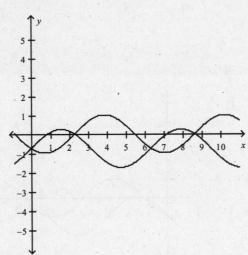

Yes, $y_1 = y_2$ because their graphs are same.

_____   20.   Write the given expression as the cosine of an angle.

$\cos 80° \cos 50° - \sin 80° \sin 50°$

a. $\cos(80°)$
b. $\cos(130°)$
c. $\cos(-100°)$
d. $\cos(50°)$
e. $\cos(30°)$

_____   21.   Use the figure to find the exact value of the trigonometric function.

$\tan 2\theta$

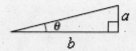

$a = 1, b = 8$

a. $\dfrac{16}{65}$

b. $\dfrac{63}{16}$

c. $\dfrac{63}{65}$

d. $\dfrac{16}{63}$

e. $\dfrac{65}{63}$

_____   22.   Use the half-angle formulas to simplify the expression.

$$-\sqrt{\dfrac{1-\cos 10x}{1+\cos 10x}}$$

a. $-|\tan x|$
b. $-|5\tan 5x|$
c. $-|5\tan 10x|$
d. $-|\tan 5x|$
e. $-|5\tan x|$

____ 23.   Use the sum-to-product formulas to select the sum or difference as a product.

$\cos 3\theta + \cos 6\theta$

a. $2\cos\dfrac{9\theta}{2}\cos\left(-\dfrac{3\theta}{2}\right)$

b. $2\cos\dfrac{9\theta}{2}\sin\left(-\dfrac{3\theta}{2}\right)$

c. $2\cos\dfrac{9\theta}{2}\cos\left(\dfrac{3\theta}{2}\right)$

d. $2\cos\left(-\dfrac{9\theta}{2}\right)\cos\dfrac{3\theta}{2}$

e. $2\cos\dfrac{9\theta}{2}\sin\left(\dfrac{3\theta}{2}\right)$

____ 24.   Evaluate the expression.

$\tan\dfrac{a}{2}$

a. $\cos a + \cot a$
b. $\cos a - \cot a$
c. $\csc a - \cot a$
d. $\csc a - \tan a$
e. $\csc a + \cot a$

_____   25.   Use the figure below to find the exact value of the given trigonometric expression.

$\cot\dfrac{x}{2}$

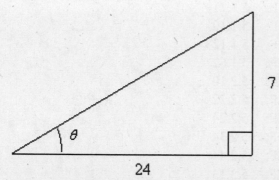

a. $\cot\dfrac{x}{2} = \dfrac{7\sqrt{2}}{10}$

b. $\cot\dfrac{x}{2} = \dfrac{7}{12}$

c. $\cot\dfrac{x}{2} = \dfrac{1}{7}$

d. $\cot\dfrac{x}{2} = \dfrac{\sqrt{2}}{10}$

e. $\cot\dfrac{x}{2} = 7$

Ch 5 Form C
Answer Section

1.	ANS:	E	PTS:	1	REF:	5.1.15
2.	ANS:	E	PTS:	1	REF:	5.1.71
3.	ANS:	E	PTS:	1	REF:	5.1.101
4.	ANS:	E	PTS:	1	REF:	5.1.123
5.	ANS:	A	PTS:	1	REF:	5.1.62
6.	ANS:	A	PTS:	1	REF:	5.2.10
7.	ANS:	E	PTS:	1	REF:	5.2.22
8.	ANS:	B	PTS:	1	REF:	5.2.24
9.	ANS:	C	PTS:	1	REF:	5.2.34
10.	ANS:	D	PTS:	1	REF:	5.2.44
11.	ANS:	D	PTS:	1	REF:	5.3.13
12.	ANS:	E	PTS:	1	REF:	5.3.24
13.	ANS:	E	PTS:	1	REF:	5.3.42
14.	ANS:	E	PTS:	1	REF:	5.3.83
15.	ANS:	E	PTS:	1	REF:	5.3.43
16.	ANS:	E	PTS:	1	REF:	5.4.32
17.	ANS:	C	PTS:	1	REF:	5.4.64
18.	ANS:	B	PTS:	1	REF:	5.4.100a
19.	ANS:	E	PTS:	1	REF:	5.4.110
20.	ANS:	B	PTS:	1	REF:	5.4.39
21.	ANS:	D	PTS:	1	REF:	5.5.13
22.	ANS:	D	PTS:	1	REF:	5.5.75
23.	ANS:	A	PTS:	1	REF:	5.5.94
24.	ANS:	C	PTS:	1	REF:	5.5.119
25.	ANS:	E	PTS:	1	REF:	5.5.58

Ch 5 Form D

_____ 1.   Use the given values to evaluate (if possible) three trigonometric functions $\cos x, \sin x,$ $\cot x$.

$$\tan x = \frac{2}{15}, \sec x = -\frac{11}{15}$$

a.
$$\cos x = \frac{15}{11}$$
$$\sin x = -\frac{2}{11}$$
$$\cot x = \frac{15}{2}$$

b.
$$\cos x = -\frac{15}{11}$$
$$\sin x = \frac{2}{11}$$
$$\cot x = \frac{15}{2}$$

c.
$$\cos x = -\frac{15}{11}$$
$$\sin x = -\frac{2}{11}$$
$$\cot x = -\frac{15}{2}$$

d.
$$\cos x = -\frac{15}{11}$$
$$\sin x = -\frac{2}{11}$$
$$\cot x = \frac{15}{2}$$

e.
$$\cos x = \frac{15}{11}$$
$$\sin x = \frac{2}{11}$$
$$\cot x = \frac{15}{2}$$

_____ 2.   Perform the multiplication and use the fundamental identities to simplify.

$(\cos x + \sin x)^2$

a. $1 + 2\sin x \cos x$
b. $2 + 2\sin x \cos x$
c. $1 + 2\sin x + \cos x$
d. $1 + \sin x + \cos x$
e. $1 + \sin x \cos x$

_____ 3.   Use the trigonometric substitution to select the algebraic expression as a trigonometric function of θ, where $0 < \theta < \dfrac{\pi}{2}$.

$\sqrt{25x^2 + 36}$, $5x = 6\tan\theta$

a. $-5\sec\theta$
b. $25\tan\theta$
c. $5\tan\theta$
d. $6\sec\theta$
e. $25\sec\theta$

_____ 4.   The forces acting on an object weighing   X units on an inclined plane positioned at an angle of θ with the horizontal (see figure) are modeled by

$\mu X\cos\theta = X\sin\theta$

where μ is the coefficient of friction. Solve the equation for μ and simplify the result.

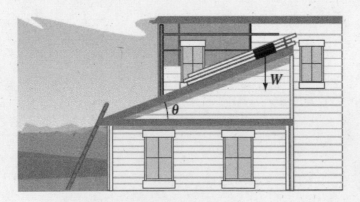

a. $\mu = \tan\theta$
b. $\mu = \cot\theta$
c. $\mu = \cos\theta$
d. $\mu = \sin\theta$
e. $\mu = \csc\theta$

____ 5.   Factor; then use fundamental identities to simplify the expression below and determine which of the following is *not* equivalent.

$\cot^2 \alpha \tan^2 \alpha + \cot^2 \alpha$

a. $\dfrac{1}{\sin^2 \alpha}$

b. $\sec^2 \alpha$

c. $\csc^2 \alpha$

d. $1 + \cot^2 \alpha$

e. $\dfrac{1}{1 - \cos^2 \alpha}$

____ 6.   Evaluate the following expression.

$\sec y \cos y$

a. 1

b. 3

c. 0

d. 2

e. 4

____ 7.   Evaluate the following expression.

$\sec^5 x (\sec x \tan x) - \sec^3 x (\sec x \tan x)$

a. $\sec^3 x \tan^5 x$

b. $\sec^4 x \tan x$

c. $4 \sec x \tan^4 x$

d. $\sec^4 x \tan^3 x$

e. $\sec^3 x \tan^3 x$

____ 8.   Evaluate the following expression.

$\dfrac{\sec 5\theta - 1}{1 - \cos 5\theta}$

a. $\sec 5\theta - \cos 5\theta$

b. $\cos 5\theta$

c. $-\sec 5\theta$

d. $\sec 5\theta$

e. $-\cos 5\theta$

_____ 9.   Evaluate the following expression.

$$\frac{11\cos\left[\left(\dfrac{\pi}{2}\right)-x\right]}{\sin\left[\left(\dfrac{\pi}{2}\right)-x\right]}$$

a. $11\tan x$
b. $11\cot x$
c. $-11\tan x$
d. $-11\cot x$
e. $12\tan x$

_____ 10.   Evaluate the following expression.

$$4\sec^2 y - 4\cot^2\left(\frac{\pi}{2}-y\right)$$

a.   0
b. -4
c.   5
d. -5
e.   4

_____ 11.   Solve the following equation.

$$3\sqrt{3}\csc x - 6 = 0$$

a. $\dfrac{\pi}{3}+2n\pi,\ \dfrac{2\pi}{3}+2n\pi$

b. $\dfrac{\pi}{3}+\pi,\ \dfrac{2\pi}{3}+2n\pi$

c. $\dfrac{\pi}{2}+2n\pi,\ \dfrac{2\pi}{3}+2n\pi$

d. $\dfrac{\pi}{4}+2n\pi,\ \dfrac{2\pi}{4}+2n\pi$

e. $\dfrac{\pi}{3}+2n\pi,\ \dfrac{2\pi}{3}+\pi$

_____   12.   Solve the following equation.

$$\cos 2x(4\cos x + 2) = 0$$

a. $\dfrac{\pi}{3} + n\pi, \dfrac{\pi}{3} + n\pi$

b. $\dfrac{\pi}{2} + n\pi, \dfrac{2\pi}{5} + n\pi$

c. $\dfrac{\pi}{4} + \dfrac{n\pi}{2}, \dfrac{2\pi}{3} + 2n\pi, \dfrac{4\pi}{3} + 2n\pi$

d. $\dfrac{2\pi}{3} + n\pi, \dfrac{2\pi}{3} + n\pi$

e. $\dfrac{4\pi}{3} + n\pi, \dfrac{2\pi}{3} + n\pi, \dfrac{4\pi}{3} + 2n\pi$

_____   13.   Solve the multiple-angle equation.

$$5\sec 4x = 10$$

a. $\dfrac{\pi}{12} - \dfrac{n\pi}{3}, \dfrac{5\pi}{12} + \dfrac{n\pi}{2}$

b. $\dfrac{3\pi}{4} + \dfrac{n\pi}{3}, \dfrac{\pi}{12} + \dfrac{n\pi}{2}$

c. $\dfrac{5\pi}{12} + \dfrac{n\pi}{3}, \dfrac{\pi}{12} + \dfrac{n\pi}{2}$

d. $\dfrac{\pi}{2} + \dfrac{n\pi}{3}, \dfrac{\pi}{12} + \dfrac{n\pi}{2}$

e. $\dfrac{\pi}{12} + \dfrac{n\pi}{2}, \dfrac{5\pi}{12} + \dfrac{n\pi}{2}$

_____   14.   Use a graphing utility to select the correct graph the function.

Functions   *Trigonometic functions*

$$f(x) = 2(\sin x \cos x) \qquad 2\left(-\sin^2 x - \cos^2 x\right) = 0$$

a.

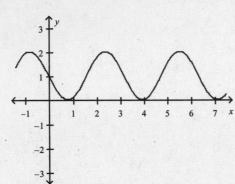

d.

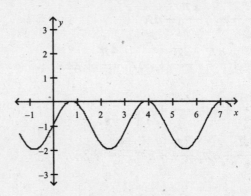

b.

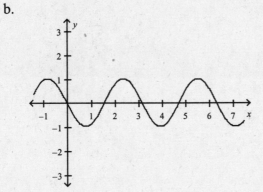

e.

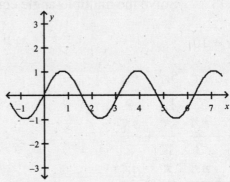

c.

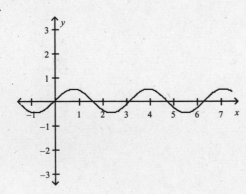

_____ 15.   Solve the multiple-angle equation.

$$\cos \frac{x}{2} = -\frac{\sqrt{3}}{2}$$

a. $x = \frac{7\pi}{6} + 2n\pi$ and $\frac{11\pi}{6} + 2n\pi$, where n is an integer

b. $x = \frac{5\pi}{3} + 2n\pi$ and $\frac{8\pi}{3} + 2n\pi$, where n is an integer

c. $x = \frac{5\pi}{3} + 4n\pi$ and $\frac{7\pi}{3} + 4n\pi$, where n is an integer

d. $x = \frac{5\pi}{6} + 2n\pi$ and $\frac{7\pi}{6} + 2n\pi$, where n is an integer

e. $x = \frac{2\pi}{3} + 2n\pi$ and $\frac{5\pi}{3} + 2n\pi$, where n is an integer

_____ 16.   Find the expression as the sine or cosine of an angle.

$$\cos 140° \cos 30° - \sin 140° \sin 30°$$

a. $\cos 170°$
b. $\sin 170°$
c. $\cos 140°$
d. $\sin 110°$
e. $\cos 110°$

_____ 17.   Simplify the expression algebraically.

$$\frac{7}{\sqrt{2}} \cos\left(\frac{5\pi}{4} - x\right)$$

a. $\frac{7}{2}\left(\cos \frac{5x}{4} + \sin \frac{5x}{4}\right)$

b. $-\frac{7}{2}(\cos x + \sin x)$

c. $\frac{7}{2}(\cos x - \sin x)$

d. $\frac{7}{2}(\sin x - \cos x)$

e. $\frac{7}{2}\left(\cos \frac{5x}{4} - \sin \frac{5x}{4}\right)$

____   18.   Use the formula $a \sin B\theta + b \cos B\theta = \sqrt{a^2 + b^2} \sin(B\theta + C)$, where $C = \arctan(b/a), a > 0$, to find the trigonometric expression in the following forms.

$y = \sqrt{a^2 + b^2} \sin(B\theta + C)$

$4 \sin 2\theta + 2 \cos 2\theta$

a. $2\sqrt{5} \sin(2\theta - 0.4636)$
b. $\sin(2\theta + 0.4636)$
c. $2\sqrt{5} \sin(\theta + 0.4636)$
d. $2\sqrt{5} \sin(\theta - 0.4636)$
e. $2\sqrt{5} \sin(2\theta + 0.4636)$

____   19.   Use a graphing utility to select correct graph y_1 and y_2 in the same viewing window. Use the graphs to determine whether $y_1 = y_2$. Explain your reasoning.

$y_1 = \sin(x + 6), y_2 = \sin x + \sin 6$

a.

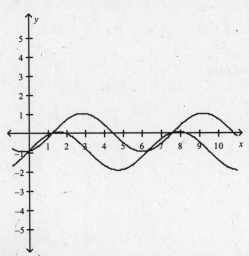

No, $y_1 = y_2$ because their graphs are different.

d.

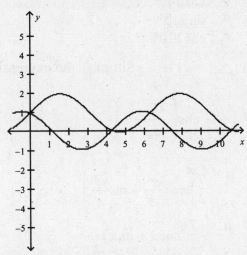

No, $y_1 \neq y_2$ because their graphs are Same.

b.

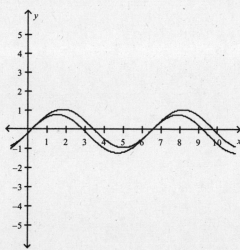

No, $y_1 \neq y_2$ because their graphs are different.

e.

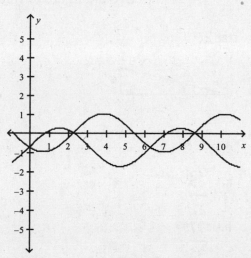

Yes, $y_1 = y_2$ because their graphs are same.

c.

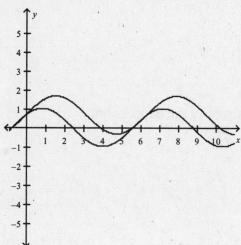

Yes, $y_1 = y_2$ because their graphs are different.

____ 20. Write the given expression as the cosine of an angle.

$\cos 70° \cos 55° - \sin 70° \sin 55°$

a. $\cos(55°)$
b. $\cos(70°)$
c. $\cos(-110°)$
d. $\cos(15°)$
e. $\cos(125°)$

_____ 21.   Use the figure to find the exact value of the trigonometric function.

$\tan 2\theta$

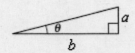

$a = 1, b = 6$

a. $\dfrac{35}{12}$

b. $\dfrac{37}{35}$

c. $\dfrac{35}{37}$

d. $\dfrac{12}{37}$

e. $\dfrac{12}{35}$

_____ 22.   Use the half-angle formulas to simplify the expression.

$-\sqrt{\dfrac{1 - \cos 6x}{1 + \cos 6x}}$

a. $-|3 \tan 6x|$
b. $-|3 \tan x|$
c. $-|3 \tan 3x|$
d. $-|\tan x|$
e. $-|\tan 3x|$

_____ 23.   Use the sum-to-product formulas to select the sum or difference as a product.

$\cos 3\theta + \cos 4\theta$

a.
$$2\cos\frac{7\theta}{2}\sin\left(\frac{\theta}{2}\right)$$

b.
$$2\cos\left(-\frac{7\theta}{2}\right)\cos\frac{\theta}{2}$$

c.
$$2\cos\frac{7\theta}{2}\cos\left(-\frac{\theta}{2}\right)$$

d.
$$2\cos\frac{7\theta}{2}\cos\left(\frac{\theta}{2}\right)$$

e.
$$2\cos\frac{7\theta}{2}\sin\left(-\frac{\theta}{2}\right)$$

_____ 24.   Evaluate the expression.

$$\tan\frac{u}{2}$$

a. $\cos u + \cot u$
b. $\csc u - \cot u$
c. $\csc u + \cot u$
d. $\cos u - \cot u$
e. $\csc u - \tan u$

_____ 25.   Use the figure below to find the exact value of the given trigonometric expression.

$\cos\dfrac{x}{2}$

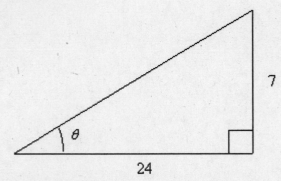

a. $\cos\dfrac{x}{2} = 7$

b. $\cos\dfrac{x}{2} = \dfrac{7\sqrt{2}}{10}$

c. $\cos\dfrac{x}{2} = \dfrac{\sqrt{2}}{10}$

d. $\cos\dfrac{x}{2} = \dfrac{1}{7}$

e. $\cos\dfrac{x}{2} = \dfrac{7}{12}$

Ch 5 Form D
Answer Section

1.	ANS: D	PTS: 1	REF:	5.1.15
2.	ANS: A	PTS: 1	REF:	5.1.71
3.	ANS: D	PTS: 1	REF:	5.1.101
4.	ANS: A	PTS: 1	REF:	5.1.123
5.	ANS: B	PTS: 1	REF:	5.1.62
6.	ANS: A	PTS: 1	REF:	5.2.10
7.	ANS: D	PTS: 1	REF:	5.2.22
8.	ANS: D	PTS: 1	REF:	5.2.24
9.	ANS: A	PTS: 1	REF:	5.2.34
10.	ANS: E	PTS: 1	REF:	5.2.44
11.	ANS: A	PTS: 1	REF:	5.3.13
12.	ANS: C	PTS: 1	REF:	5.3.24
13.	ANS: E	PTS: 1	REF:	5.3.42
14.	ANS: E	PTS: 1	REF:	5.3.83
15.	ANS: C	PTS: 1	REF:	5.3.43
16.	ANS: A	PTS: 1	REF:	5.4.32
17.	ANS: B	PTS: 1	REF:	5.4.64
18.	ANS: E	PTS: 1	REF:	5.4.100a
19.	ANS: B	PTS: 1	REF:	5.4.110
20.	ANS: E	PTS: 1	REF:	5.4.39
21.	ANS: E	PTS: 1	REF:	5.5.13
22.	ANS: E	PTS: 1	REF:	5.5.75
23.	ANS: C	PTS: 1	REF:	5.5.94
24.	ANS: B	PTS: 1	REF:	5.5.119
25.	ANS: B	PTS: 1	REF:	5.5.58

Ch 5

_____ 1. Use the given values to evaluate (if possible) three trigonometric functions $\csc x$, $\tan x$, $\cot x$.

$$\cos\left(\frac{\pi}{2} - x\right) = \frac{3}{5}, \quad \cos x = \frac{4}{5}$$

a.
$$\csc x = -\frac{5}{3}$$
$$\tan x = \frac{3}{4}$$
$$\cot x = \frac{4}{3}$$

b.
$$\csc x = \frac{5}{3}$$
$$\tan x = -\frac{3}{4}$$
$$\cot x = \frac{4}{3}$$

c.
$$\csc x = \frac{5}{3}$$
$$\tan x = \frac{3}{4}$$
$$\cot x = \frac{4}{3}$$

d.
$$\csc x = \frac{5}{3}$$
$$\tan x = \frac{3}{4}$$
$$\cot x = -\frac{4}{3}$$

e.
$$\csc x = \frac{3}{5}$$
$$\tan x = \frac{3}{4}$$
$$\cot x = \frac{4}{3}$$

_____ 2.   By using a graphing utility to complete the following table. Round your answer to four decimal places.

x	0.6	0.8	1.0	1.2	1.4	1.6	1.8
y_1	---	---	---	---	---	---	---
y_2	---	---	---	---	---	---	---

$$y_1 = \frac{\cos x}{1 - \sin x}, \; y_2 = \frac{1 + \sin x}{\cos x}$$

a.

x	0.6	0.8	1.0	1.2	1.4	1.6	1.8
y_1	1.8958	2.4650	3.4082	5.3319	11.6814	−68.4797	−8.6876
y_2	1.8958	2.4650	3.4082	5.3319	11.6814	−68.4797	−8.6876

b.

x	0.6	0.8	1.0	1.2	1.4	1.6	1.8
y_1	−1.8958	2.4650	3.4082	5.3319	11.6814	−68.4797	−8.6876
y_2	−1.8958	2.4650	3.4082	5.3319	11.6814	−68.4797	−8.6876

c.

x	0.6	0.8	1.0	1.2	1.4	1.6	1.8
y_1	1.8958	2.4650	3.4082	−5.3319	11.6814	−68.4797	−8.6876
y_2	1.8958	2.4650	3.4082	−5.3319	11.6814	−68.4797	−8.6876

d.

x	0.6	0.8	1.0	1.2	1.4	1.6	1.8
y_1	1.8958	2.4650	−3.4082	5.3319	11.6814	−68.4797	−8.6876
y_2	1.8958	2.4650	−3.4082	5.3319	11.6814	−68.4797	−8.6876

e.

x	0.6	0.8	1.0	1.2	1.4	1.6	1.8
y_1	1.8958	2.4650	3.4082	5.3319	−11.6814	−68.4797	−8.6876
y_2	1.8958	2.4650	3.4082	5.3319	−11.6814	−68.4797	−8.6876

_____ 3.   Use the trigonometric substitution to select the algebraic expression as a trigonometric function of θ, where $0 < \theta < \dfrac{\pi}{2}$.

$\sqrt{10 - x^2}, x = \sqrt{10}\sin\theta$

a. $10\sin\theta$
b. $\sqrt{10}\sin\theta$
c. $-\sqrt{10}\cos\theta$
d. $\sqrt{10}\cos\theta$
e. $10\cos\theta$

_____ 4.   Find the rate of change of the function $f(x) = -\csc x - \sin x$.

a. $\csc x\cot x - \cos x$
b. $\cos x - \tan x\sec x$
c. $\cos x + 1$
d. $\cos x + \sec x$
e. $-\cos x\cos$

_____ 5.   Which of the following is equivalent to the given expression?

$\dfrac{\sin^2 x}{1 - \cos x}$

a. $1 + \cos x$
b. $\cot x\sin x + \tan x$
c. $\tan x + \sin x$
d. $\tan x\cot x - \cos x$
e. $\csc x + \cot x$

_____ 6.   Evaluate the following expression.

$(1 + \sin\alpha)(1 - \sin\alpha)$

a. $-\cos^2\alpha$
b. $\sin^2\alpha$
c. $\cos^2\alpha$
d. $-2\sin^2\alpha$
e. $2\cos^2\alpha$

_____ 7.   Use the cofunction identities to evaluate the expression without using a calculator.

$\cos^2 55° + \cos^2 35°$

a. 4
b. -3
c. 3
d. 1
e. -1

_____ 8.   Evaluate the following expression.

$\sec x - \cos x$

a. $\sin x \csc x$
b. $-\sin x \cot x$
c. $\sin x \tan x$
d. $-\sin x \tan x$
e. $\sin x \cot x$

_____ 9.   Evaluate the following expression.

$$\frac{6 \csc(-11x)}{\sec(-11x)}$$

a. $-6 \csc(-11x)$
b. $-11 \cot 6x$
c. $-6 \cot 11x$
d. $6 \csc(-11x)$
e. $6 \cot 11x$

_____ 10. Evaluate the following expression.

$$\tan\left(\sin^{-1}x\right)$$

a. $\dfrac{x}{\sqrt{1-x^2}}$

b. $\dfrac{x}{\sqrt{1+x^2}}$

c. $\dfrac{x}{\sqrt{x^2-1}}$

d. $\dfrac{-x}{\sqrt{1+x^2}}$

e. $\dfrac{-x}{\sqrt{1-x^2}}$

_____ 11. Solve the following equation.

$$9\cot x^2 - 3 = 0$$

a. $\dfrac{4\pi}{3}+n\pi,\ \dfrac{2\pi}{3}+n\pi$

b. $\dfrac{\pi}{3}+n\pi,\ \dfrac{\pi}{3}+n\pi$

c. $\dfrac{2\pi}{3}+n\pi,\ \dfrac{2\pi}{3}+n\pi$

d. $\dfrac{\pi}{3}+n\pi,\ \dfrac{2\pi}{3}+n\pi$

e. $\dfrac{\pi}{2}+n\pi,\ \dfrac{2\pi}{5}+n\pi$

_____ 12.   Find all solutions of the following equation in the interval $[0, 2\pi)$.

$4 \sec^2 x - 4 = 0$

a. $0, \dfrac{5\pi}{3}$

b. $0, \pi$

c. $\pi, \dfrac{2\pi}{3}$

d. $2\pi, \dfrac{3\pi}{4}$

e. $0, \dfrac{\pi}{2}$

_____ 13.   Use inverse functions where needed to find all solutions of the equation in the interval $[0, 2\pi)$.

$\cot^2 x - 9 = 0$

a. $\arctan\left(\dfrac{1}{3}\right), \arctan\left(\dfrac{1}{3}\right) + \pi, \arctan\left(\dfrac{1}{3}\right) + \pi, \arctan\left(\dfrac{1}{3}\right) + \pi$

b. $\arctan\left(\dfrac{1}{3}\right), \arctan\left(\dfrac{1}{3}\right) + 2\pi, \arctan\left(-\dfrac{1}{3}\right) + 2\pi, \arctan\left(-\dfrac{1}{3}\right) + 2\pi$

c. $\arctan\left(\dfrac{1}{3}\right), \arctan\left(\dfrac{1}{3}\right) + \pi, \arctan\left(\dfrac{1}{3}\right) + \pi, \arctan\left(\dfrac{1}{3}\right) + 2\pi$

d. $\arctan\left(\dfrac{1}{3}\right), \arctan\left(\dfrac{1}{3}\right) + 2\pi, \arctan\left(-\dfrac{1}{3}\right) + \pi, \arctan\left(-\dfrac{1}{3}\right) + 2\pi$

e. $\arctan\left(\dfrac{1}{3}\right), \arctan\left(\dfrac{1}{3}\right) + \pi, \arctan\left(-\dfrac{1}{3}\right) + \pi, \arctan\left(-\dfrac{1}{3}\right) + 2\pi$

_____ 14.   Determine whether the statement is true or false. Justify your answer.

The equation $2 \sin 4t - 1 = 0$ has two times the number of solutions in the interval $[0, 2\pi)$ as the equation $2 \sin t - 1 = 0$.

a.   False
b.   True

_____ 15. Use a graphing utility to approximate the solutions (to three decimal places) of the given equation in the interval $\left(-\dfrac{\pi}{2}, \dfrac{\pi}{2}\right)$.

$6\sin^3 x + 18\sin^2 x = 5\sin x + 15$

a. $x = -1.150, 1.150$

b. $x = -0.825, 1.336$

c. $x = 1.265$

d. $x = -1.193, 0, 1.193$

e. $x = -1.265, 0.398$

_____ 16. Find the expression as the tangent of an angle.

$\dfrac{\tan 100° - \tan 30°}{1 + \tan 100° \tan 30°}$

a. $\tan^{-1} 100°$

b. $\tan 130°$

c. $\tan^{-1} 70°$

d. $\tan 70°$

e. $\tan 30°$

_____ 17. Simplify the expression algebraically.

$\sin(4x + 4y)\sin(4x - 4y)$

a. $\sin^2 4x + \sin^2 4y$

b. $\sin^2 x - \sin^2 4y$

c. $\sin^2 4x - \sin^2 4y$

d. $\sin^2 4x - \sin^2 y$

e. $\sin^2 x - \sin^2 y$

_____   18.   Use the formula $a \sin B\theta + b \cos B\theta = \sqrt{a^2 + b^2} \sin(B\theta + C)$, where $C = \arctan(b/a), a > 0$, to find the trigonometric expression in the following forms.

$$y = \sqrt{a^2 + b^2} \sin(B\theta + C)$$

$3 \sin 2\theta + 5 \cos 2\theta$

a. $\sqrt{34} \, \sin(\theta + 1.0304)$
b. $\sqrt{34} \, \sin(2\theta + 1.0304)$
c. $\sin(2\theta + 1.0304)$
d. $\sqrt{34} \, \sin(2\theta - 1.0304)$
e. $\sqrt{34} \, \sin(\theta - 1.0304)$

_____   19.   Simplify the following expression algebraically.

$\cos(\pi + x)$

a. $-\cos x$
b. $-\dfrac{3}{2} \cos x$
c. $\dfrac{3}{2} \cos x$
d. $\cos x$
e. $-\sin x$

_____   20.   Find the exact value of the given expression.

$\cos \dfrac{7\pi}{12} \cos \dfrac{\pi}{6} - \sin \dfrac{7\pi}{12} \sin \dfrac{\pi}{6}$

a. $\dfrac{\left(\sqrt{3} + 1\right)\left(2\sqrt{2}\right)}{8}$

b. $-\dfrac{\sqrt{2}}{2}$

c. $\dfrac{\left(\sqrt{3} - 1\right)\left(2\sqrt{2}\right)}{8}$

d. $-\dfrac{1}{2}$

e. $\dfrac{\sqrt{3}}{2}$

____   21.   Use the figure to find the exact value of the trigonometric function.

$\csc 2\theta$

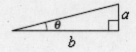

$a = 1, b = 4$

a. $\dfrac{9}{17}$

b. $\dfrac{17}{8}$

c. $\dfrac{8}{17}$

d. $\dfrac{17}{9}$

e. $\dfrac{8}{9}$

____   22.   Use the product-to-sum formulas to select the product as a sum or difference.

$\sin \dfrac{\pi}{4} \cos \dfrac{\pi}{8}$

a. $\dfrac{1}{2}\left(\sin \dfrac{3\pi}{8} - \cos \dfrac{\pi}{8} \right)$

b. $\dfrac{1}{2}\left(\sin \dfrac{3\pi}{8} + \sin \dfrac{\pi}{8} \right)$

c. $\left(\sin \dfrac{3\pi}{8} + \cos \dfrac{\pi}{8} \right)$

d. $\dfrac{1}{2}\left(\sin \dfrac{3\pi}{8} + \cos \dfrac{\pi}{8} \right)$

e. $\dfrac{1}{2}\left(\sin \dfrac{3\pi}{8} - \sin \dfrac{\pi}{8} \right)$

_____ 23.   Use the figure to find the exact value of the trigonometric function.

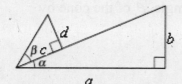

$a = 10, b = 5$

$c = 4, d = 3$

$\sin 2\alpha$

a. $\dfrac{125}{100}$

b. $\dfrac{101}{4}$

c. $\dfrac{10}{125}$

d. $\dfrac{100}{125}$

e. $\dfrac{5}{101}$

____ 24.   The mach number M of an airplane is the ratio of its speed to the speed of sound. When an airplane travels faster than the speed of sound, the sound waves form a cone behind the airplane (see figure). The mach number is related to the apex angle θ of the cone by $\sin(\theta/4) = 1/M$.

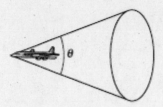

Rewrite the equation in terms of θ.

a. $\theta = \sin\left(\dfrac{1}{M}\right)$

b. $\theta = 4\sin\left(\dfrac{1}{M}\right)$

c. $\theta = 4\sin^{-1}\left(\dfrac{1}{M}\right)$

d. $\theta = \sin^{-1}\left(\dfrac{1}{M}\right)$

e. $\theta = 4\sin^{-1}\left(\dfrac{4}{M}\right)$

____ 25.   Use the half-angle formula to simplify the given expression.

$$\sqrt{\dfrac{1+\cos 4x}{2}}$$

a. $\cos 2x$

b. $\cos 16x$

c. $\cos x$

d. $\cos 4x$

e. $\cos 8x$

Ch 5 Form E
Answer Section

1.	ANS:	C	PTS:	1	REF:	5.1.18
2.	ANS:	A	PTS:	1	REF:	5.1.87
3.	ANS:	D	PTS:	1	REF:	5.1.104
4.	ANS:	A	PTS:	1	REF:	5.1.126
5.	ANS:	A	PTS:	1	REF:	5.1.81
6.	ANS:	C	PTS:	1	REF:	5.2.13
7.	ANS:	D	PTS:	1	REF:	5.2.66
8.	ANS:	C	PTS:	1	REF:	5.2.26
9.	ANS:	C	PTS:	1	REF:	5.2.36
10.	ANS:	A	PTS:	1	REF:	5.2.47
11.	ANS:	D	PTS:	1	REF:	5.3.16
12.	ANS:	B	PTS:	1	REF:	5.3.26
13.	ANS:	E	PTS:	1	REF:	5.3.69
14.	ANS:	A	PTS:	1	REF:	5.3.99
15.	ANS:	A	PTS:	1	REF:	5.3.50
16.	ANS:	D	PTS:	1	REF:	5.4.34
17.	ANS:	C	PTS:	1	REF:	5.4.68
18.	ANS:	B	PTS:	1	REF:	5.4.102a
19.	ANS:	A	PTS:	1	REF:	5.4.72
20.	ANS:	B	PTS:	1	REF:	5.4.38
21.	ANS:	B	PTS:	1	REF:	5.5.15
22.	ANS:	B	PTS:	1	REF:	5.5.81
23.	ANS:	D	PTS:	1	REF:	5.5.107
24.	ANS:	C	PTS:	1	REF:	5.5.137d
25.	ANS:	A	PTS:	1	REF:	5.5.63

Ch 5 Form F

_____   1.   Use the given values to evaluate (if possible) three trigonometric functions $\csc x$, $\tan x$, $\cot x$.

$$\cos\left(\frac{\pi}{2}-x\right)=\frac{2}{5}, \quad \cos x=\frac{3}{5}$$

a.
$$\csc x=\frac{2}{5}$$

$$\tan x=\frac{2}{3}$$

$$\cot x=\frac{3}{2}$$

b.
$$\csc x=\frac{5}{2}$$

$$\tan x=\frac{2}{3}$$

$$\cot x=-\frac{3}{2}$$

c.
$$\csc x=-\frac{5}{2}$$

$$\tan x=\frac{2}{3}$$

$$\cot x=\frac{3}{2}$$

d.
$$\csc x=\frac{5}{2}$$

$$\tan x=\frac{2}{3}$$

$$\cot x=\frac{3}{2}$$

e.
$$\csc x=\frac{5}{2}$$

$$\tan x=-\frac{2}{3}$$

$$\cot x=\frac{3}{2}$$

_____ 2.   By using a graphing utility to complete the following table. Round your answer to four decimal places.

x	0.2	0.4	0.6	0.8	1.0	1.2	1.4
y_1	---	---	---	---	---	---	---
y_2	---	---	---	---	---	---	---

$$y_1 = \frac{\cos x}{1 - \sin x}, \, y_2 = \frac{1 + \sin x}{\cos x}$$

a.

x	0.2	0.4	0.6	0.8	1.0	1.2	1.4
y_1	1.2230	1.5085	−1.8958	2.4650	3.4082	5.3319	11.6814
y_2	1.2230	1.5085	−1.8958	2.4650	3.4082	5.3319	11.6814

b.

x	0.2	0.4	0.6	0.8	1.0	1.2	1.4
y_1	1.2230	1.5085	1.8958	2.4650	3.4082	5.3319	11.6814
y_2	1.2230	1.5085	1.8958	2.4650	3.4082	5.3319	11.6814

c.

x	0.2	0.4	0.6	0.8	1.0	1.2	1.4
y_1	−1.2230	1.5085	1.8958	2.4650	3.4082	5.3319	11.6814
y_2	−1.2230	1.5085	1.8958	2.4650	3.4082	5.3319	11.6814

d.

x	0.2	0.4	0.6	0.8	1.0	1.2	1.4
y_1	1.2230	1.5085	1.8958	2.4650	−3.4082	5.3319	11.6814
y_2	1.2230	1.5085	1.8958	2.4650	−3.4082	5.3319	11.6814

e.

x	0.2	0.4	0.6	0.8	1.0	1.2	1.4
y_1	1.2230	1.5085	1.8958	−2.4650	3.4082	5.3319	11.6814
y_2	1.2230	1.5085	1.8958	−2.4650	3.4082	5.3319	11.6814

_____ 3.   Use the trigonometric substitution to select the algebraic expression as a trigonometric function of θ, where $0 < \theta < \dfrac{\pi}{2}$.

$\sqrt{13 - x^2}, x = \sqrt{13}\sin\theta$

a. $\sqrt{13}\sin\theta$
b. $13\cos\theta$
c. $\sqrt{13}\cos\theta$
d. $-\sqrt{13}\cos\theta$
e. $13\sin\theta$

_____ 4.   Find the rate of change of the function $f(x) = -\csc x - \cos x$.

a. $\sin x + 1$
b. $\sin x \sin$
c. $\sin x - \tan x \sec x$
d. $\sin x + \sec x$
e. $\csc x \cot x - \sin x$

_____ 5.   Which of the following is equivalent to the given expression?

$\dfrac{\sin^2 x}{1 - \cos x}$

a. $\cot x \sin x + \tan x$
b. $1 + \cos x$
c. $\tan x \cot x - \cos x$
d. $\tan x + \sin x$
e. $\csc x + \cot x$

_____ 6.   Evaluate the following expression.

$3(1 + \sin\alpha)(1 - \sin\alpha)$

a. $-4\sin^2\alpha$
b. $4\cos^2\alpha$
c. $3\sin^2\alpha$
d. $-3\cos^2\alpha$
e. $3\cos^2\alpha$

_____ 7.   Use the cofunction identities to evaluate the expression without using a calculator.

$\cos^2 60° + \cos^2 30°$

a. -2
b. 3
c. -1
d. 2
e. 1

_____ 8.   Evaluate the following expression.

$\sec 3x - \cos 3x$

a. $-3 \sin 3x \cot 3x$
b. $-\sin 3x \tan 3x$
c. $3 \sin x \cot x$
d. $\sin 3x \tan 3x$
e. $\sin 3x \csc 3x$

_____ 9.   Evaluate the following expression.

$$\frac{8 \csc(-9x)}{\sec(-9x)}$$

a. $-8 \csc(-9x)$
b. $-8 \cot 9x$
c. $8 \cot 9x$
d. $-9 \cot 8x$
e. $8 \csc(-9x)$

_____ 10.   Evaluate the following expression.

$$5\tan\left(\sin^{-1}x\right)$$

a. $\dfrac{5x}{\sqrt{x^2-1}}$

b. $\dfrac{5x}{\sqrt{1-x^2}}$

c. $\dfrac{-5x}{\sqrt{1-x^2}}$

d. $\dfrac{-5x}{\sqrt{1+x^2}}$

e. $\dfrac{5x}{\sqrt{1+x^2}}$

_____ 11.   Solve the following equation.

$$3\cot x^2 - 1 = 0$$

a. $\dfrac{2\pi}{3}+n\pi,\ \dfrac{2\pi}{3}+n\pi$

b. $\dfrac{4\pi}{3}+n\pi,\ \dfrac{2\pi}{3}+n\pi$

c. $\dfrac{\pi}{3}+n\pi,\ \dfrac{\pi}{3}+n\pi$

d. $\dfrac{\pi}{2}+n\pi,\ \dfrac{2\pi}{5}+n\pi$

e. $\dfrac{\pi}{3}+n\pi,\ \dfrac{2\pi}{3}+n\pi$

_____ 12.   Find all solutions of the following equation in the interval $[0, 2\pi)$.

$3\sec^2 x - 3 = 0$

a. $0, \dfrac{\pi}{2}$

b. $\pi, \dfrac{2\pi}{3}$

c. $0, \pi$

d. $0, \dfrac{5\pi}{3}$

e. $2\pi, \dfrac{3\pi}{4}$

_____ 13.   Use inverse functions where needed to find all solutions of the equation in the interval $[0, 2\pi)$.

$\cot^2 x - 36 = 0$

a. $\arctan\left(\dfrac{1}{6}\right), \arctan\left(\dfrac{1}{6}\right) + 2\pi, \arctan\left(-\dfrac{1}{6}\right) + \pi, \arctan\left(-\dfrac{1}{6}\right) + 2\pi$

b. $\arctan\left(\dfrac{1}{6}\right), \arctan\left(\dfrac{1}{6}\right) + \pi, \arctan\left(-\dfrac{1}{6}\right) + \pi, \arctan\left(-\dfrac{1}{6}\right) + 2\pi$

c. $\arctan\left(\dfrac{1}{6}\right), \arctan\left(\dfrac{1}{6}\right) + 2\pi, \arctan\left(-\dfrac{1}{6}\right) + 2\pi, \arctan\left(-\dfrac{1}{6}\right) + 2\pi$

d. $\arctan\left(\dfrac{1}{6}\right), \arctan\left(\dfrac{1}{6}\right) + \pi, \arctan\left(\dfrac{1}{6}\right) + \pi, \arctan\left(\dfrac{1}{6}\right) + 2\pi$

e. $\arctan\left(\dfrac{1}{6}\right), \arctan\left(\dfrac{1}{6}\right) + \pi, \arctan\left(\dfrac{1}{6}\right) + \pi, \arctan\left(\dfrac{1}{6}\right) + \pi$

_____ 14.   Determine whether the statement is true or false. Justify your answer.

The equation $2\sin 4t - 1 = 0$ has one times the number of solutions in the interval $[0, 2\pi)$ as the equation $2\sin t - 1 = 0$.

a. False

b. True

_____ 15. Use a graphing utility to approximate the solutions (to three decimal places) of the given equation in the interval $\left(-\frac{\pi}{2}, \frac{\pi}{2} \right)$.

$6\sin^3 x + 18\sin^2 x = 5\sin x + 15$

a. $x = -1.150, 1.150$
b. $x = 1.265$
c. $x = -1.265, 0.398$
d. $x = -0.825, 1.336$
e. $x = -1.193, 0, 1.193$

_____ 16. Find the expression as the tangent of an angle.

$$\frac{\tan 130° - \tan 40°}{1 + \tan 130° \tan 40°}$$

a. $\tan 170°$
b. $\tan 40°$
c. $\tan 90°$
d. $\tan^{-1} 130°$
e. $\tan^{-1} 90°$

_____ 17. Simplify the expression algebraically.

$\sin\left(6x + 6y \right) \sin\left(6x - 6y \right)$

a. $\sin^2 x - \sin^2 6y$
b. $\sin^2 6x + \sin^2 6y$
c. $\sin^2 6x - \sin^2 y$
d. $\sin^2 x - \sin^2 y$
e. $\sin^2 6x - \sin^2 6y$

_____ 18.   Use the formula $a \sin B\theta + b \cos B\theta = \sqrt{a^2 + b^2} \, \sin(B\theta + C)$, where $C = \arctan(b/a), a > 0$, to find the trigonometric expression in the following forms.

$$y = \sqrt{a^2 + b^2} \, \sin(B\theta + C)$$

$$8 \sin 2\theta + 2 \cos 2\theta$$

a. $2\sqrt{17} \, \sin(2\theta + 0.245)$
b. $\sin(2\theta + 0.245)$
c. $2\sqrt{17} \, \sin(2\theta - 0.245)$
d. $2\sqrt{17} \, \sin(\theta - 0.245)$
e. $2\sqrt{17} \, \sin(\theta + 0.245)$

_____ 19.   Simplify the following expression algebraically.

$$9 \cos(\pi + x)$$

a. $-9 \cos x$
b. $\dfrac{3}{2} \cos x$

c. $-\dfrac{3}{2} \cos x$

d. $9 \cos x$
e. $-9 \sin x$

_____ 20.   Find the exact value of the given expression.

$$\cos \frac{7\pi}{12} \cos \frac{\pi}{6} - \sin \frac{7\pi}{12} \sin \frac{\pi}{6}$$

a. $\dfrac{\left(\sqrt{3} + 1\right)\left(2\sqrt{2}\right)}{8}$

b. $\dfrac{\left(\sqrt{3} - 1\right)\left(2\sqrt{2}\right)}{8}$

c. $\dfrac{\sqrt{3}}{2}$

d. $-\dfrac{\sqrt{2}}{2}$

e. $-\dfrac{1}{2}$

____ 21.　Use the figure to find the exact value of the trigonometric function.

$\csc 2\theta$

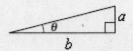

$a = 1, b = 6$

a. $\dfrac{12}{37}$

b. $\dfrac{12}{13}$

c. $\dfrac{37}{13}$

d. $\dfrac{37}{12}$

e. $\dfrac{13}{37}$

____ 22.　Use the product-to-sum formulas to select the product as a sum or difference.

$\sin\dfrac{\pi}{5}\cos\dfrac{\pi}{10}$

a. $\left(\sin\dfrac{3\pi}{10} + \cos\dfrac{\pi}{10}\right)$

b. $\dfrac{1}{2}\left(\sin\dfrac{3\pi}{10} + \sin\dfrac{\pi}{10}\right)$

c. $\dfrac{1}{2}\left(\sin\dfrac{3\pi}{10} + \cos\dfrac{\pi}{10}\right)$

d. $\dfrac{1}{2}\left(\sin\dfrac{3\pi}{10} - \sin\dfrac{\pi}{10}\right)$

e. $\dfrac{1}{2}\left(\sin\dfrac{3\pi}{10} - \cos\dfrac{\pi}{10}\right)$

_____   23.   Use the figure to find the exact value of the trigonometric function.

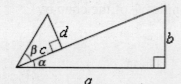

$a = 6, b = 3$

$c = 5, d = 6$

$\sin 2\alpha$

a. $\dfrac{36}{45}$

b. $\dfrac{3}{37}$

c. $\dfrac{45}{36}$

d. $\dfrac{6}{45}$

e. $\dfrac{37}{5}$

____ 24.   The mach number M of an airplane is the ratio of its speed to the speed of sound. When an airplane travels faster than the speed of sound, the sound waves form a cone behind the airplane (see figure). The mach number is related to the apex angle θ of the cone by $\sin(\theta/4) = 1/M$.

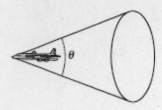

Rewrite the equation in terms of θ.

a.
$$\theta = 4\sin^{-1}\left(\frac{1}{M}\right)$$

b.
$$\theta = \sin\left(\frac{1}{M}\right)$$

c.
$$\theta = \sin^{-1}\left(\frac{1}{M}\right)$$

d.
$$\theta = 4\sin\left(\frac{1}{M}\right)$$

e.
$$\theta = 4\sin^{-1}\left(\frac{4}{M}\right)$$

____ 25.   Use the half-angle formula to simplify the given expression.

$$\sqrt{\frac{1+\cos 4x}{2}}$$

a. $\cos 8x$

b. $\cos 16x$

c. $\cos x$

d. $\cos 2x$

e. $\cos 4x$

Ch 5 Form F
Answer Section

1.	ANS:	D	PTS:	1	REF:	5.1.18
2.	ANS:	B	PTS:	1	REF:	5.1.87
3.	ANS:	C	PTS:	1	REF:	5.1.104
4.	ANS:	E	PTS:	1	REF:	5.1.126
5.	ANS:	B	PTS:	1	REF:	5.1.81
6.	ANS:	E	PTS:	1	REF:	5.2.13
7.	ANS:	E	PTS:	1	REF:	5.2.66
8.	ANS:	D	PTS:	1	REF:	5.2.26
9.	ANS:	B	PTS:	1	REF:	5.2.36
10.	ANS:	B	PTS:	1	REF:	5.2.47
11.	ANS:	E	PTS:	1	REF:	5.3.16
12.	ANS:	C	PTS:	1	REF:	5.3.26
13.	ANS:	B	PTS:	1	REF:	5.3.69
14.	ANS:	A	PTS:	1	REF:	5.3.99
15.	ANS:	A	PTS:	1	REF:	5.3.50
16.	ANS:	C	PTS:	1	REF:	5.4.34
17.	ANS:	E	PTS:	1	REF:	5.4.68
18.	ANS:	A	PTS:	1	REF:	5.4.102a
19.	ANS:	A	PTS:	1	REF:	5.4.72
20.	ANS:	D	PTS:	1	REF:	5.4.38
21.	ANS:	D	PTS:	1	REF:	5.5.15
22.	ANS:	B	PTS:	1	REF:	5.5.81
23.	ANS:	A	PTS:	1	REF:	5.5.107
24.	ANS:	A	PTS:	1	REF:	5.5.137d
25.	ANS:	D	PTS:	1	REF:	5.5.63

Ch 6 Form A

____ 1.   Use the Law of Sines to solve the triangle. Round your answer to two decimal places.

$A = 25°, B = 45°, c = 13$

a. $C = 110°, a \approx 6.85, b \approx 9.78$
b. $C = 110°, a \approx 9.78, b \approx 10.78$
c. $C = 110°, a \approx 3.72, b \approx 11.78$
d. $C = 110°, a \approx 5.85, b \approx 9.78$
e. $C = 110°, a \approx 7.85, b \approx 11.78$

____ 2.   Use the Law of Sines to solve (if possible) for c. Round your answers to two decimal places.

$A = 76°, a = 18, b = 20$

a. $c \approx 148.23$
b. $c \approx 11.49$
c. $c \approx 40.06$
d. $c \approx 32.32$
e. No Solution

____ 3.   Find values for b such that the triangle has two solutions.

$A = 46°, a = 19$

a. $19 \geq b \geq \dfrac{19}{\sin 46°}$

b. $19 \leq b \leq \dfrac{19}{\sin 46°}$

c. $19 > b > \dfrac{19}{\sin 46°}$

d. $19 < b \leq \dfrac{19}{\sin 46°}$

e. $19 < b < \dfrac{19}{\sin 46°}$

_____ 4.   Find the area of the triangle having the indicated angle and sides.

$A = 5°19', b = 4.7, c = 22$

(Round your answer to one decimal place.)

a. 4.8
b. 3.8
c. 5.8
d. 6.8
e. 9.6

_____ 5.   Given $C = 115°$, $a = 19.9$, and $c = 15.3$, use the Law of Sines to solve the triangle (if possible) for the value of b. If two solutions exist, find both. Round answer to two decimal places.
a. not possible
b. $b = 11.37$ and 15.69
c. $b = 13.81$
d. $b = 17.06$
e. $b = 10.44$ and 15.82

_____ 6.   Use the law of Cosines to solve the given triangle. Round your answer to two decimal places.

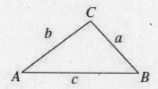

$a = 8, b = 10, c = 14$

a. $A \approx 101.53°, B \approx 44.42°, C \approx 34.05°$
b. $A \approx 34.05°, B \approx 101.53°, C \approx 44.42°$
c. $A \approx 44.42°, B \approx 44.42°, C \approx 91.16°$
d. $A \approx 44.42°, B \approx 34.05°, C \approx 101.53°$
e. $A \approx 34.05°, B \approx 44.42°, C \approx 101.53°$

_____ 7.   Use the low of Cosines to solve the given triangle. Round your answer to two decimal places.

$A = 50°, b = 4, c = 15$

a. $a \approx 15, B \approx 13.85°, C \approx 116.15°$
b. $a \approx 12.8, B \approx 116.15°, C \approx 13.85°$
c. $a \approx 4, B \approx 13.85°, C \approx 116.15°$
d. $a \approx 15, B \approx 15.85°, C \approx 114.15°$

443

e. $a \approx 12.8, B \approx 13.85°, C \approx 116.15°$

_____ 8. Use the Heron's formula to find the area of the triangle. Round your answer upto one decimal place.

$a = 2.8, b = 10.5, c = 9$

a. 5.8
b. 6.3
c. 3.4
d. 40.9
e. 11.4

_____ 9. To determine the distance between two aircraft, a tracking station continuously determines the distance to each aircraft and the angle A between them (see figure). Determine the distance a between the planes when $A = 44°$ miles, $b = 37$ miles, and $c = 22$ miles.

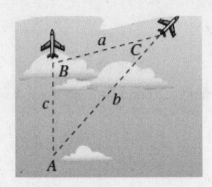

a. 35.6 miles
b. 31.81 miles
c. 26.11 miles
d. 11.27 miles
e. 54.99 miles

_____ 10. Given $a = 8$, $b = 13$, and $c = 11$, use the Law of Cosines to solve the triangle for the value of C. Round answer to two decimal places.
a. 60.33°
b. 84.78°
c. 57.42°
d. 37.79°
e. 80.44°

_____ 11.   Find **u** + **v**.

$\mathbf{u} = \langle 3,1 \rangle, \mathbf{v} = \langle 1,4 \rangle$

a. $\langle 5,6 \rangle$

b. $\langle 4,5 \rangle$

c. $\langle 5,5 \rangle$

d. $\langle 5,4 \rangle$

e. $\langle 4,4 \rangle$

_____ 12.   Find a unit vector in the direction of the given vector.

$\mathbf{u} = \langle 0,-5 \rangle$

a. $\langle -1,-1 \rangle$

b. $\langle -1,0 \rangle$

c. $\langle 0,0 \rangle$

d. $\langle 0,-1 \rangle$

e. $\langle 1,0 \rangle$

_____ 13.   Detroit Tigers pitcher Joel Zumaya was recorded throwing a pitch at a velocity of 102 miles per hour. If he threw the pitch at an angle of 38° below the horizontal, find the vertical and horizontal components of the velocity.(Round your answers to one decimal place.)

a. Vertical ≈ −61.8 mi/h, Horizontal ≈ 81.4 mi/h.
b. Vertical ≈ 80.4 mi/h, Horizontal ≈ −62.8 mi/h.
c. Vertical ≈ −62.8 mi/h, Horizontal ≈ −62.8 mi/h.
d. Vertical ≈ −62.8 mi/h, Horizontal ≈ 80.4 mi/h.
e. Vertical ≈ 62.8 mi/h, Horizontal ≈ 80.4 mi/h.

_____ 14.   Find the magnitude of vector **v.**

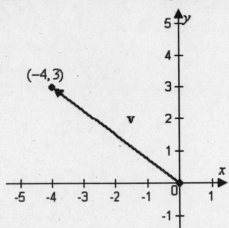

(-4, 3)

a. $\|\mathbf{v}\| = 5$
b. $\|\mathbf{v}\| = 2\sqrt{7}$
c. $\|\mathbf{v}\| = 6$
d. $\|\mathbf{v}\| = 4\sqrt{2}$
e. $\|\mathbf{v}\| = 6\sqrt{3}$

_____ 15.   Let **w** be a vector with initial point $(-6, -9)$ and terminal point $(0, 8)$. Write **w** as a linear combination of the standard unit vectors **i** and **j**.
a. $\mathbf{w} = 6\mathbf{i} + 17\mathbf{j}$
b. $\mathbf{w} = 14\mathbf{i} + 9\mathbf{j}$
c. $\mathbf{w} = -6\mathbf{i} - 17\mathbf{j}$
d. $\mathbf{w} = 3\mathbf{i} - 8\mathbf{j}$
e. $\mathbf{w} = -15\mathbf{i} + 8\mathbf{j}$

_____ 16.   Find the dot product of **u** and **v.**

$\mathbf{u} = \langle 6, 1 \rangle$

$\mathbf{v} = \langle -5, 4 \rangle$

a. -30
b. -28
c. -24
d. -26
e. -22

_____ 17.   Use the vectors $\mathbf{u} = \langle 2,6 \rangle$, $\mathbf{v} = \langle -4,4 \rangle$, and $\mathbf{w} = \langle 4,-2 \rangle$ to find the indicated quantity. State whether the result is a vector or a scalar.

$(\mathbf{v} \cdot \mathbf{u})\mathbf{w}$

a. $\langle 64,-36 \rangle$; vector

b. $\langle 64,-32 \rangle$; vector

c. −34; scalar

d. −32; scalar

e. $\langle 64,-28 \rangle$; vector

_____ 18.   Find the angle θ between the vectors.

$\mathbf{u} = \langle 5,0 \rangle$

$\mathbf{v} = \langle 0,-2 \rangle$

(Round the answer upto 1 decimal place.)

a. 40°

b. 110°

c. 50°

d. 130°

e. 90°

_____ 19.   A force of $y = 65$ pounds exerted at an angle of 30° above the horizontal is required to slide a table across a floor (see figure). The table is dragged $x = 18$ feet. Determine the work done in sliding the table.

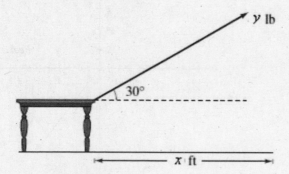

a.   1033.2 ft-lb

b.   1093.2 ft-lb

c.   1013.2 ft-lb

d.   1073.2 ft-lb

e.   1053.2 ft-lb

_____   20.   Find the angle between the vectors **u** and **v** if **u** $= -4\mathbf{i} + 2\mathbf{j}$ and **v** $= 3\mathbf{i} + 2\mathbf{j}$. Round answer to two decimal places.

a.   118.50°
b.   120.70°
c.   119.74°
d.   117.81°
e.   121.15°

_____   21.   Plot the complex number and find its absolute value.

$-6 + 8i$

a.

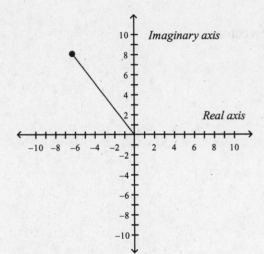

$|-6 + 8i| = 10$

d.

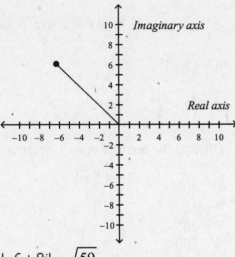

$|-6 + 8i| = \sqrt{59}$

b.

e.

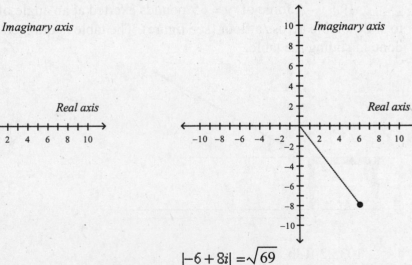

$|-6 + 8i| = \sqrt{33}$ $|-6 + 8i| = \sqrt{69}$

c.

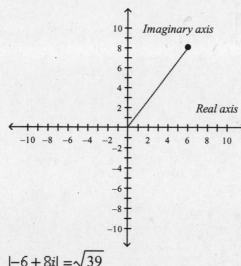

$$\left|-6+8i\right| = \sqrt{39}$$

_____ 22.   Use the formula to find the indicated roots of the complex number.
Square roots of $5(\cos 50° + i\sin 50°)$

a. $\sqrt{7}(\cos 25° + i\sin 25°)$
     $\sqrt{7}(\cos 100° - i\sin 100°)$

b. $\sqrt{5}(\cos 25° + i\sin 25°)$
     $\sqrt{5}(\cos 100° + i\sin 100°)$

c. $\sqrt{5}(\cos 25° - i\sin 25°)$
     $\sqrt{5}(\cos 100° + i\sin 100°)$

d. $\sqrt{5}(\cos 25° + i\sin 25°)$
     $\sqrt{5}(\cos 100° - i\sin 100°)$

e. $\sqrt{7}(\cos 25° - i\sin 25°)$
     $\sqrt{7}(\cos 100° - i\sin 100°)$

_____ 23.   Find the trigonometric form of the complex number shown below.
$-12i$

a. $12(\cos 0 + i\sin 0)$

b. $12\left(\cos \dfrac{3\pi}{2} + i\sin \dfrac{3\pi}{2}\right)$

c. $12\left(\cos \dfrac{\pi}{4} + i\sin \dfrac{\pi}{4}\right)$

d. $12(\cos \pi + i\sin \pi)$

e. $12\left(\cos \dfrac{\pi}{2} + i\sin \dfrac{\pi}{2}\right)$

____ 24.   Perform the operation shown below and leave the result in trigonometric form.

$$\left[2\left(\cos\frac{3\pi}{7}+i\sin\frac{3\pi}{7}\right)\right]\left[6\left(\cos\frac{4\pi}{5}+i\sin\frac{4\pi}{5}\right)\right]$$

a. $\left[12\left(\cos\frac{12\pi}{35}+i\sin\frac{12\pi}{35}\right)\right]$

b. $\left[8\left(\cos\frac{43\pi}{35}+i\sin\frac{43\pi}{35}\right)\right]$

c. $\left[8\left(\cos\frac{12\pi}{35}+i\sin\frac{12\pi}{35}\right)\right]$

d. $\left[12\left(\cos\frac{3\pi}{7}+i\sin\frac{3\pi}{7}\right)\right]$

e. $\left[12\left(\cos\frac{43\pi}{35}+i\sin\frac{43\pi}{35}\right)\right]$

____ 25.   Use DeMoivre's Theorem to find the indicated power of the complex number. Write the result in standard form.

$$10\left(\sqrt{3}+i\right)^5$$

a. $160+160\sqrt{3}i$

b. $10\sqrt{3}-10i$

c. $10+10\sqrt{3}i$

d. $-160\sqrt{3}+160i$

e. $160\sqrt{3}-160i$

Ch 6 Form A
Answer Section

1.	ANS:	D	PTS:	1	REF:	6.1.13
2.	ANS:	E	PTS:	1	REF:	6.1.27
3.	ANS:	E	PTS:	1	REF:	6.1.36b
4.	ANS:	A	PTS:	1	REF:	6.1.42
5.	ANS:	A	PTS:	1	REF:	6.1.25
6.	ANS:	E	PTS:	1	REF:	6.2.5
7.	ANS:	E	PTS:	1	REF:	6.2.14
8.	ANS:	E	PTS:	1	REF:	6.2.35
9.	ANS:	C	PTS:	1	REF:	6.2.53
10.	ANS:	C	PTS:	1	REF:	6.2.10
11.	ANS:	B	PTS:	1	REF:	6.3.31a
12.	ANS:	D	PTS:	1	REF:	6.3.40
13.	ANS:	D	PTS:	1	REF:	6.3.84
14.	ANS:	A	PTS:	1	REF:	6.3.13
15.	ANS:	A	PTS:	1	REF:	6.3.53
16.	ANS:	D	PTS:	1	REF:	6.4.7
17.	ANS:	B	PTS:	1	REF:	6.4.18
18.	ANS:	E	PTS:	1	REF:	6.4.31
19.	ANS:	C	PTS:	1	REF:	6.4.79
20.	ANS:	C	PTS:	1	REF:	6.4.34
21.	ANS:	A	PTS:	1	REF:	6.5.5
22.	ANS:	B	PTS:	1	REF:	6.5.83a
23.	ANS:	B	PTS:	1	REF:	6.5.21
24.	ANS:	E	PTS:	1	REF:	6.5.47
25.	ANS:	D	PTS:	1	REF:	6.5.72

Ch 6 Form B

_____ 1. Use the Law of Sines to solve the triangle. Round your answer to two decimal places.

$A = 35°, B = 40°, c = 13$

a. $C = 105°, a \approx 7.72, b \approx 8.65$
b. $C = 105°, a \approx 3.72, b \approx 10.65$
c. $C = 105°, a \approx 9.72, b \approx 10.65$
d. $C = 105°, a \approx 8.65, b \approx 9.65$
e. $C = 105°, a \approx 8.72, b \approx 8.65$

_____ 2. Use the Law of Sines to solve (if possible) for c. Round your answers to two decimal places.

$A = 76°, a = 18, b = 20$

a. $c \approx 32.32$
b. $c \approx 40.06$
c. $c \approx 11.49$
d. No Solution
e. $c \approx 148.23$

_____ 3. Find values for b such that the triangle has two solutions.

$A = 46°, a = 12$

a. $12 \leq b \leq \dfrac{12}{\sin 46°}$

b. $12 < b < \dfrac{12}{\sin 46°}$

c. $12 < b \leq \dfrac{12}{\sin 46°}$

d. $12 \geq b \geq \dfrac{12}{\sin 46°}$

e. $12 > b > \dfrac{12}{\sin 46°}$

_____   4.   Find the area of the triangle having the indicated angle and sides.

$A = 5°20', b = 4.6, c = 26$

(Round your answer to one decimal place.)

a. 5.6
b. 6.6
c. 7.6
d. 11.1
e. 4.6

_____   5.   Given $C = 124°$, $a = 14.9$, and $c = 10.3$, use the Law of Sines to solve the triangle (if possible) for the value of b. If two solutions exist, find both. Round answer to two decimal places.

a. $b = 9.56$ and 13.88
b. not possible
c. $b = 12.00$
d. $b = 15.25$
e. $b = 8.63$ and 14.01

_____   6.   Use the law of Cosines to solve the given triangle. Round your answer to two decimal places.

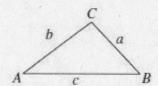

$a = 10, b = 12, c = 16$

a. $A \approx 38.62°, B \approx 92.87°, C \approx 48.51°$
b. $A \approx 48.51°, B \approx 38.62°, C \approx 92.87°$
c. $A \approx 48.51°, B \approx 48.51°, C \approx 82.98°$
d. $A \approx 92.87°, B \approx 48.51°, C \approx 38.62°$
e. $A \approx 38.62°, B \approx 48.51°, C \approx 92.87°$

_____   7.   Use the low of Cosines to solve the given triangle. Round your answer to two decimal places.

$A = 52°, b = 5, c = 16$

a. $a \approx 16, B \approx 18.96°, C \approx 109.04°$
b. $a \approx 16, B \approx 16.96°, C \approx 111.04°$
c. $a \approx 13.51, B \approx 111.04°, C \approx 16.96°$
d. $a \approx 5, B \approx 16.96°, C \approx 111.04°$
e. $a \approx 13.51, B \approx 16.96°, C \approx 111.04°$

_____ 8.   Use the Heron's formula to find the area of the triangle. Round your answer upto one decimal place.

$a = 3.1, b = 10.8, c = 9$

a.   3.6
b.   6.7
c.   6.4
d.   44.2
e.   12.3

_____ 9.   To determine the distance between two aircraft, a tracking station continuously determines the distance to each aircraft and the angle A between them (see figure). Determine the distance a between the planes when $A = 44°$ miles, $b = 37$ miles, and $c = 22$ miles.

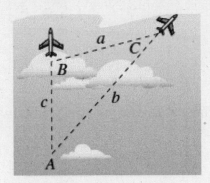

a.   31.81 miles
b.   26.11 miles
c.   11.27 miles
d.   35.6 miles
e.   54.99 miles

_____ 10.   Given $a = 5$, $b = 8$, and $c = 12$, use the Law of Cosines to solve the triangle for the value of C. Round answer to two decimal places.
a.   80.44°
b.   133.43°
c.   28.96°
d.   17.61°
e.   60.33°

____   11.   Find $\mathbf{u}+\mathbf{v}$.

$\mathbf{u} = \langle 5,1 \rangle, \mathbf{v} = \langle 1,6 \rangle$

a. $\langle 7,8 \rangle$

b. $\langle 6,6 \rangle$

c. $\langle 7,6 \rangle$

d. $\langle 6,7 \rangle$

e. $\langle 7,7 \rangle$

____   12.   Find a unit vector in the direction of the given vector.

$\mathbf{u} = \langle 0,-3 \rangle$

a. $\langle 0,0 \rangle$

b. $\langle 0,-1 \rangle$

c. $\langle 1,0 \rangle$

d. $\langle -1,0 \rangle$

e. $\langle -1,-1 \rangle$

____   13.   Detroit Tigers pitcher Joel Zumaya was recorded throwing a pitch at a velocity of 105 miles per hour. If he threw the pitch at an angle of 33° below the horizontal, find the vertical and horizontal components of the velocity.(Round your answers to one decimal place.)

a.   Vertical ≈ 88.1 mi/h, Horizontal ≈ −57.2 mi/h.
b.   Vertical ≈ −57.2 mi/h, Horizontal ≈ 88.1 mi/h.
c.   Vertical ≈ 57.2 mi/h, Horizontal ≈ 88.1 mi/h.
d.   Vertical ≈ −56.2 mi/h, Horizontal ≈ 89.1 mi/h.
e.   Vertical ≈ −57.2 mi/h, Horizontal ≈ −57.2 mi/h.

_____ 14.   Find the magnitude of vector **v**.

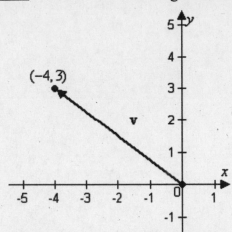

a. $\|\mathbf{v}\| = 6\sqrt{3}$
b. $\|\mathbf{v}\| = 6$
c. $\|\mathbf{v}\| = 5$
d. $\|\mathbf{v}\| = 4\sqrt{2}$
e. $\|\mathbf{v}\| = 2\sqrt{7}$

_____ 15.   Let **w** be a vector with initial point $(5, 1)$ and terminal point $(3, -3)$. Write **w** as a linear combination of the standard unit vectors **i** and **j**.
a. $\mathbf{w} = 6\mathbf{i} - 6\mathbf{j}$
b. $\mathbf{w} = 4\mathbf{i} + 6\mathbf{j}$
c. $\mathbf{w} = -8\mathbf{i} + 2\mathbf{j}$
d. $\mathbf{w} = -2\mathbf{i} - 4\mathbf{j}$
e. $\mathbf{w} = 8\mathbf{i} + 4\mathbf{j}$

_____ 16.   Find the dot product of **u** and **v**.

$\mathbf{u} = \langle 3, 1 \rangle$

$\mathbf{v} = \langle -6, 2 \rangle$

a. -14
b. -16
c. -18
d. -20
e. -12

_____ 17.   Use the vectors $\mathbf{u} = \langle 3,5 \rangle$, $\mathbf{v} = \langle -3,2 \rangle$, and $\mathbf{w} = \langle 4,-1 \rangle$ to find the indicated quantity.
State
whether the result is a vector or a scalar.

$(\mathbf{v} \cdot \mathbf{u})\mathbf{w}$

a. −1; scalar
b. $\langle 4,-1 \rangle$; vector
c. −3; scalar
d. $\langle 4,-5 \rangle$; vector
e. $\langle 4,3 \rangle$; vector

_____ 18.   Find the angle θ between the vectors.

$\mathbf{u} = \langle 1,0 \rangle$

$\mathbf{v} = \langle 0,-2 \rangle$

(Round the answer upto 1 decimal place.)

a. 30°
b. 90°
c. 110°
d. 70°
e. 125°

_____ 19.   A force of $y = 55$ pounds exerted at an angle of 30° above the horizontal is required
to slide a table across a floor (see figure). The table is dragged $x = 18$ feet. Determine the work
done in sliding the table.

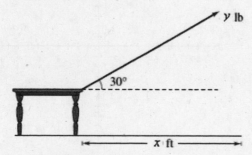

a.   917.4 ft-lb
b.   897.4 ft-lb
c.   857.4 ft-lb
d.   937.4 ft-lb
e.   877.4 ft-lb

_____ 20.   Find the angle between the vectors **u** and **v** if $\mathbf{u} = \mathbf{i} - 2\mathbf{j}$ and $\mathbf{v} = 4\mathbf{i} + 3\mathbf{j}$. Round answer to two decimal places.

a.   101.71°
b.   98.37°
c.   100.30°
d.   101.26°
e.   99.06°

_____ 21.   Plot the complex number and find its absolute value.

$-3 + 6i$

a.

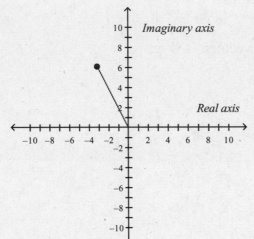

$|-3 + 6i| = 3\sqrt{5}$

d.

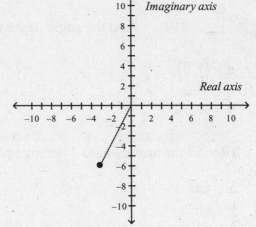

$|-3 + 6i| = \sqrt{6}$

b.

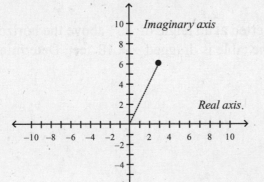

$|-3 + 6i| = 2\sqrt{3}$

e.

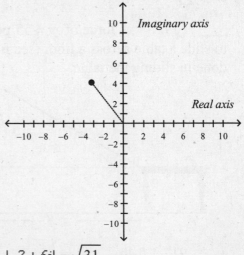

$|-3 + 6i| = \sqrt{31}$

c.

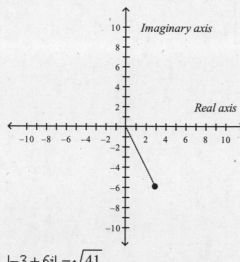

$$|-3+6i| = \sqrt{41}$$

_____ 22.   Use the formula to find the indicated roots of the complex number.

Square roots of $7(\cos 50° + i \sin 50°)$

a. $\sqrt{7}(\cos 25° + i \sin 25°)$
    $\sqrt{7}(\cos 100° - i \sin 100°)$

b. $\sqrt{9}(\cos 25° + i \sin 25°)$
    $\sqrt{9}(\cos 100° - i \sin 100°)$

c. $\sqrt{7}(\cos 25° + i \sin 25°)$
    $\sqrt{7}(\cos 100° + i \sin 100°)$

d. $\sqrt{9}(\cos 25° - i \sin 25°)$
    $\sqrt{9}(\cos 100° - i \sin 100°)$

e. $\sqrt{7}(\cos 25° - i \sin 25°)$
    $\sqrt{7}(\cos 100° + i \sin 100°)$

_____ 23.   Find the trigonometric form of the complex number shown below.

$-11i$

a. $11\left(\cos \dfrac{\pi}{2} + i \sin \dfrac{\pi}{2}\right)$

b. $11(\cos \pi + i \sin \pi)$

c. $11\left(\cos \dfrac{3\pi}{2} + i \sin \dfrac{3\pi}{2}\right)$

d. $11(\cos 0 + i \sin 0)$

e. $11\left(\cos \dfrac{\pi}{4} + i \sin \dfrac{\pi}{4}\right)$

_____ 24. Perform the operation shown below and leave the result in trigonometric form.

$$\left[2\left(\cos\frac{5\pi}{6}+i\sin\frac{5\pi}{6}\right)\right]\left[4\left(\cos\frac{2\pi}{3}+i\sin\frac{2\pi}{3}\right)\right]$$

a. $\left[8\left(\cos\dfrac{3\pi}{2}+i\sin\dfrac{3\pi}{2}\right)\right]$

b. $\left[8\left(\cos\dfrac{5\pi}{6}+i\sin\dfrac{5\pi}{6}\right)\right]$

c. $\left[6\left(\cos\dfrac{3\pi}{2}+i\sin\dfrac{3\pi}{2}\right)\right]$

d. $\left[8\left(\cos\dfrac{5\pi}{9}+i\sin\dfrac{5\pi}{9}\right)\right]$

e. $\left[6\left(\cos\dfrac{5\pi}{9}+i\sin\dfrac{5\pi}{9}\right)\right]$

_____ 25. Use DeMoivre's Theorem to find the indicated power of the complex number. Write the result in standard form.

$$-7\left(\sqrt{3}+i\right)^{13}$$

a. $-7-7\sqrt{3}i$

b. $-28672\sqrt{3}-28672i$

c. $28672-28672\sqrt{3}i$

d. $7\sqrt{3}+7i$

e. $28672\sqrt{3}+28672i$

Ch 6 Form B
Answer Section

1.	ANS: A	PTS: 1	REF:	6.1.13
2.	ANS: D	PTS: 1	REF:	6.1.27
3.	ANS: B	PTS: 1	REF:	6.1.36b
4.	ANS: A	PTS: 1	REF:	6.1.42
5.	ANS: B	PTS: 1	REF:	6.1.25
6.	ANS: E	PTS: 1	REF:	6.2.5
7.	ANS: E	PTS: 1	REF:	6.2.14
8.	ANS: E	PTS: 1	REF:	6.2.35
9.	ANS: B	PTS: 1	REF:	6.2.53
10.	ANS: B	PTS: 1	REF:	6.2.10
11.	ANS: D	PTS: 1	REF:	6.3.31a
12.	ANS: B	PTS: 1	REF:	6.3.40
13.	ANS: B	PTS: 1	REF:	6.3.84
14.	ANS: C	PTS: 1	REF:	6.3.13
15.	ANS: D	PTS: 1	REF:	6.3.53
16.	ANS: B	PTS: 1	REF:	6.4.7
17.	ANS: B	PTS: 1	REF:	6.4.18
18.	ANS: B	PTS: 1	REF:	6.4.31
19.	ANS: C	PTS: 1	REF:	6.4.79
20.	ANS: C	PTS: 1	REF:	6.4.34
21.	ANS: A	PTS: 1	REF:	6.5.5
22.	ANS: C	PTS: 1	REF:	6.5.83a
23.	ANS: C	PTS: 1	REF:	6.5.21
24.	ANS: A	PTS: 1	REF:	6.5.47
25.	ANS: B	PTS: 1	REF:	6.5.72

Ch 6 Form C

_____ 1.   Use the Law of Sines to solve for B and C. Round your answer to two decimal places.

$A = 36°, a = 8, b = 5$

a. $B \approx 29°, C \approx 115°$
b. $B \approx 21.55°, C \approx 122.45°$
c. $B \approx 105°, C \approx 39°$
d. $B \approx 115°, C \approx 29°$
e. $B \approx 122.45°, C \approx 21.55°$

_____ 2.   Use the Law of Sines to solve (if possible) the triangle. If two solutions exist, find both. Round your answers to two decimal places.

$A = 62°, a = 12.5, b = 13.9$

a. $B \approx 38.94°, C \approx 79.06°, c \approx 13.9$
b. $B \approx 89°, C \approx 29°, c \approx 8.9$
c. $B \approx 79.06°, C \approx 38.94°, c \approx 8.9$
d. $B \approx 29°, C \approx 89°, c \approx 12.5$
e.   No Solution

_____ 3.   Find values for b such that the triangle has two solutions.

$A = 18°, a = 9.8$

a.
$$9.8 < b \leq \frac{9.8}{\sin 18°}$$

b.
$$9.8 < b < \frac{9.8}{\sin 18°}$$

c.
$$9.8 > b > \frac{9.8}{\sin 18°}$$

d.
$$9.8 \leq b \leq \frac{9.8}{\sin 18°}$$

e.
$$9.8 \geq b \geq \frac{9.8}{\sin 18°}$$

_____   4.   Find the area of the triangle having the indicated angle and sides.

$C = 84°30', a = 17, b = 22$

(Round your answer to one decimal place.)

a. 188.1
b. 186.1
c. 187.1
d. 185.1
e. 372.3

_____   5.   Determine a value for b such that a triangle with $A = 48°$ and $a = 11$ has only one solution.

a. $b = 13$
b. $b = 14$
c. $b = 9$
d. $b = 12$
e. $b = 11$

_____   6.   Use the law of Cosines to solve the given triangle. Round your answer to two decimal places.

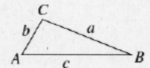

$a = 8, b = 4, c = 9$

a. $A \approx 26.38°, B \approx 62.72°, C \approx 90.9°$
b. $A \approx 90.9°, B \approx 26.38°, C \approx 62.72°$
c. $A \approx 90.9°, B \approx 62.72°, C \approx 26.38°$
d. $A \approx 62.72°, B \approx 90.9°, C \approx 26.38°$
e. $A \approx 62.72°, B \approx 26.38°, C \approx 90.9°$

_____   7.   Determine whether the Law of Sines or the Law of Cosines is needed to solve the triangle. Then solve the triangle.

$a = 11, c = 8, B = 70°$

a. Law of Sines; $A \approx 67.71°, C \approx 42.29°, b \approx 11.17$
b. Law of Cosine; $A \approx 67.71°, C \approx 42.29°, b \approx 11.17$
c. Law of Cosine; $A \approx 42.29°, C \approx 67.71°, b \approx 11.17$
d. Law of Sines; $A \approx 42.29°, C \approx 67.71°, b \approx 11.17$
e. Law of Sines; No solution

_____ 8.   Use the Heron's formula to find the area of the triangle. Round your answer upto one decimal place.

$a = 3.02, b = 0.72, c = 2.42$

a.   3.36
b.   0.09
c.   0.28
d.   0.31
e.   0.54

_____ 9.   To buy a triangular lot measuring 508 yards by 838 yards by 1118 yards. The price of the land is $2000 per acre. How much does the land cost?
(*Hint:* 1 acre = 4840 square yards)

a. $82,710.34
b. $82,810.34
c. $82,830.34
d. $82,910.34
e. $82,960.34

_____ 10.   Given $C = 115°$, $a = 12$, and $b = 8$, use the Law of Cosines to solve the triangle for the value of c. Round answer to two decimal places.
a.   16.29
b.   11.26
c.   15.57
d.   17.00
e.   14.13

_____ 11.   Find $\mathbf{u} - \mathbf{v}$.

$\mathbf{u} = \langle 0, 0 \rangle, \mathbf{v} = \langle 2, 1 \rangle$

a. $\langle -1, -2 \rangle$

b. $\langle -1, -1 \rangle$

c. $\langle -2, -1 \rangle$

d. $\langle -2, -2 \rangle$

e. $\langle -1, 0 \rangle$

_____ 12.   Find a unit vector in the direction of the given vector.

$\mathbf{v} = \mathbf{i} + \mathbf{j}$

a.
$$-\frac{\sqrt{2}}{2}\mathbf{i} + \frac{\sqrt{2}}{2}\mathbf{j}$$

b.
$$-\frac{\sqrt{2}}{2}\mathbf{i} - \frac{\sqrt{2}}{2}\mathbf{j}$$

c. $\sqrt{2}\mathbf{i} + \sqrt{2}\mathbf{j}$

d.
$$\frac{\sqrt{2}}{2}\mathbf{i} + \frac{\sqrt{2}}{2}\mathbf{j}$$

e.
$$\frac{\sqrt{2}}{2}\mathbf{i} - \frac{\sqrt{2}}{2}\mathbf{j}$$

_____ 13.   A force of F pounds is required to pull an object weighing W pounds up a ramp inclined at θ degrees from the horizontal.

Find θ if $F = 5,200$ pounds and $W = 15,000$.

a.   22.3°
b.   20.3°
c.   19.3°
d.   21.3°
e.   18.3°

_____ 14.   Find the component form of vector $\mathbf{v}$ with initial point $(3,7)$ and terminal point $(-2,-4)$.

a. $\mathbf{v} = \langle -5, 11 \rangle$

b. $\mathbf{v} = \langle -5, -11 \rangle$

c. $\mathbf{v} = \langle -4, 2 \rangle$

d. $\mathbf{v} = \langle 7, 9 \rangle$

e. $\mathbf{v} = \langle 11, -5 \rangle$

_____ 15.   Find the magnitude and direction angle of $\mathbf{v} = 6\left(\cos 85°\mathbf{i} + \sin 85°\mathbf{j} \right)$.

a. $\|\mathbf{v}\| = \sqrt{6};\ \theta = 95°$
b. $\|\mathbf{v}\| = 6;\ \theta = 95°$
c. $\|\mathbf{v}\| = \sqrt{6};\ \theta = 85°$
d. $\|\mathbf{v}\| = 6;\ \theta = 85°$
e. $\|\mathbf{v}\| = 6;\ \theta = 5°$

_____ 16.   Find the dot product of **u** and **v**.

$\mathbf{u} = \langle -3, 1 \rangle$

$\mathbf{v} = \langle 2, -3 \rangle$

a. −7
b. −5
c. −9
d. −13
e. −11

_____ 17.   Use the vectors $\mathbf{u} = \langle 5, 2 \rangle$, $\mathbf{v} = \langle -3, 2 \rangle$, and $\mathbf{w} = \langle 2, -4 \rangle$ to find the indicated quantity. State whether the result is a vector or a scalar.

$(\mathbf{u} \cdot 2\mathbf{v})\mathbf{w}$

a. 88; scalar
b. $\langle -44, 92 \rangle$; vector
c. $\langle -44, 90 \rangle$; vector
d. $\langle -44, 84 \rangle$; vector
e. $\langle -44, 88 \rangle$; vector

_____ 18.   Find the angle θ between the vectors.

$\mathbf{u} = 9\mathbf{i} - 1\mathbf{j}$

$\mathbf{v} = 5\mathbf{i} + 6\mathbf{j}$

(Round the answer upto 2 decimal places.)

a. 56.53°
b. 76.53°
c. 61.53°
d. 66.53°
e. 71.53°

_____ 19.   Given $\mathbf{u} = 5\mathbf{i} + 3\mathbf{j}$ and $\mathbf{v} = 3\mathbf{i} + 2\mathbf{j}$, find $\mathbf{u} \cdot \mathbf{v}$.
a. 9
b. 21
c. 19
d. 1
e. 15

_____   20.   Determine $\mathbf{u} \cdot \mathbf{v}$ if $\|\mathbf{u}\| = 4$, $\|\mathbf{v}\| = 3$, and $\theta = \frac{\pi}{6}$, where θ is the angle between $\mathbf{u}$ and $\mathbf{v}$.

Round answer to two decimal places.

a.   8.20

b.   9.44

c.   8.49

d.   6.00

e.   10.39

_____   21.   Plot the complex number and find its absolute value.

$-9 + 6i$

a.

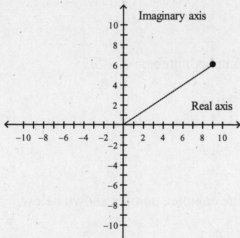

$|-9 + 6i| = 2\sqrt{21}$

d.

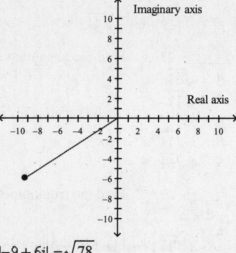

$|-9 + 6i| = \sqrt{78}$

b.

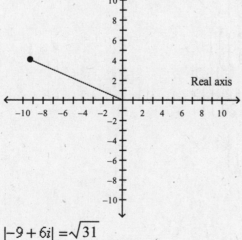

$|-9 + 6i| = \sqrt{31}$

e.

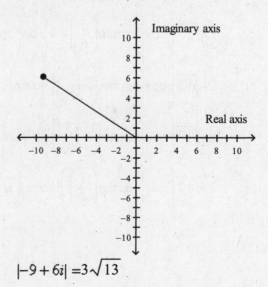

$|-9 + 6i| = 3\sqrt{13}$

c.

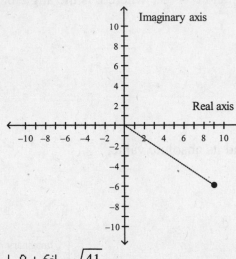

$$\left| -9 + 6i \right| = \sqrt{41}$$

_____ 22.   Find the absolute value of the complex number $-6 + 5i$.

a. $\sqrt{61}$

b. $\sqrt{11}$

c. 61

d. $3\sqrt{11}$

e. $4\sqrt{61}$

_____ 23.   Find the trigonometric form of the complex number shown below.

$-8 - 2i$

a. $2\sqrt{17}\left(\cos\left(\arctan\left(\dfrac{1}{8} \right) \right) + i\sin\left(\arctan\left(\dfrac{1}{8} \right) \right) \right)$

b. $2\sqrt{17}\left(\cos\left(\arctan\left(\dfrac{1}{6} \right) \right) + i\sin\left(\arctan\left(\dfrac{1}{6} \right) \right) \right)$

c. $2\sqrt{17}\left(\cos\left(\arctan\left(-\dfrac{3}{4} \right) \right) + i\sin\left(\arctan\left(-\dfrac{3}{4} \right) \right) \right)$

d. $2\sqrt{17}\left(\cos\left(\arctan\left(-\dfrac{3}{20} \right) \right) + i\sin\left(\arctan\left(-\dfrac{3}{20} \right) \right) \right)$

e. $2\sqrt{17}\left(\cos\left(\arctan\left(\dfrac{1}{4} \right) \right) + i\sin\left(\arctan\left(\dfrac{1}{4} \right) \right) \right)$

_____ 24.   Multiply the complex numbers below and leave the result in trigonometric form.

$$\left[0.4(\cos 110° + i \sin 110°) \right]\left[0.8(\cos 100° + i \sin 100°) \right]$$

a. $1.2(\cos 210° + i \sin 210°)$

b. $0.32(\cos 10° + i \sin 10°)$

c. $1.2(\cos 10° + i \sin 10°)$

d. $0.32(\cos 210° + i \sin 10°)$

e. $0.32(\cos 210° + i \sin 210°)$

_____ 25.   Use DeMoivre's Theorem to find the indicated power of the following complex number.

$$\left[2\left(\cos \frac{\pi}{3} + i \sin \frac{\pi}{3} \right) \right]^{12}$$

a. 2048

b. $2,048 + 2048\sqrt{3}$

c. $-4,096$

d. $4,096 + 4096\sqrt{3}$

e. $4,096$

Ch 6 Form C
Answer Section

1.	ANS:	B	PTS:	1	REF:	6.1.17
2.	ANS:	C	PTS:	1	REF:	6.1.29
3.	ANS:	B	PTS:	1	REF:	6.1.37b
4.	ANS:	B	PTS:	1	REF:	6.1.44
5.	ANS:	C	PTS:	1	REF:	6.1.35
6.	ANS:	E	PTS:	1	REF:	6.2.6
7.	ANS:	B	PTS:	1	REF:	6.2.27
8.	ANS:	E	PTS:	1	REF:	6.2.38
9.	ANS:	A	PTS:	1	REF:	6.2.61
10.	ANS:	D	PTS:	1	REF:	6.2.13
11.	ANS:	C	PTS:	1	REF:	6.3.34b
12.	ANS:	D	PTS:	1	REF:	6.3.43
13.	ANS:	B	PTS:	1	REF:	6.3.97
14.	ANS:	B	PTS:	1	REF:	6.3.19
15.	ANS:	D	PTS:	1	REF:	6.3.65
16.	ANS:	C	PTS:	1	REF:	6.4.9
17.	ANS:	E	PTS:	1	REF:	6.4.20
18.	ANS:	A	PTS:	1	REF:	6.4.35
19.	ANS:	B	PTS:	1	REF:	6.4.12
20.	ANS:	E	PTS:	1	REF:	6.4.49
21.	ANS:	E	PTS:	1	REF:	6.5.10
22.	ANS:	A	PTS:	1	REF:	6.5.10
23.	ANS:	E	PTS:	1	REF:	6.5.23
24.	ANS:	E	PTS:	1	REF:	6.5.50
25.	ANS:	E	PTS:	1	REF:	6.5.76

Ch 6 Form D

_____ 1.   Use the Law of Sines to solve for B and C. Round your answer to two decimal places.

$A = 38°, a = 8, b = 5$

a. $B \approx 113°, C \approx 29°$
b. $B \approx 103°, C \approx 39°$
c. $B \approx 29°, C \approx 113°$
d. $B \approx 22.63°, C \approx 119.37°$
e. $B \approx 119.37°, C \approx 22.63°$

_____ 2.   Use the Law of Sines to solve (if possible) the triangle. If two solutions exist, find both. Round your answers to two decimal places.

$A = 62°, a = 12.1, b = 13.5$

a. $B \approx 80.1°, C \approx 37.9°, c \approx 8.42$
b.   No Solution
c. $B \approx 29°, C \approx 89°, c \approx 12.1$
d. $B \approx 37.9°, C \approx 80.1°, c \approx 13.5$
e. $B \approx 89°, C \approx 29°, c \approx 8.42$

_____ 3.   Find values for b such that the triangle has two solutions.

$A = 30°, a = 10.6$

a. $10.6 \leq b \leq \dfrac{10.6}{\sin 30°}$

b. $10.6 < b < \dfrac{10.6}{\sin 30°}$

c. $10.6 < b \leq \dfrac{10.6}{\sin 30°}$

d. $10.6 \geq b \geq \dfrac{10.6}{\sin 30°}$

e. $10.6 > b > \dfrac{10.6}{\sin 30°}$

_____ 4.   Find the area of the triangle having the indicated angle and sides.

$C = 82°32', a = 16, b = 25$

(Round your answer to one decimal place.)

a.   198.3
b.   199.3
c.   200.3
d.   396.6
e.   197.3

_____ 5.   Determine a value for b such that a triangle with $A = 40°$ and $a = 11$ has only one solution.

a. $b = 5$
b. $b = 11$
c. $b = 13$
d. $b = 12$
e. $b = 14$

_____ 6.   Use the law of Cosines to solve the given triangle. Round your answer to two decimal places.

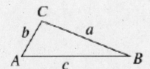

$a = 11, b = 7, c = 12$

a. $A \approx 80.28°, B \approx 64.62°, C \approx 35.1°$
b. $A \approx 80.28°, B \approx 35.1°, C \approx 64.62°$
c. $A \approx 64.62°, B \approx 80.28°, C \approx 35.1°$
d. $A \approx 64.62°, B \approx 35.1°, C \approx 80.28°$
e. $A \approx 35.1°, B \approx 64.62°, C \approx 80.28°$

_____ 7.   Determine whether the Law of Sines or the Law of Cosines is needed to solve the triangle. Then solve the triangle.

$a = 11, c = 8, B = 70°$

a.   Law of Sines; $A \approx 67.71°, C \approx 42.29°, b \approx 11.17$
b.   Law of Cosine; $A \approx 42.29°, C \approx 67.71°, b \approx 11.17$
c.   Law of Sines; No solution
d.   Law of Sines; $A \approx 42.29°, C \approx 67.71°, b \approx 11.17$
e.   Law of Cosine; $A \approx 67.71°, C \approx 42.29°, b \approx 11.17$

_____   8.   Use the Heron's formula to find the area of the triangle. Round your answer up to one decimal place.

$a = 3.03, b = 0.73, c = 2.43$

a.   3.39
b.   0.3
c.   0.09
d.   0.32
e.   0.56

_____   9.   To buy a triangular lot measuring 503 yards by 833 yards by 1113 yards. The price of the land is $2000 per acre. How much does the land cost?
(*Hint:* 1 acre = 4840 square yards)

a. $81,249.44
b. $81,149.44
c. $81,269.44
d. $81,349.44
e. $81,399.44

_____   10.   Given $C = 112°$, $a = 11$, and $b = 8$, use the Law of Cosines to solve the triangle for the value of c. Round answer to two decimal places.
a.   10.91
b.   15.84
c.   14.61
d.   13.38
e.   15.22

_____   11.   Find $\mathbf{u} - \mathbf{v}$.

$\mathbf{u} = \langle 0, 0 \rangle, \mathbf{v} = \langle 4, 3 \rangle$

a. $\langle -3, -4 \rangle$

b. $\langle -3, -3 \rangle$

c. $\langle -4, -4 \rangle$

d. $\langle -3, -2 \rangle$

e. $\langle -4, -3 \rangle$

_____ 12.   Find a unit vector in the direction of the given vector.

$\mathbf{v} = 2\mathbf{i} + 2\mathbf{j}$

a. $\dfrac{\sqrt{2}}{2}\mathbf{i} + \dfrac{\sqrt{2}}{2}\mathbf{j}$

b. $-\dfrac{\sqrt{2}}{2}\mathbf{i} - \dfrac{\sqrt{2}}{2}\mathbf{j}$

c. $\dfrac{\sqrt{2}}{2}\mathbf{i} - \dfrac{\sqrt{2}}{2}\mathbf{j}$

d. $-\dfrac{\sqrt{2}}{2}\mathbf{i} + \dfrac{\sqrt{2}}{2}\mathbf{j}$

e. $\sqrt{2}\mathbf{i} + \sqrt{2}\mathbf{j}$

_____ 13.   A force of F pounds is required to pull an object weighing W pounds up a ramp inclined at θ degrees from the horizontal.

Find θ if $F = 5,000$ pounds and $W = 14,000$.

a.   21.9°
b.   19.9°
c.   18.9°
d.   22.9°
e.   20.9°

_____ 14.   Find the component form of vector $\mathbf{v}$ with initial point $(3, 5)$ and terminal point $(-1, 6)$.

a. $\mathbf{v} = \langle -4, 1 \rangle$

b. $\mathbf{v} = \langle -2, -7 \rangle$

c. $\mathbf{v} = \langle -3, 6 \rangle$

d. $\mathbf{v} = \langle -4, -1 \rangle$

e. $\mathbf{v} = \langle -1, -4 \rangle$

_____ 15.   Find the magnitude and direction angle of $\mathbf{v} = 3\left(\cos 120°\mathbf{i} + \sin 120°\mathbf{j} \right)$.

a. $\|\mathbf{v}\| = \sqrt{3};\ \theta = 120°$
b. $\|\mathbf{v}\| = \sqrt{3};\ \theta = 60°$
c. $\|\mathbf{v}\| = 3;\ \theta = 120°$
d. $\|\mathbf{v}\| = 3;\ \theta = 60°$
e. $\|\mathbf{v}\| = 3;\ \theta = -30°$

_____ 16.   Find the dot product of **u** and **v**.

$$\mathbf{u} = \langle -4, 1 \rangle$$

$$\mathbf{v} = \langle 6, -4 \rangle$$

a. −26
b. −30
c. −24
d. −28
e. −32

_____ 17.   Use the vectors $\mathbf{u} = \langle 5, 3 \rangle$, $\mathbf{v} = \langle -5, 3 \rangle$, and $\mathbf{w} = \langle 3, -4 \rangle$ to find the indicated quantity. State whether the result is a vector or a scalar.

$$(\mathbf{u} \cdot 2\mathbf{v})\mathbf{w}$$

a.   128; scalar
b. $\langle -96, 132 \rangle$; vector
c. $\langle -96, 130 \rangle$; vector
d. $\langle -96, 124 \rangle$; vector
e. $\langle -96, 128 \rangle$; vector

_____ 18.   Find the angle θ between the vectors.

$$\mathbf{u} = 3\mathbf{i} - 1\mathbf{j}$$

$$\mathbf{v} = 8\mathbf{i} + 8\mathbf{j}$$

(Round the answer upto 2 decimal places.)

a.   73.43°
b.   78.43°
c.   83.43°
d.   68.43°
e.   63.43°

_____ 19.   Given $\mathbf{u} = -3\mathbf{i} + 5\mathbf{j}$ and $\mathbf{v} = -2\mathbf{i} + 4\mathbf{j}$, find $\mathbf{u} \cdot \mathbf{v}$.
a.   6
b.   −2
c.   −22
d.   −14
e.   26

_____ 20.   Determine $\mathbf{u} \cdot \mathbf{v}$ if $\|\mathbf{u}\| = 2$, $\|\mathbf{v}\| = 6$, and $\theta = \dfrac{\pi}{6}$, where θ is the angle between $\mathbf{u}$ and $\mathbf{v}$.

Round answer to two decimal places.

a.   8.49

b.   9.44

c.   6.00

d.   8.20

e.   10.39

_____ 21.   Plot the complex number and find its absolute value.

$-9 + 3i$

a.

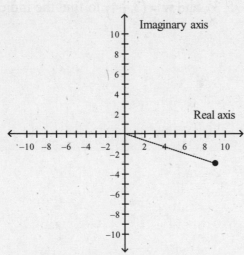

$|-9 + 3i| = \sqrt{14}$

d.

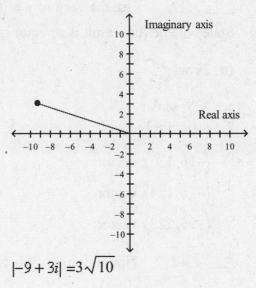

$|-9 + 3i| = 3\sqrt{10}$

b.

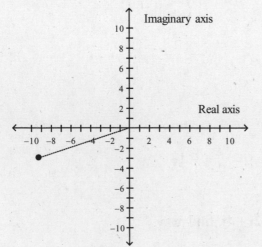

$|-9 + 3i| = \sqrt{78}$

e.

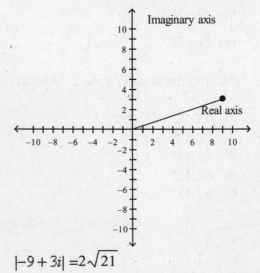

$|-9 + 3i| = 2\sqrt{21}$

c.

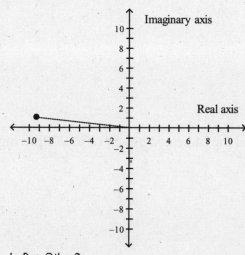

$$|-9+3i|=2$$

_____ 22.   Find the absolute value of the complex number $4+2i$.

a. $5\sqrt{5}$

b. 20

c. $2\sqrt{5}$

d. $\sqrt{6}$

e. $3\sqrt{6}$

_____ 23.   Find the trigonometric form of the complex number shown below.

$-10-2i$

a. $2\sqrt{26}\left(\cos\left(\arctan\left(\dfrac{2}{15}\right)\right)+i\sin\left(\arctan\left(\dfrac{2}{15}\right)\right)\right)$

b. $2\sqrt{26}\left(\cos\left(\arctan\left(-\dfrac{3}{5}\right)\right)+i\sin\left(\arctan\left(-\dfrac{3}{5}\right)\right)\right)$

c. $2\sqrt{26}\left(\cos\left(\arctan\left(-\dfrac{3}{25}\right)\right)+i\sin\left(\arctan\left(-\dfrac{3}{25}\right)\right)\right)$

d. $2\sqrt{26}\left(\cos\left(\arctan\left(\dfrac{1}{10}\right)\right)+i\sin\left(\arctan\left(\dfrac{1}{10}\right)\right)\right)$

e. $2\sqrt{26}\left(\cos\left(\arctan\left(\dfrac{1}{5}\right)\right)+i\sin\left(\arctan\left(\dfrac{1}{5}\right)\right)\right)$

_____ 24. Multiply the complex numbers below and leave the result in trigonometric form.

$$\left[\, 0.6(\cos 120° + i \sin 120°) \,\right]\left[\, 0.2(\cos 160° + i \sin 160°) \,\right]$$

a. $0.8(\cos 280° + i \sin 280°)$

b. $0.12(\cos 280° + i \sin 320°)$

c. $0.8(\cos 320° + i \sin 320°)$

d. $0.12(\cos 320° + i \sin 320°)$

e. $0.12(\cos 280° + i \sin 280°)$

_____ 25. Use DeMoivre's Theorem to find the indicated power of the following complex number.

$$\left[\, 2\left(\cos \frac{\pi}{3} + i \sin \frac{\pi}{3}\right) \,\right]^9$$

a. $-512 - 512\sqrt{3}$

b. $-256 - 256\sqrt{3}$

c. -512

d. -256

e. 512

Ch 6 Form D
Answer Section

1.	ANS:	D	PTS:	1	REF:	6.1.17
2.	ANS:	A	PTS:	1	REF:	6.1.29
3.	ANS:	B	PTS:	1	REF:	6.1.37b
4.	ANS:	A	PTS:	1	REF:	6.1.44
5.	ANS:	A	PTS:	1	REF:	6.1.35
6.	ANS:	D	PTS:	1	REF:	6.2.6
7.	ANS:	E	PTS:	1	REF:	6.2.27
8.	ANS:	E	PTS:	1	REF:	6.2.38
9.	ANS:	B	PTS:	1	REF:	6.2.61
10.	ANS:	B	PTS:	1	REF:	6.2.13
11.	ANS:	E	PTS:	1	REF:	6.3.34b
12.	ANS:	A	PTS:	1	REF:	6.3.43
13.	ANS:	E	PTS:	1	REF:	6.3.97
14.	ANS:	A	PTS:	1	REF:	6.3.19
15.	ANS:	C	PTS:	1	REF:	6.3.65
16.	ANS:	D	PTS:	1	REF:	6.4.9
17.	ANS:	E	PTS:	1	REF:	6.4.20
18.	ANS:	E	PTS:	1	REF:	6.4.35
19.	ANS:	E	PTS:	1	REF:	6.4.12
20.	ANS:	E	PTS:	1	REF:	6.4.49
21.	ANS:	D	PTS:	1	REF:	6.5.10
22.	ANS:	C	PTS:	1	REF:	6.5.10
23.	ANS:	E	PTS:	1	REF:	6.5.23
24.	ANS:	E	PTS:	1	REF:	6.5.50
25.	ANS:	C	PTS:	1	REF:	6.5.76

Ch 6 Form E

____ 1.   Use the Law of Sines to solve   for B and C. Round your answer to two decimal places.

$A = 145°, a = 28, b = 8$

a. $B \approx 9.43°, C = 25.57°$
b. $B \approx 25.57°, C = 9.43°$
c. $B \approx 0.18°, C \approx 39.82°$
d. $B \approx 39.82°, C \approx 0.18°$
e. $B \approx 0.18°, C \approx 32.89°$

____ 2.   Use the Law of Sines to solve (if possible) the triangle. Round your answers to two decimal places.

$A = 120°, a = b = 42$

a. $B \approx 96°, C \approx 42°, c \approx 44$
b. $B \approx 42°, C \approx 96°, c \approx 23.5$
c. $B \approx 99°, C \approx 39°, c \approx 23.5$
d. $B \approx 29°, C \approx 109°, c \approx 23.5$
e. No Solution

____ 3.   Find values for b such that the triangle has one solution.

$A = 78°, a = 302$

a.
$$b \geq 302, b = \frac{302}{\sin 78°}$$
b.
$$b \leq 302, b \neq \frac{302}{\sin 78°}$$
c.
$$b > 302, b > \frac{302}{\sin 78°}$$
d.
$$b \leq 302, b = \frac{302}{\sin 78°}$$
e.
$$b \geq 302, b \geq \frac{302}{\sin 78°}$$

_____ 4.   In the figure, α and β are positive angles.

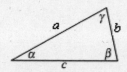

Where $a = 36, b = 9$

Use $\alpha = \arcsin\left(0.3\sin\beta\right)$ to write c as a function of β.

a.
$$c = \frac{36\sin\left[\pi - \beta - \arcsin\left(0.3\sin\beta\right)\right]}{\sin\beta}$$

b.
$$c = \frac{0.3\sin\left[\pi - \beta - \arcsin\left(36\sin\beta\right)\right]}{\sin\beta}$$

c.
$$c = \frac{36\sin\left[\pi - \beta + \arcsin\left(0.3\sin\beta\right)\right]}{\sin\beta}$$

d.
$$c = \frac{36\sin\left[\pi + \beta + \arcsin\left(0.3\sin\beta\right)\right]}{\sin\beta}$$

e.
$$c = \frac{36\sin\left[\pi + \beta - \arcsin\left(0.3\sin\beta\right)\right]}{\sin\beta}$$

_____ 5.   Determine a value for b such that a triangle with $A = 58°$ and $a = 10$ has no solution. Round your answer to the nearest hundredth.

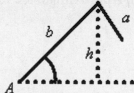

a. 2.95

b. 5.90

c. 11.69

d. 31.83

e. 2.36

_____   6.   Use the law of Cosines to solve the given triangle. Round your answer to two decimal places.

$a = 9, b = 4.5, C = 108°$

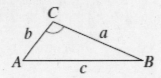

a. $A \approx 49.61°, B \approx 22.39°, c \approx 11.24$
b. $A \approx 20.39°, B \approx 20.39°, c \approx 4.5$
c. $A \approx 51.61°, B \approx 51.61°, c \approx 4.5$
d. $A \approx 20.39°, B \approx 11.24°, c \approx 11.24$
e. $A \approx 51.61°, B \approx 20.39°, c \approx 4.5$

_____   7.   Determine whether the Law of Sines or the Law of Cosines is needed to solve the triangle. Then solve the triangle. Round your answer to two decimal places.

$a = 18, b = 20, c = 14$

a.   Law of Cosines; No solution
b.   Law of Cosines; $A \approx 60.94°, B \approx 76.23°, C \approx 42.83°$
c.   Law of Sines; No solution
d.   Law of Sines; $A \approx 60.94°, B \approx 42.83°, C \approx 76.23°$
e.   Law of Sines; $A \approx 60.94°, B \approx 76.23°, C \approx 42.83°$

_____   8.   To approximate the length of a marsh, a surveyor walks   235 meters from point A to point B, then turns 74° and walks   205 meters to point C (see figure). Approximate the length of AC the marsh.

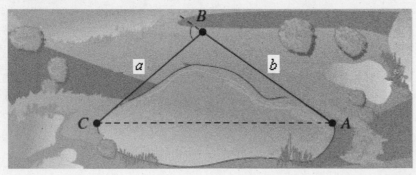

where $a = 205\,\text{m}, \; b = 235\,\text{m}$

a.   351.9 m
b.   345.9 m
c.   356.9 m
d.   357.9 m
e.   346.9 m

_____   9.   Given $a = 9$, $b = 6$, and $c = 10$, use the Law of Cosines to solve the triangle for the value of A. Round answer to two decimal places.

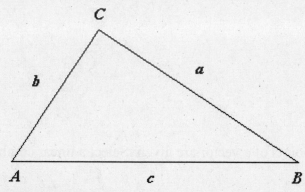

Figure not drawn to scale

a.   36.34°
b.   80.44°
c.   80.94°
d.   62.72°
e.   60.33°

_____   10.   In the figure below, $a = 8$, $b = 11$, and $d = 12$. Use this information to solve the parallelogram for β. The diagonals of the parallelogram are represented by c and d. Round answer to two decimal places.

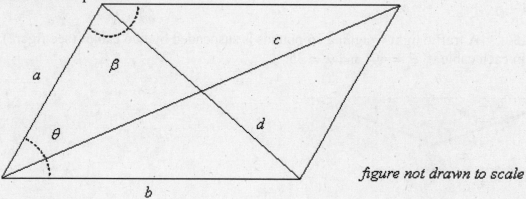

figure not drawn to scale

a.   97.49°
b.   92.25°
c.   76.53°
d.   103.47°
e.   91.50°

_____ 11.   Find $2\mathbf{u} - 3\mathbf{v}$.

$u = 2\mathbf{i}, \mathbf{v} = \mathbf{j}$

a. $4\mathbf{i} - 3\mathbf{j}$
b. $-4\mathbf{i} - 3\mathbf{j}$
c. $2\mathbf{i} - 3\mathbf{j}$
d. $4\mathbf{i} + 3\mathbf{j}$
e. $2\mathbf{i} - \mathbf{j}$

_____ 12.   The initial and terminal points of a vector are given. Select a linear combination of the standard unit vectors **i** and **j**.

Initial Point	Terminal Point
$(-7, 3)$	$(8, -4)$

a. $15\mathbf{i} - 7\mathbf{j}$
b. $-7\mathbf{i} + 15\mathbf{j}$
c. $-7\mathbf{i} - 15\mathbf{j}$
d. $15\mathbf{i} + 7\mathbf{j}$
e. $-15\mathbf{i} - 7\mathbf{j}$

_____ 13.   A traffic light weighing 16 pounds is suspended by two cables (see figure). Find the tension in each cable if $\theta_1 = 40°$ and $\theta_2 = 35°$

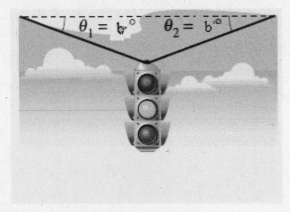

a. $T_L = 13.6$ lb; $T_R = 13.6$ lb
b. $T_L = 12.7$ lb; $T_R = 13.6$ lb
c. $T_L = 12.7$ lb; $T_R = 12.7$ lb
d. $T_L = 13.6$ lb; $T_R = 12.7$ lb
e. $T_L = 14.6$ lb; $T_R = 13.7$ lb

_____ 14.   Given $\mathbf{u} = \langle 4, -2 \rangle$ and $\mathbf{v} = \langle 3, 1 \rangle$, determine $-3\mathbf{u} + 3\mathbf{v}$.

a. $-3\mathbf{u} + 3\mathbf{v} = \langle 3, -9 \rangle$

b. $-3\mathbf{u} + 3\mathbf{v} = \langle -3, 9 \rangle$

c. $-3\mathbf{u} + 3\mathbf{v} = \langle -9, -9 \rangle$

d. $-3\mathbf{u} + 3\mathbf{v} = \langle 15, -9 \rangle$

e. $-3\mathbf{u} + 3\mathbf{v} = \langle 9, -6 \rangle$

_____ 15.   Find the component form of $\mathbf{v}$ if $\|\mathbf{v}\| = 8$ and the angle it makes with the x-axis is 150°.

a. $\langle -4, 4\sqrt{3} \rangle$

b. $\langle -8\sqrt{3}, -8 \rangle$

c. $\langle -4\sqrt{3}, 4 \rangle$

d. $\langle -8, 8\sqrt{3} \rangle$

e. $\langle -4\sqrt{2}, 4\sqrt{2} \rangle$

_____ 16.   Find the dot product of $\mathbf{u}$ and $\mathbf{v}$.

$\mathbf{u} = 6\mathbf{i} + 5\mathbf{j}$

$\mathbf{v} = 8\mathbf{i} - 3\mathbf{j}$

a. 29
b. 33
c. 37
d. 35
e. 31

_____ 17.   Use the dot product to find the magnitude of $\mathbf{u}$.

$\mathbf{u} = \langle -8, 11 \rangle$

a. $\sqrt{181}$
b. $\sqrt{187}$
c. $3\sqrt{21}$
d. $\sqrt{185}$
e. $\sqrt{183}$

____ 18. Find the projection of **u** onto **v**. Then write **u** as the sum of two orthogonal vectors, one of which is $\mathrm{proj}_v\mathbf{u}$.

$\mathbf{u} = \langle 4, 2 \rangle$

$\mathbf{v} = \langle 1, -2 \rangle$

a. $\langle 0, 0 \rangle, \langle -4, 2 \rangle$

b. $\langle 0, 0 \rangle, \langle 4, 2 \rangle$

c. $\langle 0, 0 \rangle, \langle -1, -2 \rangle$

d. $\langle 0, 0 \rangle, \langle 4, -2 \rangle$

e. $\langle 0, 0 \rangle, \langle 1, -2 \rangle$

____ 19. Given vectors $\mathbf{u} = \langle 2, 1 \rangle$ and $\mathbf{v} = \langle 1, -4 \rangle$, determine the quantity indicated below.

$(\mathbf{u} \cdot 4\mathbf{v})\mathbf{u}$

a. $\langle -28, -14 \rangle$

b. $\langle -16, -8 \rangle$

c. $\langle -72, -36 \rangle$

d. $\langle -24, -12 \rangle$

e. $\langle 8, 4 \rangle$

____ 20. Determine whether **u** are **v** and orthogonal, parallel, or neither.

$\mathbf{u} = \langle -1, -3 \rangle, \mathbf{v} = \langle -6, -4 \rangle$

a. neither
b. orthogonal
c. parallel

_____   21.   Represent the complex number graphically, and find the trigonometric form of the number.

3

a.

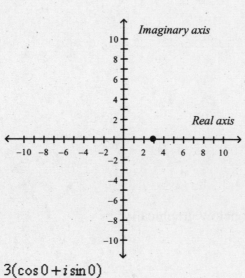

$3(\cos 0 + i \sin 0)$

d.

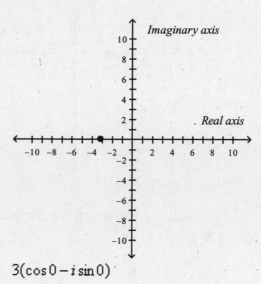

$3(\cos 0 - i \sin 0)$

b.

$3(\cos 3 - i \sin 3)$

e.

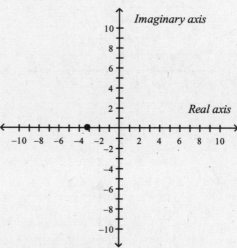

$3(\cos 3 + i \sin 3)$

c.

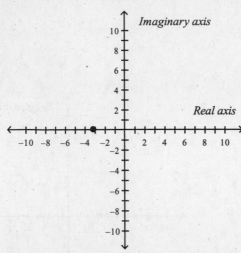

$3(\cos 3 - i \sin 3)$

_____ 22.   Represent the complex number below graphically.

$-2 - \sqrt{3}\,i$

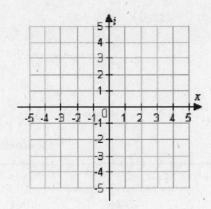

a.

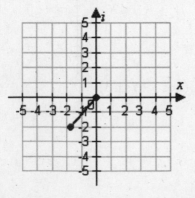

d.

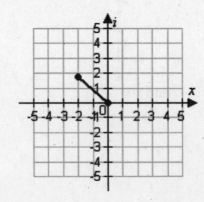

b.

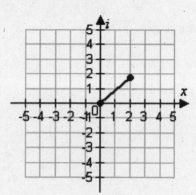

e.

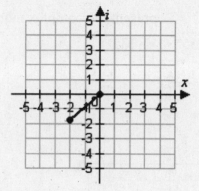

c.

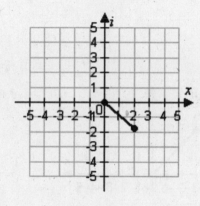

_____ 23.   Represent the complex number below graphically.

$$3\sqrt{2}\left(\cos 135° + i \sin 135°\right)$$

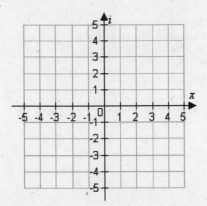

a.

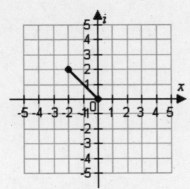

d.

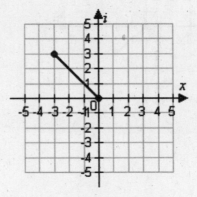

b.

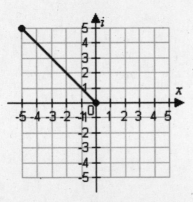

e.

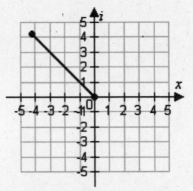

c.

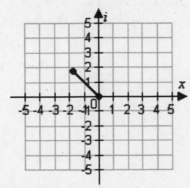

_____ 24.   Perform the indicated operation using trigonometric form. Leave answer in trigonometric form.

$(-4-4i)(5+5i)$

a.

$$20\left(\cos\frac{5\pi}{4}+i\sin\frac{5\pi}{4}\right)$$

b.

$$40\left(\cos\frac{3\pi}{2}+i\sin\frac{3\pi}{2}\right)$$

c.

$$-20\left(\cos\frac{3\pi}{4}+i\sin\frac{3\pi}{4}\right)$$

d.

$$40\left(\cos\frac{3\pi}{2}+i\sin\frac{3\pi}{2}\right)$$

e.

$$-20\left(\cos\frac{\pi}{2}+i\sin\frac{\pi}{2}\right)$$

_____ 25.   Find the cube roots of the following complex number. Write each of the roots in standard form.

343

a.

$$7,\ \frac{7}{2}+\frac{7\sqrt{3}}{2}i,\ \frac{7}{2}-\frac{7\sqrt{3}}{2}i$$

b. 7

c. $7,-7$

d.

$$-7,\ \frac{7}{2}-\frac{7\sqrt{3}}{2}i,\ \frac{7}{2}+\frac{7\sqrt{3}}{2}i$$

e.

$$7,\ -\frac{7}{2}+\frac{7\sqrt{3}}{2}i,\ -\frac{7}{2}-\frac{7\sqrt{3}}{2}i$$

Ch 6 Form E
Answer Section

1.	ANS:	B	PTS:	1	REF:	6.1.21
2.	ANS:	E	PTS:	1	REF:	6.1.31
3.	ANS:	D	PTS:	1	REF:	6.1.38a
4.	ANS:	A	PTS:	1	REF:	6.1.60c
5.	ANS:	D	PTS:	1	REF:	6.1.36c
6.	ANS:	A	PTS:	1	REF:	6.2.8
7.	ANS:	B	PTS:	1	REF:	6.2.30
8.	ANS:	A	PTS:	1	REF:	6.2.43
9.	ANS:	D	PTS:	1	REF:	6.2.6
10.	ANS:	D	PTS:	1	REF:	6.2.24
11.	ANS:	A	PTS:	1	REF:	6.3.37c
12.	ANS:	A	PTS:	1	REF:	6.3.53
13.	ANS:	D	PTS:	1	REF:	6.3.90
14.	ANS:	B	PTS:	1	REF:	6.3.31c
15.	ANS:	C	PTS:	1	REF:	6.3.70
16.	ANS:	B	PTS:	1	REF:	6.4.12
17.	ANS:	D	PTS:	1	REF:	6.4.25
18.	ANS:	B	PTS:	1	REF:	6.4.60
19.	ANS:	B	PTS:	1	REF:	6.4.20
20.	ANS:	A	PTS:	1	REF:	6.4.54
21.	ANS:	A	PTS:	1	REF:	6.5.25
22.	ANS:	A	PTS:	1	REF:	6.5.17
23.	ANS:	A	PTS:	1	REF:	6.5.36
24.	ANS:	B	PTS:	1	REF:	6.5.59
25.	ANS:	E	PTS:	1	REF:	6.5.94

Ch 6 Form F

_____   1.   Use the Law of Sines to solve   for B and C. Round your answer to two decimal places.

$A = 145°, a = 28, b = 8$

a. $B \approx 0.14°, C \approx 32.88°$
b. $B \approx 9.43°, C = 25.57°$
c. $B \approx 0.14°, C \approx 29.86°$
d. $B \approx 29.86°, C \approx 0.14°$
e. $B \approx 25.57°, C = 9.43°$

_____   2.   Use the Law of Sines to solve (if possible) the triangle. Round your answers to two decimal places.

$A = 120°, a = b = 38$

a. $B \approx 38°, C \approx 104°, c \approx 23.5$
b.   No Solution
c. $B \approx 29°, C \approx 113°, c \approx 23.5$
d. $B \approx 104°, C \approx 38°, c \approx 44$
e. $B \approx 103°, C \approx 39°, c \approx 23.5$

_____   3.   Find values for b such that the triangle has one solution.

$A = 82°, a = 332.4$

a. $b \geq 332.4, b = \dfrac{332.4}{\sin 82°}$

b. $b \geq 332.4, b \geq \dfrac{332.4}{\sin 82°}$

c. $b > 332.4, b > \dfrac{332.4}{\sin 82°}$

d. $b \leq 332.4, b = \dfrac{332.4}{\sin 82°}$

e. $b \leq 332.4, b \neq \dfrac{332.4}{\sin 82°}$

____   4.   In the figure, α and β are positive angles.

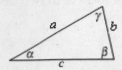

Where $a = 18, b = 9$

Use $\alpha = \arcsin\left(0.5\sin\beta\right)$ to write c as a function of β.

a.
$$c = \frac{18\sin\left[\pi + \beta + \arcsin\left(0.5\sin\beta\right)\right]}{\sin\beta}$$

b.
$$c = \frac{18\sin\left[\pi + \beta - \arcsin\left(0.5\sin\beta\right)\right]}{\sin\beta}$$

c.
$$c = \frac{0.5\sin\left[\pi - \beta - \arcsin\left(18\sin\beta\right)\right]}{\sin\beta}$$

d.
$$c = \frac{18\sin\left[\pi - \beta + \arcsin\left(0.5\sin\beta\right)\right]}{\sin\beta}$$

e.
$$c = \frac{18\sin\left[\pi - \beta - \arcsin\left(0.5\sin\beta\right)\right]}{\sin\beta}$$

____   5.   Determine a value for b such that a triangle with $A = 38°$ and $a = 3$ has no solution. Round your answer to the nearest hundredth.

a. 2.44
b. 1.22
c. 14.61
d. 0.97
e. 4.77

_____   6.   Use the law of Cosines to solve the given triangle. Round your answer to two decimal places.

$a = 11, b = 5.5, C = 118°$

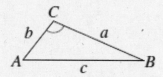

a. $A \approx 44.33°, B \approx 44.33°, c \approx 5.5$
b. $A \approx 17.67°, B \approx 14.42°, c \approx 14.42$
c. $A \approx 44.33°, B \approx 17.67°, c \approx 5.5$
d. $A \approx 17.67°, B \approx 17.67°, c \approx 5.5$
e. $A \approx 42.33°, B \approx 19.67°, c \approx 14.42$

_____   7.   Determine whether the Law of Sines or the Law of Cosines is needed to solve the triangle. Then solve the triangle. Round your answer to two decimal places.

$a = 15, b = 17, c = 11$

a.   Law of Cosines; No solution
b.   Law of Sines; $A \approx 60.35°, B \approx 39.59°, C \approx 80.05°$
c.   Law of Sines; No solution
d.   Law of Cosines; $A \approx 60.35°, B \approx 80.05°, C \approx 39.59°$
e.   Law of Sines; $A \approx 60.35°, B \approx 80.05°, C \approx 39.59°$

_____   8.   To approximate the length of a marsh, a surveyor walks   255 meters from point A to point B, then turns 83° and walks   225 meters to point C (see figure). Approximate the length of AC the marsh.

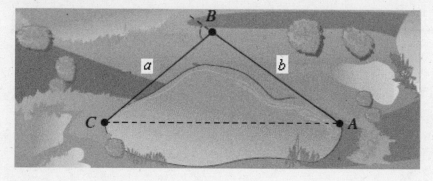

where $a = 225\,m, \; b = 255\,m$

a.   366 m
b.   360 m
c.   365 m
d.   355 m
e.   354 m

_____   9.   Given $a = 11$, $b = 10$, and $c = 15$, use the Law of Cosines to solve the triangle for the value of A. Round answer to two decimal places.

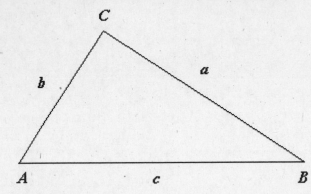

Figure not drawn to scale

a.   80.44°
b.   41.80°
c.   60.33°
d.   91.04°
e.   47.16°

_____   10.   In the figure below, $a = 9$, $b = 10$, and $d = 13$. Use this information to solve the parallelogram for β. The diagonals of the parallelogram are represented by c and d. Round answer to two decimal places.

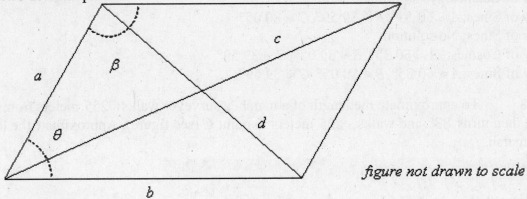

figure not drawn to scale

a.   92.66°
b.   93.82°
c.   86.18°
d.   91.04°
e.   91.50°

_____   11.   Find $2\mathbf{u} - 3\mathbf{v}$.

$u = 2\mathbf{i}, \mathbf{v} = \mathbf{j}$

a. $2\mathbf{i} - \mathbf{j}$
b. $2\mathbf{i} - 3\mathbf{j}$
c. $-4\mathbf{i} - 3\mathbf{j}$
d. $4\mathbf{i} + 3\mathbf{j}$
e. $4\mathbf{i} - 3\mathbf{j}$

_____   12.   The initial and terminal points of a vector are given. Select a linear combination of the standard unit vectors **i** and **j**.

Initial Point	Terminal Point
$(-9, 1)$	$(10, -2)$

a. $-3\mathbf{i} + 19\mathbf{j}$
b. $19\mathbf{i} - 3\mathbf{j}$
c. $-3\mathbf{i} - 19\mathbf{j}$
d. $-19\mathbf{i} - 3\mathbf{j}$
e. $19\mathbf{i} + 3\mathbf{j}$

_____ 13.   A traffic light weighing 12 pounds is suspended by two cables (see figure). Find the tension in each cable if $\theta_1 = 40°$ and $\theta_2 = 35°$

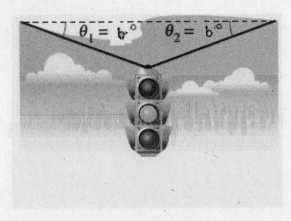

a. $T_L = 9.5\,\text{lb}; T_R = 9.5\,\text{lb}$
b. $T_L = 10.2\,\text{lb}; T_R = 9.5\,\text{lb}$
c. $T_L = 10.2\,\text{lb}; T_R = 10.2\,\text{lb}$
d. $T_L = 11.2\,\text{lb}; T_R = 10.5\,\text{lb}$
e. $T_L = 9.5\,\text{lb}; T_R = 10.2\,\text{lb}$

_____ 14.   Given $\mathbf{u} = \langle -4,-2 \rangle$ and $\mathbf{v} = \langle 5,0 \rangle$, determine $2\mathbf{u} - 2\mathbf{v}$.

a. $2\mathbf{u} - 2\mathbf{v} = \langle -8,-8 \rangle$

b. $2\mathbf{u} - 2\mathbf{v} = \langle -14,-8 \rangle$

c. $2\mathbf{u} - 2\mathbf{v} = \langle -18,-4 \rangle$

d. $2\mathbf{u} - 2\mathbf{v} = \langle 8,10 \rangle$

e. $2\mathbf{u} - 2\mathbf{v} = \langle 18,-8 \rangle$

_____ 15.   Find the component form of $\mathbf{v}$ if $\|v\| = 10$ and the angle it makes with the x-axis is 150°.

a. $\langle -10\sqrt{3}, -10 \rangle$

b. $\langle -5, 5\sqrt{3} \rangle$

c. $\langle -5\sqrt{2}, 5\sqrt{2} \rangle$

d. $\langle -10, 10\sqrt{3} \rangle$

e. $\langle -5\sqrt{3}, 5 \rangle$

_____ 16.   Find the dot product of **u** and **v**.

$\mathbf{u} = 6\mathbf{i} + 4\mathbf{j}$

$\mathbf{v} = 4\mathbf{i} - 5\mathbf{j}$

a. 2
b. 6
c. 0
d. 8
e. 4

_____ 17.   Use the dot product to find the magnitude of **u**.

$\mathbf{u} = \langle -8, 18 \rangle$

a. $14\sqrt{2}$
b. $\sqrt{386}$
c. $2\sqrt{97}$
d. $\sqrt{390}$
e. $8\sqrt{6}$

_____ 18.   Find the projection of **u** onto **v**. Then write **u** as the sum of two orthogonal vectors, one of which is $\text{proj}_{\mathbf{v}}\mathbf{u}$.

$\mathbf{u} = \langle 24, 6 \rangle$

$\mathbf{v} = \langle 1, -4 \rangle$

a. $\langle 0, 0 \rangle, \langle -24, 6 \rangle$

b. $\langle 0, 0 \rangle, \langle 1, -4 \rangle$

c. $\langle 0, 0 \rangle, \langle -1, -4 \rangle$

d. $\langle 0, 0 \rangle, \langle 24, 6 \rangle$

e. $\langle 0, 0 \rangle, \langle 24, -6 \rangle$

_____   19.   Given vectors $\mathbf{u} = \langle 2, -2 \rangle$ and $\mathbf{v} = \langle -4, 4 \rangle$, determine the quantity indicated below.

$(3\mathbf{u} \cdot 2\mathbf{v})\mathbf{u}$

a. $\langle 0, 0 \rangle$

b. $\langle -192, 192 \rangle$

c. $\langle -144, 144 \rangle$

d. $\langle 16, -16 \rangle$

e. $\langle -80, 80 \rangle$

_____   20.   Determine whether $\mathbf{u}$ are $\mathbf{v}$ and orthogonal, parallel, or neither.

$\mathbf{u} = \langle -7, 3 \rangle$, $\mathbf{v} = \langle 15, -42 \rangle$

a. neither
b. parallel
c. orthogonal

_____   21.   Represent the complex number graphically, and find the trigonometric form of the number.

6

a.

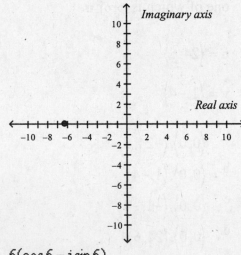

d.

$6(\cos 6 + i\sin 6)$ $6(\cos 6 - i\sin 6)$

b.

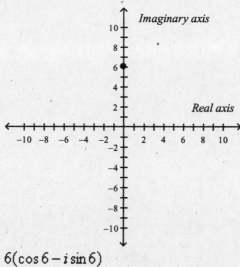

$6(\cos 6 - i \sin 6)$

e.

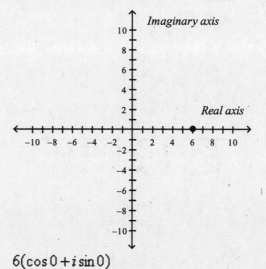

$6(\cos 0 + i \sin 0)$

c.

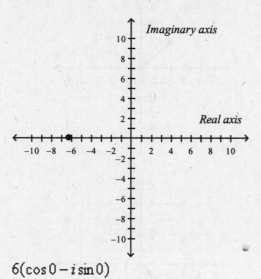

$6(\cos 0 - i \sin 0)$

_____ 22. Represent the complex number below graphically.

$-2 - \sqrt{3}i$

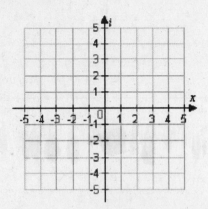

a.

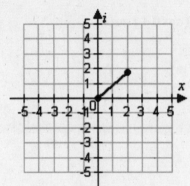

d.

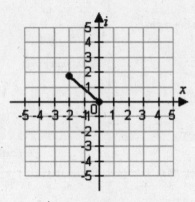

b.

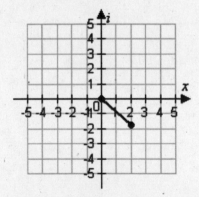

e.

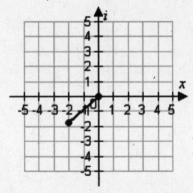

c.

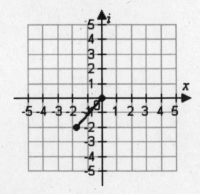

_____ 23.   Represent the complex number below graphically.

$3\sqrt{2}\left(\cos 135° + i \sin 135°\right)$

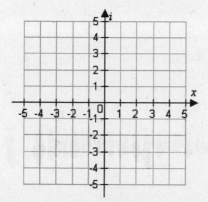

a.

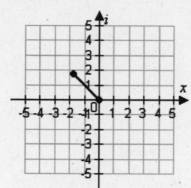

d.

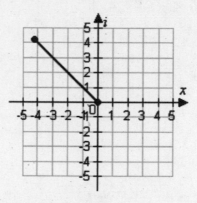

b.

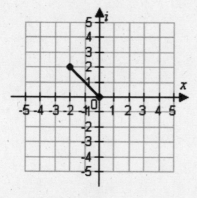

e.

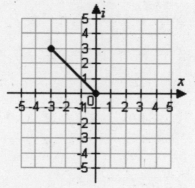

c.

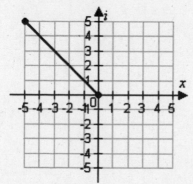

_____ 24.   Perform the indicated operation using trigonometric form. Leave answer in trigonometric form.

$(8+8i)(2+2i)$

a. $32\left(\cos\dfrac{\pi}{2}+i\sin\dfrac{\pi}{2}\right)$

b. $16\left(\cos\dfrac{\pi}{2}+i\sin\dfrac{\pi}{2}\right)$

c. $-32\left(\cos\dfrac{3\pi}{2}+i\sin\dfrac{3\pi}{2}\right)$

d. $16\left(\cos\dfrac{3\pi}{4}+i\sin\dfrac{3\pi}{4}\right)$

e. $-16\left(\cos\dfrac{5\pi}{4}+i\sin\dfrac{5\pi}{4}\right)$

_____ 25.   Find the cube roots of the following complex number. Write each of the roots in standard form.

125

a.
$$5, \frac{5}{2} + \frac{5\sqrt{3}}{2}i, \frac{5}{2} - \frac{5\sqrt{3}}{2}i$$

b.
$$5, -\frac{5}{2} + \frac{5\sqrt{3}}{2}i, -\frac{5}{2} - \frac{5\sqrt{3}}{2}i$$

c.
$$-5, \frac{5}{2} - \frac{5\sqrt{3}}{2}i, \frac{5}{2} + \frac{5\sqrt{3}}{2}i$$

d. $5, -5$

e. 5

Ch 6 Form F
Answer Section

1.	ANS:	E	PTS:	1	REF:	6.1.21
2.	ANS:	B	PTS:	1	REF:	6.1.31
3.	ANS:	D	PTS:	1	REF:	6.1.38a
4.	ANS:	E	PTS:	1	REF:	6.1.60c
5.	ANS:	C	PTS:	1	REF:	6.1.36c
6.	ANS:	E	PTS:	1	REF:	6.2.8
7.	ANS:	D	PTS:	1	REF:	6.2.30
8.	ANS:	B	PTS:	1	REF:	6.2.43
9.	ANS:	E	PTS:	1	REF:	6.2.6
10.	ANS:	B	PTS:	1	REF:	6.2.24
11.	ANS:	E	PTS:	1	REF:	6.3.37c
12.	ANS:	B	PTS:	1	REF:	6.3.53
13.	ANS:	B	PTS:	1	REF:	6.3.90
14.	ANS:	C	PTS:	1	REF:	6.3.31c
15.	ANS:	E	PTS:	1	REF:	6.3.70
16.	ANS:	E	PTS:	1	REF:	6.4.12
17.	ANS:	C	PTS:	1	REF:	6.4.25
18.	ANS:	D	PTS:	1	REF:	6.4.60
19.	ANS:	B	PTS:	1	REF:	6.4.20
20.	ANS:	A	PTS:	1	REF:	6.4.54
21.	ANS:	E	PTS:	1	REF:	6.5.25
22.	ANS:	C	PTS:	1	REF:	6.5.17
23.	ANS:	B	PTS:	1	REF:	6.5.36
24.	ANS:	A	PTS:	1	REF:	6.5.59
25.	ANS:	B	PTS:	1	REF:	6.5.94

Ch 7 Form A

_____   1.   Select the ordered pair that is a solution of the system of equations.

$$\begin{cases} 2x - y = 1 \\ 8x + y = -16 \end{cases}$$

a. $(-3, -4)$

b. $(-\frac{3}{2}, -4)$

c. $(-4, -\frac{3}{2})$

d. $(\frac{3}{2}, 4)$

e. $(3, 4)$

_____   2.   Solve the system by the method of substitution.

$$\begin{cases} 1.7x + 0.6y = 11.5 \\ 0.3x - 0.2y = 0.5 \end{cases}$$

a. $(-7, -7)$
b. $(7, 7)$
c. $(-5, -5)$
d. $(-5, 5)$
e. $(5, 5)$

_____   3.   A small software company invests $24,391$ to produce a software package that will sell for 45.36. Each unit can be produced for 69.51. How many units must be sold to break even?

a.   1110 units
b.   1010 units
c.   910 units
d.   810 units
e.   1210 units

_____ 4.   Solve the system by the method of substitution.

$$\begin{cases} -\dfrac{2}{3}x + y = 9 \\ 2x - 3y = 22 \end{cases}$$

a. $(20, 46)$

b. $(-20, -46)$

c. $\left(-\dfrac{20}{3}, \dfrac{46}{3} \right)$

d. $\left(\dfrac{20}{3}, \dfrac{46}{3} \right)$

e. No solution

_____ 5.   Solve the system by the method of elimination and check any solutions algebraically.

$$\begin{cases} x + 3y = 10 \\ x - 3y = 4 \end{cases}$$

a. $(1, 7)$

b. $(7, 1)$

c. $(-7, -1)$

d. $(7, -1)$

e. $(1, -7)$

_____ 6.   Use any method to solve the system.

$$\begin{cases} x - 5y = 25 \\ 4x + 5y = 25 \end{cases}$$

a. $(-10, -3)$

b. $(10, -3)$

c. $(5, -3)$

d. $(-3, 10)$

e. $(-3, -10)$

_____ 7.   Sixty liters of a 40% acid solution is obtained by mixing a 25% solution with a 50% solution. A system of equations in which one equation represents the amount of final mixture required and the other represents the percent of acid in the final mixture. Let x and y represent the amounts of the 25% and 50% solutions, respectively. How much of each solution is required to obtain the specified concentration of the final mixture?

$$\begin{cases} x + y = 60 \\ 0.25x + 0.5y = 24 \end{cases}$$

a.   25% solution: 24 L; 50% solution: 36 L
b.   50% solution: 24 L; 25% solution: 36 L
c.   25% solution: 40 L; 50% solution: 36 L
d.   50% solution: 40 L; 25% solution: 36 L
e.   50% solution: 24 L; 25% solution: 40 L

_____ 8.   Solve the system by the method of elimination and check any solutions algebraically.

$$\begin{cases} 2r + 4s = 15 \\ 16r + 50s = 165 \end{cases}$$

a. $\left(\dfrac{5}{2}, -\dfrac{5}{2} \right)$

b. $(15, 165)$

c. $\left(\dfrac{5}{2}, \dfrac{5}{2} \right)$

d. $\left(-\dfrac{5}{2}, \dfrac{5}{2} \right)$

e. $\left(-\dfrac{5}{2}, -\dfrac{5}{2} \right)$

____   9.   Determine whether the ordered triple is a solution of the system of equations.

$$\begin{cases} 4x + y - z = 0 \\ -8x - 6y + z = -\dfrac{7}{4} \\ 3x - y = -\dfrac{9}{4} \end{cases}$$

$$\left(\dfrac{1}{2}, \dfrac{-3}{4}, \dfrac{-7}{4} \right)$$

a.   Yes
b.   No

____   10.   Find the equation of the circle $x^2 + y^2 + Dx + Ey + F = 0$ that passes through the points.

$(0,0),(0,8),(4,4)$

a. $x^2 + y^2 - 8y = 0$
b. $x^2 - y^2 - 8y = 0$
c. $-x^2 + y^2 - 8y = 0$
d. $x^2 - y^2 + 8y = 0$
e. $x^2 + y^2 + 8y = 0$

____   11.   Find values of $x, y,$ and λ that satisfy the system. These systems arise in certain optimization problems in calculus, and λ is called a Lagrange multiplier.

$$\begin{cases} y + \lambda = 0 \\ x + \lambda = 0 \\ x + y - 14 = 0 \end{cases}$$

a. $x = 7, y = -7, \lambda = -7$
b. $x = 7, y = 7, \lambda = -7$
c. $x = 7, y = 7, \lambda = 7$
d. $x = 7, y = -7, \lambda = 7$
e. $x = -7, y = 7, \lambda = -7$

_____ 12.   Solve the system of linear equations.

$$\begin{cases} x+y+z+w=-5 \\ -2x+5y+z+5w=6 \\ 3x+z+5w=1 \\ x-3y+3z+5w=25 \end{cases}$$

a. $(-5,1,-4,3)$
b. $(3,-4,1,-5)$
c. $(-5,-4,1,3)$
d. $(-5,-4,3,1)$
e. inconsistent

_____ 13.   Write the form of the partial fraction decomposition of the rational expression. Do not solve for the constants.

$$\frac{5}{x^3-6x^2}$$

a. $\dfrac{A}{x}+\dfrac{B}{x^3}+\dfrac{C}{x-6}$

b. $\dfrac{A}{x^2}+\dfrac{B}{x-6}$

c. $\dfrac{A}{x}+\dfrac{B}{x^2}+\dfrac{C}{x-6}$

d. $\dfrac{A}{x^2}+\dfrac{B}{x^3}+\dfrac{C}{x-6}$

e. $\dfrac{A}{x}-\dfrac{B}{x^2}-\dfrac{C}{x-6}$

____ 14.   Write the partial fraction decomposition of the rational expression. Check your result algebraically.

$$\frac{39}{x^2 + 3x - 40}$$

a. $\dfrac{3}{x+5} - \dfrac{3}{x-8}$

b. $\dfrac{3}{x-5} - \dfrac{3}{x+8}$

c. $\dfrac{1}{x-5} + \dfrac{1}{x+8}$

d. $\dfrac{1}{x-5} - \dfrac{1}{x+8}$

e. $\dfrac{3}{x-5} + \dfrac{3}{x+8}$

____ 15.   Write the partial fraction decomposition of the rational expression.

$$\frac{8-x}{2x^2 + x - 1}$$

a. $\dfrac{5}{2x-1} - \dfrac{3}{x+1}$

b. $\dfrac{5}{2x-1} + \dfrac{3}{x+1}$

c. $\dfrac{5}{2x+1} - \dfrac{3}{x+1}$

d. $\dfrac{5}{2x-1} - \dfrac{3}{x-1}$

e. $\dfrac{5}{2x-1} - \dfrac{3}{x-1}$

_____   16.   Write the partial fraction decomposition of the rational expression.

$$\frac{1}{x\left(x+q\right)}$$

a. $\dfrac{1}{x}-\dfrac{1}{x+q}$

b. $\dfrac{1}{q}\left(\dfrac{1}{x}-\dfrac{1}{x+q}\right)$

c. $\dfrac{1}{x}-\dfrac{1}{x-q}$

d. $\dfrac{q}{x}-\dfrac{q}{x+q}$

e. $\dfrac{1}{q}\left(\dfrac{1}{x}+\dfrac{1}{x+q}\right)$

_____   17.   Select the correct graph of the inequality.

$x \geq 2$

a.

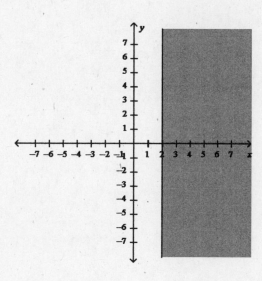

d.

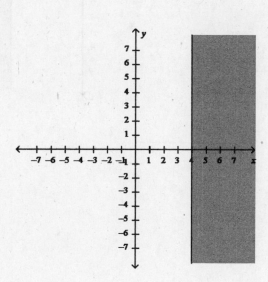

b.

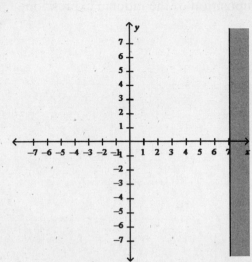

e.

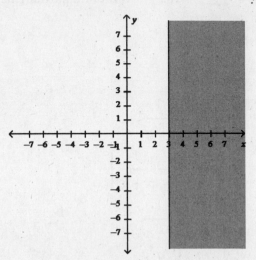

c.

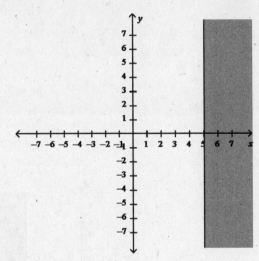

_____   18.   Select the correct graph of the inequality.

$$(x-4)^2 + (y-2)^2 > 4$$

a.

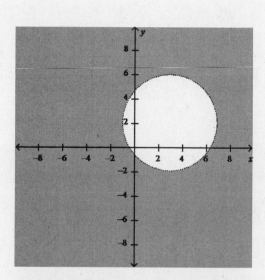

d.

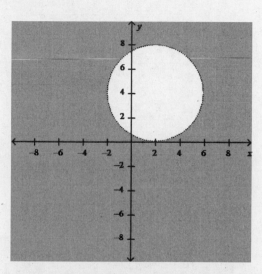

b.

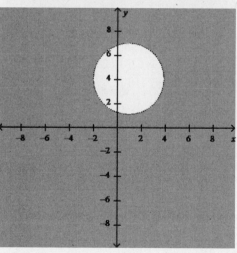

e.

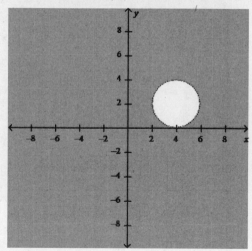

c.

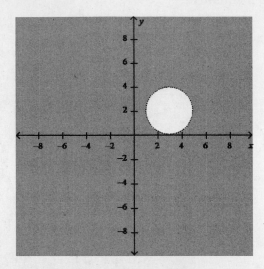

_____   19.   Select an inequalities to describe the region.

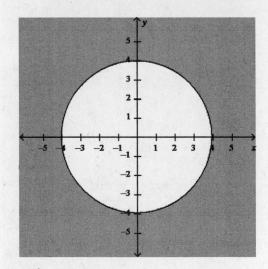

a. $x^2 + y^2 \geq 9$

b. $x^2 + y^2 \geq 16$

c. $x^2 + y^2 \geq 25$

d. $x^2 + y^2 \geq 1$

e. $x^2 + y^2 \geq 4$

____   20.   A dietitian is asked to design a special dietary supplement using two different foods. Each ounce of food X contains 20 units of calcium, 15 units of iron, and 10 units of vitamin B. Each ounce of food Y contains 10 units of calcium, 10 units of iron, and 20 units of vitamin B. The minimum daily requirements of the diet are 200 units of calcium, 150 units of iron, and 250 units of vitamin B. Write a system of inequalities describing the different amounts of food X and food Y that can be used.

a. $\begin{cases} 20x + 10y \geq 150 \\ 15x + 10y \geq 200 \\ 10x + 20y \geq 250 \\ \quad x \geq 0 \\ \quad y \geq 0 \end{cases}$

b. $\begin{cases} 20x + 10y \geq 250 \\ 15x + 10y \geq 200 \\ 10x + 20y \geq 150 \\ \quad x \geq 0 \\ \quad y \geq 0 \end{cases}$

c. $\begin{cases} 20x + 10y \geq 150 \\ 15x + 10y \geq 250 \\ 10x + 20y \geq 200 \\ \quad x \geq 0 \\ \quad y \geq 0 \end{cases}$

d. $\begin{cases} 20x + 10y \geq 200 \\ 15x + 10y \geq 150 \\ 10x + 20y \geq 250 \\ \quad x \geq 0 \\ \quad y \geq 0 \end{cases}$

e. $\begin{cases} 20x + 10y \geq 250 \\ 15x + 10y \geq 150 \\ 10x + 20y \geq 200 \\ \qquad x \geq 0 \\ \qquad y \geq 0 \end{cases}$

_____ 21. Use a graphing utility to graph the inequalities. Shade the region representing the solution set of the system.

$\begin{cases} y < x^2 - 3x - 3 \\ y > -x^2 + 2x + 2 \end{cases}$

a.

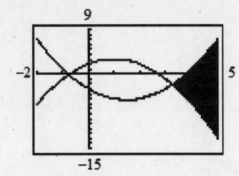

d.

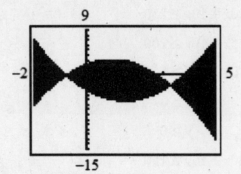

b.

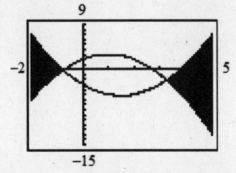

e.

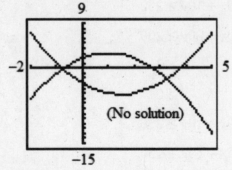

c.

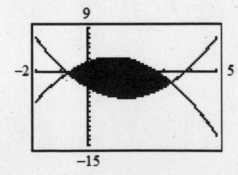

_____ 22. Find the minimum value of the objective function and where they occur, subject to the indicated constraints.

Objective function:

$$z = 7x + 6y$$

Constraints:

$$x \geq 0$$

$$y \geq 0$$

$$x + y \leq 5$$

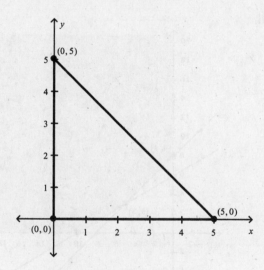

a. Minimum at $(0, 5)$: 31
b. Minimum at $(5, 0)$: 36
c. Minimum at $(0, 0)$: 0
d. Minimum at $(5, 0)$: 30
e. Minimum at $(0, 5)$: 35

____ 23. Select the region determined by the constraints. Then find the maximum value of the objective function (if possible) and where they occur, subject to the indicated constraints.

Objective function:

$z = 6x + 7y$

Constraints:

$$x \geq 0$$

$$y \geq 0$$

$$x + y \geq 8$$

$$3x + 5y \geq 30$$

a.

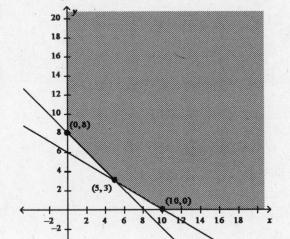

Maximum at $(10, 0)$: 60

d.

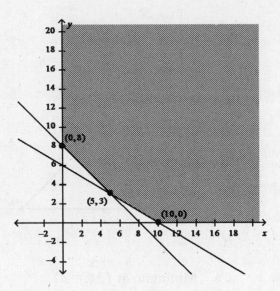

Maximum at $(0, 8)$: 56

b.

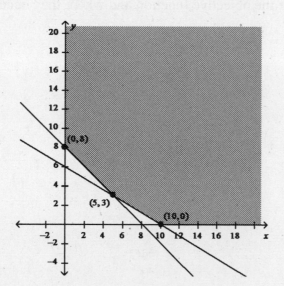

Maximum at $(3, 5)$: 52

e.

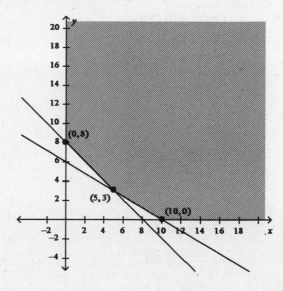

No maximum

c.

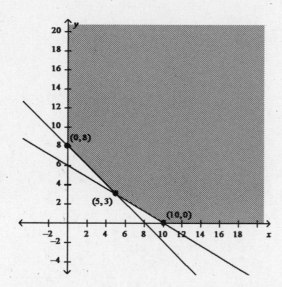

Maximum at $(5, 3)$: 51

_____   24.   Find the minimum value of the objective function and where they occur, subject to the constraints:

Objective function:

$z = 4x + y$

Constraints:

$$x \geq 0$$

$$y \geq 0$$

$$x + 4y \leq 20$$

$$x + y \leq 18$$

$$2x + 2y \leq 21$$

a.   No minimum
b.   Minimum at $(0, 0)$: 0
c.   Minimum at $\left(\dfrac{21}{2}, 0 \right)$: 42
d.   Minimum at $(5, 0)$: 20
e.   Minimum at $(18, 0)$: 72

____ 25. A humanitarian agency can use two models of vehicles for a refugee rescue mission. Each
model A vehicle costs $3000 and each model B vehicle costs $3500. Mission strategies and objectives indicate the following constraints. A total of at least 20 vehicles must be used. A model A vehicle can hold 45 boxes of supplies. A model B vehicle can hold 30 boxes of supplies. The agency
must deliver at least 690 boxes of supplies to the refugee camp. A model A vehicle can hold 20 refugees. A model B vehicle can hold 32 refugees. The agency must rescue at least 520 refugees. What
is the optimal number of vehicles of each model that should be used? What is the optimal cost?

a. 45 model A vehicles
   30 model A vehicles
   Optimal cost: $240,000
b. 10 model A vehicles
   10 model A vehicles
   Optimal cost: $65,000
c. 30 model A vehicles
   32 model A vehicles
   Optimal cost: $202,000
d. 20 model A vehicles
   32 model A vehicles
   Optimal cost: $172,000
e. 20 model A vehicles
   20 model A vehicles
   Optimal cost: $130,000

Ch 7 Form A
Answer Section

1.	ANS: B	PTS: 1	REF:	7.1.7
2.	ANS: E	PTS: 1	REF:	7.1.25
3.	ANS: B	PTS: 1	REF:	7.1.67a
4.	ANS: E	PTS: 1	REF:	7.1.30
5.	ANS: B	PTS: 1	REF:	7.2.13
6.	ANS: B	PTS: 1	REF:	7.2.39
7.	ANS: A	PTS: 1	REF:	7.2.51(c)
8.	ANS: C	PTS: 1	REF:	7.2.18
9.	ANS: B	PTS: 1	REF:	7.3.9
10.	ANS: A	PTS: 1	REF:	7.3.56
11.	ANS: B	PTS: 1	REF:	7.3.85
12.	ANS: C	PTS: 1	REF:	7.3.37
13.	ANS: C	PTS: 1	REF:	7.4.11
14.	ANS: B	PTS: 1	REF:	7.4.22
15.	ANS: A	PTS: 1	REF:	7.4.51
16.	ANS: B	PTS: 1	REF:	7.4.68
17.	ANS: A	PTS: 1	REF:	7.5.9
18.	ANS: E	PTS: 1	REF:	7.5.18
19.	ANS: B	PTS: 1	REF:	7.5.64
20.	ANS: D	PTS: 1	REF:	7.5.81(a)
21.	ANS: B	PTS: 1	REF:	7.5.56
22.	ANS: C	PTS: 1	REF:	7.6.7a
23.	ANS: E	PTS: 1	REF:	7.6.15b
24.	ANS: B	PTS: 1	REF:	7.6.28a
25.	ANS: B	PTS: 1	REF:	7.6.38

Ch 7 Form B

_____ 1. Select the ordered pair that is a solution of the system of equations.

$$\begin{cases} 2x - y = 3 \\ 8x + y = -18 \end{cases}$$

a. $(-6, -\frac{3}{2})$

b. $(\frac{3}{2}, 6)$

c. $(-3, -6)$

d. $(-\frac{3}{2}, -6)$

e. $(3, 6)$

_____ 2. Solve the system by the method of substitution.

$$\begin{cases} 1.8x + 0.6y = 9.6 \\ 0.8x - 0.2y = 2.4 \end{cases}$$

a. $(6, 6)$
b. $(-4, -4)$
c. $(-6, -6)$
d. $(4, 4)$
e. $(-4, 4)$

_____ 3. A small software company invests $24,777 to produce a software package that will sell for $45.84. Each unit can be produced for $69.46. How many units must be sold to break even?

a. 949 units
b. 849 units
c. 1249 units
d. 1149 units
e. 1049 units

____   4.   Solve the system by the method of substitution.

$$\begin{cases} -\dfrac{2}{3}x + y = 9 \\ 2x - 3y = 22 \end{cases}$$

a. $(-20, -46)$
b. $\left(\dfrac{20}{3}, \dfrac{46}{3}\right)$
c. $\left(-\dfrac{20}{3}, \dfrac{46}{3}\right)$
d. $(20, 46)$
e.   No solution

____   5.   Solve the system by the method of elimination and check any solutions algebraically.

$$\begin{cases} x + 3y = 10 \\ x - 3y = 4 \end{cases}$$

a. $(-7, -1)$
b. $(7, -1)$
c. $(7, 1)$
d. $(1, 7)$
e. $(1, -7)$

____   6.   Use any method to solve the system.

$$\begin{cases} x - 3y = 21 \\ 6x + 3y = 21 \end{cases}$$

a. $(-6, -5)$
b. $(-5, -6)$
c. $(-5, 6)$
d. $(3, -5)$
e. $(6, -5)$

_____ 7.   Thirty liters of a 30% acid solution is obtained by mixing a 27% solution with a 45% solution. A system of equations in which one equation represents the amount of final mixture required and the other represents the percent of acid in the final mixture. Let x and y represent the amounts of the 27% and 45% solutions, respectively. How much of each solution is required to obtain the specified concentration of the final mixture?

$$\begin{cases} x + y = 30 \\ 0.27x + 0.45y = 9 \end{cases}$$

a.   45% solution: 25 L; 27% solution: 30 L
b.   45% solution: 30 L; 27% solution: 5 L
c.   27% solution: 30 L; 45% solution: 5 L
d.   45% solution: 25 L; 27% solution: 5 L
e.   27% solution: 25 L; 45% solution: 5 L

_____ 8.   Solve the system by the method of elimination and check any solutions algebraically.

$$\begin{cases} 2r + 4s = 7 \\ 16r + 50s = 77 \end{cases}$$

a. $\left(-\dfrac{7}{6}, -\dfrac{7}{6} \right)$

b. $(7, 77)$

c. $\left(\dfrac{7}{6}, -\dfrac{7}{6} \right)$

d. $\left(-\dfrac{7}{6}, \dfrac{7}{6} \right)$

e. $\left(\dfrac{7}{6}, \dfrac{7}{6} \right)$

_____ 9. Determine whether the ordered triple is a solution of the system of equations.

$$\begin{cases} 4x + y - z = 0 \\ -8x - 6y + z = -\dfrac{7}{4} \\ 3x - y = -\dfrac{9}{4} \end{cases}$$

$$\left(\dfrac{1}{2}, \dfrac{-3}{4}, \dfrac{-7}{4} \right)$$

a. No
b. Yes

_____ 10. Find the equation of the circle $x^2 + y^2 + Dx + Ey + F = 0$ that passes through the points.

$(0,0), (0,8), (4,4)$

a. $x^2 - y^2 + 8y = 0$
b. $-x^2 + y^2 - 8y = 0$
c. $x^2 + y^2 + 8y = 0$
d. $x^2 + y^2 - 8y = 0$
e. $x^2 - y^2 - 8y = 0$

_____ 11. Find values of x, y, and λ that satisfy the system. These systems arise in certain optimization problems in calculus, and λ is called a Lagrange multiplier.

$$\begin{cases} y + \lambda = 0 \\ x + \lambda = 0 \\ x + y - 12 = 0 \end{cases}$$

a. $x = 6, y = 6, \lambda = 6$
b. $x = 6, y = -6, \lambda = -6$
c. $x = -6, y = 6, \lambda = -6$
d. $x = 6, y = 6, \lambda = -6$
e. $x = 6, y = -6, \lambda = 6$

____   12.   Solve the system of linear equations.

$$\begin{cases} x + y + z + w = 1 \\ 5x + 3y + 4z + w = 0 \\ -2x - 3z + 4w = 19 \\ 3x - y + z + 5w = 23 \end{cases}$$

a. $(4, -5, -1, 3)$
b. inconsistent
c. $(4, -1, -5, 3)$
d. $(3, -1, -5, 4)$
e. $(4, -1, 3, -5)$

____   13.   Write the form of the partial fraction decomposition of the rational expression. Do not solve for the constants.

$$\frac{3}{x^3 - 4x^2}$$

a. $\dfrac{A}{x^2} + \dfrac{B}{x - 4}$

b. $\dfrac{A}{x} + \dfrac{B}{x^2} + \dfrac{C}{x - 4}$

c. $\dfrac{A}{x^2} + \dfrac{B}{x^3} + \dfrac{C}{x - 4}$

d. $\dfrac{A}{x} - \dfrac{B}{x^2} - \dfrac{C}{x - 4}$

e. $\dfrac{A}{x} + \dfrac{B}{x^3} + \dfrac{C}{x - 4}$

____ 14. Write the partial fraction decomposition of the rational expression. Check your result algebraically.

$$\frac{36}{x^2+6x-27}$$

a. $\dfrac{1}{x-3}-\dfrac{1}{x+9}$

b. $\dfrac{3}{x-3}+\dfrac{3}{x+9}$

c. $\dfrac{3}{x+3}-\dfrac{3}{x-9}$

d. $\dfrac{1}{x-3}+\dfrac{1}{x+9}$

e. $\dfrac{3}{x-3}-\dfrac{3}{x+9}$

____ 15. Write the partial fraction decomposition of the rational expression.

$$\frac{5-x}{2x^2+x-1}$$

a. $\dfrac{3}{2x-1}-\dfrac{2}{x-1}$

b. $\dfrac{3}{2x-1}+\dfrac{2}{x+1}$

c. $\dfrac{3}{2x-1}-\dfrac{2}{x+1}$

d. $\dfrac{3}{2x+1}-\dfrac{2}{x+1}$

e. $\dfrac{3}{2x-1}-\dfrac{2}{x-1}$

_____   16.   Write the partial fraction decomposition of the rational expression.

$$\frac{1}{x\left(x+q\right)}$$

a. $\dfrac{1}{x} - \dfrac{1}{x-q}$

b. $\dfrac{1}{q}\left(\dfrac{1}{x} + \dfrac{1}{x+q}\right)$

c. $\dfrac{1}{x} - \dfrac{1}{x+q}$

d. $\dfrac{1}{q}\left(\dfrac{1}{x} - \dfrac{1}{x+q}\right)$

e. $\dfrac{q}{x} - \dfrac{q}{x+q}$

_____   17.   Select the correct graph of the inequality.

$x \ge 3$

a.

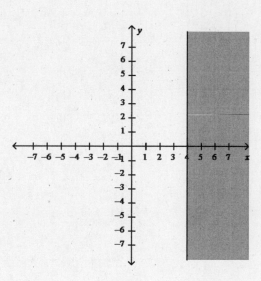

d.

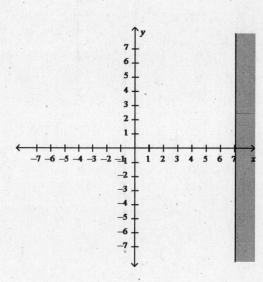

b.

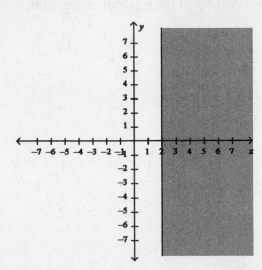

e.

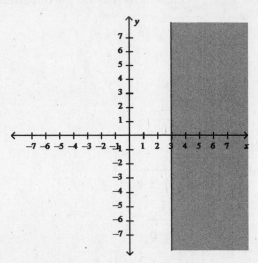

c.

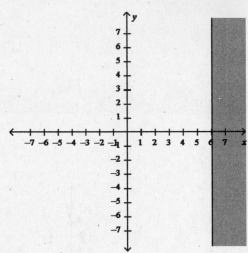

_____   18.   Select the correct graph of the inequality.

$$(x-4)^2 + (y-3)^2 > 9$$

a.

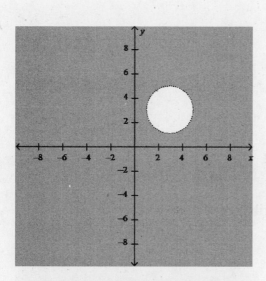

d.

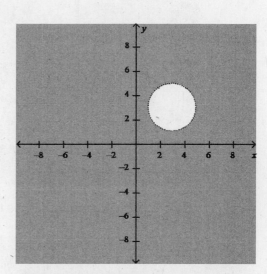

b.

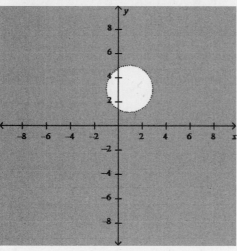

e.

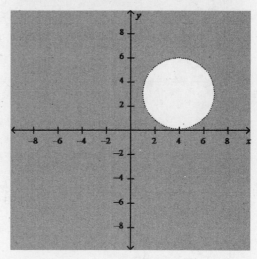

c.

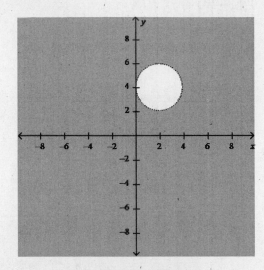

_____ 19. Select an inequalities to describe the region.

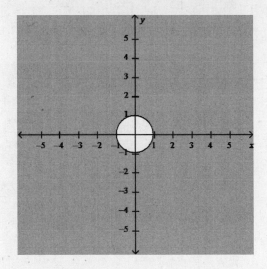

a. $x^2 + y^2 \geq 4$

b. $x^2 + y^2 \geq 16$

c. $x^2 + y^2 \geq 9$

d. $x^2 + y^2 \geq 25$

e. $x^2 + y^2 \geq 1$

____   20.   A dietitian is asked to design a special dietary supplement using two different foods. Each ounce of food X contains 20 units of calcium, 15 units of iron, and 10 units of vitamin B. Each ounce of food Y contains 10 units of calcium, 10 units of iron, and 20 units of vitamin B. The minimum daily requirements of the diet are 150 units of calcium, 100 units of iron, and 200 units of vitamin B. Write a system of inequalities describing the different amounts of food X and food Y that can be used.

a.
$$\begin{cases} 20x + 10y \geq 200 \\ 15x + 10y \geq 100 \\ 10x + 20y \geq 150 \\ x \geq 0 \\ y \geq 0 \end{cases}$$

b.
$$\begin{cases} 20x + 10y \geq 150 \\ 15x + 10y \geq 100 \\ 10x + 20y \geq 200 \\ x \geq 0 \\ y \geq 0 \end{cases}$$

c.
$$\begin{cases} 20x + 10y \geq 100 \\ 15x + 10y \geq 150 \\ 10x + 20y \geq 200 \\ x \geq 0 \\ y \geq 0 \end{cases}$$

d.
$$\begin{cases} 20x + 10y \geq 100 \\ 15x + 10y \geq 200 \\ 10x + 20y \geq 150 \\ x \geq 0 \\ y \geq 0 \end{cases}$$

e. $\begin{cases} 20x + 10y \geq 200 \\ 15x + 10y \geq 150 \\ 10x + 20y \geq 100 \\ x \geq 0 \\ y \geq 0 \end{cases}$

____ 21.   Use a graphing utility to graph the inequalities. Shade the region representing the solution set of the system.

$\begin{cases} y > x^2 - 5x + 3 \\ y < -x^2 + x + 3 \end{cases}$

a.

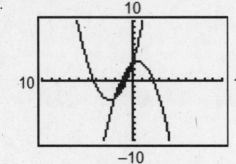

d.

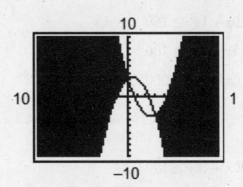

b.

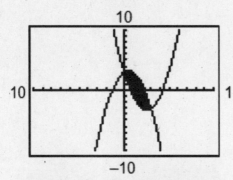

e.

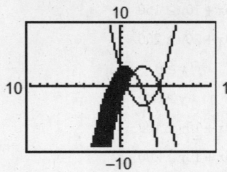

c.

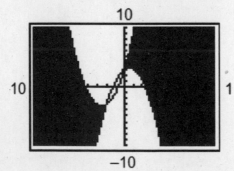

____   22.   Find the minimum value of the objective function and where they occur, subject to the indicated constraints.

Objective function:

$z = 5x + 4y$

Constraints:

$x \geq 0$

$y \geq 0$

$x + y \leq 3$

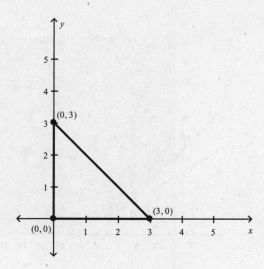

a.   Minimum at $(3,0)$: 12
b.   Minimum at $(0,3)$: 13
c.   Minimum at $(3,0)$: 16
d.   Minimum at $(0,0)$: 0
e.   Minimum at $(0,3)$: 15

_____   23.   Select the region determined by the constraints. Then find the maximum value of the objective function (if possible) and where they occur, subject to the indicated constraints.

Objective function:

$z = 5x + 6y$

Constraints:

$$x \geq 0$$

$$y \geq 0$$

$$x + y \geq 8$$

$$3x + 5y \geq 30$$

a.

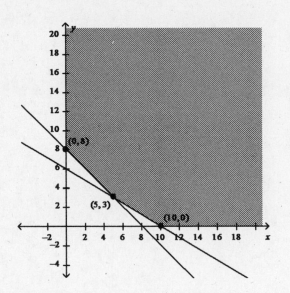

d.

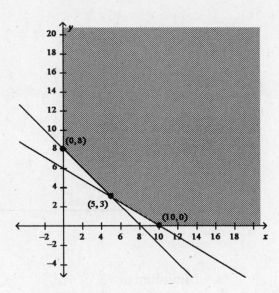

Maximum at $(0,8)$: 48   Maximum at $(10,0)$: 50

b.

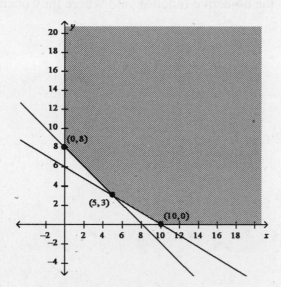

Maximum at $(3, 5)$: 44

e.

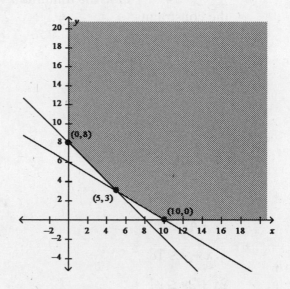

No maximum

c.

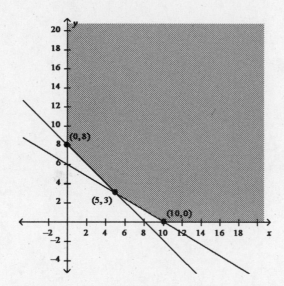

Maximum at $(5, 3)$: 43

____ 24.   Find the minimum value of the objective function and where they occur, subject to the constraints:

Objective function:

$z = 4x + y$

Constraints:

$$x \geq 0$$

$$y \geq 0$$

$$x + 4y \leq 20$$

$$x + y \leq 18$$

$$2x + 2y \leq 21$$

a. Minimum at $(0, 0)$: 0
b. Minimum at $(18, 0)$: 72
c.
    Minimum at $\left(\dfrac{21}{2}, 0 \right)$: 42

d. No minimum
e. Minimum at $(5, 0)$: 20

_____ 25.   A humanitarian agency can use two models of vehicles for a refugee rescue mission. Each
model A vehicle costs $2000 and each model B vehicle costs $2500. Mission strategies and objectives indicate the following constraints. A total of at least 20 vehicles must be used. A model A vehicle can hold 45 boxes of supplies. A model B vehicle can hold 30 boxes of supplies. The agency must deliver at least 690 boxes of supplies to the refugee camp. A model A vehicle can hold 20 refugees. A model B vehicle can hold 32 refugees. The agency must rescue at least 520 refugees. What is the optimal number of vehicles of each model that should be used? What is the optimal cost?

a. 30 model A vehicles
    32 model A vehicles
    Optimal cost: $140,000
b. 45 model A vehicles
    30 model A vehicles
    Optimal cost: $165,000
c. 20 model A vehicles
    32 model A vehicles
    Optimal cost: $120,000
d. 10 model A vehicles
    10 model A vehicles
    Optimal cost: $45,000
e. 20 model A vehicles
    20 model A vehicles
    Optimal cost: $90,000

Ch 7 Form B
Answer Section

1.	ANS:	D	PTS:	1	REF:	7.1.7
2.	ANS:	D	PTS:	1	REF:	7.1.25
3.	ANS:	E	PTS:	1	REF:	7.1.67a
4.	ANS:	E	PTS:	1	REF:	7.1.30
5.	ANS:	C	PTS:	1	REF:	7.2.13
6.	ANS:	E	PTS:	1	REF:	7.2.39
7.	ANS:	E	PTS:	1	REF:	7.2.51(c)
8.	ANS:	E	PTS:	1	REF:	7.2.18
9.	ANS:	A	PTS:	1	REF:	7.3.9
10.	ANS:	D	PTS:	1	REF:	7.3.56
11.	ANS:	D	PTS:	1	REF:	7.3.85
12.	ANS:	C	PTS:	1	REF:	7.3.37
13.	ANS:	B	PTS:	1	REF:	7.4.11
14.	ANS:	E	PTS:	1	REF:	7.4.22
15.	ANS:	C	PTS:	1	REF:	7.4.51
16.	ANS:	D	PTS:	1	REF:	7.4.68
17.	ANS:	E	PTS:	1	REF:	7.5.9
18.	ANS:	E	PTS:	1	REF:	7.5.18
19.	ANS:	E	PTS:	1	REF:	7.5.64
20.	ANS:	B	PTS:	1	REF:	7.5.81(a)
21.	ANS:	B	PTS:	1	REF:	7.5.56
22.	ANS:	D	PTS:	1	REF:	7.6.7a
23.	ANS:	E	PTS:	1	REF:	7.6.15b
24.	ANS:	A	PTS:	1	REF:	7.6.28a
25.	ANS:	D	PTS:	1	REF:	7.6.38

Ch 7 Form C

_____   1.   Select the ordered pair that is a solution of the system of equations.

$$\begin{cases} y = -5e^x \\ -7x - y = 5 \end{cases}$$

a. $\left(\dfrac{1}{-5}, 0 \right)$

b. $(0, -5)$

c. $\left(\dfrac{1}{5}, 0 \right)$

d. $(0, 5)$

e. $(-5, 0)$

_____   2.   Solve the system graphically.

$$\begin{cases} x - y = 1 \\ 6x - 3y = 15 \end{cases}$$

a. $(5, 4)$

b. $(4, 4)$

c. $(4, 3)$

d. $(-5, -4)$

e. $(-4, -3)$

_____   3.   The weekly rentals for a newly released DVD of an animated film at a local video store decreased each week. At the same time, the weekly rentals for a newly released DVD of a horror film increased each week. Models that approximate the weekly rentals R for each DVD are

$$\begin{cases} R = 340 - 36x \qquad \text{Animated film} \\ R = 40 + 24x \qquad \text{Horror film} \end{cases}$$

where x represents the number of weeks each DVD was in the store, with $x = 1$ corresponding to the first week. After how many weeks will the rentals for the two movies be equal?

a.   7 weeks

b.   3 weeks

c.   1 week

d.   9 weeks

e.   5 weeks

_____ 4.　　Solve the system by the method of substitution.

$$\begin{cases} x - y = 9 \\ x^2 - y = 23 \end{cases}$$

a.　$\left(-\dfrac{25}{3}, \dfrac{44}{3}\right)$

b.　$\left(\dfrac{25}{3}, \dfrac{44}{3}\right)$

c.　$\left(-\dfrac{25}{3}, -\dfrac{44}{3}\right)$

d.　$\left(\dfrac{25}{3}, -\dfrac{44}{3}\right)$

e.　No solution

_____   5.   Solve the system by the method of elimination.

$$\begin{cases} 2x + y = 6 \\ x - y = 3 \end{cases}$$

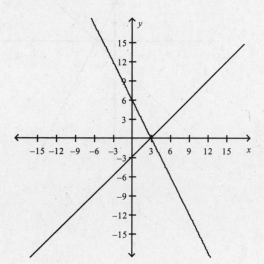

a.   (0,3)   d.   (3,−6)

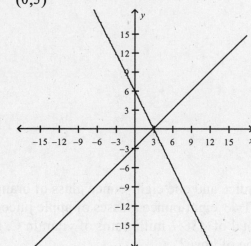   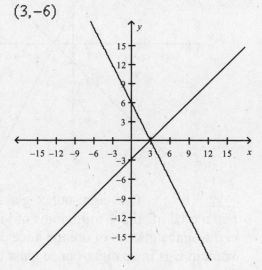

b.   (−3, 6)   e.   (−3, −6)

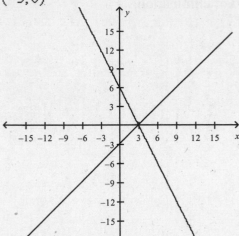 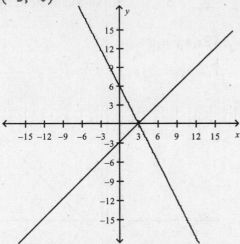

c.   (3, 0)

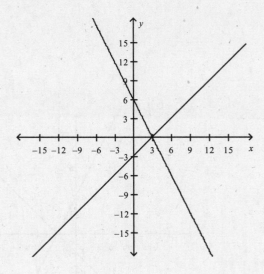

_____   6.   One eight-ounce glass of apple juice and one eight-ounce glass of orange juice contain a total of 176.4 milligrams of vitamin C. Two eight-ounce glasses of apple juice and three eight-ounce glasses of orange juice contain a total of 436.7 milligrams of vitamin C. How much vitamin C is in an eight-ounce glass of each type of juice?

a.   Apple juice: 92.5 mg; Orange juice: 92.5 mg
b.   Apple juice: 92.5 mg; Orange juice: 83.9 mg
c.   Apple juice: 83.9 mg; Orange juice: 83.9 mg
d.   Apple juice: 83.9 mg; Orange juice: 92.5 mg
e.   Apple juice: 176.4 mg; Orange juice: 83.9 mg

_____   7.   A total of $25,000$ is invested in two corporate bonds that pay 3.5% and 5% simple interest. The investor wants an annual interest income of 965 from the investments. What amount should be invested in the 3.5% bond?

a. $24,800$
b. $19,000$
c. $25,000$
d. $19,300$
e. $19,100$

_____   8.   Solve the system by the method of elimination.

$$\begin{cases} \dfrac{8}{5}x + \dfrac{1}{5}y = -\dfrac{9}{5} \\ \ 8x + y = -9 \end{cases}$$

a. $(-3, 15)$
b. $(a, -9 - 8a)$ (dependent)
c. $(5, -49)$
d.   inconsistent
e. $(-1, -1)$

_____   9.   Use back-substitution to solve the system of linear equations.

$$\begin{cases} 4x - 3y - 2z = 21 \\ \quad\ 6y - 5z = 12 \\ \qquad\quad z = -6 \end{cases}$$

a. $(0, 3, 6)$
b. $(0, -3, 6)$
c. $(-3, 6, 0)$
d. $(0, -3, -6)$
e. $(-3, -6, 0)$

_____   10.   A small corporation borrowed $774,000   to expand its clothing line. Some of the money was borrowed at 8%, some at 9%, and some at 10%. How much was borrowed at each rate if the annual interest owed was $67,500 and the amount borrowed at 8% was four times the amount borrowed at 10%?

a. $288,000 at 8%
     $414,000 at 9%
     $72,000 at 10%
b. $288,000 at 8%
     $72,000 at 9%
     $414,000 at 10%
c. $288,000 at 8%
     $72,000 at 9%
     $72,000 at 10%
d. $288,000 at 9%
     $414,000 at 8%
     $72,000 at 10%
e. $288,000 at 8%
     $72,000 at 9%
     $72,000 at 9%

_____   11.   Find values of x, y, and λ that satisfy the system. These systems arise in certain optimization problems in calculus, and λ is called a Lagrange multiplier.

$$\begin{cases} 2 + 2y + 2\lambda = 0 \\ 2x + 1 + \lambda = 0 \\ 2x + y - 92 = 0 \end{cases}$$

a. $x = 23, y = -47, \lambda = 23$
b. $x = 23, y = 46, \lambda = -47$
c. $x = 23, y = 46, \lambda = 46$
d. $x = -47, y = 46, \lambda = -47$
e. $x = 23, y = -47, \lambda = -47$

_____   12.   Find the equation of the parabola $y = ax^2 + bx + c$ that passes through the points. $(-1,4),(0,5),(1,2)$
a. $y = -2x^2 + x - 5$
b. $y = -2x^2 - x - 5$
c. $y = -x^2 - x + 4$
d. $y = -2x^2 - x + 5$
e. $y = -x^2 - x + 5$

_____ 13.   Write the form of the partial fraction decomposition of the rational expression. Do not solve for the constants.

$$\frac{7x^2 + 6}{(x-9)^3}$$

a. $\dfrac{A}{x-9} + \dfrac{B}{(x-9)^2} + \dfrac{C}{(x-9)^3}$

b. $\dfrac{A}{(x-9)^3}$

c. $\dfrac{A}{x-9} + \dfrac{B}{(x-9)^2}$

d. $\dfrac{A}{x-9} - \dfrac{B}{(x-9)^2} - \dfrac{C}{(x-9)^3}$

e. $\dfrac{A}{x-9} + \dfrac{B}{x-9} + \dfrac{C}{x-9}$

_____ 14.   Write the partial fraction decomposition of the rational expression. Check your result algebraically.

$$\frac{x+1}{x^2 - x - 30}$$

a. $\dfrac{1}{6}\left(\dfrac{7}{x-6} - \dfrac{4}{x+5}\right)$

b. $\dfrac{1}{11}\left(\dfrac{5}{x-6} - \dfrac{6}{x+5}\right)$

c. $\dfrac{1}{5}\left(\dfrac{7}{x-6} - \dfrac{4}{x+5}\right)$

d. $\dfrac{1}{11}\left(\dfrac{7}{x-6} + \dfrac{4}{x+5}\right)$

e. $\dfrac{1}{11}\left(\dfrac{7}{x-6} - \dfrac{4}{x+5}\right)$

_____ 15.   Write the partial fraction decomposition of the rational expression.

$$\frac{2x^2 + 4x + 14}{\left(x^2 + 7\right)^2}$$

a. $\dfrac{2}{x^2 + 7} + \dfrac{4}{\left(x^2 + 7\right)^2}$

b. $\dfrac{2}{x^2 + 7} + \dfrac{4x}{\left(x^2 + 7\right)^2}$

c. $\dfrac{4x + 2}{\left(x^2 + 7\right)^2}$

d. $\dfrac{2x + 14}{x^2 + 7} + \dfrac{4x}{\left(x^2 + 7\right)^2}$

e. $\dfrac{2}{x^2 + 7} - \dfrac{4x}{\left(x^2 + 7\right)^2}$

_____ 16.   Write the partial fraction decomposition of the rational expression.

$$\frac{1}{(x+1)(p-x)}$$

a. $\dfrac{1}{p+1}\left(\dfrac{1}{x+1} + \dfrac{1}{p-x}\right)$

b. $\dfrac{1}{p}\left(\dfrac{1}{x+1} + \dfrac{1}{p-x}\right)$

c. $\dfrac{1}{p+1}\left(\dfrac{1}{x+1} - \dfrac{1}{p-x}\right)$

d. $\dfrac{1}{p+1}\left(\dfrac{1}{x+1} - \dfrac{1}{p+x}\right)$

e. $\dfrac{1}{p+1}\left(\dfrac{1}{x+1} + \dfrac{1}{x}\right)$

_____ 17.   Select the correct graph of the inequality.

$y > -6$

a.

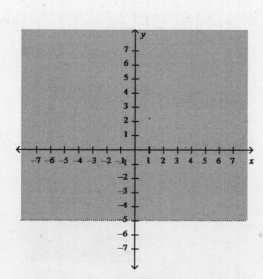

d.

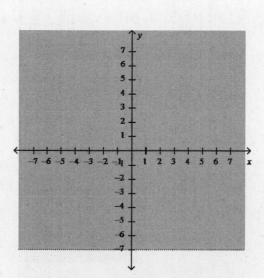

b.

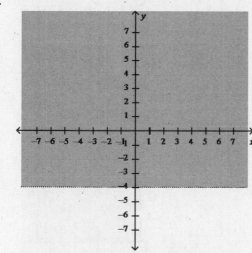

e.

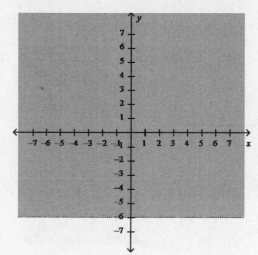

c.

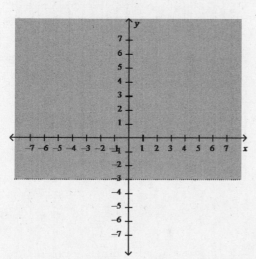

_____ 18.   Select the correct graph of the inequality.

$y < \ln x$

a.

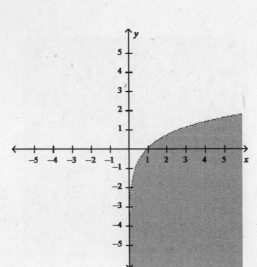

d.

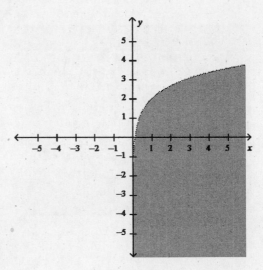

b.

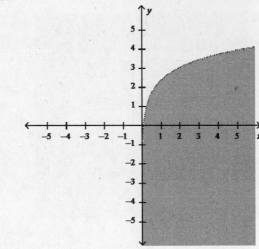

e.

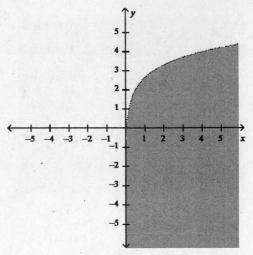

c.

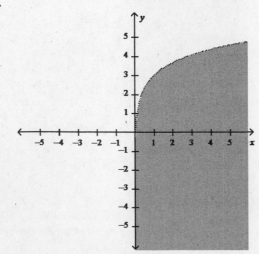

_____   19.   Write an inequality for the shaded region shown in the figure.

Rectangle: vertices at $(2,2),(6,2),(6,6),(2,6)$

a. $\begin{cases} x \geq 3 \\ x \leq 6 \\ y \geq 2 \\ y \leq 8 \end{cases}$

b. $\begin{cases} x \geq 1 \\ x \leq 6 \\ y \geq 2 \\ y \leq 8 \end{cases}$

c. $\begin{cases} x \geq 4 \\ x \leq 6 \\ y \geq 2 \\ y \leq 8 \end{cases}$

d. $\begin{cases} x \geq 5 \\ x \leq 6 \\ y \geq 2 \\ y \leq 8 \end{cases}$

e. $\begin{cases} x \geq 2 \\ x \leq 6 \\ y \geq 2 \\ y \leq 8 \end{cases}$

_____   20.   Sketch the graph of the inequality.

$(x-3)^2 + (y+1)^2 < 4$

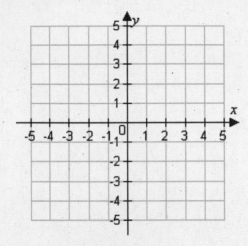

a.

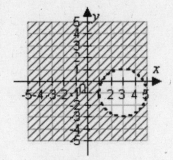

d.

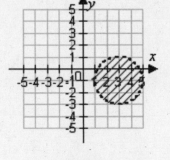

b.

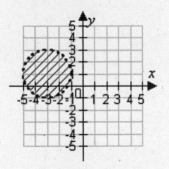

e.

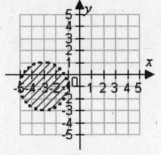

c.

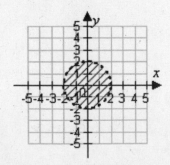

_____ 21.   Derive a set of inequalities to describe the region.

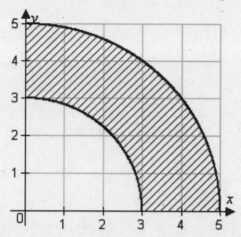

a. $\begin{cases} x^2 + y^2 \geq 9 \\ x^2 + y^2 \leq 25 \end{cases}$

b. $\begin{cases} x^2 + y^2 \geq 9 \\ x^2 + y^2 \leq 25 \\ x \geq 0 \\ y \geq 0 \end{cases}$

c. $\begin{cases} x^2 + y^2 \geq 3 \\ x^2 + y^2 \leq 5 \\ x \geq 0 \\ y \geq 0 \end{cases}$

d. $\begin{cases} x^2 + y^2 \geq 3 \\ x^2 + y^2 \leq 5 \end{cases}$

e. $\begin{cases} x^2 + y^2 \leq 9 \\ x^2 + y^2 \geq 25 \\ x \geq 0 \\ y \geq 0 \end{cases}$

_____ 22.   Find the maximum value of the objective function and where they occur, subject to the indicated constraints.

Objective function:

$z = 4x + 16y$

Constraints:

$x \geq 0$

$y \geq 0$

$2x + y \leq 10$

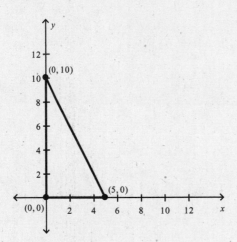

a.   Maximum at $(0,0)$: 0
b.   Maximum at $(10,0)$: 161
c.   Maximum at $(0,5)$: 41
d.   Maximum at $(0,10)$: 160
e.   Maximum at $(5,0)$: 40

_____ 23. Select the region determined by the constraints. Then find the maximum value of the objective function (if possible) and where they occur, subject to the indicated constraints.

Objective function:

$z = 8x + 7y$

Constraints:

$x \geq 0$

$y \geq 0$

$2x + 2y \geq 10$

$x + 2y \geq 6$

a.

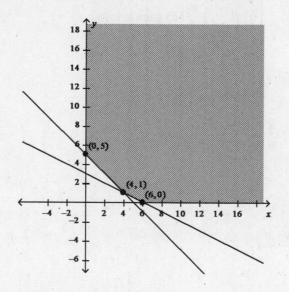

Maximum at $(0, 5)$: 35

d.

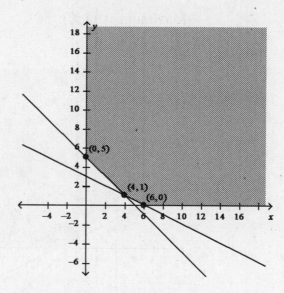

Maximum at $(4, 1)$: 39

b.

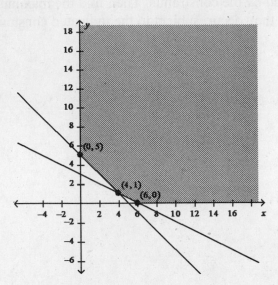

Maximum at $(5,0)$: 36

e.

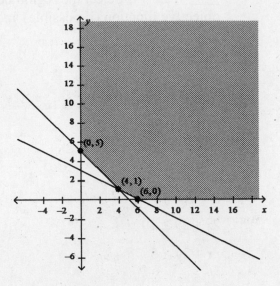

No maximum

c.

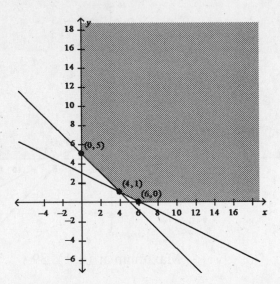

Maximum at $(6,0)$: 48

_____ 24.   The linear programming problem has an unusual characteristic. Select a graph of the solution region for the problem and describe the unusual characteristic. Find the minimum value of the objective function (if possible) and where they occur.

Objective function:

$z = 2.4x + y$

Constraints:

$x \geq 0$

$y \geq 0$

$3x + 5y \leq 15$

$5x + 2y \leq 10$

a.

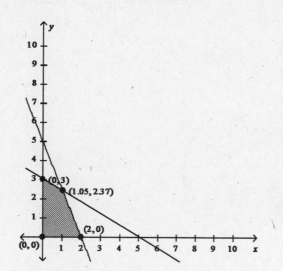

No minimum

d.

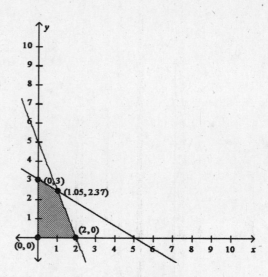

Minimum at $\left(\dfrac{20}{19}, \dfrac{45}{19} \right)$: 4.89

b.

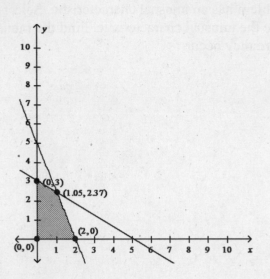

Minimum at $(0,0)$: 0

e.

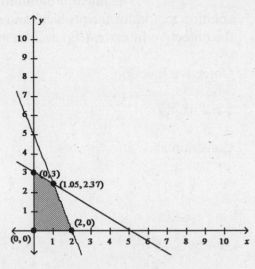

Minimum at $\left(\dfrac{20}{19}, 0\right)$: 2.53

c.

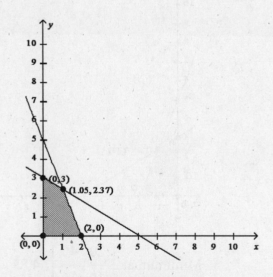

Minimum at $\left(\dfrac{45}{19}, \dfrac{20}{19}\right)$: 6.74

_____ 25. A manufacturer produces two models of elliptical cross-training exercise machines. The times for assembling, finishing, and packaging model X are 3 hours, 3 hours, and 0.8 hour, respectively. The times for model Y are 4 hours, 2.5 hours, and 0.4 hour. The total times available for assembling, finishing, and packaging are 6000 hours, 4200 hours, and 950 hours, respectively. The profits per unit are $500 for model X and $575 for model Y. What is the optimal production level for each model? What is the optimal profit?

a. 6000 units of model X
    950 units of model Y
    Optimal profit: $3,546,250
b. 950 units of model X
    6000 units of model Y
    Optimal profit: $3,925,000
c. 400 units of model X
    1200 units of model Y
    Optimal profit: $890,000
d. 950 units of model X
    4200 units of model Y
    Optimal profit: $2,890,000
e. 4200 units of model X
    950 units of model Y
    Optimal profit: $2,646,250

Ch 7 Form C
Answer Section

1.	ANS: B	PTS: 1		REF:	7.1.9
2.	ANS: C	PTS: 1		REF:	7.1.35
3.	ANS: E	PTS: 1		REF:	7.1.69a
4.	ANS: E	PTS: 1		REF:	7.1.33
5.	ANS: C	PTS: 1		REF:	7.2.5
6.	ANS: B	PTS: 1		REF:	7.2.50
7.	ANS: B	PTS: 1		REF:	7.2.53
8.	ANS: B	PTS: 1		REF:	7.2.21
9.	ANS: D	PTS: 1		REF:	7.3.12
10.	ANS: A	PTS: 1		REF:	7.3.61
11.	ANS: B	PTS: 1		REF:	7.3.88
12.	ANS: D	PTS: 1		REF:	7.3.49
13.	ANS: A	PTS: 1		REF:	7.4.13
14.	ANS: D	PTS: 1		REF:	7.4.24
15.	ANS: B	PTS: 1		REF:	7.4.55
16.	ANS: A	PTS: 1		REF:	7.4.70
17.	ANS: E	PTS: 1		REF:	7.5.11
18.	ANS: A	PTS: 1		REF:	7.5.21
19.	ANS: E	PTS: 1		REF:	7.5.67
20.	ANS: D	PTS: 1		REF:	7.5.17
21.	ANS: B	PTS: 1		REF:	7.5.65
22.	ANS: D	PTS: 1		REF:	7.6.8b
23.	ANS: E	PTS: 1		REF:	7.6.16b
24.	ANS: B	PTS: 1		REF:	7.6.29a
25.	ANS: C	PTS: 1		REF:	7.6.36

Ch 7 Form D

_____ 1.   Select the ordered pair that is a solution of the system of equations.

$$\begin{cases} y = -4e^x \\ -7x - y = 4 \end{cases}$$

a. $(-4, 0)$

b. $\left(\dfrac{1}{-4}, 0 \right)$

c. $(0, 4)$

d. $\left(\dfrac{1}{4}, 0 \right)$

e. $(0, -4)$

_____ 2.   Solve the system graphically.

$$\begin{cases} x - y = 1 \\ 7x - 5y = 17 \end{cases}$$

a. $(-6, -5)$

b. $(6, 5)$

c. $(6, 6)$

d. $(7, 6)$

e. $(-7, -6)$

_____   3.   The weekly rentals for a newly released DVD of an animated film at a local video store decreased each week. At the same time, the weekly rentals for a newly released DVD of a horror film increased each week. Models that approximate the weekly rentals R for each DVD are

$$\begin{cases} R = 352 - 16x & \text{Animated film} \\ R = 40 + 36x & \text{Horror film} \end{cases}$$

where x represents the number of weeks each DVD was in the store, with $x = 1$ corresponding to the first week. After how many weeks will the rentals for the two movies be equal?

a.   8 weeks
b.   2 weeks
c.   4 weeks
d.   6 weeks
e.   10 weeks

_____   4.   Solve the system by the method of substitution.

$$\begin{cases} x - y = 9 \\ x^2 - y = 22 \end{cases}$$

a.   No solution
b. $\left(-\dfrac{20}{3}, -\dfrac{46}{3} \right)$
c. $\left(-\dfrac{20}{3}, \dfrac{46}{3} \right)$
d. $\left(\dfrac{20}{3}, \dfrac{46}{3} \right)$
e. $\left(\dfrac{20}{3}, -\dfrac{46}{3} \right)$

_____ 5.   Solve the system by the method of elimination.

$$\begin{cases} 4x + y = 9 \\ x - y = 6 \end{cases}$$

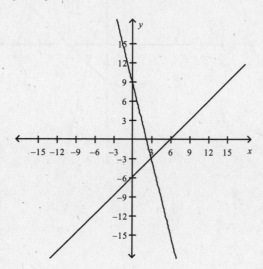

a. $(-3, 3)$

d. $(-3, 9)$

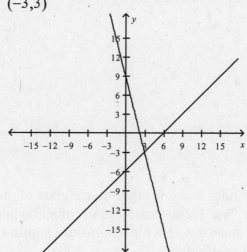

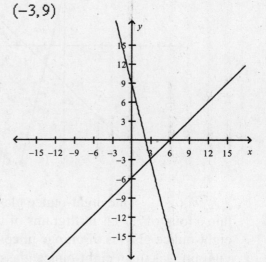

b.   (3, −9)

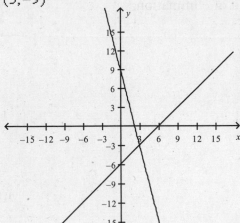

e.   (−3, −9)

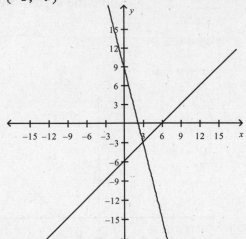

c.   (3, −3)

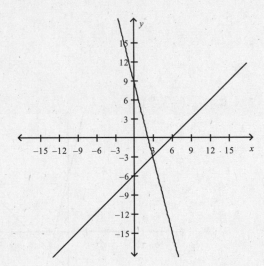

_____ 6.   One eight-ounce glass of apple juice and one eight-ounce glass of orange juice contain a total of 175.4 milligrams of vitamin C. Two eight-ounce glasses of apple juice and three eight-ounce glasses of orange juice contain a total of 432.7 milligrams of vitamin C. How much vitamin C is in an eight-ounce glass of each type of juice?

a.   Apple juice: 93.5 mg; Orange juice: 93.5 mg
b.   Apple juice: 81.9 mg; Orange juice: 93.5 mg
c.   Apple juice: 93.5 mg; Orange juice: 81.9 mg
d.   Apple juice: 81.9 mg; Orange juice: 81.9 mg
e.   Apple juice: 175.4 mg; Orange juice: 81.9 mg

_____   7.   A total of $\$23,000$ is invested in two corporate bonds that pay 3.5% and 5% simple interest. The investor wants an annual interest income of $\$895$ from the investments. What amount should be invested in the 3.5% bond?

a. $\$17,000$
b. $\$17,300$
c. $\$17,100$
d. $\$22,800$
e. $\$23,000$

_____   8.   Solve the system by the method of elimination.

$$\begin{cases} \dfrac{9}{8}x + \dfrac{1}{8}y = -\dfrac{1}{4} \\ \\ 9x + y = -2 \end{cases}$$

a. $(2,-20)$
b. $(a,-2-9a)$ (dependent)
c. $(4,-38)$
d.   inconsistent
e. $(8,-74)$

_____   9.   Use back-substitution to solve the system of linear equations.

$$\begin{cases} 4x - 3y - 2z = 21 \\ 6y - 5z = 15 \\ z = -9 \end{cases}$$

a. $(-3,-5,-9)$
b. $(-5,9,-3)$
c. $(-3,-5,9)$
d. $(-3,5,9)$
e. $(-5,-9,-3)$

_____   10.   A small corporation borrowed \$773,000   to expand its clothing line. Some of the money was borrowed at 8%, some at 9%, and some at 10%. How much was borrowed at each rate if the annual interest owed was \$67,500 and the amount borrowed at 8% was four times the amount borrowed at 10%?

a. \$276,000 at 8%
    \$69,000   at 9%
    \$69,000 at 9%
b. \$276,000 at 8%
    \$69,000   at 9%
    \$69,000 at 10%
c. \$276,000 at 8%
    \$69,000   at 9%
    \$428,000   at 10%
d. \$276,000 at 8%
    \$428,000 at 9%
    \$69,000 at 10%
e. \$276,000 at 9%
    \$428,000 at 8%
    \$69,000 at 10%

_____   11.   Find values of x, y, and λ that satisfy the system. These systems arise in certain optimization problems in calculus, and λ is called a Lagrange multiplier.

$$\begin{cases} 2+2y+2\lambda = 0 \\ 2x+1+\lambda = 0 \\ 2x+y-92 = 0 \end{cases}$$

a. $x = 23, y = 46, \lambda = -47$
b. $x = 23, y = -47, \lambda = -47$
c. $x = 23, y = 46, \lambda = 46$
d. $x = 23, y = -47, \lambda = 23$
e. $x = -47, y = 46, \lambda = -47$

_____   12.   Find the equation of the parabola $y = ax^2 + bx + c$ that passes through the points. $(0,-9),(1,-6),(2,1)$
a. $y = 2x^2 + x - 9$
b. $y = 2x^2 - x + 9$
c. $y = 2x^2 + x + 9$
d. $y = 3x^2 + x - 9$
e. $y = 3x^2 + x - 10$

_____   13.   Write the form of the partial fraction decomposition of the rational expression. Do not solve for the constants.

$$\frac{7x^2 + 6}{(x - 5)^3}$$

a. $\dfrac{A}{x - 5} + \dfrac{B}{(x - 5)^2} + \dfrac{C}{(x - 5)^3}$

b. $\dfrac{A}{x - 5} - \dfrac{B}{(x - 5)^2} - \dfrac{C}{(x - 5)^3}$

c. $\dfrac{A}{(x - 5)^3}$

d. $\dfrac{A}{x - 5} + \dfrac{B}{x - 5} + \dfrac{C}{x - 5}$

e. $\dfrac{A}{x - 5} + \dfrac{B}{(x - 5)^2}$

_____   14.   Write the partial fraction decomposition of the rational expression. Check your result algebraically.

$$\frac{x + 1}{x^2 - x - 12}$$

a. $\dfrac{1}{7}\left(\dfrac{5}{x - 4} - \dfrac{2}{x + 3}\right)$

b. $\dfrac{1}{3}\left(\dfrac{5}{x - 4} - \dfrac{2}{x + 3}\right)$

c. $\dfrac{1}{7}\left(\dfrac{3}{x - 4} - \dfrac{4}{x + 3}\right)$

d. $\dfrac{1}{7}\left(\dfrac{5}{x - 4} + \dfrac{2}{x + 3}\right)$

e. $\dfrac{1}{4}\left(\dfrac{5}{x - 4} - \dfrac{2}{x + 3}\right)$

_____ 15.   Write the partial fraction decomposition of the rational expression.

$$\frac{3x^2 + 2x + 18}{\left(x^2 + 6\right)^2}$$

a. $\dfrac{3x + 18}{x^2 + 6} + \dfrac{2x}{\left(x^2 + 6\right)^2}$

b. $\dfrac{2x + 3}{\left(x^2 + 6\right)^2}$

c. $\dfrac{3}{x^2 + 6} - \dfrac{2x}{\left(x^2 + 6\right)^2}$

d. $\dfrac{3}{x^2 + 6} + \dfrac{2x}{\left(x^2 + 6\right)^2}$

e. $\dfrac{3}{x^2 + 6} + \dfrac{2}{\left(x^2 + 6\right)^2}$

_____ 16.   Write the partial fraction decomposition of the rational expression.

$$\frac{1}{(x+1)(d-x)}$$

a. $\dfrac{1}{d+1}\left(\dfrac{1}{x+1} - \dfrac{1}{d+x}\right)$

b. $\dfrac{1}{d}\left(\dfrac{1}{x+1} + \dfrac{1}{d-x}\right)$

c. $\dfrac{1}{d+1}\left(\dfrac{1}{x+1} + \dfrac{1}{d-x}\right)$

d. $\dfrac{1}{d+1}\left(\dfrac{1}{x+1} - \dfrac{1}{d-x}\right)$

e. $\dfrac{1}{d+1}\left(\dfrac{1}{x+1} + \dfrac{1}{x}\right)$

_____   17.   Select the correct graph of the inequality.

$y > -5$

a.

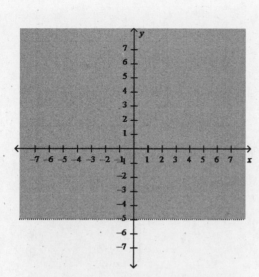

d.

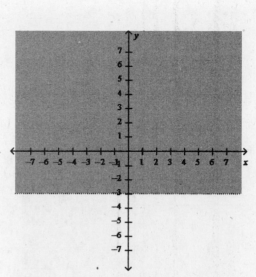

b.

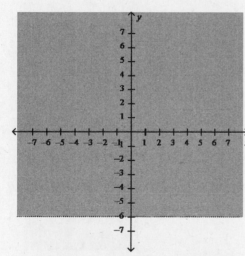

e.

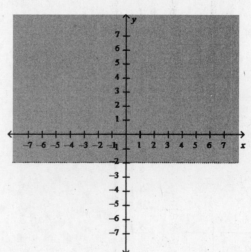

c.

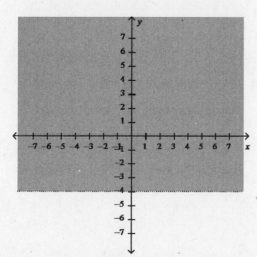

_____ 18.   Select the correct graph of the inequality.

$y < \ln 10x$

a.

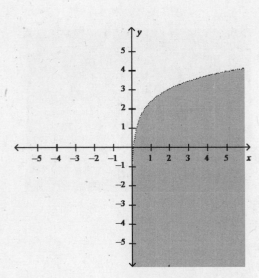

d.

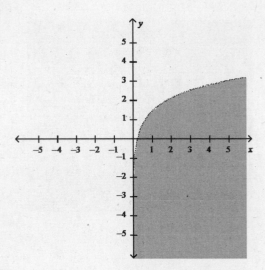

b.

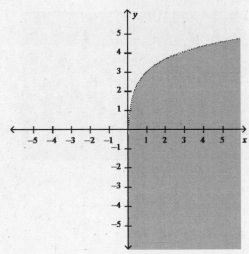

e.

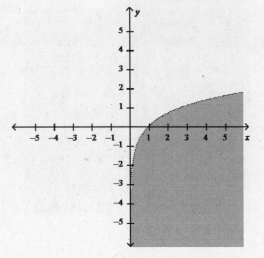

c.

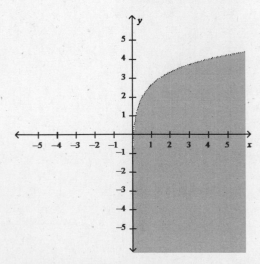

____   19.   Write an inequality for the shaded region shown in the figure.

Rectangle: vertices at $(3,5),(7,5),(7,7),(3,7)$

a. $\begin{cases} x \geq 3 \\ x \leq 7 \\ y \geq 5 \\ y \leq 7 \end{cases}$

b. $\begin{cases} x \geq 5 \\ x \leq 7 \\ y \geq 5 \\ y \leq 7 \end{cases}$

c. $\begin{cases} x \geq 2 \\ x \leq 7 \\ y \geq 5 \\ y \leq 7 \end{cases}$

d. $\begin{cases} x \geq 4 \\ x \leq 7 \\ y \geq 5 \\ y \leq 7 \end{cases}$

e. $\begin{cases} x \geq 1 \\ x \leq 7 \\ y \geq 5 \\ y \leq 7 \end{cases}$

_____ 20.   Sketch the graph of the inequality.

$(x-3)^2 + (y+1)^2 < 4$

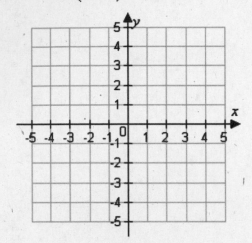

a.

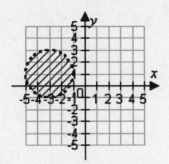

d.

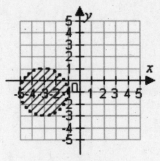

b.

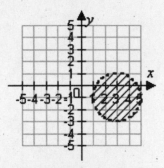

e.

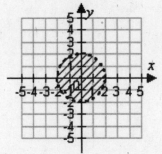

c.

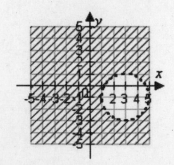

_____ 21. Derive a set of inequalities to describe the region.

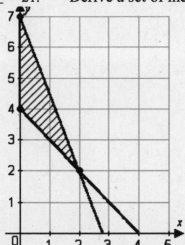

a. $\begin{cases} 5x + 2y \leq 14 \\ x + y \leq 4 \\ x \geq 0 \end{cases}$

b. $\begin{cases} 5x + 2y \geq 14 \\ x + y \leq 4 \end{cases}$

c. $\begin{cases} 5x + 2y \leq 14 \\ x + y \geq 4 \\ x \geq 0 \end{cases}$

d. $\begin{cases} 5x + 2y \leq 14 \\ x + y \geq 4 \end{cases}$

e. $\begin{cases} 5x + 2y \leq 7 \\ x + y \geq 4 \\ x \leq 0 \end{cases}$

_____ 22.   Find the maximum value of the objective function and where they occur, subject to the indicated constraints.

Objective function:

$z = 5x + 20y$

Constraints:

$x \geq 0$

$y \geq 0$

$2x + y \leq 12$

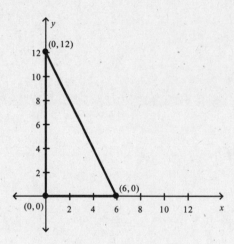

a. Maximum at $(6, 0)$: 60
b. Maximum at $(0, 0)$: 0
c. Maximum at $(0, 12)$: 240
d. Maximum at $(0, 6)$: 61
e. Maximum at $(12, 0)$: 241

_____   23.   Select the region determined by the constraints. Then find the maximum value of the objective function (if possible) and where they occur, subject to the indicated constraints.

Objective function:

$z = 7x + 6y$

Constraints:

$$x \geq 0$$

$$y \geq 0$$

$$2x + 2y \geq 10$$

$$x + 2y \geq 6$$

a.

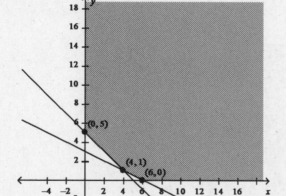

d.

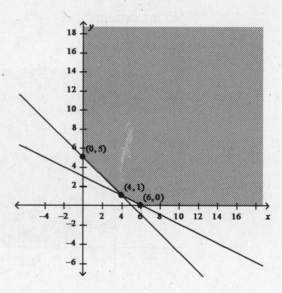

Maximum at $(0, 5)$: 30

Maximum at $(5, 0)$: 31

b.

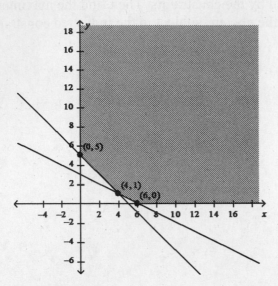

No maximum

e.

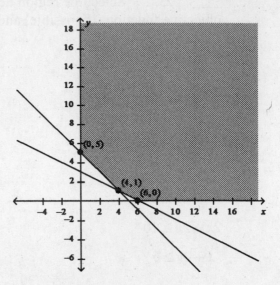

Maximum at $(4, 1)$: 34

c.

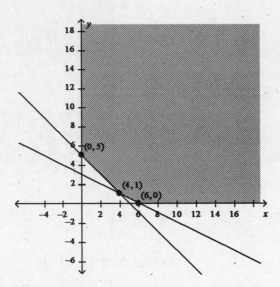

Maximum at $(6, 0)$: 42

_____ 24.   The linear programming problem has an unusual characteristic. Select a graph of the solution region for the problem and describe the unusual characteristic. Find the minimum value of the objective function (if possible) and where they occur.

Objective function:

$z = 2.6x + y$

Constraints:

$x \geq 0$

$y \geq 0$

$3x + 5y \leq 15$

$5x + 2y \leq 10$

a.

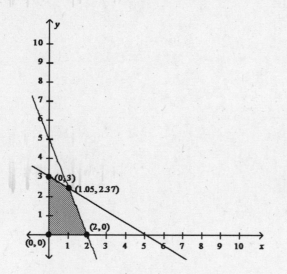

Minimum at $\left(\dfrac{45}{19}, \dfrac{20}{19} \right)$: 7.21

d.

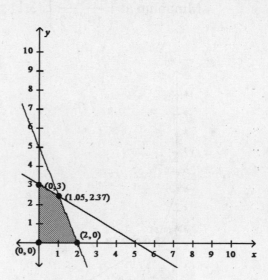

Minimum at $\left(\dfrac{20}{19}, 0 \right)$: 2.74

b.

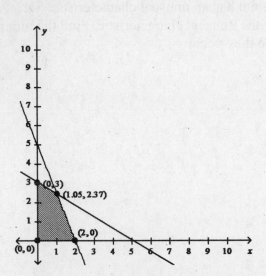

Minimum at $\left(\dfrac{20}{19}, \dfrac{45}{19}\right)$: 5.11

e.

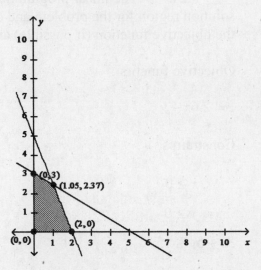

No minimum

c.

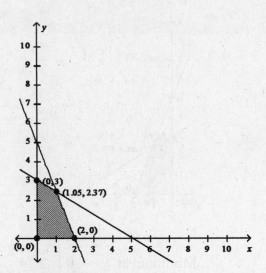

Minimum at $(0,0)$: 0

_____ 25.　　A manufacturer produces two models of elliptical cross-training exercise machines. The times for assembling, finishing, and packaging model X are 3 hours, 3 hours, and 0.8 hour, respectively. The times for model Y are 4 hours, 2.5 hours, and 0.4 hour. The total times available for assembling, finishing, and packaging are 6000 hours, 4200 hours, and 950 hours, respectively. The profits per unit are $500 for model X and $575 for model Y. What is the optimal production level for each model? What is the optimal profit?

a.　400 units of model X
　　1200 units of model Y
　　Optimal profit: $890,000
b.　950 units of model X
　　4200 units of model Y
　　Optimal profit: $2,890,000
c.　4200 units of model X
　　950 units of model Y
　　Optimal profit: $2,646,250
d.　6000 units of model X
　　950 units of model Y
　　Optimal profit: $3,546,250
e.　950 units of model X
　　6000 units of model Y
　　Optimal profit: $3,925,000

Ch 7 Form D
Answer Section

1.	ANS:	E	PTS:	1	REF:	7.1.9
2.	ANS:	B	PTS:	1	REF:	7.1.35
3.	ANS:	D	PTS:	1	REF:	7.1.69a
4.	ANS:	A	PTS:	1	REF:	7.1.33
5.	ANS:	C	PTS:	1	REF:	7.2.5
6.	ANS:	C	PTS:	1	REF:	7.2.50
7.	ANS:	A	PTS:	1	REF:	7.2.53
8.	ANS:	B	PTS:	1	REF:	7.2.21
9.	ANS:	A	PTS:	1	REF:	7.3.12
10.	ANS:	D	PTS:	1	REF:	7.3.61
11.	ANS:	A	PTS:	1	REF:	7.3.88
12.	ANS:	A	PTS:	1	REF:	7.3.49
13.	ANS:	A	PTS:	1	REF:	7.4.13
14.	ANS:	D	PTS:	1	REF:	7.4.24
15.	ANS:	D	PTS:	1	REF:	7.4.55
16.	ANS:	C	PTS:	1	REF:	7.4.70
17.	ANS:	A	PTS:	1	REF:	7.5.11
18.	ANS:	A	PTS:	1	REF:	7.5.21
19.	ANS:	A	PTS:	1	REF:	7.5.67
20.	ANS:	B	PTS:	1	REF:	7.5.17
21.	ANS:	C	PTS:	1	REF:	7.5.65
22.	ANS:	C	PTS:	1	REF:	7.6.8b
23.	ANS:	B	PTS:	1	REF:	7.6.16b
24.	ANS:	C	PTS:	1	REF:	7.6.29a
25.	ANS:	A	PTS:	1	REF:	7.6.36

Ch 7 Form E

____ 1.   Solve the system by the method of substitution. Check your solution(s) graphically.

$$\begin{cases} x - 3y = -13 \\ x + 2y = 2 \end{cases}$$

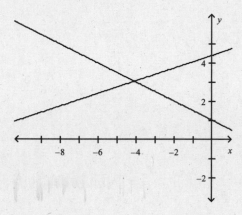

a. $(-4, 3)$
b. $(-2, 3)$
c. $(-2, -2)$
d. $(-2, -3)$
e. $(-4, -3)$

____ 2.   Solve the system graphically.

$$\begin{cases} x - y = 0 \\ 5x - 2y = 6 \end{cases}$$

a. $(2, 2)$
b. $(-4, -4)$
c. $(4, 4)$
d. $(-2, -2)$
e. $(4, 2)$

_____   3.   What are the dimensions of an isosceles right triangle with a four-inch hypotenuse and an area of 4 square inch?

a. $2\sqrt{2}$ in. × $2\sqrt{2}$ in. × 4 in.
b. $\sqrt{11}$ in. × $\sqrt{11}$ in. × 4 in.
c. 3 in. × 3 in. × 4 in.
d. $\sqrt{10}$ in. × $\sqrt{10}$ in. × 4 in.
e. $2\sqrt{3}$ in. × $2\sqrt{3}$ in. × 4 in.

_____   4.   Solve the system graphically.

$$\begin{cases} x - 3y = -4 \\ 5x + 3y = -11 \end{cases}$$

a. $(-1, -5)$
b. $\left(\dfrac{-5}{2}, -1\right)$
c. $\left(\dfrac{-5}{2}, -\dfrac{1}{2}\right)$
d. $\left(\dfrac{-5}{2}, \dfrac{1}{2}\right)$
e. $(-5, 1)$

_____   5.   Find the equilibrium point of the demand and supply equations. The equilibrium point is the price p and number of units x that satisfy both the demand and supply equations.

Demand	Supply
$p = 570 - 0.5x$	$p = 360 + 0.2x$

a. $(300, 420)$
b. $(420, -300)$
c. $(420, 300)$
d. $(-300, 420)$
e. $(-300, -420)$

_____ 6.   Solve the system by the method of elimination.

$$\begin{cases} x - y = 4 \\ -4x + 4y = 11 \end{cases}$$

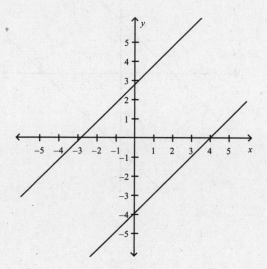

a. $(4,4)$

d. $(11,4)$

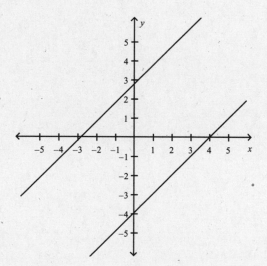

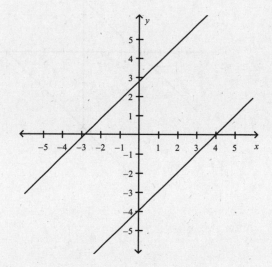

b. $(4, 11)$

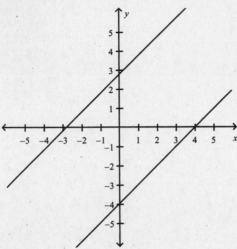

e.   No solution

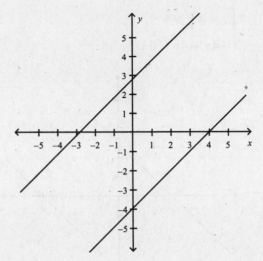

c. $(11, 11)$

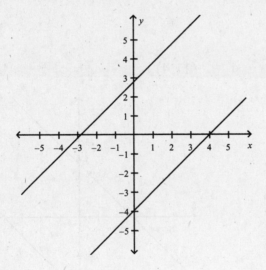

_____ 7.   Solve the system by the method of elimination and check any solutions algebraically.

$$\begin{cases} 0.05x - 0.03y = 0.21 \\ 0.07x + 0.02y = 0.16 \end{cases}$$

a. $\left(\dfrac{91}{31}, \dfrac{68}{31} \right)$

b. $\left(\dfrac{91}{31}, \dfrac{-68}{31} \right)$

c. $\left(\dfrac{-91}{31}, \dfrac{68}{31} \right)$

d. $\left(\dfrac{68}{31}, \dfrac{-91}{31} \right)$

e. $\left(\dfrac{-68}{31}, \dfrac{91}{31} \right)$

_____ 8.   Solve using any method.

$$\begin{cases} -5x + 3y = -6 \\ \quad\quad y = x - 1 \end{cases}$$

a. $\left(-3, -\dfrac{3}{5} \right)$

b. $(-7, -8)$

c. $\left(\dfrac{3}{2}, \dfrac{1}{2} \right)$

d. inconsistent

e. $\left(\dfrac{9}{2}, -\dfrac{11}{2} \right)$

_____ 9.   Solve the system of linear equations and check any solution algebraically.

$$\begin{cases} 2x + 2z = 2 \\ 5x + 3y = 4 \\ 3y - 4z = 4 \end{cases}$$

a. $(4, -8, 5)$
b. $(-4, 8, 5)$
c. $(4, 8, 5)$
d. $(-4, -8, -5)$
e. $(4, -8, -5)$

_____ 10.   Find the equation of the circle $x^2 + y^2 + Dx + Ey + F = 0$ that passes through the points.

$(0, 0), (0, 0), (3, 0)$

a. $x^2 - y^2 + 3x = 0$
b. $x^2 + y^2 + 3x = 0$
c. $x^3 + y^2 - 3x = 0$
d. $-x^2 - y^2 - 3x = 0$
e. $x^2 + y^2 - 3x = 0$

_____ 11.   In Super Bowl I, on January 15, 1967, the Green Bay Packers defeated the Kansas City Chiefs by a score of 15 to 30 . The total points scored came from 13 different scoring plays, which were a combination of touchdowns, extra-point kicks, and field goals, worth 6, 1, and 3 points, respectively. The same number of touchdowns and extra-point kicks were scored. There were six times as many touchdowns as field goals. How many touchdowns, extra-point kicks, and field goals were scored during the game?

a. 6 touchdowns, 6 extra-point kicks, 1 field goal
b. 6 touchdowns, 1 extra-point kick, 1 field goal
c. 6 touchdowns, 6 extra-point kicks, 6 field goal
d. 1 touchdown, 6 extra-point kicks, 1 field goal
e. 1 touchdown, 6 extra-point kicks, 6 field goal

_____   12.   Find the equation of the circle

$$x^2 + y^2 + Dx + Ey + F = 0$$

that passes through the points $(3, 8), (-2, 3), (8, 3)$.

a. $x^2 + y^2 - 6x - 6y - 7 = 0$

b. $x^2 + y^2 - 6x - 6y - 25 = 0$

c. $x^2 + y^2 - 3x - 3y - 7 = 0$

d. $x^2 + y^2 - 3x - 3y - 25 = 0$

e. $x^2 + y^2 - 6x - 6y + 43 = 0$

_____   13.   Write the form of the partial fraction decomposition of the rational expression. Do not solve for the constants.

$$\frac{x - 4}{6x^3 + 30x}$$

a. $\dfrac{A}{6x} + \dfrac{B}{x^2} + \dfrac{C}{5}$

b. $\dfrac{A}{6x} + \dfrac{B}{x+5} + \dfrac{C}{x+5}$

c. $\dfrac{A}{6x} + \dfrac{Bx+C}{x^2+5}$

d. $\dfrac{A}{6x} - \dfrac{Bx+C}{x^2+5}$

e. $\dfrac{A}{6x} + \dfrac{B}{x^2+5}$

____ 14. Write the partial fraction decomposition of the rational expression. Check your result algebraically.

$$\frac{5x^2 - 3x - 4}{x^3 - x}$$

a. $\dfrac{4}{x} - \dfrac{2}{x+1} - \dfrac{1}{x-1}$

b. $\dfrac{4}{x} + \dfrac{2}{x+1} + \dfrac{1}{x-1}$

c. $\dfrac{4}{x} + \dfrac{2}{x+1} - \dfrac{1}{x-1}$

d. $\dfrac{4}{x} + \dfrac{2}{x+1} - \dfrac{1}{x+1}$

e. $\dfrac{4}{x} + \dfrac{2}{x-1} - \dfrac{1}{x-1}$

____ 15. The predicted cost C (in thousands of dollars) for a company to remove $p\%$ of a chemical from its waste water is given by the model

$$C = \frac{128p}{22,500 - p^2}, \ 0 \le p < 100.$$

Write the partial fraction decomposition for the rational function. Verify your result by using the *table* feature of a graphing utility to create a table comparing the original function with the partial fractions.

a. $\dfrac{128}{150-p} - \dfrac{128}{150+p}$

b. $\dfrac{1}{150-p} - \dfrac{1}{150+p}$

c. $\dfrac{64}{150-p} - \dfrac{64}{(150-p)^2}$

d. $\dfrac{64}{150-p} + \dfrac{64}{150+p}$

e. $\dfrac{64}{150-p} - \dfrac{64}{150+p}$

_____ 16.   Write the form of the partial fraction decomposition of the rational expression. Do not solve for the constants.

$$\frac{x+8}{x\left(x^2-2\right)^2}$$

a. $\dfrac{Ax+B}{x}+\dfrac{Cx+D}{x^2-2}+\dfrac{Ex+F}{\left(x^2-2\right)^2}$

b. $\dfrac{Ax+B}{x^2-2}+\dfrac{Cx+D}{\left(x^2-2\right)^2}$

c. $\dfrac{A}{x}+\dfrac{B}{x^2-2}+\dfrac{C}{\left(x^2-2\right)^2}$

d. $\dfrac{A}{x}+\dfrac{Bx+C}{x^2-2}+\dfrac{Dx+E}{\left(x^2-2\right)^2}$

e. $\dfrac{A}{x}+\dfrac{Bx+C}{\left(x^2-2\right)^2}$

_____ 17.   Select the correct graph of the inequality.

$y < 8 - x$

a.

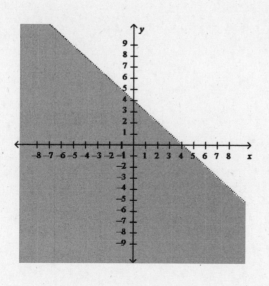

d.

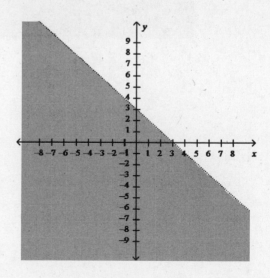

b.

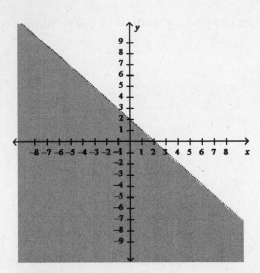

e.

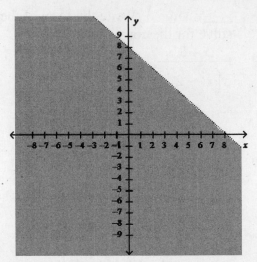

c.

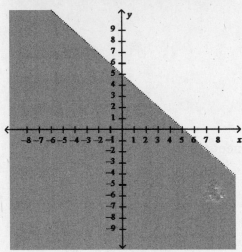

_____   18.   **Select the correct graph of the inequality.**

$y < -4.8x + 2.1$

a.

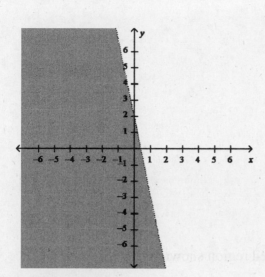

d.

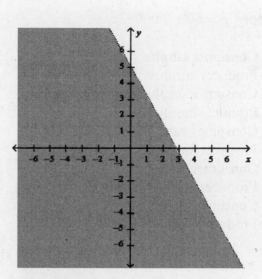

b.

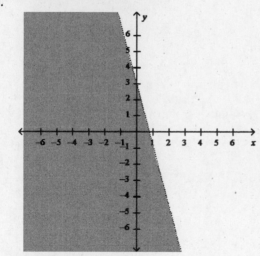

e.

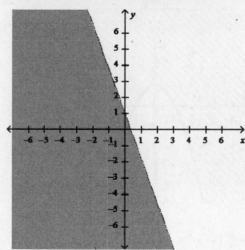

c.

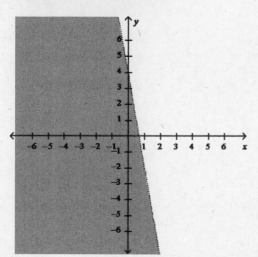

_____ 19.   Find the consumer surplus and producer surplus.

Demand $p = 150 - 0.00001x$

Supply $p = 60 + 0.00003x$

a. Consumer surplus: $\$25,312,600$
    Producer surplus: $\$75,937,600$
b. Consumer surplus: $\$25,312,650$
    Producer surplus: $\$75,937,900$
c. Consumer surplus: $\$25,312,550$
    Producer surplus: $\$75,937,700$
d. Consumer surplus: $\$25,312,500$
    Producer surplus: $\$75,937,500$
e. Consumer surplus: $\$25,312,700$
    Producer surplus: $\$75,937,800$

_____ 20.   Write an inequality for the shaded region shown in the figure.

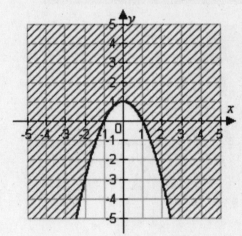

a. $y \le 1 - x^2$
b. $y \ge 1 - x^2$
c. $y \le (1-x)^2$
d. $y \ge x^2 - 1$
e. $y \ge (1-x)^2$

____ 21.   For the given supply and demand equations, find the consumer surplus.

Demand   Supply
$p = 150 - 0.00005x$ $p = 100 + 0.00003x$

a. $10,742,188
b. $5,859,375
c. $11,718,750
d. $9,765,625
e. $14,648,438

____ 22.   Find the maximum value of the objective function and where they occur, subject to the indicated constraints.

Objective function:
$z = 7x + 8y$

Constraints:

$x \geq 0$

$3x - y \leq 9$

$2x + 3y \geq 6$

$x + 4y \leq 16$

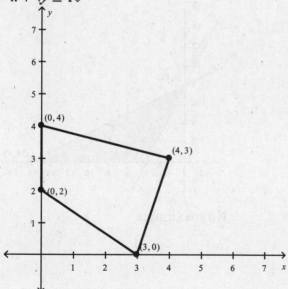

a. Maximum at $(4, 3)$: 52
b. Maximum at $(0, 4)$: 32
c. Maximum at $(0, 2)$: 16
d. Maximum at $(3, 4)$: 53
e. Maximum at $(3, 0)$: 21

_____ 23.   Select the region determined by the constraints. Then find the maximum value of the objective function (if possible) and where they occur, subject to the indicated constraints.

Objective function:

$$z = 7x + \frac{1}{2}y$$

Constraints:

$$x \geq 0$$

$$y \geq 0$$

$$\frac{1}{2}x + y \leq 8$$

$$x + \frac{1}{2}y \geq 4$$

a.

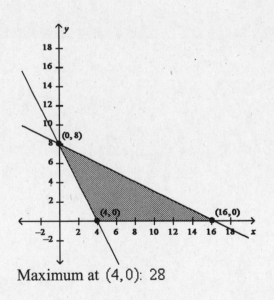

Maximum at $(4,0)$: 28

d.

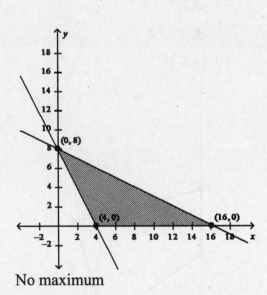

No maximum

b.

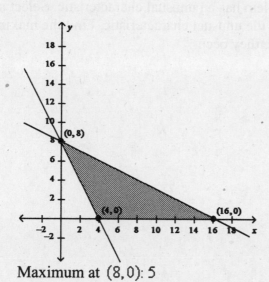

Maximum at $(8, 0)$: 5

e.

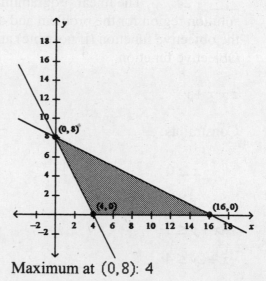

Maximum at $(0, 8)$: 4

c.

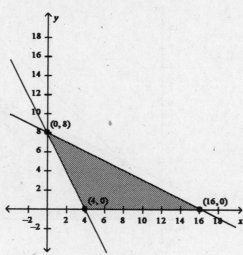

Maximum at $(16, 0)$: 112

_____   24.   The linear programming problem has an unusual characteristic. Select a graph of the solution region for the problem and describe the unusual characteristic. Find the maximum value of the objective function (if possible) and where they occur.
Objective function:

$z = x + y$

Constraints:

$$x \geq 0$$
$$y \geq 0$$
$$-x + y \leq 1$$
$$-x + 2y \leq 4$$

a.

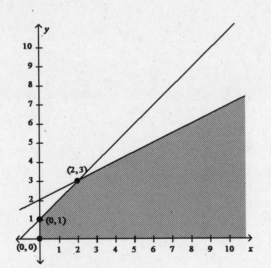

Maximum at $(2,3)$: 5

d.

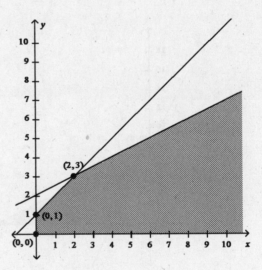

Maximum at $(0,0)$: 0

b.

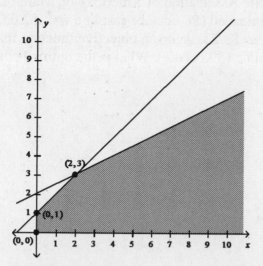

The constraints do not form a closed set of points. Therefore, $z = x + y$ is unbounded.

e.

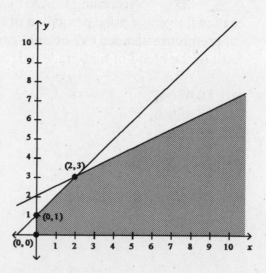

Maximum at $(3, 2)$: 5

c.

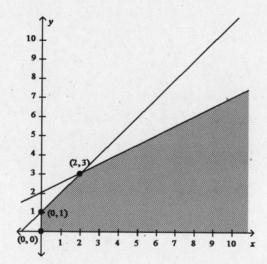

Maximum at $(0, 1)$: 1

_____ 25. According to AAA (Automobile Association of America), on March 27, 2009, the national average price per gallon of regular unleaded (86-octane) gasoline was $2.03, and the price of premium unleaded (92-octane) gasoline was $3.23. Write an objective function that models the cost of the blend of mid-grade unleaded gasoline (89-octane). What is the optimal cost?

a. $2.43/gal
b. $3.43/gal
c. $3.83/gal
d. $2.83/gal
e. $1.35/gal

Ch 7 Form E
Answer Section

1.	ANS:	A	PTS:	1	REF:	7.1.12
2.	ANS:	A	PTS:	1	REF:	7.1.44
3.	ANS:	A	PTS:	1	REF:	7.1.84
4.	ANS:	D	PTS:	1	REF:	7.1.37
5.	ANS:	A	PTS:	1	REF:	7.2.45
6.	ANS:	E	PTS:	1	REF:	7.2.9
7.	ANS:	B	PTS:	1	REF:	7.2.26
8.	ANS:	C	PTS:	1	REF:	7.2.36
9.	ANS:	B	PTS:	1	REF:	7.3.21
10.	ANS:	E	PTS:	1	REF:	7.3.58
11.	ANS:	A	PTS:	1	REF:	7.3.59
12.	ANS:	A	PTS:	1	REF:	7.3.57
13.	ANS:	C	PTS:	1	REF:	7.4.16
14.	ANS:	C	PTS:	1	REF:	7.4.27
15.	ANS:	E	PTS:	1	REF:	7.4.61
16.	ANS:	D	PTS:	1	REF:	7.4.17
17.	ANS:	E	PTS:	1	REF:	7.5.13
18.	ANS:	A	PTS:	1	REF:	7.5.27
19.	ANS:	D	PTS:	1	REF:	7.5.73
20.	ANS:	B	PTS:	1	REF:	7.5.34
21.	ANS:	D	PTS:	1	REF:	7.5.73
22.	ANS:	A	PTS:	1	REF:	7.6.10a
23.	ANS:	C	PTS:	1	REF:	7.6.14b
24.	ANS:	B	PTS:	1	REF:	7.6.30b
25.	ANS:	A	PTS:	1	REF:	7.6.42e

Ch 7 Form F

_____ 1.   Solve the system by the method of substitution. Check your solution(s) graphically.

$$\begin{cases} x - 4y = -11 \\ x + 3y = 3 \end{cases}$$

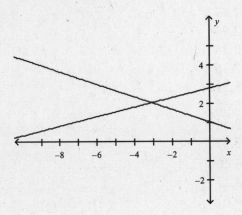

a. $(-3, 2)$
b. $(-1, -1)$
c. $(-1, 2)$
d. $(-1, -2)$
e. $(-3, -2)$

_____ 2.   Solve the system graphically.

$$\begin{cases} x - y = 0 \\ 5x - 2y = 18 \end{cases}$$

a. $(-6, -6)$
b. $(-8, -8)$
c. $(8, 8)$
d. $(8, 6)$
e. $(6, 6)$

_____ 3. What are the dimensions of an isosceles right triangle with a four-inch hypotenuse and an area of 4 square inch?

a. $\sqrt{11}$ in. $\times$ $\sqrt{11}$ in. $\times$ 4 in.
b. 3 in. $\times$ 3 in. $\times$ 4 in.
c. $2\sqrt{2}$ in. $\times$ $2\sqrt{2}$ in. $\times$ 4 in.
d. $\sqrt{10}$ in. $\times$ $\sqrt{10}$ in. $\times$ 4 in.
e. $2\sqrt{3}$ in. $\times$ $2\sqrt{3}$ in. $\times$ 4 in.

_____ 4. Solve the system graphically.

$$\begin{cases} x - 3y = -6 \\ 5x + 3y = -3 \end{cases}$$

a. $(-3, 3)$
b. $\left(\dfrac{-3}{2}, \dfrac{3}{2} \right)$
c. $\left(\dfrac{-3}{2}, -\dfrac{3}{2} \right)$
d. $(-3, -3)$
e. $\left(\dfrac{-3}{2}, -3 \right)$

_____ 5. Find the equilibrium point of the demand and supply equations. The equilibrium point is the price p and number of units x that satisfy both the demand and supply equations.

Demand	Supply
$p = 600 - 0.4x$	$p = 390 + 0.1x$

a. $(420, 432)$
b. $(-420, -432)$
c. $(432, -420)$
d. $(-420, 432)$
e. $(432, 420)$

_____ 6.   Solve the system by the method of elimination.

$$\begin{cases} x - y = 6 \\ -6x + 6y = 9 \end{cases}$$

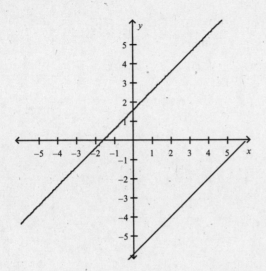

a.   No solution

d. $(6, 6)$

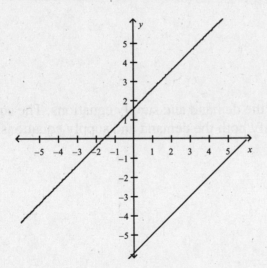

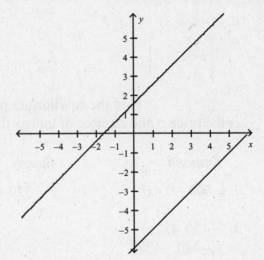

b.   (9, 9)

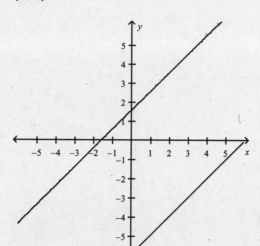

e.   (6, 9)

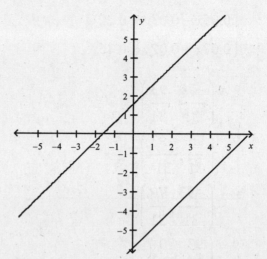

c.   (9, 6)

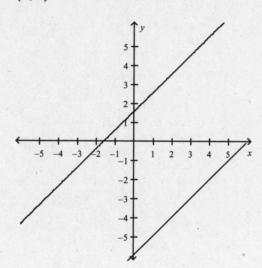

_____ 7.   Solve the system by the method of elimination and check any solutions algebraically.

$$\begin{cases} 0.05x - 0.03y = 0.22 \\ 0.07x + 0.02y = 0.16 \end{cases}$$

a. $\left(\dfrac{-70}{31}, \dfrac{93}{31} \right)$

b. $\left(\dfrac{70}{31}, \dfrac{-93}{31} \right)$

c. $\left(\dfrac{-93}{31}, \dfrac{70}{31} \right)$

d. $\left(\dfrac{93}{31}, \dfrac{70}{31} \right)$

e. $\left(\dfrac{93}{31}, \dfrac{-70}{31} \right)$

_____ 8.   Solve using any method.

$$\begin{cases} 9x + y = -18 \\ y = x + 7 \end{cases}$$

a. inconsistent

b. $\left(-\dfrac{11}{10}, \dfrac{81}{10} \right)$

c. $(-2, 5)$

d. $\left(-\dfrac{5}{2}, \dfrac{9}{2} \right)$

e. $\left(-7, -\dfrac{11}{9} \right)$

_____   9.   Solve the system of linear equations and check any solution algebraically.

$$\begin{cases} 2x + 2z = 8 \\ 5x + 3y = 10 \\ 3y - 4z = 10 \end{cases}$$

a. $(16, 30, 20)$
b. $(-16, -30, -20)$
c. $(16, -30, -20)$
d. $(-16, 30, 20)$
e. $(16, -30, 20)$

_____   10.   Find the equation of the circle $x^2 + y^2 + Dx + Ey + F = 0$ that passes through the points.

$(0, 0), (0, 0), (5, 0)$

a. $x^2 + y^2 - 5x = 0$
b. $x^2 + y^2 + 5x = 0$
c. $x^2 - y^2 + 5x = 0$
d. $-x^2 - y^2 - 5x = 0$
e. $x^3 + y^2 - 5x = 0$

_____   11.   In Super Bowl I, on January 15, 1967, the Green Bay Packers defeated the Kansas City Chiefs by a score of 15 to 30 . The total points scored came from 13 different scoring plays, which were a combination of touchdowns, extra-point kicks, and field goals, worth 6, 1, and 3 points, respectively. The same number of touchdowns and extra-point kicks were scored. There were six times as many touchdowns as field goals. How many touchdowns, extra-point kicks, and field goals were scored during the game?

a. 1 touchdown, 6 extra-point kicks, 6 field goal
b. 1 touchdown, 6 extra-point kicks, 1 field goal
c. 6 touchdowns, 6 extra-point kicks, 6 field goal
d. 6 touchdowns, 6 extra-point kicks, 1 field goal
e. 6 touchdowns, 1 extra-point kick, 1 field goal

_____ 12.   Find the equation of the circle
$$x^2 + y^2 + Dx + Ey + F = 0$$
that passes through the points $(-1, 2), (-5, -2), (3, -2)$.

a. $x^2 + y^2 + x + 2y - 11 = 0$

b. $x^2 + y^2 + 2x + 4y - 16 = 0$

c. $x^2 + y^2 + x + 2y - 16 = 0$

d. $x^2 + y^2 + 2x + 4y - 11 = 0$

e. $x^2 + y^2 + 2x + 4y + 21 = 0$

_____ 13.   Write the form of the partial fraction decomposition of the rational expression. Do not solve for the constants.

$$\frac{x - 3}{4x^3 + 8x}$$

a. $\dfrac{A}{4x} + \dfrac{B}{x^2} + \dfrac{C}{2}$

b. $\dfrac{A}{4x} + \dfrac{B}{x + 2} + \dfrac{C}{x + 2}$

c. $\dfrac{A}{4x} - \dfrac{Bx + C}{x^2 + 2}$

d. $\dfrac{A}{4x} + \dfrac{B}{x^2 + 2}$

e. $\dfrac{A}{4x} + \dfrac{Bx + C}{x^2 + 2}$

_____ 14.   Write the partial fraction decomposition of the rational expression. Check your result algebraically.

$$\frac{3x^2 - 3x - 2}{x^3 - x}$$

a. $\dfrac{2}{x} + \dfrac{2}{x+1} - \dfrac{1}{x+1}$

b. $\dfrac{2}{x} + \dfrac{2}{x+1} - \dfrac{1}{x-1}$

c. $\dfrac{2}{x} - \dfrac{2}{x+1} - \dfrac{1}{x-1}$

d. $\dfrac{2}{x} + \dfrac{2}{x-1} - \dfrac{1}{x-1}$

e. $\dfrac{2}{x} + \dfrac{2}{x+1} + \dfrac{1}{x-1}$

_____ 15.   The predicted cost C (in thousands of dollars) for a company to remove $p\%$ of a chemical from its waste water is given by the model

$$C = \frac{124p}{160,000 - p^2},\ 0 \le p < 100.$$

Write the partial fraction decomposition for the rational function. Verify your result by using the *table* feature of a graphing utility to create a table comparing the original function with the partial fractions.

a. $\dfrac{124}{400-p} - \dfrac{124}{400+p}$

b. $\dfrac{62}{400-p} - \dfrac{62}{400+p}$

c. $\dfrac{62}{400-p} + \dfrac{62}{400+p}$

d. $\dfrac{62}{400-p} - \dfrac{62}{\left(400-p\right)^2}$

e. $\dfrac{1}{400-p} - \dfrac{1}{400+p}$

____ 16. Write the form of the partial fraction decomposition of the rational expression. Do not solve for the constants.

$$\frac{x+2}{x\left(x^2-3\right)^2}$$

a. $\dfrac{A}{x}+\dfrac{Bx+C}{\left(x^2-3\right)^2}$

b. $\dfrac{A}{x}+\dfrac{B}{x^2-3}+\dfrac{C}{\left(x^2-3\right)^2}$

c. $\dfrac{A}{x}+\dfrac{Bx+C}{x^2-3}+\dfrac{Dx+E}{\left(x^2-3\right)^2}$

d. $\dfrac{Ax+B}{x^2-3}+\dfrac{Cx+D}{\left(x^2-3\right)^2}$

e. $\dfrac{Ax+B}{x}+\dfrac{Cx+D}{x^2-3}+\dfrac{Ex+F}{\left(x^2-3\right)^2}$

____ 17. Select the correct graph of the inequality.

$y < 6 - x$

a.

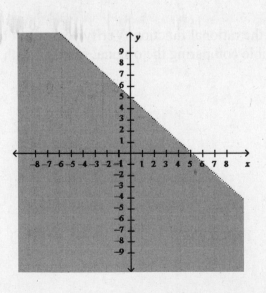

d.

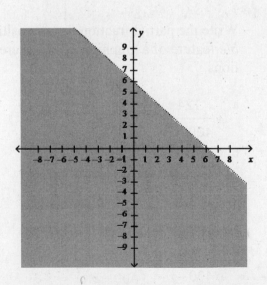

b.

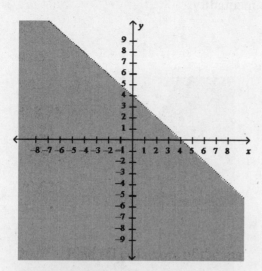

e.

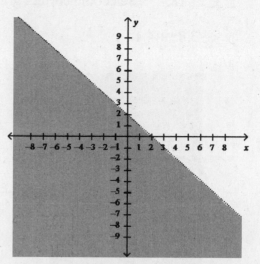

c.

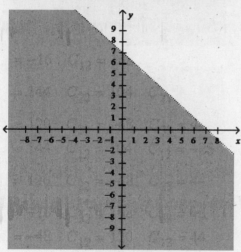

_____ 18.   Select the correct graph of the inequality.

$y < -3.8x + 4.1$

a.

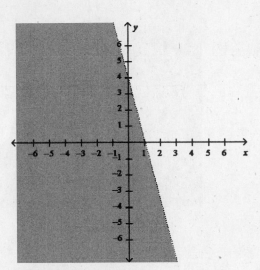

d.

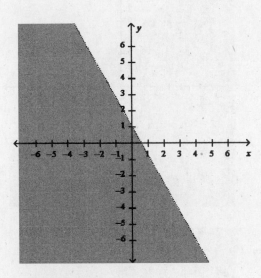

b.

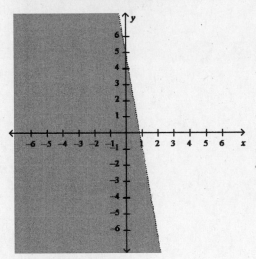

e.

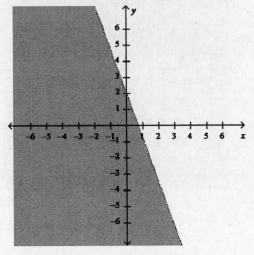

c.

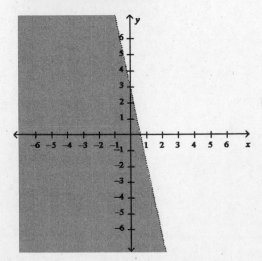

_____ 19.   Find the consumer surplus and producer surplus.

Demand $p = 190 - 0.00001x$

Supply $p = 50 + 0.00004x$

a. Consumer surplus: $39,200,150
    Producer surplus: $156,800,400
b. Consumer surplus: $39,200,000
    Producer surplus: $156,800,000
c. Consumer surplus: $39,200,200
    Producer surplus: $156,800,300
d. Consumer surplus: $39,200,050
    Producer surplus: $156,800,200
e. Consumer surplus: $39,200,100
    Producer surplus: $156,800,100

_____ 20.   Write an inequality for the shaded region shown in the figure.

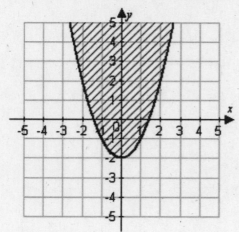

a. $y \geq x^2 - 2$
b. $y \geq 2 - x^2$
c. $y \leq 2 - x^2$
d. $y \geq x^2 + 2$
e. $y \geq (x - 2)^2$

_____   21.   For the given supply and demand equations, find the consumer surplus.

Demand   Supply

$p = 190 - 0.00005x$ $p = 140 + 0.00003x$

a. $9,765,625
b. $10,742,188
c. $5,859,375
d. $11,718,750
e. $14,648,438

_____   22.   Find the maximum value of the objective function and where they occur, subject to the indicated constraints.

Objective function:

$z = 6x + 7y$

Constraints:

$$x \geq 0$$

$$3x - y \leq 9$$

$$2x + 3y \geq 6$$

$$x + 4y \leq 16$$

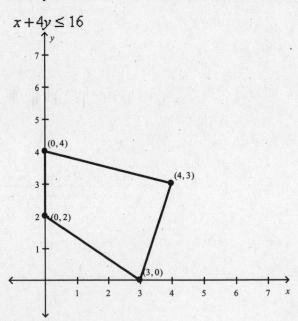

a. Maximum at $(3,4)$: 46
b. Maximum at $(0,4)$: 28
c. Maximum at $(0,2)$: 14
d. Maximum at $(3,0)$: 18
e. Maximum at $(4,3)$: 45

_____ 23. Select the region determined by the constraints. Then find the maximum value of the objective function (if possible) and where they occur, subject to the indicated constraints.

Objective function:

$$z = 7x + \frac{1}{8}y$$

Constraints:

$$x \geq 0$$

$$y \geq 0$$

$$\frac{1}{2}x + y \leq 8$$

$$x + \frac{1}{2}y \geq 4$$

a.

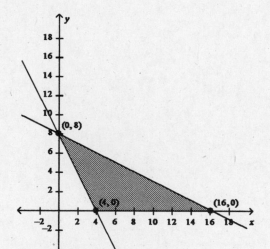

Maximum at $(4,0)$: 28

d.

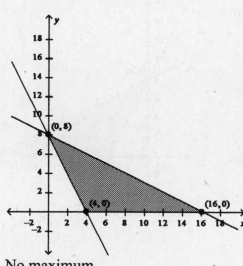

No maximum

b.

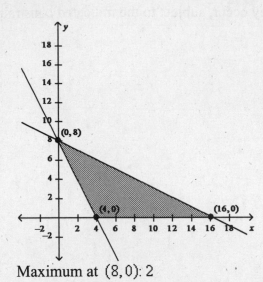

Maximum at $(8,0)$: 2

e.

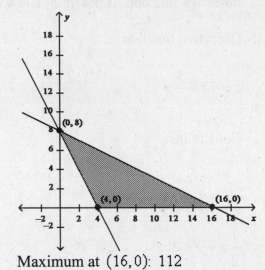

Maximum at $(16,0)$: 112

c.

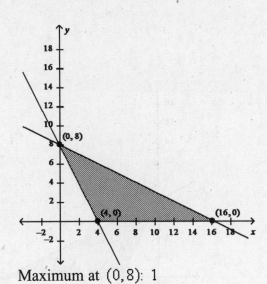

Maximum at $(0,8)$: 1

_____   24.   The linear programming problem has an unusual characteristic. Select a graph of the solution region for the problem and describe the unusual characteristic. Find the maximum value of the objective function (if possible) and where they occur.

Objective function:

$z = x + y$

Constraints:

$x \geq 0$

$y \geq 0$

$-x + y \leq 1$

$-x + 4y \leq 6$

a.

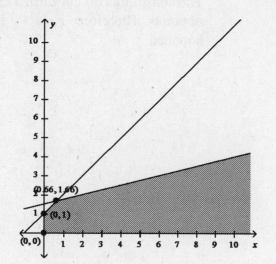

Maximum at $(1.66, 0.66)$: 2.32

d.

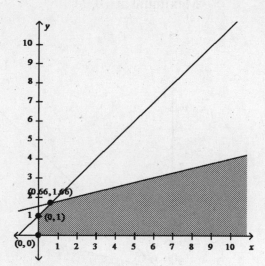

Maximum at $(0, 0)$: 0

b.

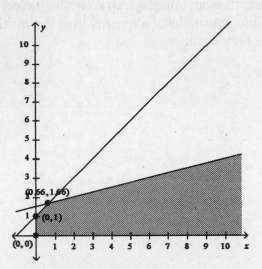

Maximum at $(0, 1)$: 1

e.

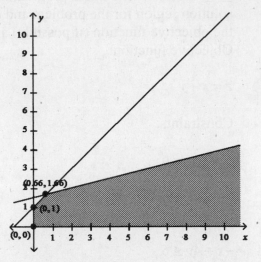

The constraints do not form a closed set of points. Therefore, $z = x + y$ is unbounded.

c.

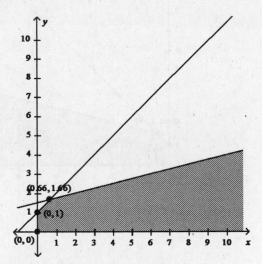

Maximum at $(0.66, 1.66)$: 2.32

_____   25.   According to AAA (Automobile Association of America), on March 27, 2009, the national average price per gallon of regular unleaded (88-octane) gasoline was $5.03, and the price of premium unleaded (94-octane) gasoline was $2.23. Write an objective function that models the cost of the blend of mid-grade unleaded gasoline (92-octane). What is the optimal cost?

a. $4.1/gal
b. $3.35/gal
c. $3.16/gal
d. $5.0966666666667/gal
e. $4.163333333333/gal

Ch 7 Form F
Answer Section

1.	ANS:	A	PTS:	1	REF:	7.1.12
2.	ANS:	E	PTS:	1	REF:	7.1.44
3.	ANS:	C	PTS:	1	REF:	7.1.84
4.	ANS:	B	PTS:	1	REF:	7.1.37
5.	ANS:	A	PTS:	1	REF:	7.2.45
6.	ANS:	A	PTS:	1	REF:	7.2.9
7.	ANS:	E	PTS:	1	REF:	7.2.26
8.	ANS:	D	PTS:	1	REF:	7.2.36
9.	ANS:	D	PTS:	1	REF:	7.3.21
10.	ANS:	A	PTS:	1	REF:	7.3.58
11.	ANS:	D	PTS:	1	REF:	7.3.59
12.	ANS:	D	PTS:	1	REF:	7.3.57
13.	ANS:	E	PTS:	1	REF:	7.4.16
14.	ANS:	B	PTS:	1	REF:	7.4.27
15.	ANS:	B	PTS:	1	REF:	7.4.61
16.	ANS:	C	PTS:	1	REF:	7.4.17
17.	ANS:	D	PTS:	1	REF:	7.5.13
18.	ANS:	A	PTS:	1	REF:	7.5.27
19.	ANS:	B	PTS:	1	REF:	7.5.73
20.	ANS:	A	PTS:	1	REF:	7.5.34
21.	ANS:	A	PTS:	1	REF:	7.5.73
22.	ANS:	E	PTS:	1	REF:	7.6.10a
23.	ANS:	E	PTS:	1	REF:	7.6.14b
24.	ANS:	E	PTS:	1	REF:	7.6.30b
25.	ANS:	A	PTS:	1	REF:	7.6.42e

Ch 8 Form A

_____ 1.   Select the order for the following matrix.

$$\begin{bmatrix} -3 & 5 & 15 & 0 \\ 0 & 0 & 2 & 2 \\ 1 & 1 & 8 & 5 \end{bmatrix}$$

a. 4×3
b. 4×2
c. 4×4
d. 3×3
e. 3×4

_____ 2.   Fill in the blank(s) using elementary row operations to form a row-equivalent matrix.

$$\begin{bmatrix} 6 & 9 & 10 \\ 4 & -3 & 6 \end{bmatrix}$$

$$\begin{bmatrix} 2 & \cdots & \dfrac{10}{3} \\ 4 & -3 & 6 \end{bmatrix}$$

a.
$$\begin{bmatrix} 2 & 7 & \dfrac{10}{3} \\ 4 & -3 & 6 \end{bmatrix}$$

b.
$$\begin{bmatrix} 2 & 8 & \dfrac{10}{3} \\ 4 & -3 & 6 \end{bmatrix}$$

c.
$$\begin{bmatrix} 2 & -3 & \dfrac{10}{3} \\ 4 & -3 & 6 \end{bmatrix}$$

d.
$$\begin{bmatrix} 2 & 5 & \dfrac{10}{3} \\ 4 & -3 & 6 \end{bmatrix}$$

e.
$$\begin{bmatrix} 2 & 3 & \dfrac{10}{3} \\ 4 & -3 & 6 \end{bmatrix}$$

_____   3.   Find the system of linear equations represented by the augmented matrix. Then use back substitution to solve. (Use variables x, y, z and if applicable.)

$$\begin{bmatrix} 1 & -1 & 2 & \vdots & 4 \\ 0 & 1 & -1 & \vdots & 2 \\ 0 & 0 & 1 & \vdots & -2 \end{bmatrix}$$

a. $\begin{cases} x - y + 2z = 4 \\ y + z = 2 \\ z = -2 \end{cases}$

$(12, 4, -2)$

b. $\begin{cases} x - y + 2z = 4 \\ y - z = -2 \\ z = 2 \end{cases}$

$(8, 0, -2)$

c. $\begin{cases} x - y + 2z = 4 \\ y + z = 2 \\ z = 2 \end{cases}$

$(-4, 4, 2)$

d. $\begin{cases} x - y + 2z = 4 \\ y - z = 2 \\ z = -2 \end{cases}$

$(8, 0, -2)$

e. $\begin{cases} x - y + 2z = 4 \\ \quad\quad y + z = -2 \\ \quad\quad\quad z = 2 \end{cases}$

$(-4, 4, 2)$

____ 4.   The currents in an electrical network are given by the solution of the system

$\begin{cases} I_1 - I_2 + I_3 = -1 \\ 3I_1 + 4I_2 = 38 \\ I_2 + 3I_3 = 23 \end{cases}$

where I_1, I_2 and I_3 are measured in amperes. Solve the system of equations using matrices.

a. $I_1 = 3, I_2 = 8, I_3 = 5$
b. $I_1 = 6, I_2 = 8, I_3 = 5$
c. $I_1 = 4, I_2 = 8, I_3 = 5$
d. $I_1 = 5, I_2 = 8, I_3 = 5$
e. $I_1 = 2, I_2 = 8, I_3 = 5$

____ 5.   Write the matrix in reduced row-echelon form.

$$\begin{bmatrix} 5 & 3 & 0 & -10 \\ 6 & 7 & -1 & -15 \\ 8 & -5 & -8 & -40 \end{bmatrix}$$

a. $\begin{bmatrix} 1 & 0 & 0 & -3 \\ 0 & 1 & 0 & 1 \\ 0 & 0 & 1 & 3 \end{bmatrix}$

b. $\begin{bmatrix} 1 & 0 & 0 & 1 \\ 0 & 1 & 0 & 1 \\ 0 & 0 & 1 & 1 \end{bmatrix}$

c. $\begin{bmatrix} 1 & 0 & 0 & -2 \\ 0 & 1 & 0 & 0 \\ 0 & 0 & 1 & 3 \end{bmatrix}$

d.
$$\begin{bmatrix} 1 & 0 & 0 & 0 \\ 0 & 1 & 0 & 0 \\ 0 & 0 & 1 & 0 \end{bmatrix}$$

e.
$$\begin{bmatrix} 1 & 0 & 0 & -2 \\ 0 & 1 & 0 & 3 \\ 0 & 0 & 1 & 0 \end{bmatrix}$$

_____   6.   Find x and y.

$$\begin{bmatrix} x & -2 \\ 7 & y \end{bmatrix} = \begin{bmatrix} -14 & -2 \\ 7 & 26 \end{bmatrix}$$

a. $x = 14, y = -26$

b. $x = \dfrac{1}{14}, y = -\dfrac{1}{26}$

c. $x = \dfrac{1}{14}, y = \dfrac{1}{26}$

d. $x = -14, y = 26$

e. $x = -\dfrac{1}{14}, y = \dfrac{1}{26}$

_____   7.   Find $A - B$.

$$A = \begin{bmatrix} 9 & -3 \\ 4 & 4 \\ -6 & 6 \end{bmatrix}, B = \begin{bmatrix} 4 & 7 \\ -2 & -2 \\ 1 & 12 \end{bmatrix}$$

a.
$$\begin{bmatrix} 5 & -10 \\ 6 & 6 \\ -7 & -6 \end{bmatrix}$$

b.
$$\begin{bmatrix} 7 & -10 \\ 6 & -6 \\ -7 & 6 \end{bmatrix}$$

c. $\begin{bmatrix} 9 & -10 \\ -7 & 6 \\ 6 & -6 \end{bmatrix}$

d. $\begin{bmatrix} 3 & 6 \\ 6 & -10 \\ -7 & -6 \end{bmatrix}$

e. $\begin{bmatrix} 1 & -10 \\ 6 & 6 \\ -7 & -6 \end{bmatrix}$

_____ 8.　　Use the matrix capabilities of a graphing utility to evaluate the expression. Round your results to three decimal places, if necessary.

$$55\left(\begin{bmatrix} 11 & -17 \\ -13 & 11 \end{bmatrix} + \begin{bmatrix} -21 & 14 \\ 16 & 8 \end{bmatrix}\right)$$

a. $\begin{bmatrix} -550 & -165 \\ 165 & 1045 \end{bmatrix}$

b. $\begin{bmatrix} -548 & -165 \\ 1045 & 165 \end{bmatrix}$

c. $\begin{bmatrix} -546 & 1045 \\ 165 & -165 \end{bmatrix}$

d. $\begin{bmatrix} -552 & 165 \\ -165 & 1045 \end{bmatrix}$

e. $\begin{bmatrix} -554 & -165 \\ 165 & 1045 \end{bmatrix}$

____ 9.   A corporation has four factories, each of which manufactures sport utility vehicles and pickup trucks. The number of units of vehicle produced at factory in one day is represented by a_{ij} in the matrix

$$A = \begin{bmatrix} 70 & 90 & 70 & 50 \\ 70 & 60 & 50 & 100 \end{bmatrix}.$$

Find the production levels if production is increased by 10%.

a.
$$\begin{bmatrix} 94 & 99 & 77 & 55 \\ 77 & 66 & 55 & 110 \end{bmatrix}$$

b.
$$\begin{bmatrix} 104 & 99 & 77 & 55 \\ 77 & 66 & 55 & 110 \end{bmatrix}$$

c.
$$\begin{bmatrix} 99 & 99 & 77 & 55 \\ 77 & 66 & 55 & 110 \end{bmatrix}$$

d.
$$\begin{bmatrix} 89 & 99 & 77 & 55 \\ 77 & 66 & 55 & 110 \end{bmatrix}$$

e.
$$\begin{bmatrix} 77 & 99 & 77 & 55 \\ 77 & 66 & 55 & 110 \end{bmatrix}$$

____ 10.   If possible, find AB.

$$A = \begin{bmatrix} -7 & -5 \\ -2 & 4 \\ 5 & -3 \end{bmatrix}, B = \begin{bmatrix} 6 \\ 4 \end{bmatrix}$$

a.
$$\begin{bmatrix} -22 \\ -28 \\ 42 \end{bmatrix}$$

b.
$$\begin{bmatrix} -62 \\ 4 \\ 18 \end{bmatrix}$$

c.
$$\begin{bmatrix} -42 & -20 \\ -12 & 16 \\ 30 & -12 \end{bmatrix}$$

d.
$$\begin{bmatrix} -22 & -28 & 42 \end{bmatrix}$$

e. not possible

_____ 11. Find the inverse of the matrix (if it exists).

$$\begin{bmatrix} 6 & 0 \\ 0 & 7 \end{bmatrix}$$

a.
$$\begin{bmatrix} \dfrac{1}{6} & 0 \\ 0 & \dfrac{1}{7} \end{bmatrix}$$

b.
$$\begin{bmatrix} \dfrac{1}{7} & 0 \\ 0 & \dfrac{1}{7} \end{bmatrix}$$

c.
$$\begin{bmatrix} \dfrac{1}{7} & 0 \\ 0 & 0 \end{bmatrix}$$

d.
$$\begin{bmatrix} 0 & \dfrac{1}{7} \\ \dfrac{1}{7} & 0 \end{bmatrix}$$

e.
$$\begin{bmatrix} \dfrac{1}{7} & 0 \\ 0 & \dfrac{1}{7} \end{bmatrix}$$

_____ 12.   Use the inverse formula $A^{-1} = \dfrac{1}{ad-bc}\begin{bmatrix} d & -b \\ -c & a \end{bmatrix}$ to find the inverse of the 2×2

matrix (if it exists).

$$\begin{bmatrix} 5 & -6 \\ -7 & 6 \end{bmatrix}$$

a.
$$-\frac{1}{12}\begin{bmatrix} 6 & 6 \\ 7 & 5 \end{bmatrix}$$

b.
$$-\frac{1}{12}\begin{bmatrix} -6 & 6 \\ 7 & -5 \end{bmatrix}$$

c.
$$-\frac{1}{12}\begin{bmatrix} -6 & -6 \\ -7 & -5 \end{bmatrix}$$

d.
$$-\frac{1}{12}\begin{bmatrix} 6 & -6 \\ 7 & 5 \end{bmatrix}$$

e.
$$-\frac{1}{12}\begin{bmatrix} -6 & -6 \\ 7 & 5 \end{bmatrix}$$

_____ 13.   Use an inverse matrix to solve (if possible) the system of linear equations.

$$\begin{cases} 18x + 12y = 13 \\ 30x + 24y = 23 \end{cases}$$

a.
$$\left(\frac{1}{2}, \frac{1}{3}\right)$$

b.
$$\left(3, \frac{1}{3}\right)$$

c.
$$\left(\frac{2}{3}, \frac{1}{3}\right)$$

d.
$$\left(\frac{1}{2}, \frac{5}{12}\right)$$

e.
$$\left(\frac{1}{2}, 5\right)$$

_____   14.   A small home business creates muffins, bones, and cookies for dogs. In addition to other ingredients, each muffin requires 2 units of beef, 3 units of chicken, and 2 units of liver. Each bone requires 1 unit of beef, 1 unit of chicken, and 1 unit of liver. Each cookie requires 2 units of beef, 1 unit of chicken, and 1.5 units of liver. Find the numbers of muffins, bones, and cookies that the company can create with the given amounts of ingredients.

500 units of beef
300 units of chicken
400 units of liver

a.   0 muffins, 100   bones, 200 cookies
b.   0 muffins, 0   bones, 300 cookies
c.   200 muffins, 100   bones, 0 cookies
d.   100 muffins,   0 bones, 200 cookies
e.   200 muffins, 100   bones, 200 cookies

_____   15.   Solve the system of linear equations
$$\begin{cases} -6x + 8y = 15 \\ -12x - 2y = -10 \end{cases}$$

using the inverse matrix $\begin{bmatrix} -\dfrac{1}{54} & -\dfrac{2}{27} \\ \dfrac{1}{9} & -\dfrac{1}{18} \end{bmatrix}$

a.
$$\begin{bmatrix} x \\ y \end{bmatrix} = \begin{bmatrix} \dfrac{10}{27} \\ -\dfrac{5}{6} \end{bmatrix}$$

b.
$$\begin{bmatrix} x \\ y \end{bmatrix} = \begin{bmatrix} \dfrac{25}{54} \\ \dfrac{20}{9} \end{bmatrix}$$

c.
$$\begin{bmatrix} x \\ y \end{bmatrix} = \begin{bmatrix} -\dfrac{25}{36} \\ -\dfrac{5}{6} \end{bmatrix}$$

d.
$$\begin{bmatrix} x \\ y \end{bmatrix} = \begin{bmatrix} -\dfrac{5}{6} \\ 0 \end{bmatrix}$$

e.

$$\begin{bmatrix} x \\ y \end{bmatrix} = \begin{bmatrix} -\dfrac{25}{54} \\[2mm] \dfrac{10}{27} \end{bmatrix}$$

_____ 16.   Find the determinant of the matrix.

[9]

a. 9
b. 0
c. −9
d. $\dfrac{1}{9}$
e. $-\dfrac{1}{9}$

_____ 17.   Find the determinant of the matrix.

$$\begin{bmatrix} -\dfrac{1}{2} & \dfrac{1}{3} \\[3mm] -27 & \dfrac{1}{3} \end{bmatrix}$$

a. $\dfrac{53}{6}$
b. $\dfrac{6}{53}$
c. $\dfrac{3}{53}$
d. $-\dfrac{53}{6}$
e. $-\dfrac{6}{53}$

____ 18. Find the determinant of the matrix by the method of expansion by cofactors. Expand using the row 1.

$$\begin{bmatrix} -7 & 6 & 5 \\ 8 & 9 & 10 \\ 6 & -7 & 5 \end{bmatrix}$$

a. -1234
b. 1235
c. -1236
d. -1235
e. -1233

____ 19. Evaluate the determinant in which the entries are functions.

$$\begin{vmatrix} x & \ln x \\ 1 & 3/x \end{vmatrix}$$

a. $x - \ln x$
b. $3x + \ln x$
c. $3 + \ln x$
d. $3x - \ln x$
e. $3 - \ln x$

____ 20. Given $A = \begin{bmatrix} 0 & -3 & -6 \\ 9 & 6 & -3 \\ 0 & -12 & -3 \end{bmatrix}$ and $B = \begin{bmatrix} -9 & 6 & 0 \\ -3 & 3 & -6 \\ -9 & -3 & -3 \end{bmatrix}$, find $|BA|$.

a. $-182,250$
b. $-153,090$
c. $218,700$
d. $273,375$
e. $290,871$

_____ 21.   Use Crammer's Rule to solve (if possible) the system of equations.

$$\begin{cases} -7x + 11y = -41 \\ 3x - 9y = 39 \end{cases}$$

a. $(-5, -2)$
b. $(2, 5)$
c. $(-2, 5)$
d. $(2, -5)$
e. $(-2, -5)$

_____ 22.   Use a determinant and the given vertices of a triangle to find the area of the triangle.

$(-4, 4), (1, 6), (2, -4)$

a. 52
b. 26
c. $\dfrac{3}{19}$
d. $\dfrac{3}{11}$
e. −26

_____ 23.   Find a value of such that the triangle with the given vertices has an area of 4 square units.

$(-4, 2), (0, 2), (-3, y)$

a. $y = 4$ or $y = -\dfrac{1}{4}$
b. $y = 4$ or $y = 0$
c. $y = -\dfrac{1}{4}$ or $y = 0$
d. $y = -4$ or $y = 0$
e. $y = \dfrac{1}{4}$ or $y = 0$

_____   24.   Use a determinant and the given vertices of a triangle to find the area of the triangle.

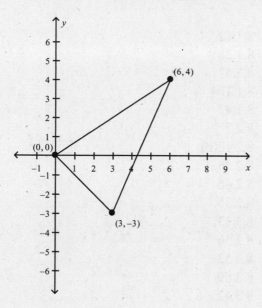

a.   16
b.   15
c. $\dfrac{2}{17}$
d. $\dfrac{5}{19}$
e.   6

_____   25.   Use a determinant to find y such that $(8,-20), (16,y)$, and $(20,-8)$ are collinear.

a. $y = -12$
b. $y = 20$
c. $y = -44$
d. $y = 4$
e. $y = -8$

Ch 8 Form A
Answer Section

1.	ANS:	E	PTS: 1	REF:	8.1.12
2.	ANS:	E	PTS: 1	REF:	8.1.28
3.	ANS:	D	PTS: 1	REF:	8.1.57
4.	ANS:	E	PTS: 1	REF:	8.1.104
5.	ANS:	C	PTS: 1	REF:	8.1.42
6.	ANS:	D	PTS: 1	REF:	8.2.7
7.	ANS:	A	PTS: 1	REF:	8.2.13(b)
8.	ANS:	A	PTS: 1	REF:	8.2.26
9.	ANS:	E	PTS: 1	REF:	8.2.66
10.	ANS:	B	PTS: 1	REF:	8.2.35
11.	ANS:	A	PTS: 1	REF:	8.3.13
12.	ANS:	A	PTS: 1	REF:	8.3.36
13.	ANS:	A	PTS: 1	REF:	8.3.52
14.	ANS:	A	PTS: 1	REF:	8.3.69
15.	ANS:	B	PTS: 1	REF:	8.3.42
16.	ANS:	A	PTS: 1	REF:	8.4.5
17.	ANS:	A	PTS: 1	REF:	8.4.19
18.	ANS:	D	PTS: 1	REF:	8.4.33a
19.	ANS:	E	PTS: 1	REF:	8.4.89
20.	ANS:	E	PTS: 1	REF:	8.4.67d
21.	ANS:	E	PTS: 1	REF:	8.5.7
22.	ANS:	B	PTS: 1	REF:	8.5.29
23.	ANS:	B	PTS: 1	REF:	8.5.33
24.	ANS:	B	PTS: 1	REF:	8.5.22
25.	ANS:	A	PTS: 1	REF:	8.5.45

Ch 8 Form B

____ 1.   Select the order for the following matrix.

$$\begin{bmatrix} -5 & 7 & 13 & 0 \\ 0 & 0 & 3 & 3 \\ 2 & 2 & 7 & 7 \end{bmatrix}$$

a. 4×3
b. 4×2
c. 4×4
d. 3×3
e. 3×4

____ 2.   Fill in the blank(s) using elementary row operations to form a row-equivalent matrix.

$$\begin{bmatrix} 9 & 12 & 7 \\ 8 & -7 & 10 \end{bmatrix}$$

$$\begin{bmatrix} 3 & \ldots & \dfrac{7}{3} \\ 8 & -7 & 10 \end{bmatrix}$$

a.
$$\begin{bmatrix} 3 & 4 & \dfrac{7}{3} \\ 8 & -7 & 10 \end{bmatrix}$$

b.
$$\begin{bmatrix} 3 & 4 & \dfrac{7}{3} \\ 8 & -7 & 10 \end{bmatrix}$$

c.
$$\begin{bmatrix} 3 & 15 & \dfrac{7}{3} \\ 8 & -7 & 10 \end{bmatrix}$$

d.
$$\begin{bmatrix} 3 & -4 & \dfrac{7}{3} \\ 8 & -7 & 10 \end{bmatrix}$$

e.
$$\begin{bmatrix} 3 & 7 & \dfrac{7}{3} \\ 8 & -7 & 10 \end{bmatrix}$$

_____ 3.   Find the system of linear equations represented by the augmented matrix. Then use back substitution to solve. (Use variables x, y, z and if applicable.)

$$\begin{bmatrix} 1 & -1 & 4 & \vdots & 6 \\ 0 & 1 & -1 & \vdots & 4 \\ 0 & 0 & 1 & \vdots & -4 \end{bmatrix}$$

a.
$$\begin{cases} x - y + 4z = 6 \\ y + z = 4 \\ z = 4 \end{cases}$$

$(-18, 8, 4)$

b.
$$\begin{cases} x - y + 4z = 6 \\ y - z = -4 \\ z = 4 \end{cases}$$

$(22, 0, -4)$

c.
$$\begin{cases} x - y + 4z = 6 \\ y + z = 4 \\ z = -4 \end{cases}$$

$(30, 8, -4)$

d.
$$\begin{cases} x - y + 4z = 6 \\ y - z = 4 \\ z = -4 \end{cases}$$

$(22, 0, -4)$

e. $\begin{cases} x - y + 4z = 6 \\ \ y + z = -4 \\ \ z = 4 \end{cases}$

$(-18, 8, 4)$

_____ 4.   The currents in an electrical network are given by the solution of the system

$\begin{cases} I_1 - I_2 + I_3 = 3 \\ 3I_1 + 4I_2 = 47 \\ I_2 + 3I_3 = 26 \end{cases}$

where I_1, I_2 and I_3 are measured in amperes. Solve the system of equations using matrices.

a. $I_1 = 9, I_2 = 8, I_3 = 6$
b. $I_1 = 8, I_2 = 8, I_3 = 6$
c. $I_1 = 6, I_2 = 8, I_3 = 6$
d. $I_1 = 7, I_2 = 8, I_3 = 6$
e. $I_1 = 5, I_2 = 8, I_3 = 6$

_____ 5.   Write the matrix in reduced row-echelon form.

$$\begin{bmatrix} 1 & 0 & -8 & -51 \\ -8 & 9 & 9 & 32 \\ -6 & 0 & 4 & -2 \end{bmatrix}$$

a. $\begin{bmatrix} 1 & 0 & 0 & 4 \\ 0 & 1 & 0 & 2 \\ 0 & 0 & 1 & 7 \end{bmatrix}$

b. $\begin{bmatrix} 1 & 0 & 0 & 5 \\ 0 & 1 & 0 & 1 \\ 0 & 0 & 1 & 7 \end{bmatrix}$

c. $\begin{bmatrix} 1 & 0 & 0 & 1 \\ 0 & 1 & 0 & 1 \\ 0 & 0 & 1 & 1 \end{bmatrix}$

d. $\begin{bmatrix} 1 & 0 & 0 & 0 \\ 0 & 1 & 0 & 0 \\ 0 & 0 & 1 & 0 \end{bmatrix}$

e. $\begin{bmatrix} 1 & 0 & 0 & 5 \\ 0 & 1 & 0 & 7 \\ 0 & 0 & 1 & 1 \end{bmatrix}$

_____ 6.   Find x and y.

$$\begin{bmatrix} x & -2 \\ 7 & y \end{bmatrix} = \begin{bmatrix} -4 & -2 \\ 7 & 22 \end{bmatrix}$$

a. $x = \dfrac{1}{4}, y = \dfrac{1}{22}$

b. $x = 4, y = -22$

c. $x = -\dfrac{1}{4}, y = \dfrac{1}{22}$

d. $x = -4, y = 22$

e. $x = \dfrac{1}{4}, y = -\dfrac{1}{22}$

_____ 7.   Find $A - B$.

$$A = \begin{bmatrix} 4 & -1 \\ 3 & 2 \\ -5 & 7 \end{bmatrix}, B = \begin{bmatrix} 1 & 5 \\ -2 & -2 \\ 2 & 8 \end{bmatrix}$$

a. $\begin{bmatrix} 7 & -6 \\ -7 & 4 \\ 5 & -1 \end{bmatrix}$

b. $\begin{bmatrix} 1 & 4 \\ 5 & -6 \\ -7 & -1 \end{bmatrix}$

c.
$$\begin{bmatrix} 5 & -6 \\ 5 & -1 \\ -7 & 4 \end{bmatrix}$$

d.
$$\begin{bmatrix} -1 & -6 \\ 4 & 5 \\ -7 & -1 \end{bmatrix}$$

e.
$$\begin{bmatrix} 3 & -6 \\ 5 & 4 \\ -7 & -1 \end{bmatrix}$$

_____   8.   Use the matrix capabilities of a graphing utility to evaluate the expression. Round your results to three decimal places, if necessary.

$$55\left(\begin{bmatrix} 19 & -10 \\ -13 & 20 \end{bmatrix} + \begin{bmatrix} -15 & 12 \\ 12 & 14 \end{bmatrix}\right)$$

a.
$$\begin{bmatrix} 218 & -55 \\ 110 & 1870 \end{bmatrix}$$

b.
$$\begin{bmatrix} 216 & 110 \\ -55 & 1870 \end{bmatrix}$$

c.
$$\begin{bmatrix} 220 & 110 \\ -55 & 1870 \end{bmatrix}$$

d.
$$\begin{bmatrix} 224 & 1870 \\ -55 & 110 \end{bmatrix}$$

e.
$$\begin{bmatrix} 222 & 110 \\ 1870 & -55 \end{bmatrix}$$

_____ 9.   A corporation has four factories, each of which manufactures sport utility vehicles and pickup trucks. The number of units of vehicle produced at factory in one day is represented by a_{ij} in the matrix

$$A = \begin{bmatrix} 90 & 50 & 70 & 50 \\ 80 & 90 & 80 & 80 \end{bmatrix}.$$

Find the production levels if production is increased by 10%.

a.
$$\begin{bmatrix} 113 & 55 & 77 & 55 \\ 88 & 99 & 88 & 88 \end{bmatrix}$$

b.
$$\begin{bmatrix} 128 & 55 & 77 & 55 \\ 88 & 99 & 88 & 88 \end{bmatrix}$$

c.
$$\begin{bmatrix} 99 & 55 & 77 & 55 \\ 88 & 99 & 88 & 88 \end{bmatrix}$$

d.
$$\begin{bmatrix} 123 & 55 & 77 & 55 \\ 88 & 99 & 88 & 88 \end{bmatrix}$$

e.
$$\begin{bmatrix} 118 & 55 & 77 & 55 \\ 88 & 99 & 88 & 88 \end{bmatrix}$$

_____ 10.   If possible, find AB.

$$A = \begin{bmatrix} 9 & -7 \\ -2 & 3 \\ -8 & -3 \end{bmatrix}, B = \begin{bmatrix} 2 \\ 8 \end{bmatrix}$$

a.
$$\begin{bmatrix} 74 \\ -28 \\ 8 \end{bmatrix}$$

b.
$$\begin{bmatrix} 74 & -28 & 8 \end{bmatrix}$$

c.
$$\begin{bmatrix} 18 & -56 \\ -4 & 24 \\ -16 & -24 \end{bmatrix}$$

d.
$$\begin{bmatrix} -38 \\ 20 \\ -40 \end{bmatrix}$$

e. not possible

_____ 11.   Find the inverse of the matrix (if it exists).

$$\begin{bmatrix} 3 & 0 \\ 0 & 4 \end{bmatrix}$$

a.
$$\begin{bmatrix} \dfrac{1}{4} & 0 \\ 0 & 0 \end{bmatrix}$$

b.
$$\begin{bmatrix} \dfrac{1}{3} & 0 \\ 0 & \dfrac{1}{4} \end{bmatrix}$$

c.
$$\begin{bmatrix} \dfrac{1}{4} & 0 \\ 0 & \dfrac{1}{4} \end{bmatrix}$$

d.
$$\begin{bmatrix} 0 & \dfrac{1}{4} \\ \dfrac{1}{4} & 0 \end{bmatrix}$$

e.
$$\begin{bmatrix} \dfrac{1}{4} & 0 \\ 0 & \dfrac{1}{4} \end{bmatrix}$$

_____ 12.   Use the inverse formula $A^{-1} = \dfrac{1}{ad - bc} \begin{bmatrix} d & -b \\ -c & a \end{bmatrix}$ to find the inverse of the 2×2 matrix (if it exists).

$$\begin{bmatrix} 2 & -3 \\ -4 & 3 \end{bmatrix}$$

a. $-\dfrac{1}{6}\begin{bmatrix} -3 & -3 \\ -4 & -2 \end{bmatrix}$

b. $-\dfrac{1}{6}\begin{bmatrix} -3 & -3 \\ 4 & 2 \end{bmatrix}$

c. $-\dfrac{1}{6}\begin{bmatrix} -3 & 3 \\ 4 & -2 \end{bmatrix}$

d. $-\dfrac{1}{6}\begin{bmatrix} 3 & -3 \\ 4 & 2 \end{bmatrix}$

e. $-\dfrac{1}{6}\begin{bmatrix} 3 & 3 \\ 4 & 2 \end{bmatrix}$

_____ 13.   Use an inverse matrix to solve (if possible) the system of linear equations.

$$\begin{cases} 18x + 12y = 14 \\ 30x + 24y = 24 \end{cases}$$

a. $\left(\dfrac{2}{3}, 3\right)$

b. $\left(\dfrac{2}{3}, \dfrac{1}{6}\right)$

c. $\left(\dfrac{5}{6}, \dfrac{1}{6}\right)$

d. $\left(\dfrac{2}{3}, \dfrac{1}{4}\right)$

e. $\left(4, \dfrac{1}{6}\right)$

_____ 14.   A small home business creates muffins, bones, and cookies for dogs. In addition to other ingredients, each muffin requires 2 units of beef, 3 units of chicken, and 2 units of liver. Each bone requires 1 unit of beef, 1 unit of chicken, and 1 unit of liver. Each cookie requires 2 units of beef, 1 unit of chicken, and 1.5 units of liver. Find the numbers of muffins, bones, and cookies that the company can create with the given amounts of ingredients.

500 units of beef
300 units of chicken
400 units of liver

a. 200 muffins, 100 bones, 200 cookies
b. 0 muffins, 100 bones, 200 cookies
c. 0 muffins, 0 bones, 300 cookies
d. 100 muffins, 0 bones, 200 cookies
e. 200 muffins, 100 bones, 0 cookies

_____ 15. Solve the system of linear equations

$$\begin{cases} -8x - 4y = 3 \\ -16x + 8y = -2 \end{cases}$$

using the inverse matrix $\begin{bmatrix} -\dfrac{1}{16} & -\dfrac{1}{32} \\ -\dfrac{1}{8} & \dfrac{1}{16} \end{bmatrix}$

a.
$$\begin{bmatrix} x \\ y \end{bmatrix} = \begin{bmatrix} -\dfrac{9}{128} \\ -\dfrac{1}{8} \end{bmatrix}$$

b.
$$\begin{bmatrix} x \\ y \end{bmatrix} = \begin{bmatrix} -\dfrac{1}{8} \\ -\dfrac{1}{2} \end{bmatrix}$$

c.
$$\begin{bmatrix} x \\ y \end{bmatrix} = \begin{bmatrix} -\dfrac{3}{32} \\ \dfrac{1}{32} \end{bmatrix}$$

d.
$$\begin{bmatrix} x \\ y \end{bmatrix} = \begin{bmatrix} -\dfrac{1}{8} \\ 0 \end{bmatrix}$$

e.
$$\begin{bmatrix} x \\ y \end{bmatrix} = \begin{bmatrix} \dfrac{1}{32} \\ -\dfrac{1}{8} \end{bmatrix}$$

____   16.   Find the determinant of the matrix.

[5]

a. 0

b. $-\dfrac{1}{5}$

c. $\dfrac{1}{5}$

d. 5

e. −5

____   17.   Find the determinant of the matrix.

$$\begin{bmatrix} -\dfrac{1}{2} & \dfrac{1}{3} \\[2mm] -12 & \dfrac{1}{3} \end{bmatrix}$$

a. $\dfrac{23}{6}$

b. $\dfrac{6}{23}$

c. $-\dfrac{23}{6}$

d. $-\dfrac{6}{23}$

e. $\dfrac{3}{23}$

_____   18.   Find the determinant of the matrix by the method of expansion by cofactors. Expand using the row 1.

$$\begin{bmatrix} -6 & 5 & 4 \\ 7 & 8 & 9 \\ 5 & -6 & 4 \end{bmatrix}$$

a. −758
b. 759
c. −759
d. −757
e. −760

_____   19.   Evaluate the determinant in which the entries are functions.

$$\begin{vmatrix} x & \ln x \\ 1 & 2/x \end{vmatrix}$$

a. $2 + \ln x$
b. $2x + \ln x$
c. $2x - \ln x$
d. $x - \ln x$
e. $2 - \ln x$

_____   20.   Given $A = \begin{bmatrix} 0 & 3 & 6 \\ -9 & -6 & 3 \\ 0 & 12 & 3 \end{bmatrix}$ and $B = \begin{bmatrix} 9 & -6 & 0 \\ 3 & -3 & 6 \\ 9 & 3 & 3 \end{bmatrix}$, find $|BA|$.

a. 273,375
b. −182,250
c. 290,871
d. 218,700
e. −153,090

_____ 21.   Use Crammer's Rule to solve (if possible) the system of equations.

$$\begin{cases} -7x + 11y = -52 \\ 3x - 9y = 48 \end{cases}$$

a. $(2,6)$
b. $(-6,-2)$
c. $(2,-6)$
d. $(-2,6)$
e. $(-2,-6)$

_____ 22.   Use a determinant and the given vertices of a triangle to find the area of the triangle.

$(-4,4),(1,5),(2,-5)$

a. $-\dfrac{51}{2}$

b. $\dfrac{2}{19}$

c. $\dfrac{51}{2}$

d. 51

e. $\dfrac{4}{11}$

_____ 23.   Find a value of such that the triangle with the given vertices has an area of 4 square units.

$(-2,3),(0,5),(-1,y)$

a. $y = -\dfrac{1}{8}$ or $y = 0$

b. $y = 8$ or $y = -\dfrac{1}{8}$

c. $y = 8$ or $y = 0$

d. $y = \dfrac{1}{8}$ or $y = 0$

e. $y = -8$ or $y = 0$

_____ 24.   Use a determinant and the given vertices of a triangle to find the area of the triangle.

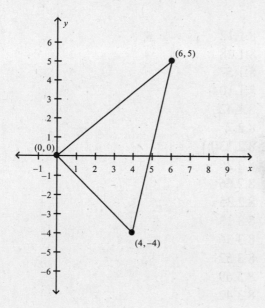

a. 6
b. 16
c. $\dfrac{3}{19}$
d. 22
e. $\dfrac{6}{17}$

_____ 25.   Use a determinant to find y such that $(8,-20)$, $(16,y)$, and $(20,-8)$ are collinear.
a. $y = 20$
b. $y = -44$
c. $y = -8$
d. $y = -12$
e. $y = 4$

Ch 8 Form B
Answer Section

1.	ANS:	E	PTS:	1	REF:	8.1.12
2.	ANS:	B	PTS:	1	REF:	8.1.28
3.	ANS:	D	PTS:	1	REF:	8.1.57
4.	ANS:	E	PTS:	1	REF:	8.1.104
5.	ANS:	B	PTS:	1	REF:	8.1.42
6.	ANS:	D	PTS:	1	REF:	8.2.7
7.	ANS:	E	PTS:	1	REF:	8.2.13(b)
8.	ANS:	C	PTS:	1	REF:	8.2.26
9.	ANS:	C	PTS:	1	REF:	8.2.66
10.	ANS:	D	PTS:	1	REF:	8.2.35
11.	ANS:	B	PTS:	1	REF:	8.3.13
12.	ANS:	E	PTS:	1	REF:	8.3.36
13.	ANS:	B	PTS:	1	REF:	8.3.52
14.	ANS:	B	PTS:	1	REF:	8.3.69
15.	ANS:	B	PTS:	1	REF:	8.3.42
16.	ANS:	D	PTS:	1	REF:	8.4.5
17.	ANS:	A	PTS:	1	REF:	8.4.19
18.	ANS:	C	PTS:	1	REF:	8.4.33a
19.	ANS:	E	PTS:	1	REF:	8.4.89
20.	ANS:	C	PTS:	1	REF:	8.4.67d
21.	ANS:	E	PTS:	1	REF:	8.5.7
22.	ANS:	C	PTS:	1	REF:	8.5.29
23.	ANS:	C	PTS:	1	REF:	8.5.33
24.	ANS:	D	PTS:	1	REF:	8.5.22
25.	ANS:	D	PTS:	1	REF:	8.5.45

Ch 8 Form C

_____ 1.   Select the order for the following matrix.

$$\begin{bmatrix} 9 & -8 & 7 & 5 \end{bmatrix}$$

a. 2×2
b. 4×4
c. 3×1
d. 4×1
e. 1×4

_____ 2.   Identify the elementary row operation being performed to obtain the new row-equivalent matrix.

Original Matrix   _New Row-Equivalent Matrix_

$$\begin{bmatrix} -4 & 6 & 1 \\ 4 & -1 & -9 \end{bmatrix}$$ $$\begin{bmatrix} 20 & 0 & -53 \\ 4 & -1 & -9 \end{bmatrix}$$

a.   Add 6 times Row 2 to Row 1.
b.   Add 3 times Row 1 to Row 2.
c.   Add 6 times Row 1 to Row 2.
d.   Add 4 times Row 2 to Row 1.
e.   Add 3 times Row 2 to Row 1.

_____ 3.   An augmented matrix that represents a system of linear equations (in variables x, y, z and w if applicable) has been reduced using Gauss-Jordan elimination. Find the solution represented by the augmented matrix.

$$\begin{bmatrix} 1 & 0 & 0 & \vdots & -4 \\ 0 & 1 & 0 & \vdots & -10 \\ 0 & 0 & 1 & \vdots & 4 \end{bmatrix}$$

a. $(-4, 10, 4)$
b. $(4, -10, 4)$
c. $(-4, -10, 4)$
d. $(-4, -10, -4)$
e. $(-4, 4, -10)$

_____ 4.   Use the matrix capabilities of a graphing utility to reduce the augmented matrix corresponding to the system of equations, and solve the system.

$$\begin{cases} x + 2y + 2z + 4w = 24 \\ 3x + 6y + 5z + 12w = 65 \\ x + 3y - 3z + 2w = -9 \\ 6x - y - z + w = -22 \end{cases}$$

a. $(-2, 4, 7, -1)$
b. $(-2, -4, 7, 1)$
c. $(-2, 4, -7, 1)$
d. $(-2, -4, -7, -1)$
e. $(-2, 4, 7, 1)$

_____ 5.   Use matrices to solve the system of equations (if possible). Use Gaussian elimination with back-substitution or Gauss-Jordan elimination.

$$\begin{cases} 9x + 8y = 31 \\ -x - 4y = -19 \end{cases}$$

a. $x = 5, y = -1$
b. $x = 1, y = -5$
c. $x = -1, y = 5$
d. $x = 5, y = 1$
e. no solution

_____ 6.   Find x and y.

$$\begin{bmatrix} 16 & 4 & 16 & 4 \\ -3 & 13 & 15 & 16 \\ 0 & 2 & 22 & 0 \end{bmatrix} = \begin{bmatrix} 16 & 4 & 7x+2 & 4 \\ -3 & 13 & 15 & 8x \\ 0 & 2 & 3y-5 & 0 \end{bmatrix}$$

a. $x = -2, y = 9$
b. $x = 2, y = -9$
c. $x = -2, y = -9$
d. $x = 16, y = 22$
e. $x = 2, y = 9$

_____ 7.   Find $3A - 2B$.

$$A = \begin{bmatrix} 7 & -4 \\ 4 & 5 \\ -3 & 5 \end{bmatrix}, B = \begin{bmatrix} 3 & 6 \\ -1 & -2 \\ 2 & 12 \end{bmatrix}$$

a. $\begin{bmatrix} 17 & -24 \\ 14 & -9 \\ -13 & 19 \end{bmatrix}$

b. $\begin{bmatrix} 15 & -24 \\ 14 & 19 \\ -13 & -9 \end{bmatrix}$

c. $\begin{bmatrix} 13 & 19 \\ 14 & -24 \\ -13 & -9 \end{bmatrix}$

d. $\begin{bmatrix} 11 & -24 \\ 19 & 14 \\ -13 & -9 \end{bmatrix}$

e. $\begin{bmatrix} 19 & -24 \\ -13 & 19 \\ 14 & -9 \end{bmatrix}$

_____ 8.   If possible, find AB and state the order of the result.

$$A = \begin{bmatrix} 0 & 5 & 0 \\ 5 & 0 & 5 \\ 2 & 4 & -2 \end{bmatrix}, B = \begin{bmatrix} -1 & 8 \\ 4 & -3 \\ 7 & -7 \end{bmatrix}$$

a. $\begin{bmatrix} 18 & -15 \\ 5 & 30 \\ 0 & 18 \end{bmatrix}$

Order: 3×2

b. $\begin{bmatrix} 20 & -15 \\ 30 & 5 \\ 0 & 18 \end{bmatrix}$

Order: 3×2

c. $\begin{bmatrix} 24 & 5 \\ 30 & -15 \\ 0 & 18 \end{bmatrix}$

Order: 3×2

d. $\begin{bmatrix} 22 & -15 \\ 0 & 5 \\ 30 & 18 \end{bmatrix}$

Order: 3×2

e. $\begin{bmatrix} 16 & -15 \\ 30 & 5 \\ 18 & 0 \end{bmatrix}$

Order: 3×2

_____ 9.   Find x and y.

$$\begin{bmatrix} x+2 & 6 & 8y \\ 1 & -2x & 6 \\ -1 & y-1 & 6 \end{bmatrix} = \begin{bmatrix} -x+6 & 6 & -24 \\ 1 & -4 & 6 \\ -1 & -4 & 6 \end{bmatrix}$$

a. $x = -3, y = 3$
b. $x = 3, y = -4$
c.   no solution
d. $x = 2, y = -3$
e. $x = 2, y = -4$

_____ 10.   Use the matrix capabilities of a graphing utility to find AB, if possible.

$$A = \begin{bmatrix} -2 & -2 \\ 7 & 2 \\ 6 & 4 \\ -5 & 3 \end{bmatrix}, B = \begin{bmatrix} -7 & 2 & -3 & 9 \\ 7 & 7 & 4 & 6 \end{bmatrix}$$

a.
$$\begin{bmatrix} 0 \\ 28 \\ -6 \\ -27 \end{bmatrix}$$

b.
$$\begin{bmatrix} 0 & -18 & -2 & -30 \\ -35 & 28 & -13 & 75 \\ -14 & 40 & -2 & 78 \\ 56 & 11 & 27 & -27 \end{bmatrix}$$

c.
$$\begin{bmatrix} 28 & 10 & 14 & -6 \\ -63 & 0 & -29 & 51 \\ -70 & -16 & -34 & 30 \\ 14 & -31 & 3 & -63 \end{bmatrix}$$

d.   not possible

e.
$$\begin{bmatrix} 0 & -35 & -14 & 56 \\ -18 & 28 & 40 & 11 \\ -2 & -13 & -2 & 27 \\ -30 & 75 & 78 & -27 \end{bmatrix}$$

_____ 11. Find the inverse of the matrix (if it exists).

$$\begin{bmatrix} 2 & -3 \\ 3 & -4 \end{bmatrix}$$

a.
$$\begin{bmatrix} -4 & 3 \\ 3 & 2 \end{bmatrix}$$

b.
$$\begin{bmatrix} -4 & -3 \\ -3 & -2 \end{bmatrix}$$

c.
$$\begin{bmatrix} -4 & 3 \\ -3 & 2 \end{bmatrix}$$

d.
$$\begin{bmatrix} -4 & -3 \\ -3 & 2 \end{bmatrix}$$

e.
$$\begin{bmatrix} -4 & -3 \\ 3 & 2 \end{bmatrix}$$

_____ 12.   Use the inverse formula $A^{-1} = \dfrac{1}{ad-bc}\begin{bmatrix} d & -b \\ -c & a \end{bmatrix}$ to find the inverse of the 2×2

matrix (if it exists).

$$\begin{bmatrix} -13 & 4 \\ 6 & 3 \end{bmatrix}$$

a.
$$-\frac{1}{63}\begin{bmatrix} -3 & 4 \\ 6 & -13 \end{bmatrix}$$

b.
$$-\frac{1}{63}\begin{bmatrix} -3 & -4 \\ -6 & -13 \end{bmatrix}$$

c.
$$-\frac{1}{63}\begin{bmatrix} 3 & -4 \\ 6 & 13 \end{bmatrix}$$

d.
$$-\frac{1}{63}\begin{bmatrix} 3 & -4 \\ -6 & -13 \end{bmatrix}$$

e.
$$-\frac{1}{63}\begin{bmatrix} -3 & -4 \\ 6 & 13 \end{bmatrix}$$

_____ 13.   Use an inverse matrix to solve (if possible) the system of linear equations.

$$\begin{cases} 0.2x - 0.6y = 16.4 \\ -x + 1.4y = -22.8 \end{cases}$$

a. $(-29, -37)$
b. $(-27, -37)$
c. $(-28, -37)$
d. $(-28, -35)$
e. $(-29, -36)$

____ 14.   A small home business creates muffins, bones, and cookies for dogs. In addition to other ingredients, each muffin requires 2 units of beef, 3 units of chicken, and 2 units of liver. Each bone requires 1 unit of beef, 1 unit of chicken, and 1 unit of liver. Each cookie requires 2 units of beef, 1 unit of chicken, and 1.5 units of liver. Find the numbers of muffins, bones, and cookies that the company can create with the given amounts of ingredients.

600 units of beef
550 units of chicken
525 units of liver

a.   100 muffins, 100   bones, 150 cookies
b.   100 muffins, 100   bones, 550 cookies
c.   150 muffins, 100   bones, 100 cookies
d.   150 muffins, 100   bones, 150 cookies
e.   100 muffins,   100 bones, 150 cookies

____ 15.   Solve the system of linear equations

$$\begin{cases} 9x + 9y + 9z = -2 \\ 27x + 45y + 36z = 6 \\ 27x + 54y + 45z = -4 \end{cases}$$

using the inverse matrix $\dfrac{1}{9}\begin{bmatrix} 1 & 1 & -1 \\ -3 & 2 & -1 \\ 3 & -3 & 2 \end{bmatrix}$.

a.
$$\begin{bmatrix} x \\ y \\ z \end{bmatrix} = \begin{bmatrix} \dfrac{8}{9} \\ \dfrac{22}{9} \\ -\dfrac{32}{9} \end{bmatrix}$$

b.
$$\begin{bmatrix} x \\ y \\ z \end{bmatrix} = \begin{bmatrix} \dfrac{22}{9} \\ -\dfrac{32}{9} \\ \dfrac{8}{9} \end{bmatrix}$$

c.

$$\begin{bmatrix} x \\ y \\ z \end{bmatrix} = \begin{bmatrix} -\dfrac{32}{9} \\ \dfrac{8}{9} \\ \dfrac{22}{9} \end{bmatrix}$$

d.

$$\begin{bmatrix} x \\ y \\ z \end{bmatrix} = \begin{bmatrix} -\dfrac{10}{9} \\ \dfrac{4}{3} \\ -\dfrac{8}{9} \end{bmatrix}$$

e.

$$\begin{bmatrix} x \\ y \\ z \end{bmatrix} = \begin{bmatrix} \dfrac{10}{9} \\ -\dfrac{2}{3} \\ \dfrac{4}{9} \end{bmatrix}$$

_____   16.   Find the determinant of the matrix.

$$\begin{bmatrix} -3 & 0 \\ 4 & 7 \end{bmatrix}$$

a. $-\dfrac{1}{21}$

b. 21

c. $\dfrac{1}{21}$

d. -21

e. 0

_____   17.   Find all minors of the matrix.

$$\begin{bmatrix} 4 & 5 \\ 1 & -2 \end{bmatrix}$$

a. $M_{11} = -2, M_{12} = 1, M_{21} = 5, M_{22} = 4$
b. $M_{11} = 5, M_{12} = 1, M_{21} = 2, M_{22} = 4$
c. $M_{11} = 4, M_{12} = 5, M_{21} = 1, M_{22} = 2$
d. $M_{11} = -2, M_{12} = -1, M_{21} = -5, M_{22} = -4$
e. $M_{11} = 1, M_{12} = 2, M_{21} = 4, M_{22} = 5$

_____   18.   Use the matrix capabilities of a graphing utility to evaluate the determinant.

$$\begin{bmatrix} 6 & 6 & -9 \\ 0 & -4 & 7 \\ 6 & 4 & 3 \end{bmatrix}$$

a.   −202
b.   −204
c.   −203
d.   −206
e.   −205

_____   19.   Find the determinant of the matrix $\begin{bmatrix} -\dfrac{3}{2} & -\dfrac{1}{2} \\ 6 & \dfrac{1}{3} \end{bmatrix}$.

a. $-\dfrac{53}{6}$

b. $-\dfrac{7}{2}$

c. $\dfrac{5}{2}$

d. $-\dfrac{9}{4}$

e. $\dfrac{3}{4}$

_____ 20.   Solve for x given the following equation involving a determinant.

$$\begin{vmatrix} x+5 & 2 \\ -1 & x+2 \end{vmatrix} = 0$$

a. $x = -4, -3$
b. $x = 4, -3$
c. $x = -8, -6$
d. $x = -4, 3$
e. $x = 4, 3$

_____ 21.   Use Crammer's Rule to solve (if possible) the system of equations.

$$\begin{cases} 5x - 4y + z = -5 \\ -x + 2y - 2z = 4 \\ 3x + y + z = 0 \end{cases}$$

a. $(0, -1, -1)$
b. $(0, 1, 0)$
c. $(0, 1, -1)$
d. $(0, -1, 1)$
e. $(0, 1, 1)$

_____ 22.   Find y such that the points are collinear.

$(2, -3), (5, y), (4, -5)$

a. $y = -6$
b. $y = -3$
c. $y = -4$
d. $y = -5$
e. $y = 6$

_____ 23.   Find a value of such that the triangle with the given vertices has an area of 6 square units.

$(2, 0), (5, -3), (-2, y)$

a. $y = -8$ or $y = -4$
b. $y = 8$ or $y = -4$
c. $y = 8$ or $y = 0$
d. $y = 0$ or $y = 4$
e. $y = 8$ or $y = 4$

24. Use a determinant and the given vertices of a triangle to find the area of the triangle.

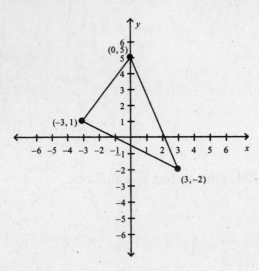

a. $\dfrac{2}{19}$

b. $\dfrac{6}{17}$

c. $\dfrac{33}{2}$

d. 37

e. 35

25. Use a determinant to determine whether the points $(9,-7),(7,-9)$ and $(12,-5)$ are collinear.

a. $\begin{vmatrix} 9 & -7 & 1 \\ 7 & -9 & 1 \\ 12 & -5 & 1 \end{vmatrix} = 2$; therefore, the points are not collinear.

b. $\begin{vmatrix} 9 & -7 & 1 \\ 7 & -9 & 1 \\ 12 & -5 & 1 \end{vmatrix} = 0$; therefore, the points are collinear.

Ch 8 Form C
Answer Section

1.	ANS:	E	PTS:	1	REF:	8.1.10
2.	ANS:	A	PTS:	1	REF:	8.1.35
3.	ANS:	C	PTS:	1	REF:	8.1.61
4.	ANS:	E	PTS:	1	REF:	8.1.88
5.	ANS:	C	PTS:	1	REF:	8.1.63
6.	ANS:	E	PTS:	1	REF:	8.2.9
7.	ANS:	B	PTS:	1	REF:	8.2.13(d)
8.	ANS:	B	PTS:	1	REF:	8.2.34
9.	ANS:	D	PTS:	1	REF:	8.2.10
10.	ANS:	B	PTS:	1	REF:	8.2.43
11.	ANS:	C	PTS:	1	REF:	8.3.15
12.	ANS:	D	PTS:	1	REF:	8.3.36
13.	ANS:	A	PTS:	1	REF:	8.3.54
14.	ANS:	A	PTS:	1	REF:	8.3.71
15.	ANS:	A	PTS:	1	REF:	8.3.46
16.	ANS:	D	PTS:	1	REF:	8.4.8
17.	ANS:	A	PTS:	1	REF:	8.4.25a
18.	ANS:	B	PTS:	1	REF:	8.4.55
19.	ANS:	C	PTS:	1	REF:	8.4.19
20.	ANS:	A	PTS:	1	REF:	8.4.83
21.	ANS:	C	PTS:	1	REF:	8.5.16
22.	ANS:	A	PTS:	1	REF:	8.5.45
23.	ANS:	C	PTS:	1	REF:	8.5.36
24.	ANS:	C	PTS:	1	REF:	8.5.24
25.	ANS:	A	PTS:	1	REF:	8.5.40

Ch 8 Form D

_____ 1. Select the order for the following matrix.

$$\begin{bmatrix} 7 & -6 & 5 & 2 \end{bmatrix}$$

a. 3×1
b. 4×4
c. 1×4
d. 2×2
e. 4×1

_____ 2. Identify the elementary row operation being performed to obtain the new row-equivalent matrix.

Original Matrix

$$\begin{bmatrix} -3 & 4 & 1 \\ 2 & -1 & -7 \end{bmatrix}$$

New Row-Equivalent Matrix

$$\begin{bmatrix} 5 & 0 & -27 \\ 2 & -1 & -7 \end{bmatrix}$$

a. Add 2 times Row 1 to Row 2.
b. Add 4 times Row 1 to Row 2.
c. Add 2 times Row 2 to Row 1.
d. Add 3 times Row 2 to Row 1.
e. Add 4 times Row 2 to Row 1.

_____ 3. An augmented matrix that represents a system of linear equations (in variables x, y, z and w if applicable) has been reduced using Gauss-Jordan elimination. Find the solution represented by the augmented matrix.

$$\begin{bmatrix} 1 & 0 & 0 & \vdots & -4 \\ 0 & 1 & 0 & \vdots & -10 \\ 0 & 0 & 1 & \vdots & 4 \end{bmatrix}$$

a. $(-4, -10, 4)$
b. $(-4, 4, -10)$
c. $(-4, -10, -4)$
d. $(4, -10, 4)$
e. $(-4, 10, 4)$

_____   4.   Use the matrix capabilities of a graphing utility to reduce the augmented matrix corresponding to the system of equations, and solve the system.

$$\begin{cases} x + 2y + 2z + 4w = 17 \\ 3x + 6y + 5z + 12w = 45 \\ x + 3y - 3z + 2w = -16 \\ 6x - y - z + w = -35 \end{cases}$$

a. $(-5, 1, -6, 2)$
b. $(-5, -1, 6, 2)$
c. $(-5, 1, 6, -2)$
d. $(-5, -1, -6, -2)$
e. $(-5, 1, 6, 2)$

_____   5.   Use matrices to solve the system of equations (if possible). Use Gaussian elimination with back-substitution or Gauss-Jordan elimination.

$$\begin{cases} 7x + 5y = -3 \\ -4x + 5y = 41 \end{cases}$$

a. $x = 5, y = -4$
b. $x = -4, y = 5$
c. no solution
d. $x = 4, y = -5$
e. $x = 5, y = 4$

_____   6.   Find x and y.

$$\begin{bmatrix} 16 & 4 & 27 & 4 \\ -3 & 13 & 15 & 27 \\ 0 & 2 & 22 & 0 \end{bmatrix} = \begin{bmatrix} 16 & 4 & 7x+6 & 4 \\ -3 & 13 & 15 & 9x \\ 0 & 2 & 3y-5 & 0 \end{bmatrix}$$

a. $x = 3, y = -9$
b. $x = -3, y = 9$
c. $x = 27, y = 22$
d. $x = -3, y = -9$
e. $x = 3, y = 9$

_____ 7. Find $3A - 2B$.

$$A = \begin{bmatrix} 8 & -2 \\ 3 & 4 \\ -5 & 4 \end{bmatrix}, B = \begin{bmatrix} 4 & 8 \\ -3 & -6 \\ 1 & 8 \end{bmatrix}$$

a. $\begin{bmatrix} 16 & -22 \\ 15 & 24 \\ -17 & -4 \end{bmatrix}$

b. $\begin{bmatrix} 18 & -22 \\ 15 & -4 \\ -17 & 24 \end{bmatrix}$

c. $\begin{bmatrix} 20 & -22 \\ -17 & 24 \\ 15 & -4 \end{bmatrix}$

d. $\begin{bmatrix} 12 & -22 \\ 24 & 15 \\ -17 & -4 \end{bmatrix}$

e. $\begin{bmatrix} 14 & 24 \\ 15 & -22 \\ -17 & -4 \end{bmatrix}$

_____ 8.   If possible, find AB and state the order of the result.

$$A = \begin{bmatrix} 0 & 2 & 0 \\ 5 & 0 & 5 \\ 2 & 6 & -2 \end{bmatrix}, B = \begin{bmatrix} -3 & 7 \\ 2 & -3 \\ 8 & -8 \end{bmatrix}$$

a. $\begin{bmatrix} 2 & -6 \\ -5 & 25 \\ -10 & 12 \end{bmatrix}$

Order: 3×2

b. $\begin{bmatrix} 0 & -6 \\ 25 & -5 \\ 12 & -10 \end{bmatrix}$

Order: 3×2

c. $\begin{bmatrix} 6 & -6 \\ -10 & -5 \\ 25 & 12 \end{bmatrix}$

Order: 3×2

d. $\begin{bmatrix} 4 & -6 \\ 25 & -5 \\ -10 & 12 \end{bmatrix}$

Order: 3×2

e. $\begin{bmatrix} 8 & -5 \\ 25 & -6 \\ -10 & 12 \end{bmatrix}$

Order: 3×2

_____ 9.   Find x and y.

$$\begin{bmatrix} x+6 & -9 & 6y \\ 5 & -9x & 1 \\ 6 & y+1 & 9 \end{bmatrix} = \begin{bmatrix} 0x+11 & -9 & 12 \\ 5 & -45 & 1 \\ 6 & 3 & 9 \end{bmatrix}$$

a. $x = 5, y = 1$

b. $x = 5, y = 2$

c. $x = 6, y = 1$

d. $x = 2, y = 6$

e.   no solution

_____ 10.　　Use the matrix capabilities of a graphing utility to find AB, if possible.

$$A = \begin{bmatrix} 4 & 2 \\ -7 & -8 \\ -3 & 9 \\ -4 & 2 \end{bmatrix}, \; B = \begin{bmatrix} 0 & -2 & 8 & 0 \\ -4 & -6 & -9 & 9 \end{bmatrix}$$

a.　not possible

b.
$$\begin{bmatrix} 8 & 4 & 50 & -18 \\ -32 & -34 & -128 & 72 \\ 36 & 60 & 57 & -81 \\ 8 & 20 & -14 & -18 \end{bmatrix}$$

c.
$$\begin{bmatrix} -8 & -20 & 14 & 18 \\ 32 & 62 & 16 & -72 \\ -36 & -48 & -105 & 81 \\ -8 & -4 & -50 & 18 \end{bmatrix}$$

d.
$$\begin{bmatrix} -8 & 32 & -36 & -8 \\ -20 & 62 & -48 & -4 \\ 14 & 16 & -105 & -50 \\ 18 & -72 & 81 & 18 \end{bmatrix}$$

e.
$$\begin{bmatrix} -8 \\ 62 \\ -42 \\ 18 \end{bmatrix}$$

_____ 11.   Find the inverse of the matrix (if it exists).

$$\begin{bmatrix} 2 & -3 \\ 3 & -4 \end{bmatrix}$$

a.
$$\begin{bmatrix} -4 & -3 \\ -3 & -2 \end{bmatrix}$$

b.
$$\begin{bmatrix} -4 & 3 \\ -3 & 2 \end{bmatrix}$$

c.
$$\begin{bmatrix} -4 & -3 \\ -3 & 2 \end{bmatrix}$$

d.
$$\begin{bmatrix} -4 & 3 \\ 3 & 2 \end{bmatrix}$$

e.
$$\begin{bmatrix} -4 & -3 \\ 3 & 2 \end{bmatrix}$$

_____ 12.   Use the inverse formula $A^{-1} = \dfrac{1}{ad - bc} \begin{bmatrix} d & -b \\ -c & a \end{bmatrix}$ to find the inverse of the 2×2 matrix (if it exists).

$$\begin{bmatrix} -11 & 2 \\ 4 & 1 \end{bmatrix}$$

a. $-\dfrac{1}{19} \begin{bmatrix} -1 & -2 \\ 4 & 11 \end{bmatrix}$

b. $-\dfrac{1}{19} \begin{bmatrix} -1 & 2 \\ 4 & -11 \end{bmatrix}$

c. $-\dfrac{1}{19} \begin{bmatrix} -1 & -2 \\ -4 & -11 \end{bmatrix}$

d. $-\dfrac{1}{19} \begin{bmatrix} 1 & -2 \\ -4 & -11 \end{bmatrix}$

e. $-\dfrac{1}{19} \begin{bmatrix} 1 & -2 \\ 4 & 11 \end{bmatrix}$

_____ 13.   Use an inverse matrix to solve (if possible) the system of linear equations.

$$\begin{cases} 0.2x - 0.6y = 22.4 \\ -x + 1.4y = -28.8 \end{cases}$$

a. $(-43, -50)$
b. $(-44, -52)$
c. $(-44, -51)$
d. $(-42, -52)$
e. $(-43, -52)$

_____ 14.   A small home business creates muffins, bones, and cookies for dogs. In addition to other ingredients, each muffin requires 2 units of beef, 3 units of chicken, and 2 units of liver. Each bone requires 1 unit of beef, 1 unit of chicken, and 1 unit of liver. Each cookie requires 2 units of beef, 1 unit of chicken, and 1.5 units of liver. Find the numbers of muffins, bones, and cookies that the company can create with the given amounts of ingredients.

500 units of beef
450 units of chicken
425 units of liver

a.   150 muffins, 0 bones, 150 cookies
b.   100 muffins, 100 bones, 450 cookies
c.   150 muffins, 0 bones, 100 cookies
d.   100 muffins, 0 bones, 150 cookies
e.   0 muffins, 100 bones, 150 cookies

_____ 15.   Solve the system of linear equations

$$\begin{cases} 7x + 7y + 7z = 1 \\ 21x + 35y + 28z = -3 \\ 21x + 42y + 35z = 2 \end{cases}$$

using the inverse matrix $\dfrac{1}{7}\begin{bmatrix} 1 & 1 & -1 \\ -3 & 2 & -1 \\ 3 & -3 & 2 \end{bmatrix}$.

a.
$$\begin{bmatrix} x \\ y \\ z \end{bmatrix} = \begin{bmatrix} \dfrac{5}{7} \\ -\dfrac{6}{7} \\ \dfrac{4}{7} \end{bmatrix}$$

b.
$$\begin{bmatrix} x \\ y \\ z \end{bmatrix} = \begin{bmatrix} -\dfrac{11}{7} \\ \dfrac{16}{7} \\ -\dfrac{4}{7} \end{bmatrix}$$

c.

$$\begin{bmatrix} x \\ y \\ z \end{bmatrix} = \begin{bmatrix} \dfrac{16}{7} \\ -\dfrac{4}{7} \\ -\dfrac{11}{7} \end{bmatrix}$$

d.

$$\begin{bmatrix} x \\ y \\ z \end{bmatrix} = \begin{bmatrix} -\dfrac{4}{7} \\ -\dfrac{11}{7} \\ \dfrac{16}{7} \end{bmatrix}$$

e.

$$\begin{bmatrix} x \\ y \\ z \end{bmatrix} = \begin{bmatrix} -\dfrac{5}{7} \\ \dfrac{3}{7} \\ -\dfrac{2}{7} \end{bmatrix}$$

_____ 16.   Find the determinant of the matrix.

$$\begin{bmatrix} -9 & 0 \\ 10 & 6 \end{bmatrix}$$

a. $\dfrac{1}{54}$

b. $-\dfrac{1}{54}$

c. -54

d. 0

c. 54

_____ 17.   Find all minors of the matrix.

$$\begin{bmatrix} 5 & 6 \\ 5 & -10 \end{bmatrix}$$

a. $M_{11} = -10,\ M_{12} = -5,\ M_{21} = -6,\ M_{22} = -5$
b. $M_{11} = 5,\ M_{12} = 10,\ M_{21} = 5,\ M_{22} = 6$
c. $M_{11} = 6,\ M_{12} = 5,\ M_{21} = 10,\ M_{22} = 5$
d. $M_{11} = -10,\ M_{12} = 5,\ M_{21} = 6,\ M_{22} = 5$
e. $M_{11} = 5,\ M_{12} = 6,\ M_{21} = 5,\ M_{22} = 10$

_____ 18.   Use the matrix capabilities of a graphing utility to evaluate the determinant.

$$\begin{bmatrix} 9 & 6 & -3 \\ 0 & -6 & 6 \\ 6 & 7 & 2 \end{bmatrix}$$

a. -379
b. -380
c. -377
d. -378
e. -376

_____ 19.   Find the determinant of the matrix $\begin{bmatrix} -\dfrac{3}{5} & \dfrac{6}{5} \\ 3 & -\dfrac{1}{3} \end{bmatrix}$.

a. $\dfrac{24}{35}$
b. $-\dfrac{12}{35}$
c. $\dfrac{19}{5}$
d. $-\dfrac{17}{5}$
e. $-\dfrac{7}{5}$

_____ 20.   Solve for x given the following equation involving a determinant.

$$\begin{vmatrix} x+1 & -14 \\ -1 & x-4 \end{vmatrix} = 0$$

a. $x = 3, 6$
b. $x = 3, -6$
c. $x = -3, -6$
d. $x = -3, 6$
e. $x = -6, 12$

_____ 21.   Use Crammer's Rule to solve (if possible) the system of equations.

$$\begin{cases} 5x - 4y + z = -18 \\ -x + 2y - 2z = 12 \\ 3x + y + z = 2 \end{cases}$$

a. $(0,-4,2)$
b. $(0,-4,-2)$
c. $(0,4,2)$
d. $(0,4,-2)$
e. $(0,4,0)$

_____ 22.   Find y such that the points are collinear.

$(5,-5), (4,y), (6,-5)$

a. $y = -2$
b. $y = -4$
c. $y = 5$
d. $y = -3$
e. $y = -5$

_____ 23.   Find a value of such that the triangle with the given vertices has an area of 6 square units.

$(4,0), (8,-2), (-2,y)$

a. $y = 6$ or $y = 0$
b. $y = -6$ or $y = -2$
c. $y = 6$ or $y = -2$
d. $y = 0$ or $y = 2$
e. $y = 6$ or $y = 2$

_____ 24. Use a determinant and the given vertices of a triangle to find the area of the triangle.

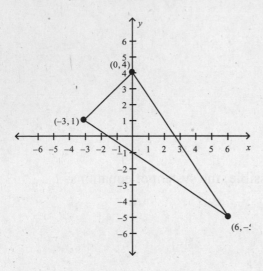

a. $\dfrac{45}{2}$

b. 49

c. $\dfrac{4}{19}$

d. $\dfrac{4}{17}$

e. 47

_____ 25. Use a determinant to determine whether the points $(-7,-9), (-9,-11)$ and $(-4,-7)$ are collinear.

a. $\begin{vmatrix} -7 & -9 & 1 \\ -9 & -11 & 1 \\ -4 & -7 & 1 \end{vmatrix} = 0$; therefore, the points are collinear.

b. $\begin{vmatrix} -7 & -9 & 1 \\ -9 & -11 & 1 \\ -4 & -7 & 1 \end{vmatrix} = 2$; therefore, the points are not collinear.

Ch 8 Form D
Answer Section

1.	ANS:	C	PTS:	1	REF:	8.1.10
2.	ANS:	E	PTS:	1	REF:	8.1.35
3.	ANS:	A	PTS:	1	REF:	8.1.61
4.	ANS:	E	PTS:	1	REF:	8.1.88
5.	ANS:	B	PTS:	1	REF:	8.1.63
6.	ANS:	E	PTS:	1	REF:	8.2.9
7.	ANS:	A	PTS:	1	REF:	8.2.13(d)
8.	ANS:	D	PTS:	1	REF:	8.2.34
9.	ANS:	B	PTS:	1	REF:	8.2.10
10.	ANS:	C	PTS:	1	REF:	8.2.43
11.	ANS:	B	PTS:	1	REF:	8.3.15
12.	ANS:	D	PTS:	1	REF:	8.3.36
13.	ANS:	B	PTS:	1	REF:	8.3.54
14.	ANS:	D	PTS:	1	REF:	8.3.71
15.	ANS:	D	PTS:	1	REF:	8.3.46
16.	ANS:	C	PTS:	1	REF:	8.4.8
17.	ANS:	D	PTS:	1	REF:	8.4.25a
18.	ANS:	D	PTS:	1	REF:	8.4.55
19.	ANS:	D	PTS:	1	REF:	8.4.19
20.	ANS:	D	PTS:	1	REF:	8.4.83
21.	ANS:	D	PTS:	1	REF:	8.5.16
22.	ANS:	E	PTS:	1	REF:	8.5.45
23.	ANS:	A	PTS:	1	REF:	8.5.36
24.	ANS:	A	PTS:	1	REF:	8.5.24
25.	ANS:	B	PTS:	1	REF:	8.5.40

Ch 8 Form E

_____ 1.   Select the augmented matrix for the system of linear equations.

$$\begin{cases} 8x - 5y + z = 16 \\ 17x \quad\;\; - 9z = 14 \end{cases}$$

a.
$$\begin{bmatrix} 8 & -5 & 1 & \vdots & 16 \\ 17 & -9 & 14 & \vdots & 0 \end{bmatrix}$$

b.
$$\begin{bmatrix} 8 & -5 & 1 & \vdots & 16 \\ 17 & -9 & 0 & \vdots & 14 \end{bmatrix}$$

c.
$$\begin{bmatrix} 8 & 5 & 1 & \vdots & 16 \\ 17 & 0 & -9 & \vdots & 14 \end{bmatrix}$$

d.
$$\begin{bmatrix} 8 & -5 & 1 & \vdots & 16 \\ 17 & 0 & 9 & \vdots & 14 \end{bmatrix}$$

e.
$$\begin{bmatrix} 8 & -5 & 1 & \vdots & 16 \\ 17 & 0 & -9 & \vdots & 14 \end{bmatrix}$$

_____   2.   Perform the sequence of row operations on the following matrix.
Add R_3 to R_4.

$$\begin{bmatrix} 8 & 1 \\ 0 & 3 \\ -4 & 5 \\ 5 & 1 \end{bmatrix}$$

a.
$$\begin{bmatrix} 8 & 1 \\ 0 & 3 \\ 9 & 6 \\ 5 & 1 \end{bmatrix}$$

b.
$$\begin{bmatrix} 8 & 1 \\ 0 & 3 \\ -4 & 5 \\ 13 & 9 \end{bmatrix}$$

c.
$$\begin{bmatrix} 8 & 1 \\ 0 & 3 \\ 1 & 6 \\ 5 & 1 \end{bmatrix}$$

d.
$$\begin{bmatrix} 8 & 1 \\ 0 & 3 \\ -4 & 5 \\ 9 & 13 \end{bmatrix}$$

e.
$$\begin{bmatrix} 8 & 1 \\ 0 & 3 \\ -4 & 5 \\ 1 & 6 \end{bmatrix}$$

_____   3.   Use matrices to find the system of equations (if possible). Use Gaussian elimination with

back-substitution or Gauss-Jordan elimination.

$$\begin{cases} 2x + 6y = 10 \\ 2x + 3y = 7 \end{cases}$$

a. $(10, 1)$
b. $(2, 1)$
c. $(2, -6)$
d. $(-2, 1)$
e. $(2, -1)$

_____   4.   Write the system of linear equations represented by the augmented matrix. (Use variables x, y, z, and w.)

$$\begin{bmatrix} -2 & 0 & 0 & -7 & \vdots & -5 \\ -3 & -4 & 0 & 0 & \vdots & 5 \\ 0 & 4 & -1 & 5 & \vdots & 6 \\ 0 & 0 & 7 & 6 & \vdots & -3 \end{bmatrix}$$

a. $\begin{cases} -2x \quad\quad\quad\; -7w = -5 \\ -3x - 4y \quad\quad\quad = 5 \\ \quad\quad 4y - z + 5w = 6 \\ \quad\quad 7y + 6z \quad\; = -3 \end{cases}$

b. $\begin{cases} -2x \quad\; -7z \quad\; = -5 \\ -3x \quad\; -4z \quad\; = 5 \\ \quad\quad 4y - z + 5w = 6 \\ \quad\quad 7zz + 6w = -3 \end{cases}$

c. $\begin{cases} -2x - 7y \quad\quad = -5 \\ -3x - 4y \quad\quad = 5 \\ \quad\; 4x - y + 5z = 6 \\ \quad\; 7x + 6y \quad\quad = -3 \end{cases}$

d. $\begin{cases} -2x \quad\quad\quad\; -7w = -5 \\ -3x - 4y \quad\quad\quad = 5 \\ \quad\quad 4y - z + 5w = 6 \\ \quad\quad 7z + 6w = -3 \end{cases}$

e. $\begin{cases} -2x \quad\; -7z \quad\; = -5 \\ -3x - 4y \quad\quad\; = 5 \\ \quad\quad 4y - z + 5w = 6 \\ \quad\quad 7zz + 5w = -3 \end{cases}$

_____ 5.   Determine whether the two systems of linear equations yield the same solutions. If so, find the solutions using matrices.

$$\begin{cases} x + 5y - 6z = -14 \\ y - 7z = -45 \\ z = 7 \end{cases}$$

$$\begin{cases} x + 4y + 3z = 33 \\ y - 7z = -45 \\ z = 7 \end{cases}$$

a. $x = -8, y = -4, z = 7$
b. $x = 8, y = 4, z = 7$
c. $x = -4, y = 7, z = 8$
d.   The systems yield different solutions.
e. $x = 4, y = 7, z = 8$

_____ 6.   Find $A - B$.

$$A = \begin{bmatrix} 5 & -5 \\ 2 & -5 \end{bmatrix}, B = \begin{bmatrix} 2 & -5 \\ -5 & 5 \end{bmatrix}$$

a.
$$\begin{bmatrix} 7 & 0 \\ -10 & 7 \end{bmatrix}$$

b.
$$\begin{bmatrix} 5 & -10 \\ 7 & 0 \end{bmatrix}$$

c.
$$\begin{bmatrix} -1 & 0 \\ 7 & -10 \end{bmatrix}$$

d.
$$\begin{bmatrix} 1 & 0 \\ 7 & -10 \end{bmatrix}$$

e.
$$\begin{bmatrix} 3 & 0 \\ 7 & -10 \end{bmatrix}$$

_____ 7.   Find $3A - 2B$.

$$A = \begin{bmatrix} -1 & 3 & 0 \\ 2 & -4 & 4 \\ 2 & 8 & -3 \\ 0 & 8 & -6 \\ -4 & -3 & 0 \end{bmatrix}, B = \begin{bmatrix} -3 & 9 & 2 \\ 2 & -2 & -5 \\ 8 & -8 & -2 \\ 5 & 4 & -2 \\ 0 & 4 & -4 \end{bmatrix}$$

a.
$$\begin{bmatrix} 3 & -9 & -4 \\ 2 & -8 & 22 \\ -10 & 40 & -5 \\ -10 & 16 & -14 \\ -12 & -17 & 8 \end{bmatrix}$$

b.
$$\begin{bmatrix} 1 & -9 & -4 \\ -10 & -8 & -14 \\ -10 & 40 & -5 \\ 2 & 16 & 22 \\ -12 & -17 & 8 \end{bmatrix}$$

c.
$$\begin{bmatrix} 7 & -9 & -4 \\ 22 & -8 & 2 \\ -10 & 40 & -5 \\ -14 & 16 & -10 \\ -12 & -17 & 8 \end{bmatrix}$$

d.
$$\begin{bmatrix} -1 & -9 & -4 \\ 2 & -8 & 22 \\ -12 & 40 & 8 \\ -10 & 16 & -14 \\ -10 & -17 & -5 \end{bmatrix}$$

e.
$$\begin{bmatrix} 5 & -9 & -4 \\ 2 & -8 & 22 \\ -5 & 40 & -10 \\ -10 & 16 & -14 \\ 8 & -17 & -12 \end{bmatrix}$$

_____   8.   Use Gauss-Jordan elimination on the augmented matrix $[A \vdots B]$ to solve for the matrix X.

$$\begin{cases} -x_1 + x_2 = 8 \\ -2x_1 + x_2 = 0 \end{cases}$$

a.
$$\begin{bmatrix} -8 \\ -16 \end{bmatrix}$$

b.
$$\begin{bmatrix} 8 \\ 16 \end{bmatrix}$$

c.
$$\begin{bmatrix} 8 \\ -16 \end{bmatrix}$$

d.
$$\begin{bmatrix} -8 \\ 16 \end{bmatrix}$$

e.
$$\begin{bmatrix} 16 \\ 8 \end{bmatrix}$$

_____ 9.   If possible, find $2A - 5B$.

$$A = \begin{bmatrix} -1 & 9 & -4 \\ 3 & 6 & 4 \end{bmatrix}, B = \begin{bmatrix} -4 & 8 & -6 \\ 2 & 0 & 5 \end{bmatrix}$$

a.
$$\begin{bmatrix} -22 & 58 & -38 \\ 16 & 12 & 33 \end{bmatrix}$$

b.   not possible

c.
$$\begin{bmatrix} 1 & 0 & 0 \\ 0 & 1 & 0 \end{bmatrix}$$

d.
$$\begin{bmatrix} -5 & 17 & -10 \\ 5 & 6 & 9 \end{bmatrix}$$

e.
$$\begin{bmatrix} 18 & -22 & 22 \\ -4 & 12 & -17 \end{bmatrix}$$

_____ 10.   Write the system of linear equations as a matrix equation $AX = B$, and use

Gauss-Jordan elimination on the augmented matrix $\begin{bmatrix} A & \vdots & B \end{bmatrix}$ to solve for the matrix X.

$$\begin{cases} x_1 + 2x_2 = -8 \\ 5x_1 - 5x_2 = -10 \end{cases}$$

a.
$$\begin{bmatrix} 1 & 2 \\ 5 & -5 \end{bmatrix} \begin{bmatrix} -8 \\ -4 \end{bmatrix} = \begin{bmatrix} -10 \\ -2 \end{bmatrix}$$

b.
$$\begin{bmatrix} 1 & 2 \\ 5 & -5 \end{bmatrix} = \begin{bmatrix} -8 \\ -10 \end{bmatrix}$$

c.
$$\begin{bmatrix} 1 & 2 \\ 5 & -5 \end{bmatrix} \begin{bmatrix} -4 \\ -8 \end{bmatrix} = \begin{bmatrix} -2 \\ -10 \end{bmatrix}$$

d.
$$\begin{bmatrix} 1 & 2 \\ 5 & -5 \end{bmatrix} \begin{bmatrix} -4 \\ -2 \end{bmatrix} = \begin{bmatrix} -8 \\ -10 \end{bmatrix}$$

e.
$$\begin{bmatrix} 1 & 2 \\ 5 & -5 \end{bmatrix} \begin{bmatrix} -8 \\ -10 \end{bmatrix} = \begin{bmatrix} -4 \\ -2 \end{bmatrix}$$

_____   11.   Find the inverse of the matrix (if it exists).

$$\begin{bmatrix} -9 & 0 & 0 \\ 6 & 0 & 0 \\ 5 & 9 & 11 \end{bmatrix}$$

a. $\begin{bmatrix} 9 & 0 & 0 \\ 6 & 0 & 0 \\ 5 & 9 & 11 \end{bmatrix}$

b.   Does not exist

c. $\begin{bmatrix} -9 & 0 & 0 \\ -6 & 0 & 0 \\ -5 & 9 & 11 \end{bmatrix}$

d. $\begin{bmatrix} -9 & 0 & 0 \\ -6 & 0 & 0 \\ 5 & 9 & 11 \end{bmatrix}$

e. $\begin{bmatrix} -9 & 0 & 0 \\ -6 & 0 & 0 \\ -5 & -9 & -11 \end{bmatrix}$

_____   12.   Solve the system of linear equations.

$x - 2y = 9$

$2x - 3y = 7$

a. $(-13, -11)$
b. $(13, 11)$
c. $(-7, -13)$
d. $(-13, 7)$
e. $(-13, 11)$

_____   13.   A florist is creating 10 centerpieces for the tables at a wedding reception. Roses cost $5.50 each, lilies cost $6 each, and irises cost $3 each. The customer has a budget of $300   allocated for the centerpieces and wants each centerpiece to contain 12 flowers, with twice as many roses as the number of irises and lilies combined.

Write a system of linear equations that represents the situation.

a.
$$\begin{cases} 5.5r + 6l + 3i = 300 \\ r + 2l + 2i = 0 \\ r + l + i = 120 \end{cases}$$

b.
$$\begin{cases} 5.5r + 6l + 3i = 300 \\ -r + 2l + 2i = 0 \\ r + l + i = 120 \end{cases}$$

c.
$$\begin{cases} 5.5r - 6l - 3i = 300 \\ -r - 2l - 2i = 0 \\ r - l - i = 120 \end{cases}$$

d.
$$\begin{cases} 5.5r - 6l + 3i = 300 \\ -r + 2l + 2i = 0 \\ r + l + i = 120 \end{cases}$$

e.
$$\begin{cases} 5.5r + 6l - 3i = 300 \\ -r + 2l + 2i = 0 \\ r + l + i = 120 \end{cases}$$

_____   14.   Find the inverse of the matrix $\begin{bmatrix} 8 & 8 & 8 \\ 24 & 40 & 32 \\ 24 & 48 & 40 \end{bmatrix}$.

a. $-\dfrac{1}{8}\begin{bmatrix} 1 & 0 & -1 \\ -3 & 2 & -1 \\ 2 & -3 & 3 \end{bmatrix}$

b. $8\begin{bmatrix} 1 & 1 & 1 \\ -3 & 0 & -1 \\ 3 & -3 & 2 \end{bmatrix}$

c. $\dfrac{1}{8}\begin{bmatrix} 1 & 1 & 1 \\ -3 & 2 & -1 \\ 3 & -3 & 2 \end{bmatrix}$

d. $-8\begin{bmatrix} 3 & 1 & 0 \\ -3 & 1 & -1 \\ 1 & -3 & 2 \end{bmatrix}$

e. $\dfrac{1}{8}\begin{bmatrix} 1 & 1 & 1 \\ 0 & -2 & -1 \\ 3 & -3 & 2 \end{bmatrix}$

_____ 15. Solve the system of linear equations

$$\begin{cases} 8x_1 - 16x_2 - -8x_3 - 16x_4 = 0 \\ 24x_1 - 40x_2 - 16x_3 - 24x_4 = -15 \\ 16x_1 - 40x_2 - 16x_3 - 40x_4 = 10 \\ -8x_1 + 32x_2 + 32x_3 + 88x_4 = 0 \end{cases}$$

using the inverse matrix $\dfrac{1}{8}\begin{bmatrix} -24 & 7 & 1 & -2 \\ -10 & 3 & 0 & -1 \\ -29 & 7 & 3 & -2 \\ 12 & -3 & -1 & 1 \end{bmatrix}$.

a.
$$\begin{bmatrix} x_1 \\ x_2 \\ x_3 \\ x_4 \end{bmatrix} = \begin{bmatrix} -\dfrac{95}{8} \\ -\dfrac{45}{8} \\ -\dfrac{75}{8} \\ \dfrac{35}{8} \end{bmatrix}$$

d.
$$\begin{bmatrix} x_1 \\ x_2 \\ x_3 \\ x_4 \end{bmatrix} = \begin{bmatrix} 0 \\ -\dfrac{5}{8} \\ 0 \\ -\dfrac{5}{4} \end{bmatrix}$$

b.
$$\begin{bmatrix} x_1 \\ x_2 \\ x_3 \\ x_4 \end{bmatrix} = \begin{bmatrix} -\dfrac{15}{8} \\ \dfrac{5}{8} \\ 0 \\ \dfrac{5}{4} \end{bmatrix}$$

e.
$$\begin{bmatrix} x_1 \\ x_2 \\ x_3 \\ x_4 \end{bmatrix} = \begin{bmatrix} -\dfrac{35}{8} \\ -\dfrac{25}{4} \\ \dfrac{45}{8} \\ -\dfrac{45}{8} \end{bmatrix}$$

c.
$$\begin{bmatrix} x_1 \\ x_2 \\ x_3 \\ x_4 \end{bmatrix} = \begin{bmatrix} -\dfrac{45}{8} \\ -\dfrac{95}{8} \\ 0 \\ \dfrac{35}{8} \end{bmatrix}$$

_____ 16. Find the determinant of the matrix.

$$\begin{bmatrix} 9 & 2 \\ -3 & 3 \end{bmatrix}$$

a. -21
b. 21
c. 33
d. -33
e. $-\dfrac{1}{21}$

_____ 17. Find all the cofactors of the matrix.

$$\begin{bmatrix} 0 & 8 \\ 5 & -10 \end{bmatrix}$$

a. $C_{11} = -10, C_{12} = -5, C_{21} = -8, C_{22} = 0$
b. $C_{11} = 10, C_{12} = 5, C_{21} = 8, C_{22} = 0$
c. $C_{11} = -8, C_{12} = -5, C_{21} = 0, C_{22} = 10$
d. $C_{11} = 0, C_{12} = -8, C_{21} = -5, C_{22} = 10$
e. $C_{11} = 0, C_{12} = -5, C_{21} = -8, C_{22} = 10$

_____ 18. Find $|AB|$.

$$A = \begin{bmatrix} -4 & 0 \\ 0 & 6 \end{bmatrix}, \ B = \begin{bmatrix} 2 & 0 \\ 0 & -4 \end{bmatrix}$$

a. 192
b. 190
c. 191
d. 194
e. 193

_____ 19.   Use the matrix capabilities of a graphing utility to find the determinant of the matrix

$$\begin{bmatrix} 12 & 18 & 6 \\ 0 & 30 & -12 \\ 0 & 0 & -12 \end{bmatrix}.$$

a. -432

b. 0

c. -4320

d. -1080

e. 6480

_____ 20.   Find all cofactors of the matrix $\begin{bmatrix} -9 & 6 & -24 \\ -9 & -6 & 18 \\ 3 & -9 & -18 \end{bmatrix}.$

a. $C_{11} = 270 \quad C_{12} = -108 \quad C_{13} = 99$

     $C_{21} = 324 \quad C_{22} = 234 \quad C_{23} = -63$

     $C_{31} = -36 \quad C_{32} = 378 \quad C_{33} = 108$

b. $C_{11} = 270 \quad C_{12} = 99 \quad C_{13} = -108$

     $C_{21} = 324 \quad C_{22} = -63 \quad C_{23} = 234$

     $C_{31} = -36 \quad C_{32} = 108 \quad C_{33} = 378$

c. $C_{11} = -108 \quad C_{12} = 270 \quad C_{13} = 99$

     $C_{21} = 234 \quad C_{22} = 324 \quad C_{23} = -63$

     $C_{31} = 378 \quad C_{32} = -36 \quad C_{33} = 108$

d. $C_{11} = -36 \quad C_{12} = 378 \quad C_{13} = 108$

     $C_{21} = 324 \quad C_{22} = 234 \quad C_{23} = -63$

     $C_{31} = 270 \quad C_{32} = -108 \quad C_{33} = 99$

e. $C_{11} = 324 \quad C_{12} = 234 \quad C_{13} = -63$

     $C_{21} = 270 \quad C_{22} = -108 \quad C_{23} = 99$

     $C_{31} = -36 \quad C_{32} = 378 \quad C_{33} = 108$

_____ 21. Use a determinant to find an equation of the line passing through the points.

$(-3, 2), (1, 1)$

a. $x + 4y + 5 = 0$
b. $x + 4y - 5 = 5$
c. $x - 4y - 5 = 0$
d. $x + 4y - 5 = 0$
e. $x - 4y + 5 = 0$

_____ 22. Use Crammer's Rule to solve (if possible) the system of equations.

$$\begin{cases} -0.4x + 0.8y = 1.8 \\ 0.2x + 0.3y = 2.2 \end{cases}$$

a. $\left(\dfrac{30}{7}, -\dfrac{31}{7} \right)$

b. $\left(-\dfrac{30}{7}, \dfrac{31}{7} \right)$

c. $\left(\dfrac{30}{7}, \dfrac{31}{7} \right)$

d. $\left(\dfrac{31}{7}, \dfrac{30}{7} \right)$

e. $\left(-\dfrac{30}{7}, -\dfrac{31}{7} \right)$

_____ 23. Use a determinant to determine whether the points
$(x_1, y_1) = (-8, -15), (x_2, y_2) = (0, 5)$ and $(x_3, y_3) = (4, 15)$ are collinear.

a.

True. The points are collinear because $\begin{vmatrix} -8 & -15 & 1 \\ 0 & 5 & 1 \\ 4 & 15 & 1 \end{vmatrix} = 0.$

b.

False. The points are not collinear because $\begin{vmatrix} -8 & -15 & 1 \\ 0 & 5 & 1 \\ 4 & 15 & 1 \end{vmatrix} = 0.$

____ 24.   Use Cramer's Rule to solve the following system of linear equations:

$$\begin{cases} 14x - 21y + 14z = 1 \\ -21x + 14y + 7z = 2 \\ 28x + 7y - 21z = 3 \end{cases}$$

a. $x = \dfrac{2}{7}, y = \dfrac{29}{98}, z = \dfrac{26}{147}$

b. $x = \dfrac{3}{14}, y = \dfrac{33}{98}, z = \dfrac{13}{49}$

c. $x = \dfrac{3}{7}, y = \dfrac{57}{98}, z = \dfrac{18}{49}$

d. $x = \dfrac{2}{7}, y = \dfrac{19}{49}, z = \dfrac{18}{49}$

e. $x = \dfrac{5}{14}, y = \dfrac{26}{49}, z = \dfrac{43}{147}$

____ 25.   Find the uncoded 1×3 row matrices for the message "MERRY CHRISTMAS"; then

encode the message using the encoding matrix $\begin{bmatrix} 0 & -5 & 1 \\ -4 & 1 & 4 \\ 4 & 5 & 0 \end{bmatrix}$.

a.   Uncoded: $\begin{bmatrix} 13 & 5 & 18 \end{bmatrix} \begin{bmatrix} 18 & 25 & 0 \end{bmatrix} \begin{bmatrix} 3 & 8 & 18 \end{bmatrix} \begin{bmatrix} 9 & 19 & 20 \end{bmatrix}$

$\begin{bmatrix} 13 & 1 & 19 \end{bmatrix}$

Encoded: $\begin{bmatrix} 72 & 31 & 17 \end{bmatrix} \begin{bmatrix} 52 & 30 & 33 \end{bmatrix} \begin{bmatrix} -100 & -65 & 118 \end{bmatrix}$

$\begin{bmatrix} 40 & 83 & 35 \end{bmatrix} \begin{bmatrix} 4 & 74 & 85 \end{bmatrix}$

b.   Uncoded: $\begin{bmatrix} 13 & 5 & 18 \end{bmatrix} \begin{bmatrix} 18 & 25 & 0 \end{bmatrix} \begin{bmatrix} 3 & 8 & 18 \end{bmatrix} \begin{bmatrix} 9 & 19 & 20 \end{bmatrix}$

$\begin{bmatrix} 13 & 1 & 19 \end{bmatrix}$

Encoded: $\begin{bmatrix} -100 & -65 & 118 \end{bmatrix} \begin{bmatrix} 40 & 83 & 35 \end{bmatrix} \begin{bmatrix} 4 & 74 & 85 \end{bmatrix}$

$\begin{bmatrix} 72 & 31 & 17 \end{bmatrix} \begin{bmatrix} 52 & 30 & 33 \end{bmatrix}$

c. Uncoded: $\begin{bmatrix} 13 & 5 & 18 \end{bmatrix}\begin{bmatrix} 18 & 25 & 0 \end{bmatrix}\begin{bmatrix} 3 & 8 & 18 \end{bmatrix}\begin{bmatrix} 9 & 19 & 20 \end{bmatrix}$

$\begin{bmatrix} 13 & 1 & 19 \end{bmatrix}$

Encoded: $\begin{bmatrix} 40 & 83 & 35 \end{bmatrix}\begin{bmatrix} 4 & 74 & 85 \end{bmatrix}\begin{bmatrix} 72 & 31 & 17 \end{bmatrix}$

$\begin{bmatrix} 52 & 30 & 33 \end{bmatrix}\begin{bmatrix} -100 & -65 & 118 \end{bmatrix}$

d. Uncoded: $\begin{bmatrix} 13 & 5 & 18 \end{bmatrix}\begin{bmatrix} 18 & 25 & 0 \end{bmatrix}\begin{bmatrix} 3 & 8 & 18 \end{bmatrix}\begin{bmatrix} 9 & 19 & 20 \end{bmatrix}$

$\begin{bmatrix} 13 & 1 & 19 \end{bmatrix}$

Encoded: $\begin{bmatrix} 52 & 30 & 33 \end{bmatrix}\begin{bmatrix} -100 & -65 & 118 \end{bmatrix}\begin{bmatrix} 40 & 83 & 35 \end{bmatrix}$

$\begin{bmatrix} 4 & 74 & 85 \end{bmatrix}\begin{bmatrix} 72 & 31 & 17 \end{bmatrix}$

e. Uncoded: $\begin{bmatrix} 13 & 5 & 18 \end{bmatrix}\begin{bmatrix} 18 & 25 & 0 \end{bmatrix}\begin{bmatrix} 3 & 8 & 18 \end{bmatrix}\begin{bmatrix} 9 & 19 & 20 \end{bmatrix}$

$\begin{bmatrix} 13 & 1 & 19 \end{bmatrix}$

Encoded: $\begin{bmatrix} 4 & 74 & 85 \end{bmatrix}\begin{bmatrix} 72 & 31 & 17 \end{bmatrix}\begin{bmatrix} 52 & 30 & 33 \end{bmatrix}$

$\begin{bmatrix} -100 & -65 & 118 \end{bmatrix}\begin{bmatrix} 40 & 83 & 35 \end{bmatrix}$

Ch 8 Form E
Answer Section

1.	ANS:	E	PTS:	1	REF:	8.1.19
2.	ANS:	E	PTS:	1	REF:	8.1.40
3.	ANS:	B	PTS:	1	REF:	8.1.64
4.	ANS:	D	PTS:	1	REF:	8.1.25
5.	ANS:	D	PTS:	1	REF:	8.1.92
6.	ANS:	E	PTS:	1	REF:	8.2.11(b)
7.	ANS:	A	PTS:	1	REF:	8.2.16(d)
8.	ANS:	B	PTS:	1	REF:	8.2.57(b)
9.	ANS:	E	PTS:	1	REF:	8.2.11d
10.	ANS:	D	PTS:	1	REF:	8.2.60
11.	ANS:	B	PTS:	1	REF:	8.3.21
12.	ANS:	A	PTS:	1	REF:	8.3.43
13.	ANS:	B	PTS:	1	REF:	8.3.74a
14.	ANS:	C	PTS:	1	REF:	8.3.19
15.	ANS:	A	PTS:	1	REF:	8.3.48
16.	ANS:	C	PTS:	1	REF:	8.4.9
17.	ANS:	A	PTS:	1	REF:	8.4.26b
18.	ANS:	A	PTS:	1	REF:	8.4.63d
19.	ANS:	C	PTS:	1	REF:	8.4.55
20.	ANS:	A	PTS:	1	REF:	8.4.29
21.	ANS:	D	PTS:	1	REF:	8.5.49
22.	ANS:	C	PTS:	1	REF:	8.5.11
23.	ANS:	A	PTS:	1	REF:	8.5.74
24.	ANS:	D	PTS:	1	REF:	8.5.16
25.	ANS:	D	PTS:	1	REF:	8.5.56

Ch 8 Form F

_____ 1.   Select the augmented matrix for the system of linear equations.

$$\begin{cases} 8x - 4y + z = 15 \\ 17x \quad\ - 9z = 13 \end{cases}$$

a.
$$\begin{bmatrix} 8 & -4 & 1 & \vdots & 15 \\ 17 & 0 & -9 & \vdots & 13 \end{bmatrix}$$

b.
$$\begin{bmatrix} 8 & -4 & 1 & \vdots & 15 \\ 17 & -9 & 0 & \vdots & 13 \end{bmatrix}$$

c.
$$\begin{bmatrix} 8 & 4 & 1 & \vdots & 15 \\ 17 & 0 & -9 & \vdots & 13 \end{bmatrix}$$

d.
$$\begin{bmatrix} 8 & -4 & 1 & \vdots & 15 \\ 17 & -9 & 13 & \vdots & 0 \end{bmatrix}$$

e.
$$\begin{bmatrix} 8 & -4 & 1 & \vdots & 15 \\ 17 & 0 & 9 & \vdots & 13 \end{bmatrix}$$

_____ 2. Perform the sequence of row operations on the following matrix.
Add R_3 to R_4.

$$\begin{bmatrix} 7 & 1 \\ 0 & 2 \\ -3 & 4 \\ 4 & 1 \end{bmatrix}$$

a.
$$\begin{bmatrix} 7 & 1 \\ 0 & 2 \\ -3 & 4 \\ 7 & 11 \end{bmatrix}$$

b.
$$\begin{bmatrix} 7 & 1 \\ 0 & 2 \\ -3 & 4 \\ 1 & 5 \end{bmatrix}$$

c.
$$\begin{bmatrix} 7 & 1 \\ 0 & 2 \\ 7 & 5 \\ 4 & 1 \end{bmatrix}$$

d.
$$\begin{bmatrix} 7 & 1 \\ 0 & 2 \\ -3 & 4 \\ 11 & 7 \end{bmatrix}$$

e.
$$\begin{bmatrix} 7 & 1 \\ 0 & 2 \\ 1 & 5 \\ 4 & 1 \end{bmatrix}$$

_____ 3.   Use matrices to find the system of equations (if possible). Use Gaussian elimination with
back-substitution or Gauss-Jordan elimination.

$$\begin{cases} 2x + 6y = 16 \\ 2x + 3y = 13 \end{cases}$$

a. $(-2, 1)$
b. $(5, -1)$
c. $(5, -6)$
d. $(16, 1)$
e. $(5, 1)$

_____   4.   Write the system of linear equations represented by the augmented matrix. (Use variables x, y, z, and w.)

$$\begin{bmatrix} -4 & 0 & 0 & -9 & \vdots & 9 \\ 3 & -4 & 0 & 0 & \vdots & -4 \\ 0 & 8 & 2 & 3 & \vdots & -5 \\ 0 & 0 & 5 & -9 & \vdots & -2 \end{bmatrix}$$

a. $\begin{cases} -4x \quad\quad - 9z \quad\quad = 9 \\ 3x - 4y \quad\quad\quad = -4 \\ \quad\quad 8y + 2z + 3w = -5 \\ \quad\quad\quad 5zz + 3w = -2 \end{cases}$

b. $\begin{cases} -4x \quad\quad\quad - 9w = 9 \\ 3x - 4y \quad\quad\quad = -4 \\ \quad\quad 8y + 2z + 3w = -5 \\ \quad\quad\quad 5z - 9w = -2 \end{cases}$

c. $\begin{cases} -4x \quad\quad\quad - 9w = 9 \\ 3x - 4y \quad\quad\quad = -4 \\ \quad\quad 8y + 2z + 3w = -5 \\ \quad\quad 5y - 9z \quad\quad = -2 \end{cases}$

d. $\begin{cases} -4x - 9y \quad\quad = 9 \\ 3x - 4y \quad\quad = -4 \\ 8x + 2y + 3z = -5 \\ 5x - 9y \quad\quad = -2 \end{cases}$

e. $\begin{cases} -4x \quad\quad - 9z \quad\quad = 9 \\ 3x \quad - 4z \quad\quad = -4 \\ \quad\quad 8y + 2z + 3w = -5 \\ \quad\quad\quad 5zz - 9w = -2 \end{cases}$

_____ 5. Determine whether the two systems of linear equations yield the same solutions. If so, find the solutions using matrices.

$$\begin{cases} x + 9y - 4z = -70 \\ \quad\quad y + 6z = -8 \\ \quad\quad\quad z = 0 \end{cases}$$

$$\begin{cases} x - -9y - 8z = 69 \\ \quad\quad y - 7z = -8 \\ \quad\quad\quad z = 0 \end{cases}$$

a. $x = -8, y = 0, z = 2$
b. $x = -2, y = 8, z = 0$
c. $x = 8, y = 0, z = 2$
d. $x = 2, y = -8, z = 0$
e. The systems yield different solutions.

_____ 6. Find $A - B$.

$$A = \begin{bmatrix} 1 & -1 \\ 3 & -1 \end{bmatrix}, B = \begin{bmatrix} 3 & -1 \\ -1 & 6 \end{bmatrix}$$

a.
$$\begin{bmatrix} 0 & -7 \\ 4 & 0 \end{bmatrix}$$

b.
$$\begin{bmatrix} 2 & 0 \\ -7 & 4 \end{bmatrix}$$

c.
$$\begin{bmatrix} -2 & 0 \\ 4 & -7 \end{bmatrix}$$

d.
$$\begin{bmatrix} -6 & 0 \\ 4 & -7 \end{bmatrix}$$

e.
$$\begin{bmatrix} -4 & 0 \\ 4 & -7 \end{bmatrix}$$

_____ 7.   Find $3A - 2B$.

$$A = \begin{bmatrix} -3 & 3 & 0 \\ 2 & -1 & 4 \\ 6 & 7 & -3 \\ 0 & 8 & -4 \\ -2 & -3 & 0 \end{bmatrix}, B = \begin{bmatrix} -2 & 5 & 2 \\ 2 & -4 & -6 \\ 10 & -9 & -2 \\ 2 & 4 & -4 \\ 0 & 4 & -3 \end{bmatrix}$$

a.
$$\begin{bmatrix} -5 & -1 & -4 \\ 2 & 5 & 24 \\ -2 & 39 & -5 \\ -4 & 16 & -4 \\ -6 & -17 & 6 \end{bmatrix}$$

b.
$$\begin{bmatrix} -3 & -1 & -4 \\ 2 & 5 & 24 \\ -5 & 39 & -2 \\ -4 & 16 & -4 \\ 6 & -17 & -6 \end{bmatrix}$$

c.
$$\begin{bmatrix} -9 & -1 & -4 \\ 2 & 5 & 24 \\ -6 & 39 & 6 \\ -4 & 16 & -4 \\ -2 & -17 & -5 \end{bmatrix}$$

d.
$$\begin{bmatrix} -7 & -1 & -4 \\ -4 & 5 & -4 \\ -2 & 39 & -5 \\ 2 & 16 & 24 \\ -6 & -17 & 6 \end{bmatrix}$$

e.
$$\begin{bmatrix} -1 & -1 & -4 \\ 24 & 5 & 2 \\ -2 & 39 & -5 \\ -4 & 16 & -4 \\ -6 & -17 & 6 \end{bmatrix}$$

_____ 8. Use Gauss-Jordan elimination on the augmented matrix $[A\!:\!B]$ to solve for the matrix X.

$$\begin{cases} -x_1 + x_2 = 7 \\ -2x_1 + x_2 = 0 \end{cases}$$

a.
$$\begin{bmatrix} -7 \\ 14 \end{bmatrix}$$

b.
$$\begin{bmatrix} -7 \\ -14 \end{bmatrix}$$

c.
$$\begin{bmatrix} 7 \\ -14 \end{bmatrix}$$

d.
$$\begin{bmatrix} 14 \\ 7 \end{bmatrix}$$

e.
$$\begin{bmatrix} 7 \\ 14 \end{bmatrix}$$

_____ 9.   If possible, find $2A + 3B$.

$$A = \begin{bmatrix} 1 & -3 & -2 \\ -7 & 2 & 6 \end{bmatrix}, B = \begin{bmatrix} -4 & 3 & -5 \\ 8 & 2 & -5 \end{bmatrix}$$

a.
$$\begin{bmatrix} 1 & 0 & 0 \\ 0 & 1 & 0 \end{bmatrix}$$

b.
$$\begin{bmatrix} -10 & 3 & -19 \\ 10 & 10 & -3 \end{bmatrix}$$

c.   not possible

d.
$$\begin{bmatrix} -3 & 0 & -7 \\ 1 & 4 & 1 \end{bmatrix}$$

e.
$$\begin{bmatrix} 14 & -15 & 11 \\ -38 & -2 & 27 \end{bmatrix}$$

_____ 10.   Write the system of linear equations as a matrix equation $AX = B$, and use Gauss-Jordan elimination on the augmented matrix $\begin{bmatrix} A & \vdots & B \end{bmatrix}$ to solve for the matrix X.

$$\begin{cases} x_1 - 3x_2 = 0 \\ -3x_1 - 2x_2 = -33 \end{cases}$$

a.
$$\begin{bmatrix} 1 & -3 \\ -3 & -2 \end{bmatrix}\begin{bmatrix} 0 \\ -33 \end{bmatrix} = \begin{bmatrix} 9 \\ 3 \end{bmatrix}$$

b.
$$\begin{bmatrix} 1 & -3 \\ -3 & -2 \end{bmatrix} = \begin{bmatrix} 0 \\ -33 \end{bmatrix}$$

c.
$$\begin{bmatrix} 1 & -3 \\ -3 & -2 \end{bmatrix}\begin{bmatrix} 9 \\ 3 \end{bmatrix} = \begin{bmatrix} 0 \\ -33 \end{bmatrix}$$

d.
$$\begin{bmatrix} 1 & -3 \\ -3 & -2 \end{bmatrix}\begin{bmatrix} 9 \\ 0 \end{bmatrix} = \begin{bmatrix} 3 \\ -33 \end{bmatrix}$$

e.
$$\begin{bmatrix} 1 & -3 \\ -3 & -2 \end{bmatrix}\begin{bmatrix} 0 \\ 9 \end{bmatrix} = \begin{bmatrix} -33 \\ 3 \end{bmatrix}$$

_____   11.   Find the inverse of the matrix (if it exists).

$$\begin{bmatrix} -7 & 0 & 0 \\ 4 & 0 & 0 \\ 3 & 7 & 9 \end{bmatrix}$$

a. $\begin{bmatrix} -7 & 0 & 0 \\ -4 & 0 & 0 \\ 3 & 7 & 9 \end{bmatrix}$

b.   Does not exist

c. $\begin{bmatrix} 7 & 0 & 0 \\ 4 & 0 & 0 \\ 3 & 7 & 9 \end{bmatrix}$

d. $\begin{bmatrix} -7 & 0 & 0 \\ -4 & 0 & 0 \\ -3 & -7 & -9 \end{bmatrix}$

e. $\begin{bmatrix} -7 & 0 & 0 \\ -4 & 0 & 0 \\ -3 & 7 & 9 \end{bmatrix}$

_____   12.   Solve the system of linear equations.

$x - 2y = 9$

$2x - 3y = 7$

a. $(-13, 7)$
b. $(-7, -13)$
c. $(-13, 11)$
d. $(-13, -11)$
e. $(13, 11)$

____   13.   A florist is creating 10 centerpieces for the tables at a wedding reception. Roses cost $4.50 each, lilies cost $8 each, and irises cost $4 each. The customer has a budget of $300 allocated for the centerpieces and wants each centerpiece to contain 12 flowers, with twice as many roses as the number of irises and lilies combined.

Write a system of linear equations that represents the situation.

a.
$$\begin{cases} 4.5r - 8l - 4i = 300 \\ -r - 2l - 2i = 0 \\ r - l - i = 120 \end{cases}$$

b.
$$\begin{cases} 4.5r - 8l + 4i = 300 \\ -r + 2l + 2i = 0 \\ r + l + i = 120 \end{cases}$$

c.
$$\begin{cases} 4.5r + 8l + 4i = 300 \\ -r + 2l + 2i = 0 \\ r + l + i = 120 \end{cases}$$

d.
$$\begin{cases} 4.5r + 8l + 4i = 300 \\ r + 2l + 2i = 0 \\ r + l + i = 120 \end{cases}$$

e.
$$\begin{cases} 4.5r + 8l - 4i = 300 \\ -r + 2l + 2i = 0 \\ r + l + i = 120 \end{cases}$$

_____ 14.   Find the inverse of the matrix $\begin{bmatrix} 2 & 2 & 2 \\ 6 & 10 & 8 \\ 6 & 12 & 10 \end{bmatrix}$.

a.
$$-\frac{1}{2}\begin{bmatrix} 1 & 0 & -1 \\ -3 & 2 & -1 \\ 2 & -3 & 3 \end{bmatrix}$$

b.
$$\frac{1}{2}\begin{bmatrix} 1 & 1 & 1 \\ -3 & 2 & -1 \\ 3 & -3 & 2 \end{bmatrix}$$

c.
$$-2\begin{bmatrix} 3 & 1 & 0 \\ -3 & 1 & -1 \\ 1 & -3 & 2 \end{bmatrix}$$

d.
$$2\begin{bmatrix} 1 & 1 & 1 \\ -3 & 0 & -1 \\ 3 & -3 & 2 \end{bmatrix}$$

e.
$$\frac{1}{2}\begin{bmatrix} 1 & 1 & 1 \\ 0 & -2 & -1 \\ 3 & -3 & 2 \end{bmatrix}$$

_____   15.   Solve the system of linear equations

$$\begin{cases} 8x_1 - 16x_2 - -8x_3 - 16x_4 = 0 \\ 24x_1 - 40x_2 - 16x_3 - 24x_4 = -9 \\ 16x_1 - 40x_2 - 16x_3 - 40x_4 = 6 \\ -8x_1 + 32x_2 + 32x_3 + 88x_4 = 0 \end{cases}$$

using the inverse matrix $\dfrac{1}{8}\begin{bmatrix} -24 & 7 & 1 & -2 \\ -10 & 3 & 0 & -1 \\ -29 & 7 & 3 & -2 \\ 12 & -3 & -1 & 1 \end{bmatrix}$.

a.
$$\begin{bmatrix} x_1 \\ x_2 \\ x_3 \\ x_4 \end{bmatrix} = \begin{bmatrix} 0 \\ -\dfrac{3}{8} \\ 0 \\ -\dfrac{3}{4} \end{bmatrix}$$

d.
$$\begin{bmatrix} x_1 \\ x_2 \\ x_3 \\ x_4 \end{bmatrix} = \begin{bmatrix} -\dfrac{9}{8} \\ \dfrac{3}{8} \\ 0 \\ \dfrac{3}{4} \end{bmatrix}$$

b.
$$\begin{bmatrix} x_1 \\ x_2 \\ x_3 \\ x_4 \end{bmatrix} = \begin{bmatrix} -\dfrac{21}{8} \\ -\dfrac{15}{4} \\ \dfrac{27}{8} \\ -\dfrac{27}{8} \end{bmatrix}$$

e.
$$\begin{bmatrix} x_1 \\ x_2 \\ x_3 \\ x_4 \end{bmatrix} = \begin{bmatrix} -\dfrac{57}{8} \\ -\dfrac{27}{8} \\ -\dfrac{45}{8} \\ \dfrac{21}{8} \end{bmatrix}$$

c.
$$\begin{bmatrix} x_1 \\ x_2 \\ x_3 \\ x_4 \end{bmatrix} = \begin{bmatrix} -\dfrac{27}{8} \\ -\dfrac{57}{8} \\ 0 \\ \dfrac{21}{8} \end{bmatrix}$$

_____ 16.   Find the determinant of the matrix.

$$\begin{bmatrix} 9 & 4 \\ -3 & 5 \end{bmatrix}$$

a. -33
b. -57
c. 33
d. $-\dfrac{1}{33}$
e. 57

_____ 17.   Find all the cofactors of   the matrix.

$$\begin{bmatrix} 0 & 7 \\ 4 & -8 \end{bmatrix}$$

a. $C_{11} = 0, C_{12} = -7, C_{21} = -4, C_{22} = 8$
b. $C_{11} = -7, C_{12} = -4, C_{21} = 0, C_{22} = 8$
c. $C_{11} = 8, C_{12} = 4, C_{21} = 7, C_{22} = 0$
d. $C_{11} = 0, C_{12} = -4, C_{21} = -7, C_{22} = 8$
e. $C_{11} = -8, C_{12} = -4, C_{21} = -7, C_{22} = 0$

_____ 18.   Find $|AB|$.

$$A = \begin{bmatrix} -5 & 0 \\ 0 & 2 \end{bmatrix}, \ B = \begin{bmatrix} 2 & 0 \\ 0 & -5 \end{bmatrix}$$

a. 99
b. 101
c. 102
d. 98
e. 100

_____   19.   Use the matrix capabilities of a graphing utility to find the determinant of the matrix

$$\begin{bmatrix} 17 & 25.5 & 8.5 \\ 0 & 42.5 & -17 \\ 0 & 0 & -17 \end{bmatrix}.$$

a. $18,423.75$
b. -1228.25
c. $-12,282.5$
d. 0
e. -3070.625

_____   20.   Find all cofactors of the matrix $\begin{bmatrix} 6 & -4 & 16 \\ 6 & 4 & -12 \\ -2 & 6 & 12 \end{bmatrix}.$

a. $C_{11} = -16 \quad C_{12} = 168 \quad C_{13} = 48$

   $C_{21} = 144 \quad C_{22} = 104 \quad C_{23} = -28$

   $C_{31} = 120 \quad C_{32} = -48 \quad C_{33} = 44$

b. $C_{11} = 144 \quad C_{12} = 104 \quad C_{13} = -28$

   $C_{21} = 120 \quad C_{22} = -48 \quad C_{23} = 44$

   $C_{31} = -16 \quad C_{32} = 168 \quad C_{33} = 48$

c. $C_{11} = -48 \quad C_{12} = 120 \quad C_{13} = 44$

   $C_{21} = 104 \quad C_{22} = 144 \quad C_{23} = -28$

   $C_{31} = 168 \quad C_{32} = -16 \quad C_{33} = 48$

d. $C_{11} = 120 \quad C_{12} = -48 \quad C_{13} = 44$

   $C_{21} = 144 \quad C_{22} = 104 \quad C_{23} = -28$

   $C_{31} = -16 \quad C_{32} = 168 \quad C_{33} = 48$

e. $C_{11} = 120 \quad C_{12} = 44 \quad C_{13} = -48$

   $C_{21} = 144 \quad C_{22} = -28 \quad C_{23} = 104$

   $C_{31} = -16 \quad C_{32} = 48 \quad C_{33} = 168$

_____ 21. Use a determinant to find an equation of the line passing through the points.

$(-4, 2), (1, 1)$

a. $x + 5y + 6 = 0$
b. $x - 5y + 6 = 0$
c. $x - 5y - 6 = 0$
d. $x + 5y - 6 = 0$
e. $x + 5y - 6 = 5$

_____ 22. Use Crammer's Rule to solve (if possible) the system of equations.

$$\begin{cases} -0.4x + 0.8y = 1.6 \\ 0.2x + 0.3y = 2.3 \end{cases}$$

a. $\left(\dfrac{34}{7}, \dfrac{31}{7} \right)$

b. $\left(-\dfrac{34}{7}, -\dfrac{31}{7} \right)$

c. $\left(-\dfrac{34}{7}, \dfrac{31}{7} \right)$

d. $\left(\dfrac{31}{7}, \dfrac{34}{7} \right)$

e. $\left(\dfrac{34}{7}, -\dfrac{31}{7} \right)$

_____ 23. Use a determinant to determine whether the points
$(x_1, y_1) = (-7, -4), (x_2, y_2) = (0, 3)$ and $(x_3, y_3) = (4, 7)$ are collinear.

a. False. The points are not collinear because $\begin{vmatrix} -7 & -4 & 1 \\ 0 & 3 & 1 \\ 4 & 7 & 1 \end{vmatrix} = 0.$

b. True. The points are collinear because $\begin{vmatrix} -7 & -4 & 1 \\ 0 & 3 & 1 \\ 4 & 7 & 1 \end{vmatrix} = 0.$

_____   24.   Use Cramer's Rule to solve the following system of linear equations:

$$\begin{cases} 18x - 27y + 18z = 6 \\ -27x + 18y + 9z = 5 \\ 36x + 9y - 27z = 6 \end{cases}$$

a. $x = \dfrac{17}{18}, y = \dfrac{74}{63}, z = \dfrac{166}{189}$

b. $x = \dfrac{17}{27}, y = \dfrac{148}{189}, z = \dfrac{166}{189}$

c. $x = \dfrac{11}{18}, y = \dfrac{59}{63}, z = \dfrac{100}{189}$

d. $x = \dfrac{11}{18}, y = \dfrac{50}{63}, z = \dfrac{136}{189}$

e. $x = \dfrac{2}{3}, y = \dfrac{13}{21}, z = \dfrac{32}{63}$

_____   25.   Find the uncoded 1×3 row matrices for the message "MERRY CHRISTMAS"; then

encode the message using the encoding matrix $\begin{bmatrix} 0 & 3 & 1 \\ -1 & 1 & 1 \\ 1 & -3 & 0 \end{bmatrix}$.

a.   Uncoded: $\begin{bmatrix} 13 & 5 & 18 \end{bmatrix} \begin{bmatrix} 18 & 25 & 0 \end{bmatrix} \begin{bmatrix} 3 & 8 & 18 \end{bmatrix} \begin{bmatrix} 9 & 19 & 20 \end{bmatrix}$

$\begin{bmatrix} 13 & 1 & 19 \end{bmatrix}$

Encoded: $\begin{bmatrix} 1 & -14 & 28 \end{bmatrix} \begin{bmatrix} 18 & -17 & 14 \end{bmatrix} \begin{bmatrix} 13 & -10 & 18 \end{bmatrix}$

$\begin{bmatrix} -25 & 79 & 43 \end{bmatrix} \begin{bmatrix} 10 & -37 & 11 \end{bmatrix}$

b.   Uncoded: $\begin{bmatrix} 13 & 5 & 18 \end{bmatrix} \begin{bmatrix} 18 & 25 & 0 \end{bmatrix} \begin{bmatrix} 3 & 8 & 18 \end{bmatrix} \begin{bmatrix} 9 & 19 & 20 \end{bmatrix}$

$\begin{bmatrix} 13 & 1 & 19 \end{bmatrix}$

Encoded: $\begin{bmatrix} 18 & -17 & 14 \end{bmatrix} \begin{bmatrix} 13 & -10 & 18 \end{bmatrix} \begin{bmatrix} -25 & 79 & 43 \end{bmatrix}$

$\begin{bmatrix} 10 & -37 & 11 \end{bmatrix} \begin{bmatrix} 1 & -14 & 28 \end{bmatrix}$

c.   Uncoded: $\begin{bmatrix} 13 & 5 & 18 \end{bmatrix}\begin{bmatrix} 18 & 25 & 0 \end{bmatrix}\begin{bmatrix} 3 & 8 & 18 \end{bmatrix}\begin{bmatrix} 9 & 19 & 20 \end{bmatrix}$

$\begin{bmatrix} 13 & 1 & 19 \end{bmatrix}$

Encoded: $\begin{bmatrix} -25 & 79 & 43 \end{bmatrix}\begin{bmatrix} 10 & -37 & 11 \end{bmatrix}\begin{bmatrix} 1 & -14 & 28 \end{bmatrix}$

$\begin{bmatrix} 18 & -17 & 14 \end{bmatrix}\begin{bmatrix} 13 & -10 & 18 \end{bmatrix}$

d.   Uncoded: $\begin{bmatrix} 13 & 5 & 18 \end{bmatrix}\begin{bmatrix} 18 & 25 & 0 \end{bmatrix}\begin{bmatrix} 3 & 8 & 18 \end{bmatrix}\begin{bmatrix} 9 & 19 & 20 \end{bmatrix}$

$\begin{bmatrix} 13 & 1 & 19 \end{bmatrix}$

Encoded: $\begin{bmatrix} 10 & -37 & 11 \end{bmatrix}\begin{bmatrix} 1 & -14 & 28 \end{bmatrix}\begin{bmatrix} 18 & -17 & 14 \end{bmatrix}$

$\begin{bmatrix} 13 & -10 & 18 \end{bmatrix}\begin{bmatrix} -25 & 79 & 43 \end{bmatrix}$

e.   Uncoded: $\begin{bmatrix} 13 & 5 & 18 \end{bmatrix}\begin{bmatrix} 18 & 25 & 0 \end{bmatrix}\begin{bmatrix} 3 & 8 & 18 \end{bmatrix}\begin{bmatrix} 9 & 19 & 20 \end{bmatrix}$

$\begin{bmatrix} 13 & 1 & 19 \end{bmatrix}$

Encoded: $\begin{bmatrix} 13 & -10 & 18 \end{bmatrix}\begin{bmatrix} -25 & 79 & 43 \end{bmatrix}\begin{bmatrix} 10 & -37 & 11 \end{bmatrix}$

$\begin{bmatrix} 1 & -14 & 28 \end{bmatrix}\begin{bmatrix} 18 & -17 & 14 \end{bmatrix}$

Ch 8 Form F
Answer Section

1.	ANS:	A	PTS:	1	REF:	8.1.19
2.	ANS:	B	PTS:	1	REF:	8.1.40
3.	ANS:	E	PTS:	1	REF:	8.1.64
4.	ANS:	B	PTS:	1	REF:	8.1.25
5.	ANS:	E	PTS:	1	REF:	8.1.92
6.	ANS:	C	PTS:	1	REF:	8.2.11(b)
7.	ANS:	A	PTS:	1	REF:	8.2.16(d)
8.	ANS:	E	PTS:	1	REF:	8.2.57(b)
9.	ANS:	B	PTS:	1	REF:	8.2.11d
10.	ANS:	C	PTS:	1	REF:	8.2.60
11.	ANS:	B	PTS:	1	REF:	8.3.21
12.	ANS:	D	PTS:	1	REF:	8.3.43
13.	ANS:	C	PTS:	1	REF:	8.3.74a
14.	ANS:	B	PTS:	1	REF:	8.3.19
15.	ANS:	E	PTS:	1	REF:	8.3.48
16.	ANS:	E	PTS:	1	REF:	8.4.9
17.	ANS:	E	PTS:	1	REF:	8.4.26b
18.	ANS:	E	PTS:	1	REF:	8.4.63d
19.	ANS:	C	PTS:	1	REF:	8.4.55
20.	ANS:	D	PTS:	1	REF:	8.4.29
21.	ANS:	D	PTS:	1	REF:	8.5.49
22.	ANS:	A	PTS:	1	REF:	8.5.11
23.	ANS:	B	PTS:	1	REF:	8.5.74
24.	ANS:	B	PTS:	1	REF:	8.5.16
25.	ANS:	E	PTS:	1	REF:	8.5.56

Ch 9 Form A

_____   1.   Select the first five terms of the sequence. (Assume that n begins with 1.)

$a_n = 4n + 7$

a. $4, 8, 12, 16, 20$
b. $4, 11, 12, 19, 20$
c. $4, 15, 12, 23, 20$
d. $0, 11, 15, 19, 23$
e. $11, 15, 19, 23, 27$

_____   2.   Write an expression for the apparent nth term of the sequence. (Assume that n begins with 1.)

$3, 8, 13, 18, 23, \ldots$

a. $a_n = 2n + 5$
b. $a_n = 5n + 2$
c. $a_n = -5n - 2$
d. $a_n = 5n - 2$
e. $a_n = 2n - 5$

_____   3.   Write the first five terms of the sequence defined recursively. Use the pattern to write the nth term of the sequence as a function of n. (Assume that n begins with 1.)
$a_1 = 5, \ a_{k+1} = -2a_k$
a. $a_n = 5n$
b. $a_n = 5(-2)^{n-1}$
c. $a_n = (-10)^{n-1}$
d. $a_n = 5(-2)^n$
e. $a_n = (-10)^n$

_____   4.   Determine whether the sequence is arithmetic. If so, find the common difference.

$128, 64, 32, 16, 8 \ldots$

a.   Arithmetic sequence, $d = 24$
b.   Arithmetic sequence, $d = -120$
c.   Arithmetic sequence, $d = 8$
d.   Arithmetic sequence, $d = -8$
e.   Not an arithmetic sequence

_____   5.   Write the first five terms of the sequence. Determine whether the sequence is arithmetic. If so, find the common difference. (Assume that n begins with 1.)

$$a_n = 3 + (n-3)6$$

a. $15, 9, 3, -3, -9$
Arithmetic sequence
$d = -6$

b. $27, 21, 15, 9, 3$
Arithmetic sequence
$d = -6$

c. $-9, -3, 3, 9, 15$
Arithmetic sequence
$d = -6$

d. $3, 9, 15, 21, 27$
Arithmetic sequence
$d = 6$

e. $-9, -3, 3, 9, 15$
Arithmetic sequence
$d = 6$

_____   6.   Write the first five terms of the arithmetic sequence defined recursively.

$$a_1 = \frac{9}{8}, \; a_{n+1} = a_n - \frac{3}{8}$$

a. $\dfrac{9}{8}, \dfrac{3}{4}, \dfrac{3}{8}, 0, -\dfrac{3}{8}$

b. $\dfrac{9}{8}, \dfrac{3}{8}, -\dfrac{3}{8}, 0, \dfrac{3}{4}$

c. $\dfrac{9}{8}, \dfrac{3}{8}, \dfrac{3}{4}, -\dfrac{3}{4}, 0$

d. $\dfrac{9}{8}, \dfrac{3}{4}, \dfrac{3}{8}, 0, -\dfrac{3}{4}$

e. $\dfrac{3}{4}, \dfrac{3}{8}, 0, -\dfrac{3}{8}, \dfrac{9}{8}$

_____ 7.   The first two terms of the arithmetic sequence are given. Find the indicated term.

$a_1 = 2, a_2 = 7, a_9 = \boxed{}$

a. 52
b. 23
c. 47
d. 42
e. 21

_____ 8.   Determine whether the sequence is geometric. If so, find the common ratio.

$25, 20, 15, 10, \ldots$

a. Not a geometric sequence
b. Geometric sequence, $r = 6$
c. Geometric sequence, $r = 7$
d. Geometric sequence, $r = 4$
e. Geometric sequence, $r = 5$

_____ 9.   Use summation notation to write the sum.

$15 + 45 + 135 + \cdots + 10935$

a. $\displaystyle\sum_{x=1}^{7} 15(3)^{x}$

b. $\displaystyle\sum_{x=1}^{7} 15(3)^{x-1}$

c. $\displaystyle\sum_{x=1}^{6} 15(3)^{x-1}$

d. $\displaystyle\sum_{x=1}^{7} 3^{x-1}$

e. $\displaystyle\sum_{x=1}^{7} 15(3)^{x+1}$

_____ 10.   Write the nth term of the geometric sequence as a function of n.

$a_1 = 8, a_{k+1} = 5a_k$

a. $a_n = 8(5)^{n-1}$

b. $a_n = 8\left(\dfrac{1}{5}\right)^{n-1}$

c. $a_n = 3 + 5n$

d. $a_n = 5(8)^{n-1}$

e. $a_n = 8(5)^n$

_____ 11.   Find the sum using the formulas for the sums of powers of integers.

$$\sum_{n=1}^{17} n$$

a.   1,785

b.   23,409

c.   306

d.   10,710

e.   153

_____   12.   Write the first six terms of the sequence beginning with the given term. Then calculate the first and second differences of the sequence. State whether the sequence has a linear model, a quadratic model, or neither.

$a_1 = 5$

$a_n = a_{n-1} - n$

a. $5, 3, 0, -4, -9, -15$
     First differences: $-2, -3, -4, -5, -6$
     Second differences: $1, 1, 1, 1$
     Quadratic
b. $0, 5, 3, 0, -4, -9$
     First differences: $-2, -3, -4, -5, -6$
     Second differences: $1, 1, 1, 1$
     Linear
c. $5, 3, 0, -4, -9, -15$
     First differences: $-2, -3, -4, -5, -6$
     Second differences: $-1, -1, -1, -1$
     Quadratic
d. $0, 5, 3, 0, -4, -9$
     First differences: $5, -2, -3, -4, -5$
     Second differences: $1, 1, 1, 1$
     Quadratic
e. $0, 5, 3, 0, -4, -9$
     First differences: $5, -2, -3, -4, -5$
     Second differences: $-1, -1, -1, -1$
     Quadratic

_____   13.   Find a formula for the sum of the first n terms of the sequence.

$9, 13, 17, 21, 25, \ldots$

a. $S_n = n(2n + 7)$
b. $S_n = n(2n + 1)$
c. $S_n = n(3n - 1)$
d. $S_n = n(3n + 1)$
e. $S_n = \dfrac{(n + 1)}{n}$

_____ 14. Find a formula for the sum of the n terms of the sequence.

$$\frac{1}{5}, \frac{2}{25}, \frac{4}{125}, \frac{8}{625}, \cdots$$

a. $\dfrac{2^{x-1}}{5^x}$

b. $\dfrac{1}{5^x}$

c. $-\dfrac{2^x - 5^x}{3\left(5^x\right)}$

d. $\dfrac{2^x + 5^x}{7(5)^x}$

e. $-\dfrac{2\left(2^x - 5^x\right)}{3\left(5^x\right)}$

_____ 15. Calculate the binomial coefficient.

$$\begin{pmatrix} 12 \\ 8 \end{pmatrix}$$

a. 496
b. 495
c. 497
d. 493
e. 498

_____ 16. Expand the binomial by using Pascal's Triangle to determine the coefficients.

$$\left(x + 5y\right)^5$$

a. $x^5 + 25x^4y - 250x^3y^2 + 1250x^2y^3 + 3125xy^4 - 3125y^5$
b. $x^5 - 25x^4y + 250x^3y^2 + 1250x^2y^3 + 3125xy^4 - 3125y^5$
c. $x^5 + 25x^4y + 250x^3y^2 - 1250x^2y^3 + 3125xy^4 + 3125y^5$
d. $x^5 + 25x^4y - 250x^3y^2 + 1250x^2y^3 + 3125xy^4 + 3125y^5$
e. $x^5 + 25x^4y + 250x^3y^2 + 1250x^2y^3 + 3125xy^4 + 3125y^5$

_____   17.   Expand the expression in the difference quotient and simplify.

$$\frac{f(x+h)-f(x)}{h}$$ Difference quotient

$$f(x)=(2x)^3$$

a. $$\frac{12x^2+6xh-h^2}{h}$$

b. $12x^2+6xh-h^2$

c. $12x^2+6xh+h^2$

d. $$\frac{12x^2+6xh+h^2}{h}$$

e. $6x^2-6xh-h^2$

_____   18.   Determine the number of ways a computer can randomly generate one or more such integers from 1 through 20.

An even integer

a.   6
b.   12
c.   14
d.   8
e.   10

_____   19.   A customer can choose one of two amplifiers, one of three compact disc players, and one of five speaker models for an entertainment system. Determine the number of possible system configurations.

a.   25
b.   35
c.   30
d.   40
e.   20

_____   20.   How many three-digit numbers can be formed under following condition?

The leading digit cannot be zero and the number must be even.

a.   550
b.   900
c.   450
d.   350
e.   400

_____ 21. In how many ways can five children posing for a photograph line up in a row?

a. 1,120
b. 170
c. 220
d. 120
e. 620

_____ 22. Evaluate: $_9P_4$

a. 126
b. undefined
c. 3024
d. 36
e. 15,120

_____ 23. Find the probability for the experiment of tossing a coin four times. Use the sample space

$$S = \{HHHH, HHHT, HHTH, HHTT, HTHH, HTHT, HTTH, HTTT, THHH, THHT, THTH,$$

$$THTT, TTHH, TTHT, TTTH, TTTT\}.$$

The probability of getting exactly two tails.

a. $\dfrac{3}{8}$

b. $\dfrac{1}{2}$

c. $\dfrac{1}{3}$

d. $\dfrac{1}{4}$

e. $\dfrac{1}{8}$

_____ 24. The educational attainment of the United States population age 25 years or older in 2007 is shown in the circle graph. Use the fact that the population of people 25 years or older was approximately 194.32 million in 2007. Estimate the number of people 25 years or older who have advanced degrees.

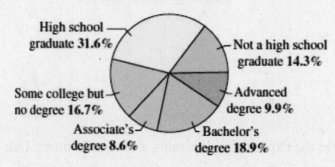

Educational Attainment

a. 59.24 million
b. 49.24 million
c. 19.24 million
d. 29.24 million
e. 39.24 million

_____ 25. In a high school graduating class of 128 students, 52 are on the honor roll. Of these, 43 are going on to college; of the other 76 students, 56 are going on to college. A student is selected at random from the class. What is the probability that the person chosen is going to college.

a. $\dfrac{7}{16}$

b. $\dfrac{43}{128}$

c. $\dfrac{99}{128}$

d. $\dfrac{128}{99}$

e. $\dfrac{16}{7}$

Ch 9 Form A
Answer Section

1.	ANS:	E	PTS:	1	REF:	9.1.9
2.	ANS:	D	PTS:	1	REF:	9.1.48
3.	ANS:	B	PTS:	1	REF:	9.1.70
4.	ANS:	E	PTS:	1	REF:	9.2.8
5.	ANS:	E	PTS:	1	REF:	9.2.18
6.	ANS:	A	PTS:	1	REF:	9.2.45
7.	ANS:	D	PTS:	1	REF:	9.2.47
8.	ANS:	A	PTS:	1	REF:	9.3.8
9.	ANS:	B	PTS:	1	REF:	9.3.87
10.	ANS:	A	PTS:	1	REF:	9.3.29
11.	ANS:	E	PTS:	1	REF:	9.4.50
12.	ANS:	C	PTS:	1	REF:	9.4.67
13.	ANS:	A	PTS:	1	REF:	9.4.43
14.	ANS:	C	PTS:	1	REF:	9.4.45
15.	ANS:	B	PTS:	1	REF:	9.5.11
16.	ANS:	E	PTS:	1	REF:	9.5.43
17.	ANS:	C	PTS:	1	REF:	9.5.67
18.	ANS:	E	PTS:	1	REF:	9.6.8
19.	ANS:	C	PTS:	1	REF:	9.6.15
20.	ANS:	C	PTS:	1	REF:	9.6.24d
21.	ANS:	D	PTS:	1	REF:	9.6.39
22.	ANS:	C	PTS:	1	REF:	9.6.31
23.	ANS:	A	PTS:	1	REF:	9.7.16
24.	ANS:	C	PTS:	1	REF:	9.7.44b
25.	ANS:	C	PTS:	1	REF:	9.7.50a

Ch 9 Form B

_____ 1.   Select the first five terms of the sequence. (Assume that n begins with 1.)

$a_n = 4n + 5$

a. $0, 9, 13, 17, 21$
b. $4, 8, 12, 16, 20$
c. $9, 13, 17, 21, 25$
d. $4, 13, 12, 21, 20$
e. $4, 9, 12, 17, 20$

_____ 2.   Write an expression for the apparent nth term of the sequence. (Assume that n begins with 1.)

$6, 14, 22, 30, 38, \ldots$

a. $a_n = 8n - 2$
b. $a_n = 8n + 2$
c. $a_n = -8n - 2$
d. $a_n = 2n - 8$
e. $a_n = 2n + 8$

_____ 3.   Write the first five terms of the sequence defined recursively. Use the pattern to write the nth term of the sequence as a function of n. (Assume that n begins with 1.)

$a_1 = -7, \ a_{k+1} = 3a_k$

a. $a_n = -7n$
b. $a_n = -7(3)^{n-1}$
c. $a_n = (-21)^n$
d. $a_n = (-21)^{n-1}$
e. $a_n = -7(3)^n$

_____ 4.   Determine whether the sequence is arithmetic. If so, find the common difference.

$80, 40, 20, 10, 5 \ldots$

a. Arithmetic sequence, $d = -75$
b. Arithmetic sequence, $d = -5$
c. Arithmetic sequence, $d = 15$
d. Arithmetic sequence, $d = 5$
e. Not an arithmetic sequence

_____ 5.   Write the first five terms of the sequence. Determine whether the sequence is arithmetic. If so, find the common difference. (Assume that n begins with 1.)

$$a_n = 2 + (n-2)5$$

a. $-3, 2, 7, 12, 17$
    Arithmetic sequence
    $d = 5$
b. $12, 17, 22, 27, 32$
    Arithmetic sequence
    $d = 5$
c. $32, 27, 22, 17, 12$
    Arithmetic sequence
    $d = -5$
d. $17, 12, 7, 2, -3$
    Arithmetic sequence
    $d = -5$
e. $-3, 2, 7, 12, 17$
    Arithmetic sequence
    $d = -5$

_____ 6.   Write the first five terms of the arithmetic sequence defined recursively.

$$a_1 = \frac{7}{8}, \ a_{n+1} = a_n - \frac{1}{8}$$

a. $\dfrac{7}{8}, \dfrac{5}{8}, \dfrac{3}{4}, \dfrac{1}{4}, \dfrac{1}{2}$

b. $\dfrac{7}{8}, \dfrac{3}{4}, \dfrac{5}{8}, \dfrac{1}{2}, \dfrac{3}{8}$

c. $\dfrac{3}{4}, \dfrac{5}{8}, \dfrac{1}{2}, \dfrac{3}{8}, \dfrac{7}{8}$

d. $\dfrac{7}{8}, \dfrac{3}{4}, \dfrac{5}{8}, \dfrac{1}{2}, \dfrac{1}{4}$

e. $\dfrac{7}{8}, \dfrac{5}{8}, \dfrac{3}{8}, \dfrac{1}{2}, \dfrac{3}{4}$

_____ 7.   The first two terms of the arithmetic sequence are given. Find the indicated term.

$a_1 = 4, a_2 = -2, a_9 = \boxed{}$

a. −50
b. 26
c. −56
d. −44
e. 30

_____ 8.   Determine whether the sequence is geometric. If so, find the common ratio.

$50, 45, 40, 35, \ldots$

a. Not a geometric sequence
b. Geometric sequence, $r = 6$
c. Geometric sequence, $r = 5$
d. Geometric sequence, $r = 7$
e. Geometric sequence, $r = 4$

_____ 9.   Use summation notation to write the sum.

$11 + 33 + 99 + \cdots + 8019$

a. $\displaystyle\sum_{x=1}^{7} 3^{x-1}$

b. $\displaystyle\sum_{x=1}^{7} 11(3)^{x-1}$

c. $\displaystyle\sum_{x=1}^{6} 11(3)^{x-1}$

d. $\displaystyle\sum_{x=1}^{7} 11(3)^{x+1}$

e. $\displaystyle\sum_{x=1}^{7} 11(3)^{x}$

_____ 10. Write the nth term of the geometric sequence as a function of n.

$a_1 = 2, a_{k+1} = -4a_k$

a. $a_n = 2(-4)^n$

b. $a_n = 6 - 4n$

c. $a_n = -4(2)^{n-1}$

d. $a_n = 2\left(-\dfrac{1}{4}\right)^{n-1}$

e. $a_n = 2(-4)^{n-1}$

_____ 11. Find the sum using the formulas for the sums of powers of integers.

$\displaystyle\sum_{n=1}^{17} n$

a. 153

b. 306

c. 23,409

d. 1,785

e. 10,710

____   12.   Write the first six terms of the sequence beginning with the given term. Then calculate the first and second differences of the sequence. State whether the sequence has a linear model, a quadratic model, or neither.

$a_1 = 9$

$a_n = a_{n-1} - n$

a. $9, 7, 4, 0, -5, -11$
      First differences: $-2, -3, -4, -5, -6$
      Second differences: $-1, -1, -1, -1$
      Quadratic
b. $0, 9, 7, 4, 0, -5$
      First differences: $-2, -3, -4, -5, -6$
      Second differences: $1, 1, 1, 1$
      Linear
c. $0, 9, 7, 4, 0, -5$
      First differences: $9, -2, -3, -4, -5$
      Second differences: $-1, -1, -1, -1$
      Quadratic
d. $0, 9, 7, 4, 0, -5$
      First differences: $9, -2, -3, -4, -5$
      Second differences: $1, 1, 1, 1$
      Quadratic
e. $9, 7, 4, 0, -5, -11$
      First differences: $-2, -3, -4, -5, -6$
      Second differences: $1, 1, 1, 1$
      Quadratic

____   13.   Find a formula for the sum of the first n terms of the sequence.

$21, 25, 29, 33, 37, \ldots$

a. $S_n = n(2n + 1)$
b. $S_n = n(5n + 1)$
c. $S_n = \dfrac{(n + 1)}{n}$
d. $S_n = n(2n + 19)$
e. $S_n = n(5n - 1)$

_____   14.   Find a formula for the sum of the n terms of the sequence.

$\dfrac{1}{5}, \dfrac{2}{25}, \dfrac{4}{125}, \dfrac{8}{625}, \ldots$

a. $-\dfrac{2^x - 5^x}{3\left(5^x\right)}$

b. $-\dfrac{2\left(2^x - 5^x\right)}{3\left(5^x\right)}$

c. $\dfrac{2^x + 5^x}{7(5)^x}$

d. $\dfrac{2^{x-1}}{5^x}$

e. $\dfrac{1}{5^x}$

_____   15.   Calculate the binomial coefficient.

$\begin{pmatrix} 10 \\ 6 \end{pmatrix}$

a.   208
b.   212
c.   213
d.   211
e.   210

_____   16.   Expand the binomial by using Pascal's Triangle to determine the coefficients.

$\left(x + 2y\right)^5$

a. $x^5 + 10x^4y + 40x^3y^2 + 80x^2y^3 + 80xy^4 + 32y^5$
b. $x^5 + 10x^4y + 40x^3y^2 - 80x^2y^3 + 80xy^4 + 32y^5$
c. $x^5 + 10x^4y - 40x^3y^2 + 80x^2y^3 + 80xy^4 + 32y^5$
d. $x^5 - 10x^4y + 40x^3y^2 + 80x^2y^3 + 80xy^4 - 32y^5$
e. $x^5 + 10x^4y - 40x^3y^2 + 80x^2y^3 + 80xy^4 - 32y^5$

_____   17.   Expand the expression in the difference quotient and simplify.

$$\frac{f(x+h)-f(x)}{h}$$ Difference quotient

$$f(x) = (x)^3$$

a. $3x^2 + 3xh + h^2$
b. $\dfrac{3x^2 + 3xh + h^2}{h}$

c. $\dfrac{3x^2 + 3xh - h^2}{h}$

d. $3x^2 - 3xh - h^2$
e. $3x^2 + 3xh - h^2$

_____   18.   Determine the number of ways a computer can randomly generate one or more such integers from 1 through 28.

An even integer

a. 14
b. 12
c. 16
d. 18
e. 10

_____   19.   A customer can choose one of five amplifiers, one of two compact disc players, and one of five speaker models for an entertainment system. Determine the number of possible system configurations.

a. 55
b. 40
c. 60
d. 50
e. 45

_____   20.   How many six-digit numbers can be formed under following condition?

The leading digit cannot be zero and the number must be even.

a. 450,000
b. 449,900
c. 450,100
d. 449,950
e. 900,000

_____ 21.   In how many ways can nine children posing for a photograph line up in a row?

a. 363,380
b. 362,980
c. 362,880
d. 363,880
e. 362,930

_____ 22.   Evaluate: $_8P_2$

a. undefined
b. 28
c. 56
d. 16
e. 20,160

_____ 23.   Find the probability for the experiment of tossing a coin three times. Use the sample space

$$S = \{HHH, HHT, HTH,, HTT, THH, THT, TTH, TTT\}.$$

The probability of getting exactly two tails.

a. $\dfrac{1}{8}$

b. $\dfrac{1}{2}$

c. $\dfrac{1}{3}$

d. $\dfrac{3}{8}$

e. $\dfrac{1}{4}$

_____ 24.   The educational attainment of the United States population age 25 years or older in 2007 is shown in the circle graph. Use the fact that the population of people 25 years or older was approximately 251.32 million in 2007. Estimate the number of people 25 years or older who have advanced degrees.

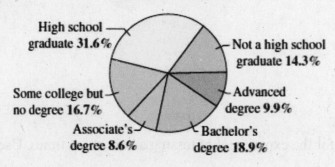

a. 24.88 million
b. 44.88 million
c. 64.88 million
d. 34.88 million
e. 54.88 million

_____ 25.   In a high school graduating class of 128 students, 52 are on the honor roll. Of these, 45 are going on to college; of the other 76 students, 57 are going on to college. A student is selected at random from the class. What is the probability that the person chosen is going to college.

a. $\dfrac{128}{57}$

b. $\dfrac{51}{64}$

c. $\dfrac{57}{128}$

d. $\dfrac{64}{51}$

e. $\dfrac{45}{128}$

Ch 9 Form B
Answer Section

1.	ANS:	C	PTS:	1	REF:	9.1.9
2.	ANS:	A	PTS:	1	REF:	9.1.48
3.	ANS:	B	PTS:	1	REF:	9.1.70
4.	ANS:	E	PTS:	1	REF:	9.2.8
5.	ANS:	A	PTS:	1	REF:	9.2.18
6.	ANS:	B	PTS:	1	REF:	9.2.45
7.	ANS:	D	PTS:	1	REF:	9.2.47
8.	ANS:	A	PTS:	1	REF:	9.3.8
9.	ANS:	B	PTS:	1	REF:	9.3.87
10.	ANS:	E	PTS:	1	REF:	9.3.29
11.	ANS:	A	PTS:	1	REF:	9.4.50
12.	ANS:	A	PTS:	1	REF:	9.4.67
13.	ANS:	D	PTS:	1	REF:	9.4.43
14.	ANS:	A	PTS:	1	REF:	9.4.45
15.	ANS:	E	PTS:	1	REF:	9.5.11
16.	ANS:	A	PTS:	1	REF:	9.5.43
17.	ANS:	A	PTS:	1	REF:	9.5.67
18.	ANS:	A	PTS:	1	REF:	9.6.8
19.	ANS:	D	PTS:	1	REF:	9.6.15
20.	ANS:	A	PTS:	1	REF:	9.6.24d
21.	ANS:	C	PTS:	1	REF:	9.6.39
22.	ANS:	C	PTS:	1	REF:	9.6.31
23.	ANS:	D	PTS:	1	REF:	9.7.16
24.	ANS:	A	PTS:	1	REF:	9.7.44b
25.	ANS:	B	PTS:	1	REF:	9.7.50a

Ch 9 Form C

_____   1.   Select the first five terms of the sequence. (Assume that n begins with 1.)

$a_n = (-3)^n$

a. $-3, -6, -9, -12, -15$
b. $1, -3, 9, -27, 81$
c. $-3, -6, -9, -27, -15$
d. $-3, 9, -27, 81, -243$
e. $-3, 9, -9, 81, -15$

_____   2.   Write an expression for the apparent nth term of the sequence. (Assume that n begins with 1.)

$$\frac{1}{6}, \frac{5}{36}, \frac{25}{216}, \frac{125}{1296}, \ldots$$

a. $a_n = \dfrac{5^{n-1}}{6^n}$

b. $a_n = \dfrac{5^n}{6^n}$

c. $a_n = \dfrac{5^{n+1}}{6^{n+1}}$

d. $a_n = \dfrac{5^{n+1}}{6^n}$

e. $a_n = \dfrac{5^{n-1}}{6^{n-1}}$

_____   3.   Simplify the factorial expression.

$\dfrac{9!}{6!}$

a. 3024
b. 504
c. 5040
d. $\dfrac{3}{2}$
e. 72

_____ 4.   Determine whether the sequence is arithmetic. If so, find the common difference.

$\ln 4, \ln 5, \ln 6, \ln 7, \ln 8 \ldots$

a.   Arithmetic sequence, $d = -0.56$
b.   Arithmetic sequence, $d = -0.22$
c.   Arithmetic sequence, $d = 0.22$
d.   Arithmetic sequence, $d = 0.41$
e.   Not an arithmetic sequence

_____ 5.   Write the first five terms of the sequence. Determine whether the sequence is arithmetic. If so, find the common difference. (Assume that n begins with 1.)

$a_n = 3^{n-1}$

a. $81, 27, 9, 3, 1$
     Arithmetic sequence
     $d = 3$
b. $1, 3, 9, 27, 81$
     Arithmetic sequence
     $d = 3$
c. $81, 27, 9, 3, 1$
     Not an Arithmetic sequence
d. $1, 3, 9, 27, 81$
     Not an Arithmetic sequence
e. $1, 3, 9, 27, 81$
     Arithmetic sequence
     $d = -3$

_____ 6.   Determine whether the sequence is arithmetic. If so, find the common difference.
$-9, -12, -15, -18, -21$
a. -9
b. -3
c.   not arithmetic
d. -6
e. 3

_____ 7.   Find the indicated nth partial sum of the arithmetic sequence.
$-3.6, -1.3, 1, 3.3, \ldots., n=15$
a.   193.4
b.   187.5
c.   181.6
d.   222
e. -343.5

_____   8.   Find the first five terms of the geometric sequence.

$a_1 = 7, r = 2$

a. $10, 20, 40, 80, 160$
b. $4, 8, 16, 32, 64$
c. $5, 10, 20, 40, 80$
d. $14, 28, 56, 112, 224$
e. $7, 14, 28, 56, 112$

_____   9.   Use summation notation to write the sum.

$0.4 + 1.6 + 6.4 + \cdots + 409.6$

a.
$$\sum_{x=1}^{8} 0.4(4)^x$$

b.
$$\sum_{x=1}^{7} 0.4(4)^{x-1}$$

c.
$$\sum_{x=1}^{6} (4)^{x-1}$$

d.
$$\sum_{x=1}^{6} 0.4(4)^{x-1}$$

e.
$$\sum_{x=1}^{8} 0.4(4)^{x+1}$$

_____   10.   Find the indicated nth term of the geometric sequence.

4th term: $a_3 = \dfrac{4}{9}, a_6 = \dfrac{4}{243}$

a. $\dfrac{4}{243}$

b. $\dfrac{4}{27}$

c. $\dfrac{4}{81}$

d. $\dfrac{4}{9}$

e. $\dfrac{3}{64}$

_____ 11.   Find the sum using the formulas for the sums of powers of integers.

$$\sum_{n=1}^{3} n^4$$

a. 36
b. 98
c. 276
d. 84
e. 14

_____ 12.   Write the first six terms of the sequence beginning with the given term. Then calculate the first and second differences of the sequence. State whether the sequence has a linear model, a quadratic model, or neither.

$$a_0 = 3$$

$$a_n = a_{n-1} + n$$

a. 3, 4, 6, 9, 13, 18
    First differences: $-1, -1, -1, -1$
    Second differences: 1, 2, 3, 4, 5
    Linear
b. 3, 4, 6, 9, 13, 18
    First differences: 1, 2, 3, 4, 5
    Second differences: 1, 1, 1, 1
    Quadratic
c. 0, 3, 4, -6, 9, -13
    First differences: 3, 1, 2, 3, 4
    Second differences: $-1, 1, -1, 1$
    Neither
d. 3, -4, 6, -9, 13, -18
    First differences: $-1, 1, -1, 1$
    Second differences: 1, 2, 3, 4, 5
    Neither
e. 0, 3, 4, 6, 9, 13
    First differences: 3, 1, 2, 3, 4
    Second differences: $-1, 1, -1, 1$
    Quadratic

_____ 13.   The table shows the numbers a_n (in thousands) of Alaskan residents from 2002 through 2007. (Source: U.S. Census Bureau)

Year	Number of residents, a_n
2002	646
2003	656
2004	662
2005	670
2006	682
2007	696

Find the first differences of the data shown in the table.

a. $14, 10, 6, 8, 12$
b. $10, 6, 8, 14, 12$
c. $10, 6, 8, 12, 14$
d. $6, 10, 8, 12, 14$
e. $10, 6, 12, 8, 14$

_____ 14.   Find the sum using the formulas for the sums of powers of integers.

$$\sum_{n=1}^{13} 6n - 2n^2$$

a. -832
b. 364
c. -3276
d. -1092
e. -260

_____ 15.   Evaluate using Pascal's Triangle.

$$\begin{pmatrix} 9 \\ 6 \end{pmatrix}$$

a. 84
b. 86
c. 85
d. 82
e. 83

_____ 16.   Find the specified nth term in the expansion of the binomial.

$$(x - 7y)^5, n = 3$$

a. $490x^3y^2$
b. $490x^5y^3$
c. $490x^3y^3$
d. $490x^2y^2$
e. $490x^2y^3$

_____ 17.   Calculate the binomial coefficient: $_{10}C_8$
a. 1
b. 80
c. 0
d. 45
e. 1,814,400

_____ 18.   Determine the number of ways a computer can randomly generate one or more such integers from 1 through 40.

An integer that is divisible by 4

a. 10
b. 6
c. 12
d. 8
e. 14

_____ 19.   A college student is preparing a course schedule for the next semester. The student may select one of four mathematics courses, one of five science courses, and one of five courses from the social sciences and humanities. How many schedules are possible?

a. 105
b. 95
c. 110
d. 100
e. 90

_____ 20.   Evaluate $_nP_r$.

$_{18}P_2$

a. 420
b. 380
c. 306
d. 153
e. 342

_____ 21.   There are three processes involved in assembling a product, and these processes can be performed in any order. The management wants to test each order to determine which is the least time-consuming. How many different orders will have to be tested?

a. 1,006
b. 506
c. 106
d. 56
e. 6

_____ 22.   Fifteen weightlifters are competing in the dead-lift competition. In how many ways can the weightlifters finish first, second, and third (no ties)?
a. 6
b. 3
c. 45
d. 2730
e. 3375

_____   23.   Find the probability for the experiment of tossing a six-sided die twice.

The sum is 4.

a. $\dfrac{1}{12}$

b. $\dfrac{1}{36}$

c.   12

d.   9

e. $\dfrac{1}{9}$

_____   24.   The educational attainment of the United States population age 25 years or older in 2007 is shown in the circle graph. Use the fact that the population of people 25 years or older was approximately 294.32 million in 2007. Estimate the number of people 25 years or older who have high school diplomas.

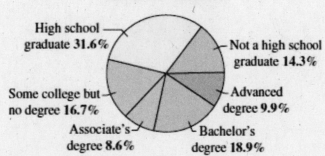

Educational Attainment

a.   252.23 million
b.   272.23 million
c.   282.23 million
d.   262.23 million
e.   292.23 million

_____ 25.   Find the probability for the experiment of drawing two marbles (without replacement) from a bag containing   three green,   six yellow, and   four red marbles such that the marbles are different colors.

a. $\dfrac{2}{13}$

b. $\dfrac{9}{13}$

c. $\dfrac{3}{2}$

d. $\dfrac{9}{26}$

e. $\dfrac{2}{3}$

Ch 9 Form C
Answer Section

1.	ANS:	D	PTS:	1	REF:	9.1.13
2.	ANS:	A	PTS:	1	REF:	9.1.54
3.	ANS:	B	PTS:	1	REF:	9.1.77
4.	ANS:	E	PTS:	1	REF:	9.2.13
5.	ANS:	D	PTS:	1	REF:	9.2.20
6.	ANS:	B	PTS:	1	REF:	9.2.7
7.	ANS:	B	PTS:	1	REF:	9.2.61
8.	ANS:	E	PTS:	1	REF:	9.3.18
9.	ANS:	D	PTS:	1	REF:	9.3.91
10.	ANS:	B	PTS:	1	REF:	9.3.49
11.	ANS:	B	PTS:	1	REF:	9.4.53
12.	ANS:	B	PTS:	1	REF:	9.4.70
13.	ANS:	C	PTS:	1	REF:	9.4.79a
14.	ANS:	D	PTS:	1	REF:	9.4.55
15.	ANS:	A	PTS:	1	REF:	9.5.16
16.	ANS:	A	PTS:	1	REF:	9.5.47
17.	ANS:	D	PTS:	1	REF:	9.5.5
18.	ANS:	A	PTS:	1	REF:	9.6.11
19.	ANS:	D	PTS:	1	REF:	9.6.17
20.	ANS:	C	PTS:	1	REF:	9.6.32
21.	ANS:	E	PTS:	1	REF:	9.6.42
22.	ANS:	D	PTS:	1	REF:	9.6.63
23.	ANS:	A	PTS:	1	REF:	9.7.25
24.	ANS:	A	PTS:	1	REF:	9.7.44a
25.	ANS:	B	PTS:	1	REF:	9.7.34

Ch 9 Form D

_____ 1.   Select the first five terms of the sequence. (Assume that n begins with 1.)

$a_n = (-2)^n$

a. $-2, -4, -6, -8, -10$
b. $-2, 4, -6, 16, -10$
c. $-2, 4, -8, 16, -32$
d. $1, -2, 4, -8, 16$
e. $-2, -4, -6, -8, -10$

_____ 2.   Write an expression for the apparent nth term of the sequence. (Assume that n begins with 1.)

$$\frac{1}{5}, \frac{4}{25}, \frac{16}{125}, \frac{64}{625}, \dots$$

a. $a_n = \dfrac{4^{n+1}}{5^{n+1}}$

b. $a_n = \dfrac{4^{n-1}}{5^n}$

c. $a_n = \dfrac{4^n}{5^n}$

d. $a_n = \dfrac{4^{n-1}}{5^{n-1}}$

e. $a_n = \dfrac{4^{n+1}}{5^n}$

_____ 3.   Simplify the factorial expression.

$\dfrac{7!}{4!}$

a.   42
b. $\dfrac{7}{4}$
c.   840
d.   210
e.   1680

_____   4.   Determine whether the sequence is arithmetic. If so, find the common difference.

$\ln 3, \ln 4, \ln 5, \ln 6, \ln 7 \ldots$

a.   Arithmetic sequence, $d = -0.29$
b.   Arithmetic sequence, $d = 0.51$
c.   Arithmetic sequence, $d = 0.29$
d.   Arithmetic sequence, $d = -0.69$
e.   Not an arithmetic sequence

_____   5.   Write the first five terms of the sequence. Determine whether the sequence is arithmetic. If so, find the common difference. (Assume that n begins with 1.)

$a_n = 4^{n-1}$

a. $1, 4, 16, 64, 256$
     Arithmetic sequence
     $d = 4$
b. $256, 64, 16, 4, 1$
     Not an Arithmetic sequence
c. $1, 4, 16, 64, 256$
     Not an Arithmetic sequence
d. $1, 4, 16, 64, 256$
     Arithmetic sequence
     $d = -4$
e. $256, 64, 16, 4, 1$
     Arithmetic sequence
     $d = 4$

_____   6.   Determine whether the sequence is arithmetic. If so, find the common difference.
$-9, -13, -17, -21, -25$
a. -9
b.   not arithmetic
c. 4
d. -5
e. -4

_____   7.   Find the indicated nth partial sum of the arithmetic sequence.
$3.7, 8.4, 13.1, 17.8, \ldots, n=85$
a.   17,493
b.   17,093
c.   17,094
d.   13,609
e.   17,095

_____ 8.   Find the first five terms of the geometric sequence.

$a_1 = 7, r = 2$

a. $14, 28, 56, 112, 224$
b. $5, 10, 20, 40, 80$
c. $7, 14, 28, 56, 112$
d. $10, 20, 40, 80, 160$
e. $4, 8, 16, 32, 64$

_____ 9.   Use summation notation to write the sum.

$0.8 + 3.2 + 12.8 + \cdots + 819.2$

a. $\displaystyle\sum_{n=1}^{7} 0.8(4)^{n-1}$

b. $\displaystyle\sum_{n=1}^{8} 0.8(4)^{n+1}$

c. $\displaystyle\sum_{n=1}^{6} (4)^{n-1}$

d. $\displaystyle\sum_{n=1}^{8} 0.8(4)^{n}$

e. $\displaystyle\sum_{n=1}^{6} 0.8(4)^{n-1}$

_____ 10.   Find the indicated nth term of the geometric sequence.

5th term: $a_4 = -\dfrac{3}{64}, a_7 = -\dfrac{3}{4096}$

a. $\dfrac{4}{81}$

b. $-\dfrac{3}{64}$

c. $-\dfrac{3}{1024}$

d. $-\dfrac{3}{4096}$

e. $-\dfrac{3}{256}$

_____ 11. Find the sum using the formulas for the sums of powers of integers.

$$\sum_{n=1}^{2} n^4$$

a. 9
b. 30
c. 5
d. 33
e. 17

_____ 12. Write the first six terms of the sequence beginning with the given term. Then calculate the first and second differences of the sequence. State whether the sequence has a linear model, a quadratic model, or neither.

$$a_0 = 0$$

$$a_n = a_{n-1} + n$$

a. 0, 1, 3, 6, 10, 15
    First differences: $-1, -1, -1, -1$
    Second differences: 1, 2, 3, 4, 5
    Linear
b. 0, 0, 1, 3, 6, 10
    First differences: 0, 1, 2, 3, 4
    Second differences: $-1, 1, -1, 1$
    Quadratic
c. 0, 0, 1, -3, 6, -10
    First differences: 0, 1, 2, 3, 4
    Second differences: $-1, 1, -1, 1$
    Neither
d. 0, -1, 3, -6, 10, -15
    First differences: $-1, 1, -1, 1$
    Second differences: 1, 2, 3, 4, 5
    Neither
e. 0, 1, 3, 6, 10, 15
    First differences: 1, 2, 3, 4, 5
    Second differences: 1, 1, 1, 1
    Quadratic

_____ 13.   The table shows the numbers a_n (in thousands) of Alaskan residents from 2002 through 2007. (Source: U.S. Census Bureau)

Year	Number of residents, a_n
2002	649
2003	652
2004	660
2005	678
2006	690
2007	693

Find the first differences of the data shown in the table.

a.   3, 8, 18, 3, 12
b.   3, 8, 12, 18, 3
c.   8, 3, 18, 12, 3
d.   3, 3, 8, 18, 12
e.   3, 8, 18, 12, 3

_____ 14.   Find the sum using the formulas for the sums of powers of integers.

$$\sum_{n=1}^{15} 6n - 5n^2$$

a.   −5480
b.   −1035
c.   −4445
d.   120
e.   −16,440

_____ 15.   Evaluate using Pascal's Triangle.

$$\begin{pmatrix} 7 \\ 4 \end{pmatrix}$$

a. 34
b. 37
c. 35
d. 33
e. 36

_____ 16.   Find the specified nth term in the expansion of the binomial.

$$(x - 9y)^5, n = 3$$

a. $810x^3y^3$
b. $810x^2y^3$
c. $810x^3y^2$
d. $810x^5y^3$
e. $810x^2y^2$

_____ 17.   Calculate the binomial coefficient: $_{14}C_4$

a. 56
b. 1001
c. 0
d. 24,024
e. 1

_____ 18.   Determine the number of ways a computer can randomly generate one or more such integers from 1 through 56.

An integer that is divisible by 4

a. 14
b. 10
c. 18
d. 12
e. 16

_____   19.   A college student is preparing a course schedule for the next semester. The student may select one of three mathematics courses, one of four science courses, and one of five courses from the social sciences and humanities. How many schedules are possible?

a. 60
b. 55
c. 70
d. 50
e. 65

_____   20.   Evaluate $_xP_y$.

$_{20}P_2$

a. 190
b. 380
c. 420
d. 462
e. 506

_____   21.   There are seven processes involved in assembling a product, and these processes can be performed in any order. The management wants to test each order to determine which is the least time-consuming. How many different orders will have to be tested?

a. 6,040
b. 5,040
c. 5,540
d. 5,090
e. 5,140

_____   22.   Fourteen weightlifters are competing in the dead-lift competition. In how many ways can the weightlifters finish first, second, and third (no ties)?
a. 2744
b. 6
c. 42
d. 3
e. 2184

_____   23.   Find the probability for the experiment of tossing a six-sided die twice.

The sum is 4.

a. $\dfrac{1}{9}$

b. $\dfrac{1}{36}$

c.   9

d.   12

e. $\dfrac{1}{12}$

_____   24.   The educational attainment of the United States population age 25 years or older in 2007 is shown in the circle graph. Use the fact that the population of people 25 years or older was approximately 248.32 million in 2007. Estimate the number of people 25 years or older who have high school diplomas.

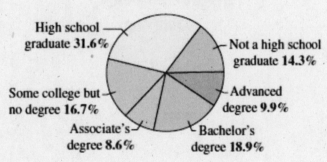

Educational Attainment

a.   222.81 million
b.   212.81 million
c.   242.81 million
d.   232.81 million
e.   252.81 million

____   25.   Find the probability for the experiment of drawing two marbles (without replacement) from a bag containing   three green,   four yellow, and   five red marbles such that the marbles are different colors.

a. $\dfrac{47}{66}$

b. $\dfrac{1}{6}$

c. $\dfrac{2}{3}$

d. $\dfrac{47}{30}$

e. $\dfrac{47}{132}$

Ch 9 Form D
Answer Section

1.	ANS:	C	PTS:	1	REF:	9.1.13
2.	ANS:	B	PTS:	1	REF:	9.1.54
3.	ANS:	D	PTS:	1	REF:	9.1.77
4.	ANS:	E	PTS:	1	REF:	9.2.13
5.	ANS:	C	PTS:	1	REF:	9.2.20
6.	ANS:	E	PTS:	1	REF:	9.2.7
7.	ANS:	C	PTS:	1	REF:	9.2.61
8.	ANS:	C	PTS:	1	REF:	9.3.18
9.	ANS:	E	PTS:	1	REF:	9.3.91
10.	ANS:	E	PTS:	1	REF:	9.3.49
11.	ANS:	E	PTS:	1	REF:	9.4.53
12.	ANS:	E	PTS:	1	REF:	9.4.70
13.	ANS:	E	PTS:	1	REF:	9.4.79a
14.	ANS:	A	PTS:	1	REF:	9.4.55
15.	ANS:	C	PTS:	1	REF:	9.5.16
16.	ANS:	C	PTS:	1	REF:	9.5.47
17.	ANS:	B	PTS:	1	REF:	9.5.5
18.	ANS:	A	PTS:	1	REF:	9.6.11
19.	ANS:	A	PTS:	1	REF:	9.6.17
20.	ANS:	B	PTS:	1	REF:	9.6.32
21.	ANS:	B	PTS:	1	REF:	9.6.42
22.	ANS:	E	PTS:	1	REF:	9.6.63
23.	ANS:	E	PTS:	1	REF:	9.7.25
24.	ANS:	B	PTS:	1	REF:	9.7.44a
25.	ANS:	A	PTS:	1	REF:	9.7.34

Ch 9 Form E

_____ 1. Select the first five terms of the sequence. (Assume that n begins with 1.)

$$a_n = \frac{n+13}{n}$$

a. $-14, \dfrac{15}{2}, -\dfrac{16}{3}, \dfrac{17}{4}, -\dfrac{18}{5}$

b. $14, \dfrac{15}{2}, \dfrac{16}{3}, \dfrac{17}{4}, \dfrac{18}{5}$

c. $14, -\dfrac{15}{2}, -\dfrac{16}{3}, -\dfrac{17}{4}, -\dfrac{18}{5}$

d. $13, 14, \dfrac{15}{2}, \dfrac{16}{3}, \dfrac{17}{4}$

e. $\dfrac{1}{14}, \dfrac{2}{15}, \dfrac{3}{16}, \dfrac{4}{17}, \dfrac{5}{18}$

_____ 2. Write an expression for the apparent nth term of the sequence. (Assume that n begins with 1.)

$0, 2, 0, 2, 0, \ldots$

a. $a_n = (-1)^n + 1$

b. $a_n = 1^n - 1$

c. $a_n = (-1)^{n+1}$

d. $a_n = (-1)^n - 1$

e. $a_n = (-1)^{n-1} + 1$

_____ 3.   Find the sum.

$$\sum_{k=1}^{3} \frac{1}{k^2 + 3}$$

a. $\dfrac{12}{11}$

b.   1

c. $\dfrac{1}{12}$

d. $\dfrac{10}{21}$

e. $\dfrac{37}{60}$

_____ 4.   Write the first five terms of the sequence. Determine whether the sequence is arithmetic. If so, find the common difference. (Assume that n begins with 1.)

$a_n = 6 + 2n$

a.   10, 12, 14, 16, 18
     Arithmetic sequence
     $d = 2$
b.   18, 16, 14, 12, 10
     Arithmetic sequence
     $d = -2$
c.   8, 10, 12, 14, 16
     Arithmetic sequence
     $d = -2$
d.   8, 10, 12, 14, 16
     Arithmetic sequence
     $d = 2$
e.   16, 14, 12, 10, 8
     Arithmetic sequence
     $d = -2$

_____ 5.   Find a formula for a_n for the arithmetic sequence.

$a_1 = 14, d = 3$

a. $a_n = -3n + 11$
b. $a_n = 3n - 11$
c. $a_n = 3n - 17$
d. $a_n = -3n + 17$
e. $a_n = 3n + 11$

_____ 6.   Find a formula for a_n for the arithmetic sequence.

$a_1 = 8, d = 4$

a. $a_n = 8\left(\dfrac{1}{4}\right)^{n-1}$

b. $a_n = 83n$

c. $a_n = 84^{n-1}$

d. $a_n = 4 + 4n$

e. $a_n = 4 + 8(n-1)$

_____ 7.   Match the arithmetic sequence with its graph from the choices below.

$a_n = 35 - 3n$

a.

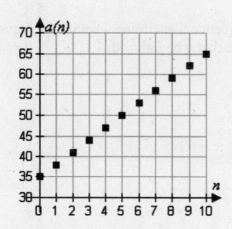

d.

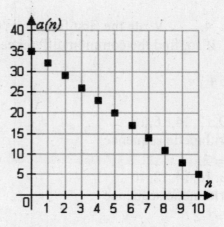

b.

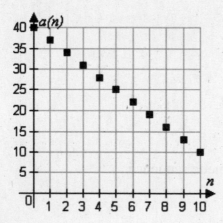

e.

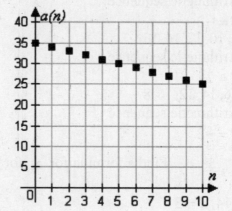

c.

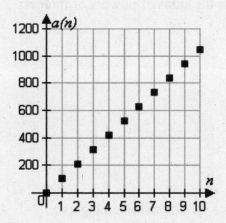

_____   8.   Find the first five terms of the geometric sequence.

$a_1 = 2, r = \pi$

a. $2, \pi, 2\pi^2, 2\pi^3, 2\pi^4$
b. $2, 2\pi^2, 2\pi^3, 2\pi^4, 2\pi^5$
c. $2, \pi, \pi^2, \pi^3, \pi^4$
d. $2, \pi^2, \pi^3, \pi^4, \pi^5$
e. $2, 2\pi, 2\pi^2, 2\pi^3, 2\pi^4$

_____   9.   A principal of \$5000 is invested at 8% interest. Find the amount after 10 years if the interest is compounded   annually.

a.   \$10796.62
b.   \$10794.62
c.   \$10798.62
d.   \$10795.62
e.   \$10797.62

_____   10.   Find the sum of the finite geometric sequence.

$$\sum_{n=1}^{5} 3\left(\frac{2}{5}\right)^{n-1}$$

a. $\dfrac{48}{5}$

b. $\dfrac{203}{125}$

c. 1031

d. $\dfrac{15,561}{1250}$

e. $\dfrac{3093}{625}$

_____ 11.   Find the sum using the formulas for the sums of powers of integers.

$$\sum_{i=1}^{6} \left(5i - 9i^3 \right)$$

a. $-1,764$
b. $-3,864$
c. $4,095$
d. $2,730$
e. -441

_____ 12.   Use mathematical induction to solve for all positive integers n.

A factor of $\left(n^3 + 6n^2 + 5n \right)$ is:

a. 8
b. 5
c. 3
d. 7
e. 6

_____ 13.   Find P_{k+1} for the given P_k.

$$P_k = \frac{2}{k(k+1)}$$

a. $P_{k+1} = \frac{2}{k(k+1)} + 1$

b. $P_{k+1} = \frac{4}{(k+1)(k+2)}$

c. $P_{k+1} = \frac{2}{k(k+2)}$

d. $P_{k+1} = \frac{2}{k(k+1)} + \frac{2}{(k+1)(k+2)}$

e. $P_{k+1} = \frac{2}{(k+1)(k+2)}$

_____ 14.   Select the formula for positive integer n using mathematical induction.

$5 + 8 + 11 + 24 + \ldots + (3n + 2) = ?$

a. $\dfrac{n}{6}(3n + 7)$

b. $\dfrac{n}{4}(3n + 7)$

c. $n(3n + 7)$

d. $\dfrac{n}{2}(3n + 7)$

e. $3n + 7$

_____ 15.   Use the Binomial Theorem to expand and simplify the expression.

$(x + 4)^4$

a. $x^4 - 16x^3 - 96x^2 - 256x - 256$

b. $x^4 + 16x^3 - 96x^2 + 256x + 256$

c. $x^4 + 16x^3 + 96x^2 - 256x + 256$

d. $x^4 - 16x^3 + 96x^2 + 256x + 256$

e. $x^4 + 16x^3 + 96x^2 + 256x + 256$

_____ 16.   Find the specified nth term in the expansion of the binomial.

$(3a + 4b)^5, n = 5$

a. $3,840ab^4$

b. $3,840a^4b^4$

c. $3,840a^4b$

d. $3,840a^5b^5$

e. $3,840ab$

_____ 17.   Use the Binomial Theorem to expand and simplify the expression.

$(p + 4)^5$

a. $p^4 + 16p^3 + 96p^2 + 256p + 256$

b. $p^5 + 16p^4 + 144p^3 + 576p^2 + 1024p + 1024$

c. $p^5 + 20p^4 + 160p^3 + 640p^2 + 1280p + 1024$

d. $p^5 + 20p^4 + 240p^3 + 960p^2 + 1280p + 1024$

e. $p^5 + 20p^4 + 160p^3 + 640p^2 + 1280p$

_____ 18.   Determine the number of ways a computer can randomly generate one or more such integers from 1 through 14.

Two *distinct* integers whose sum is 9

a. 12
b. 10
c. 8
d. 6
e. 4

_____ 19.   In how many ways can a six-question true-false exam be answered? (Assume that no questions are omitted.)

a. 69
b. 64
c. 74
d. 54
e. 59

_____ 20.   Evaluate $_nP_r$.

$_{105}P_5$

a. 114,725,520
b. 1,124,760
c. 1,158,727,752,000
d. 11,587,277,520
e. 96,560,646

_____ 21.   Eight sprinters have qualified for the finals in the 100-meter dash at the NCAA national track meet. In how many ways can the sprinters come in first, second, and third? (Assume there are no ties.)

a. 386
b. 536
c. 336
d. 436
e. 486

_____   22.   Find the number of diagonals of a dodecagon (12 sides). (A line segment connecting any two nonadjacent vertices is called a *diagonal* of the polygon.)

a. 54
b. 132
c. 144
d. 12
e. 24

_____   23.   You are given the probability that an event *will* happen. Find the probability that the event *will not* happen.

$P(E) = 0.82$

a. 0.28
b. 0.23
c. 0.18
d. 0.82
e. 0.33

_____   24.   The educational attainment of the United States population age 25 years or older in 2007 is shown in the circle graph. Use the fact that the population of people 25 years or older was approximately 9.4 million in 2007 and Associate's degree $a = 9.4\%$, Bachelor's degree $b = 17.4\%$, Advanced degree $c = 11.3\%$ and Nota a high school graduate $d = 13.6\%$. Find the probability that a person 25 years or older selected at random has earned an Associate's degree or higher.

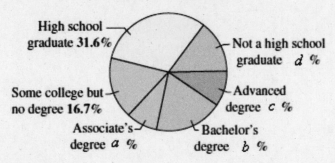

Educational Attainment

a. 1.381
b. 4.381
c. 2.381
d. 3.381
e. 0.381

____ 25.   In order to be certified, an EMT trainee (EMT stands for "emergency medical technician") must pass a written examination. A study of 72 trainees is conducted to assess the effectiveness of exam-preparation seminars in reducing the failure rate. The data are summarized below.

	0 seminars attended	1 seminar attended	2 seminars attended	Total
Passed exam	4	16	17	37
Failed exam	7	14	14	35
Total	11	30	31	72

Find the probability that the trainee attended one seminar and passed the exam.

a. $\dfrac{8}{15}$

b. $\dfrac{8}{21}$

c. $\dfrac{2}{9}$

d. $\dfrac{5}{12}$

e. $\dfrac{16}{37}$

Ch 9 Form E
Answer Section

1.	ANS:	B	PTS:	1	REF:	9.1.15
2.	ANS:	A	PTS:	1	REF:	9.1.59
3.	ANS:	D	PTS:	1	REF:	9.1.91
4.	ANS:	D	PTS:	1	REF:	9.2.15
5.	ANS:	E	PTS:	1	REF:	9.2.24
6.	ANS:	D	PTS:	1	REF:	9.2.23
7.	ANS:	D	PTS:	1	REF:	9.2.76
8.	ANS:	E	PTS:	1	REF:	9.3.24
9.	ANS:	B	PTS:	1	REF:	9.3.114a
10.	ANS:	E	PTS:	1	REF:	9.3.68
11.	ANS:	B	PTS:	1	REF:	9.4.57
12.	ANS:	C	PTS:	1	REF:	9.4.37
13.	ANS:	E	PTS:	1	REF:	9.4.5
14.	ANS:	D	PTS:	1	REF:	9.4.13
15.	ANS:	E	PTS:	1	REF:	9.5.19
16.	ANS:	A	PTS:	1	REF:	9.5.50
17.	ANS:	C	PTS:	1	REF:	9.5.19
18.	ANS:	C	PTS:	1	REF:	9.6.13
19.	ANS:	B	PTS:	1	REF:	9.6.19
20.	ANS:	D	PTS:	1	REF:	9.6.36
21.	ANS:	C	PTS:	1	REF:	9.6.50
22.	ANS:	A	PTS:	1	REF:	9.6.73
23.	ANS:	C	PTS:	1	REF:	9.7.35
24.	ANS:	E	PTS:	1	REF:	9.7.44e
25.	ANS:	C	PTS:	1	REF:	9.7.43a

Ch 9 Form F

_____   1.   Select the first five terms of the sequence. (Assume that n begins with 1.)

$$a_n = \frac{n+11}{n}$$

a.
$$12, -\frac{13}{2}, -\frac{14}{3}, -\frac{15}{4}, -\frac{16}{5}$$

b.
$$-12, \frac{13}{2}, -\frac{14}{3}, \frac{15}{4}, -\frac{16}{5}$$

c.
$$11, 12, \frac{13}{2}, \frac{14}{3}, \frac{15}{4}$$

d.
$$12, \frac{13}{2}, \frac{14}{3}, \frac{15}{4}, \frac{16}{5}$$

e.
$$\frac{1}{12}, \frac{2}{13}, \frac{3}{14}, \frac{4}{15}, \frac{5}{16}$$

_____   2.   Write an expression for the apparent nth term of the sequence. (Assume that n begins with 1.)

$0, 2, 0, 2, 0, \ldots$

a. $a_n = (-1)^{n+1}$

b. $a_n = (-1)^n - 1$

c. $a_n = (-1)^{n-1} + 1$

d. $a_n = (-1)^n + 1$

e. $a_n = 1^n - 1$

____ 3.   Find the sum.

$$\sum_{k=1}^{3} \frac{1}{k^2+5}$$

a. $\dfrac{22}{63}$

b. $\dfrac{1}{14}$

c. $\dfrac{12}{11}$

d. 1

e. $\dfrac{73}{168}$

____ 4.   Write the first five terms of the sequence. Determine whether the sequence is arithmetic. If so, find the common difference. (Assume that n begins with 1.)

$a_n = 5 + 4n$

a. $9, 13, 17, 21, 25$
   Arithmetic sequence
   $d = -4$
b. $25, 21, 17, 13, 9$
   Arithmetic sequence
   $d = -4$
c. $29, 25, 21, 17, 13$
   Arithmetic sequence
   $d = -4$
d. $9, 13, 17, 21, 25$
   Arithmetic sequence
   $d = 4$
e. $13, 17, 21, 25, 29$
   Arithmetic sequence
   $d = 4$

____ 5.   Find a formula for a_n for the arithmetic sequence.

$a_1 = 17, d = 6$

a. $a_n = -6n + 11$
b. $a_n = -6n + 23$
c. $a_n = 6n - 11$
d. $a_n = 6n - 23$
e. $a_n = 6n + 11$

_____ 6.   Find a formula for a_n for the arithmetic sequence.

$a_1 = 5, d = 6$

a. $a_n = 56^{n-1}$

b. $a_n = 6 + 5(n-1)$

c. $a_n = 55n$

d.
$$a_n = 5\left(\frac{1}{6}\right)^{n-1}$$

e. $a_n = -1 + 6n$

_____ 7.   Match the arithmetic sequence with its graph from the choices below.

$a_n = -7 + 2n$

a.

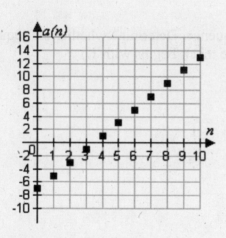

d.

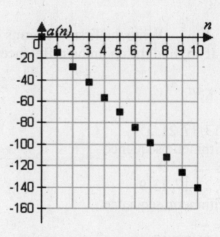

b.

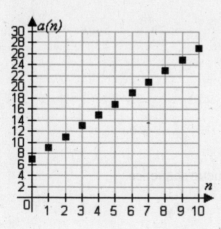

e.

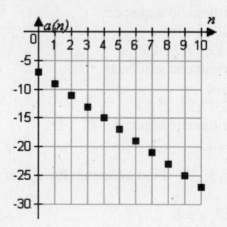

c.

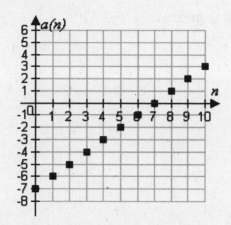

_____ 8.   Find the first five terms of the geometric sequence.

$a_1 = 5, r = \pi$

a. $5, \pi, \pi^2, \pi^3, \pi^4$
b. $5, \pi^2, \pi^3, \pi^4, \pi^5$
c. $5, \pi, 5\pi^2, 5\pi^3, 5\pi^4$
d. $5, 5\pi^2, 5\pi^3, 5\pi^4, 5\pi^5$
e. $5, 5\pi, 5\pi^2, 5\pi^3, 5\pi^4$

_____ 9.   A principal of $2000 is invested at 5% interest. Find the amount after 10 years if the interest is compounded   annually.

a. $3260.79
b. $3257.79
c. $3261.79
d. $3259.79
e. $3258.79

_____   10.   Find the sum of the finite geometric sequence.

$$\sum_{n=1}^{6} 3\left(-\frac{3}{8}\right)^{n-1}$$

a. $-\dfrac{729}{8}$

b. $\dfrac{71,295}{32,768}$

c. $\dfrac{3001}{4096}$

d. $23,765$

e. $-\dfrac{190,849}{32,768}$

_____   11.   Find the sum using the formulas for the sums of powers of integers.

$$\sum_{i=1}^{7} \left(5i - 7i^3\right)$$

a. $4,200$

b. -784

c. $-3,136$

d. $-5,348$

e. $4,900$

_____   12.   Use mathematical induction to solve for all positive integers n.

A factor of $\left(n^3 + 7n^2 + 6n\right)$ is:

a.   7

b.   6

c.   3

d.   8

e.   9

_____ 13. Find P_{k+1} for the given P_k.

$$P_k = \frac{5}{k(k+1)}$$

a. $P_{k+1} = \dfrac{25}{(k+1)(k+2)}$

b. $P_{k+1} = \dfrac{5}{k(k+1)} + \dfrac{5}{(k+1)(k+2)}$

c. $P_{k+1} = \dfrac{5}{k(k+2)}$

d. $P_{k+1} = \dfrac{5}{k(k+1)} + 1$

e. $P_{k+1} = \dfrac{5}{(k+1)(k+2)}$

_____ 14. Select the formula for positive integer n using mathematical induction.

$$9 + 14 + 19 + 80 + \ldots + (5n + 4) = ?$$

a. $\dfrac{n}{6}(5n + 13)$

b. $\dfrac{n}{2}(5n + 13)$

c. $n(5n + 13)$

d. $\dfrac{n}{4}(5n + 13)$

e. $5n + 13$

_____ 15. Use the Binomial Theorem to expand and simplify the expression.

$(x + 3)^4$

a. $x^4 - 12x^3 + 54x^2 + 108x + 81$
b. $x^4 - 12x^3 - 54x^2 - 108x - 81$
c. $x^4 + 12x^3 + 54x^2 + 108x + 81$
d. $x^4 + 12x^3 + 54x^2 - 108x + 81$
e. $x^4 + 12x^3 - 54x^2 + 108x + 81$

_____ 16.   Find the specified *n*th term in the expansion of the binomial.

$(8a + 9b)^5, n = 5$

a. $262,440a^4b$
b. $262,440a^5b^5$
c. $262,440ab$
d. $262,440a^4b^4$
e. $262,440ab^4$

_____ 17.   Use the Binomial Theorem to expand and simplify the expression.

$(z - 4)^5$

a. $z^5 - 20z^4 + 240z^3 - 960z^2 + 1280z - 1024$
b. $z^4 - 16z^3 + 96z^2 - 256z + 256$
c. $z^5 - 16z^4 + 144z^3 - 576z^2 + 1024z - 1024$
d. $z^5 - 20z^4 + 160z^3 - 640z^2 + 1280z$
e. $z^5 - 20z^4 + 160z^3 - 640z^2 + 1280z - 1024$

_____ 18.   Determine the number of ways a computer can randomly generate one or more such integers from 1 through 16.

Two *distinct* integers whose sum is 9

a. 6
b. 4
c. 10
d. 8
e. 12

_____ 19.   In how many ways can a seven-question true-false exam be answered? (Assume that no questions are omitted.)

a. 128
b. 133
c. 138
d. 118
e. 123

_____   20.   Evaluate $_nP_r$.

$_{120}P_5$

a.   22,869,362,880
b.   2,629,976,731,200
c.   1,685,040
d.   197,149,680
e.   190,578,024

_____   21.   Six sprinters have qualified for the finals in the 100-meter dash at the NCAA national track meet. In how many ways can the sprinters come in first, second, and third? (Assume there are no ties.)

a.   170
b.   120
c.   220
d.   320
e.   270

_____   22.   Find the number of diagonals of a nonagon (9 sides). (A line segment connecting any two nonadjacent vertices is called a *diagonal* of the polygon.)

a.   81
b.   72
c.   18
d.   9
e.   27

_____   23.   You are given the probability that an event *will* happen. Find the probability that the event *will not* happen.

$P(E) = 0.94$

a.   0.16
b.   0.11
c.   0.06
d.   0.21
e.   0.94

_____ 24. The educational attainment of the United States population age 25 years or older in 2007 is shown in the circle graph. Use the fact that the population of people 25 years or older was approximately 7.1 million in 2007 and Associate's degree $a = 7.1\%$, Bachelor's degree $b = 16.8\%$, Advanced degree $c = 11.6\%$ and Nota high school graduate $d = 16.2\%$. Find the probability that a person 25 years or older selected at random has earned an Associate's degree or higher.

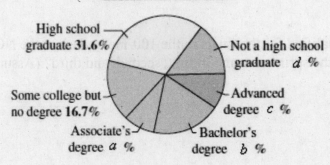

Educational Attainment

High school graduate 31.6%

Not a high school graduate d %

Some college but no degree 16.7%

Advanced degree c %

Associate's degree a %

Bachelor's degree b %

a. 1.355
b. 3.355
c. 2.355
d. 4.355
e. 0.355

_____   25.   In order to be certified, an EMT trainee (EMT stands for "emergency medical technician") must pass a written examination. A study of 64 trainees is conducted to assess the effectiveness of exam-preparation seminars in reducing the failure rate. The data are summarized below.

	0 seminars attended	1 seminar attended	2 seminars attended	Total
Passed exam	5	15	13	33
Failed exam	8	13	10	31
Total	13	28	23	64

Find the probability that the trainee attended one seminar and passed the exam.

a. $\dfrac{15}{64}$

b. $\dfrac{15}{28}$

c. $\dfrac{5}{12}$

d. $\dfrac{5}{11}$

e. $\dfrac{7}{16}$

Ch 9 Form F
Answer Section

1.	ANS:	D	PTS:	1	REF:	9.1.15
2.	ANS:	D	PTS:	1	REF:	9.1.59
3.	ANS:	A	PTS:	1	REF:	9.1.91
4.	ANS:	D	PTS:	1	REF:	9.2.15
5.	ANS:	E	PTS:	1	REF:	9.2.24
6.	ANS:	E	PTS:	1	REF:	9.2.23
7.	ANS:	A	PTS:	1	REF:	9.2.76
8.	ANS:	E	PTS:	1	REF:	9.3.24
9.	ANS:	B	PTS:	1	REF:	9.3.114a
10.	ANS:	B	PTS:	1	REF:	9.3.68
11.	ANS:	D	PTS:	1	REF:	9.4.57
12.	ANS:	C	PTS:	1	REF:	9.4.37
13.	ANS:	E	PTS:	1	REF:	9.4.5
14.	ANS:	B	PTS:	1	REF:	9.4.13
15.	ANS:	C	PTS:	1	REF:	9.5.19
16.	ANS:	E	PTS:	1	REF:	9.5.50
17.	ANS:	E	PTS:	1	REF:	9.5.19
18.	ANS:	D	PTS:	1	REF:	9.6.13
19.	ANS:	A	PTS:	1	REF:	9.6.19
20.	ANS:	A	PTS:	1	REF:	9.6.36
21.	ANS:	B	PTS:	1	REF:	9.6.50
22.	ANS:	E	PTS:	1	REF:	9.6.73
23.	ANS:	C	PTS:	1	REF:	9.7.35
24.	ANS:	E	PTS:	1	REF:	9.7.44e
25.	ANS:	A	PTS:	1	REF:	9.7.43a

Ch 10 Form A

_____   1.   Find the slope of the line with inclination θ. Round your answer to four decimal places.

$\theta = 2.88$ radians

a. $m \approx -0.4677$
b. $m \approx -0.5677$
c. $m \approx -0.3677$
d. $m \approx -0.2677$
e. $m \approx -0.6677$

_____   2.   Find the angle θ (in radians and degrees) between the lines. Round your answer to four decimal places for radians and round your answer to one decimal places for degree.

$x - 2y = 9$

$10x + 2y = 7$

a. $\theta \approx 1.3045$ radians $\approx 72.7°$
b. $\theta \approx 1.3045$ radians $\approx 74.7°$
c. $\theta \approx 1.3045$ radians $\approx 73.7°$
d. $\theta \approx 1.3045$ radians $\approx 75.7°$
e. $\theta \approx 1.3045$ radians $\approx 76.7°$

_____   3.   The given   points represent the vertices of a triangle. Select the triangle ABC in the coordinate plane.

$A = (0,0), B = (6,7), C = (7,-2)$

a.

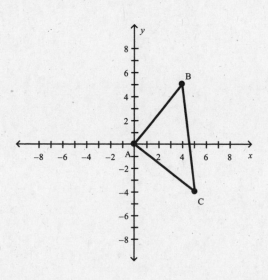

d.

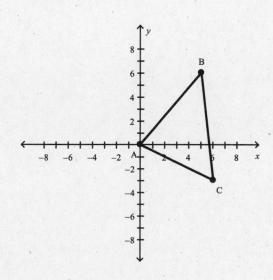

b.

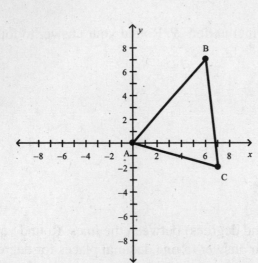

e.

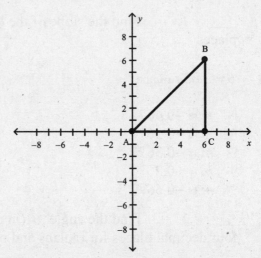

c.

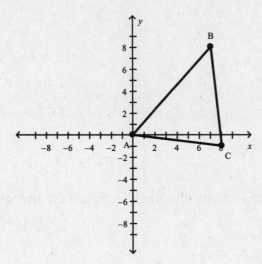

_____ 4.   Select the graph of the following equation

$x^2 = 2y$

a.

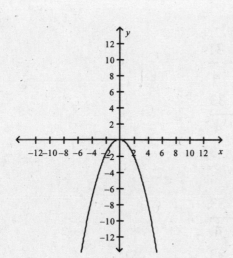

d.

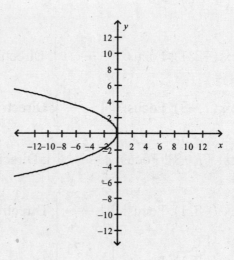

b.

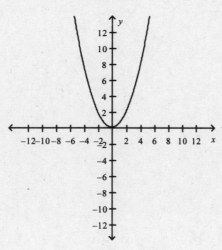

e.

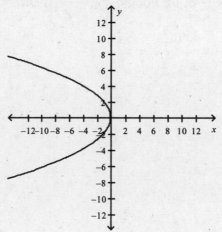

c.

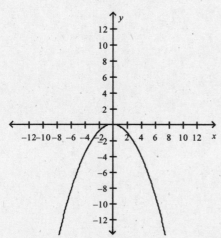

_____ 5.   Find the vertex, focus, and directrix of the parabola.

$$(x+8)+(y-1)^2 = 0$$

a.
    Vertex: $(-8, 1)$; Focus: $\left(-\dfrac{33}{4}, 1\right)$; Directrix: $x = -\dfrac{31}{4}$

b.
    Vertex: $(1, -8)$; Focus: $\left(1, -\dfrac{31}{4}\right)$; Directrix: $x = -\dfrac{33}{4}$

c.
    Vertex: $(1, -8)$; Focus: $\left(-\dfrac{31}{4}, 1\right)$; Directrix: $x = -\dfrac{33}{4}$

d.
    Vertex: $(-8, 1)$; Focus: $\left(1, -\dfrac{33}{4}\right)$; Directrix: $x = -\dfrac{33}{4}$

e.
    Vertex: $(-8, 1)$; Focus: $\left(1, -\dfrac{31}{4}\right)$; Directrix: $x = -\dfrac{33}{4}$

_____   6.   Roads are often designed with parabolic surfaces to allow rain to drain off. A particular road that is 32 feet wide is 0.2 foot higher in the center than it is on the sides (see figure).
Find an equation of the parabola that models the road surface. (Assume that the origin is at the center
of the road.)

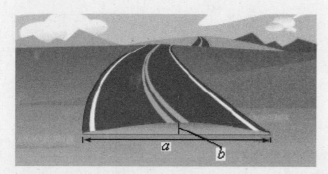

where $a = 32$ ft, $b = 0.2$ ft

a. $x^2 = -1280y$ or $y = -\dfrac{1}{1280}x^2$

b. $y^2 = -1280x$ or $x = -\dfrac{1}{1280}y^2$

c. $x^2 = 1280y$ or $y = \dfrac{1}{1280}x^2$

d. $y^2 = 1280x$ or $x = \dfrac{1}{1280}y^2$

e. $x^2 = 32y$ or $y = \dfrac{1}{32}x^2$

_____ 7.   Select the graph for following equation.

$$\frac{(x+2)^2}{16} + \frac{(y+2)^2}{9} = 1$$

a.

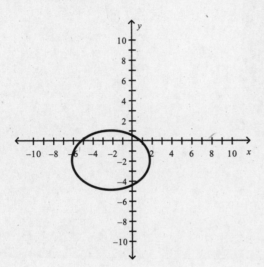

d.

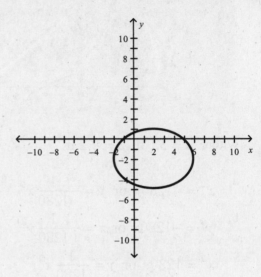

b.

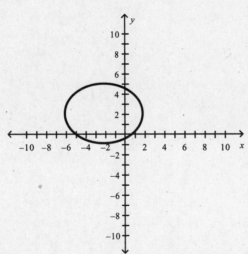

e.

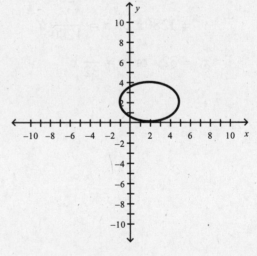

c.

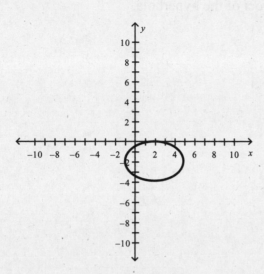

____ 8.   Identify the conic as a circle or an ellipse then find the center.

$$\frac{x^2}{64} + \frac{y^2}{64} = 1$$

a. Circle
    Center: $(0,0)$
b. Ellipse
    Center: $(0,0)$

____ 9.   Find the standard form of the equation of the ellipse with the given characteristics.
foci: $(-4,-9), (-4,-3)$ endpoints of the major axis: $(-4,-14), (-4,2)$

a.
$$\frac{(x+4)^2}{64} + \frac{(y+6)^2}{55} = 1$$

b.
$$\frac{(x-4)^2}{55} + \frac{(y-6)^2}{64} = 1$$

c.
$$\frac{(x-6)^2}{64} + \frac{(y-4)^2}{55} = 1$$

d.
$$\frac{(x+6)^2}{64} + \frac{(y+4)^2}{55} = 1$$

e.
$$\frac{(x+4)^2}{55} + \frac{(y+6)^2}{64} = 1$$

____   10.   Find the center, vertices and foci of the hyperbola.

$$\frac{y^2}{49} - \frac{x^2}{64} = 1$$

a. Center: $(0,0)$
    Vertices: $(0,8)$
    Foci: $\left(0, \sqrt{113}\right)$

b. Center: $(0,0)$
    Vertices: $(\pm 8, 0)$
    Foci: $\left(\pm\sqrt{113}, 0\right)$

c. Center: $(0,0)$
    Vertices: $(\pm 8, 0)$
    Foci: $\left(\sqrt{113}, 0\right)$

d. Center: $(0,0)$
    Vertices: $(8,0)$
    Foci: $\left(\pm\sqrt{113}, 0\right)$

e. Center: $(0,0)$
    Vertices: $(0,\pm 7)$
    Foci: $\left(0,\pm\sqrt{113}\right)$

____   11.   Select the graph of the equation as a circle, a parabola, an ellipse, or a hyperbola.

$$y^2 + 8x + 4y + 28 = 0$$

a. Ellipse
b. Hyperbola
c. Circle
d. Parabola
e. None of the above

_____   12.   The $x'y'$-coordinate system has been rotated θ degrees from the xy-coordinate system. The coordinates of a point in the xy-coordinate system are given. Find the coordinates of the point in the rotated coordinate system.

$\theta = 30°$, $(2,6)$

a. $\left(\sqrt{3}+3, 3\sqrt{3}+1 \right)$

b. $\left(\sqrt{3}+3, 3\sqrt{3}-1 \right)$

c. $\left(\dfrac{3-\sqrt{3}}{2}, \dfrac{3\sqrt{3}+1}{2} \right)$

d. $\left(\sqrt{3}-3, 3\sqrt{3}-1 \right)$

e. $\left(\dfrac{3-\sqrt{3}}{2}, \dfrac{3\sqrt{3}+3}{2} \right)$

_____   13.   Use the discriminant to classify the graph.

$x^2 + xy + 8y^2 + x + y - 8 = 0$

a. The graph is a cone.
b. The graph is a parabola.
c. The graph is a ellipse or circle.
d. The graph is a hyperbola.
e. The graph is a line.

_____   14.   Eliminate the parameter and write the corresponding rectangular equation whose graph represents the curve.

$x = \dfrac{1}{4}t$

$y = t^2$

a. $y = x^2$

b. $y = -4x^2$

c. $y = 4x^2$

d. $y = 16x^2$

e. $y = -16x^2$

_____ 15.   Find a set of parametric equations for the rectangular equation.

$$t = 7 - x$$

$$y = \frac{1}{x}$$

a.
$$x = t - 7, \ y = \frac{1}{(t+7)}$$

b.
$$x = 7 + t, \ y = \frac{1}{(-t+7)}$$

c.
$$x = 7 - t, \ y = \frac{-1}{(t-7)}$$

d.
$$x = 7 + t, \ y = \frac{1}{(t-7)}$$

e.
$$x = t - 7, \ y = \frac{-1}{(t+7)}$$

_____ 16.   A projectile is launched at a height of h feet above the ground at an angle of θ with the horizontal. The initial velocity is v_0 feet per second, and the path of the projectile is modeled by the parametric equations

$$x = \left(v_0 \cos \theta\right)t \ \text{ and } \ y = h + \left(v_0 \sin \theta\right)t - 16t^2.$$

Select the correct graph of the path of a projectile launched from ground level at the value of θ and v_0.

$$\theta = 15°, \ v_0 = 100 \text{ feet per second}$$

a.

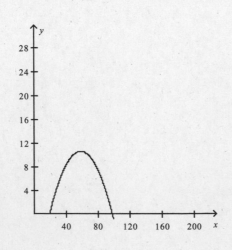

d.

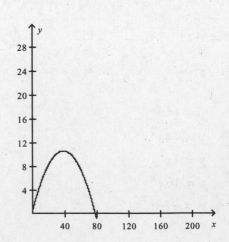

b.

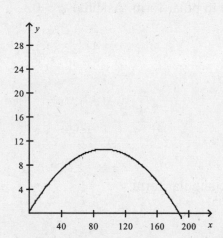

e.

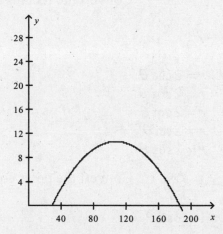

c.

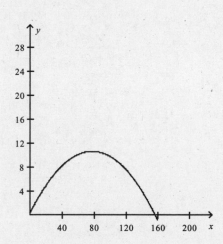

_____ 17.   A point in polar coordinates is given. Convert the point to rectangular coordinates. Round your answers to one decimal places.

$(-7, 3.66)$

a. Rectangular coordinates: $(3.7, 7.0)$
b. Rectangular coordinates: $(6.1, 3.5)$
c. Rectangular coordinates: $(-6.1, -3.5)$
d. Rectangular coordinates: $(-3.5, -6.1)$
e. Rectangular coordinates: $(3.5, 6.1)$

_____ 18.   Convert the rectangular equation to polar form. Assume $a > 0$.

$y = 2$

a. $r = 2\csc\theta$
b. $r = 2\cos\theta$
c. $r = 2\cot\theta$
d. $r = 2\sin\theta$
e. $r = 2\sec\theta$

_____ 19.   Convert the polar equation to rectangular form.

$r = 10\cos 2\theta$

a. $\left(x^2 + y^2\right)^2 = 100\left(x^2 - y^2\right)^2$

b. $\left(x^2 + y^2\right)^3 = 10\left(x^2 - y^2\right)^3$

c. $\left(x^2 + y^2\right)^3 = 100\left(x^2 - y^2\right)^3$

d. $\left(x^2 + y^2\right)^3 = 10\left(x^2 - y^2\right)^2$

e. $\left(x^2 + y^2\right)^3 = 100\left(x^2 - y^2\right)^2$

_____   20.   Select the graph of the polar equation using symmetry, zeros, maximum *r*-values, and any
other additional points.

$$r = -\frac{3\pi}{5}$$

a.   Symmetric with respect to $\theta = \frac{\pi}{2}$, polar

axis, pole

Circle with radius $\frac{3\pi}{5}$

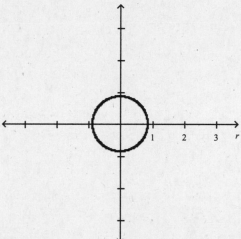

d.   Symmetric with respect to $\theta = \frac{\pi}{2}$, polar

axis, pole

Circle with radius $\frac{3\pi}{5}$

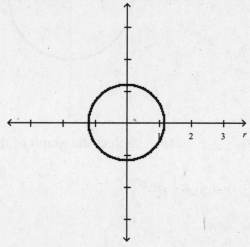

b.   Symmetric with respect to $\theta = \frac{\pi}{2}$, polar

axis, pole

Circle with radius $\frac{3\pi}{5}$

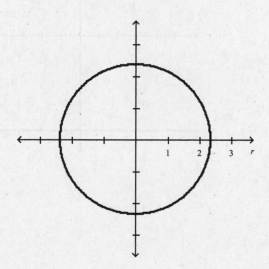

e.   Symmetric with respect to $\theta = \frac{\pi}{2}$, polar

axis, pole

Circle with radius $\frac{3\pi}{5}$

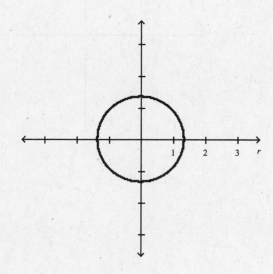

c.   Symmetric with respect to $\theta = \dfrac{\pi}{2}$, polar

axis, pole

Circle with radius $\dfrac{3\pi}{5}$

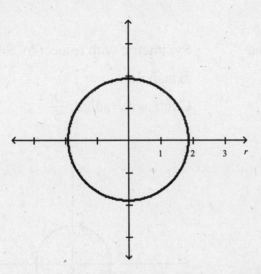

_____   21.   Select the graph of the equation.

$$r = 5\sec\left(\theta - \dfrac{\pi}{2}\right)$$

a.

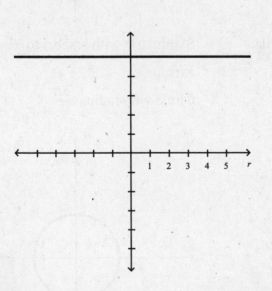

d.

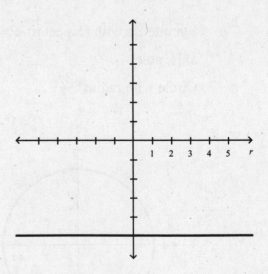

b.

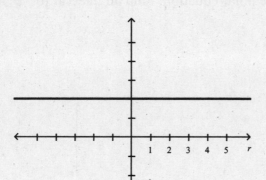

e.

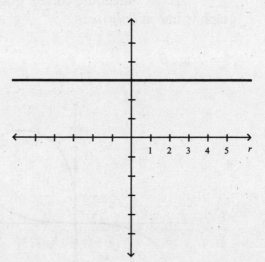

c.

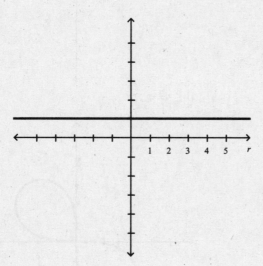

_____ 22. Select the correct graph of the polar equation. Find an interval for θ for which the graph is traced *only once*.

$r^2 = 9\sin 2\theta$

a.

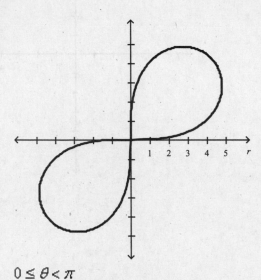

$0 \le \theta < \pi$

d.

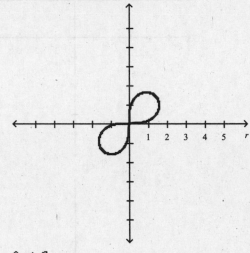

$0 \le \theta < \pi$

b.

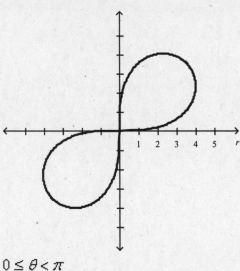

$0 \le \theta < \pi$

e.

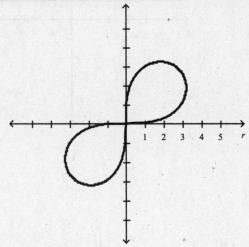

$0 \le \theta < \pi$

c.

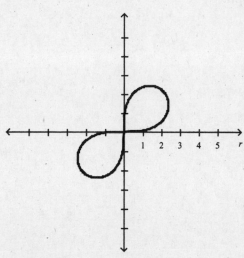

$0 \leq \theta < \pi$

____ 23.   Find a polar equation of the conic with its focus at the pole.

Conics	Eccentricity	Directrix
Parabola	$e = 1$	$x = -2$

a. $r = \dfrac{2}{1 - \sin \theta}$

b. $r = \dfrac{2}{1 - \cos \theta}$

c. $r = \dfrac{-2}{1 - \cos \theta}$

d. $r = \dfrac{2}{1 + \sin \theta}$

e. $r = \dfrac{2}{1 + \cos \theta}$

_____ 24.   Select the polar equation of graph.

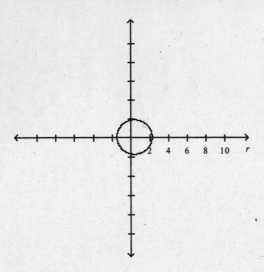

a. $\dfrac{7}{4-\cos\theta}$

b. $\dfrac{7}{4-\sin\theta}$

c. $\dfrac{1}{4-\cos\theta}$

d. $\dfrac{7}{4+\sin\theta}$

e. $\dfrac{7}{4+\cos\theta}$

_____ 25. Find a polar equation of the conic with its focus at the pole.

Conics   *Vertex or vertices*

Parabola $(6, \pi)$

a. $\dfrac{12}{1 + \cos \theta}$

b. $\dfrac{-12}{1 - \sin \theta}$

c. $\dfrac{12}{1 + \sin \theta}$

d. $\dfrac{12}{1 - \sin \theta}$

e. $\dfrac{12}{1 - \cos \theta}$

Ch 10 Form A
Answer Section

1.	ANS:	D	PTS:	1	REF:	10.1.12
2.	ANS:	B	PTS:	1	REF:	10.1.41
3.	ANS:	B	PTS:	1	REF:	10.1.60a
4.	ANS:	B	PTS:	1	REF:	10.2.14
5.	ANS:	A	PTS:	1	REF:	10.2.40
6.	ANS:	A	PTS:	1	REF:	10.2.73a
7.	ANS:	A	PTS:	1	REF:	10.3.10
8.	ANS:	A	PTS:	1	REF:	10.3.31a
9.	ANS:	E	PTS:	1	REF:	10.3.28
10.	ANS:	E	PTS:	1	REF:	10.4.11
11.	ANS:	D	PTS:	1	REF:	10.4.63
12.	ANS:	B	PTS:	1	REF:	10.5.8
13.	ANS:	C	PTS:	1	REF:	10.5.50a
14.	ANS:	D	PTS:	1	REF:	10.6.9b
15.	ANS:	C	PTS:	1	REF:	10.6.47b
16.	ANS:	C	PTS:	1	REF:	10.6.62a
17.	ANS:	B	PTS:	1	REF:	10.7.28
18.	ANS:	A	PTS:	1	REF:	10.7.72
19.	ANS:	E	PTS:	1	REF:	10.7.104
20.	ANS:	C	PTS:	1	REF:	10.8.26
21.	ANS:	A	PTS:	1	REF:	10.8.78d
22.	ANS:	C	PTS:	1	REF:	10.8.63
23.	ANS:	B	PTS:	1	REF:	10.9.39
24.	ANS:	A	PTS:	1	REF:	10.9.10
25.	ANS:	E	PTS:	1	REF:	10.9.47

Ch 10 Form B

_____   1.   Find the slope of the line with inclination θ. Round your answer to four decimal places.

$\theta = 2.48$ radians

a. $m \approx -1.0787$
b. $m \approx -1.1787$
c. $m \approx -0.7787$
d. $m \approx -0.8787$
e. $m \approx -0.9787$

_____   2.   Find the angle θ (in radians and degrees) between the lines. Round your answer to four decimal places for radians and round your answer to one decimal places for degree.

$x - 2y = 10$

$14x + 2y = 9$

a. $\theta \approx 1.2490$ radians $\approx 69.6°$
b. $\theta \approx 1.2490$ radians $\approx 70.6°$
c. $\theta \approx 1.2490$ radians $\approx 71.6°$
d. $\theta \approx 1.2490$ radians $\approx 73.6°$
e. $\theta \approx 1.2490$ radians $\approx 72.6°$

_____   3.   The given points represent the vertices of a triangle. Select the triangle ABC in the coordinate plane.

$A = (0,0), B = (6,7), C = (7,-1)$

a.

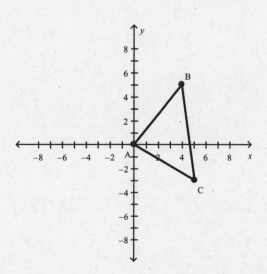

d.

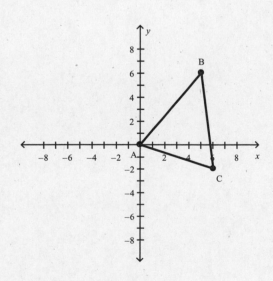

b.

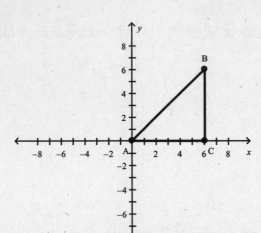

e.

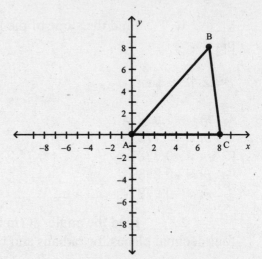

c.

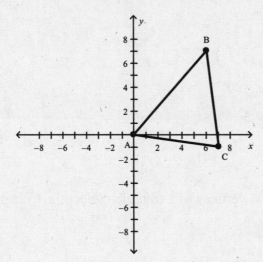

_____   4.   Select the graph of the following equation

$x^2 = 6y$

a.

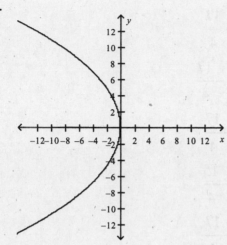

d.

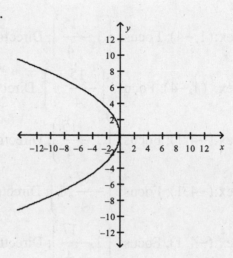

b.

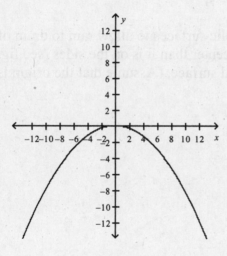

e.

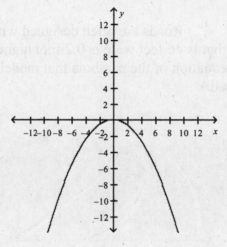

c.

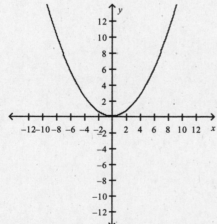

_____   5.   Find the vertex, focus, and directrix of the parabola.

$$(x+4)+\left(y-1\right)^2 = 0$$

a.
  Vertex: $(1,-4)$; Focus: $\left(1,-\dfrac{15}{4}\right)$; Directrix: $x=-\dfrac{17}{4}$

b.
  Vertex: $(1,-4)$; Focus: $\left(-\dfrac{15}{4},1\right)$; Directrix: $x=-\dfrac{17}{4}$

c.
  Vertex: $(-4,1)$; Focus: $\left(1,-\dfrac{15}{4}\right)$; Directrix: $x=-\dfrac{17}{4}$

d.
  Vertex: $(-4,1)$; Focus: $\left(-\dfrac{17}{4},1\right)$; Directrix: $x=-\dfrac{15}{4}$

e.
  Vertex: $(-4,1)$; Focus: $\left(1,-\dfrac{17}{4}\right)$; Directrix: $x=-\dfrac{17}{4}$

_____   6.   Roads are often designed with parabolic surfaces to allow rain to drain off. A particular road that is 46 feet wide is 0.2 foot higher in the center than it is on the sides (see figure). Find an equation of the parabola that models the road surface. (Assume that the origin is at the center of the road.)

where $a = 46$ ft, $b = 0.2$ ft

a.
  $y^2 = -2645x$ or $x=-\dfrac{1}{2645}y^2$

b.
  $x^2 = 2645y$ or $y=\dfrac{1}{2645}x^2$

c.
  $y^2 = 2645x$ or $x=\dfrac{1}{2645}y^2$

d.
  $x^2 = 46y$ or $y=\dfrac{1}{46}x^2$

e.
  $x^2 = -2645y$ or $y=-\dfrac{1}{2645}x^2$

_____ 7.   Select the graph for following equation.

$$\frac{(x+2)^2}{25} + \frac{(y+2)^2}{16} = 1$$

a.

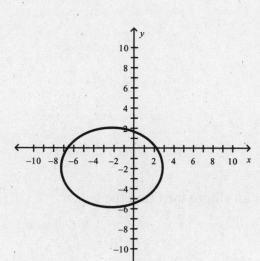

d.

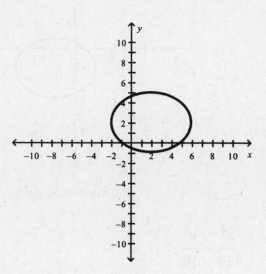

b.

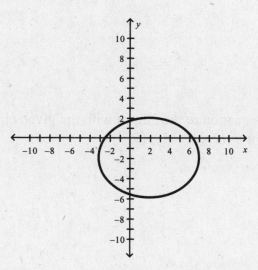

e.

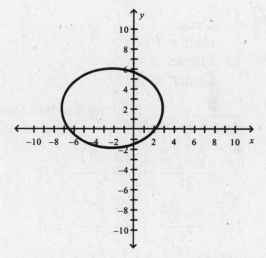

c.

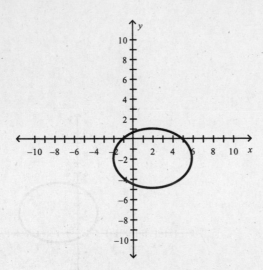

_____ 8.   Identify the conic as a circle or an ellipse then find the center.

$$\frac{x^2}{16} + \frac{y^2}{16} = 1$$

a. Circle
    Center: $(0,0)$
b. Ellipse
    Center: $(0,0)$

_____ 9.   Find the standard form of the equation of the ellipse with the given characteristics.
foci: $(9,-7), (9,3)$ endpoints of the major axis: $(9,-11), (9,7)$

a.
$$\frac{(x+2)^2}{81} + \frac{(y-9)^2}{56} = 1$$

b.
$$\frac{(x+9)^2}{56} + \frac{(y-2)^2}{81} = 1$$

c.
$$\frac{(x-2)^2}{81} + \frac{(y+9)^2}{56} = 1$$

d.
$$\frac{(x-9)^2}{56} + \frac{(y+2)^2}{81} = 1$$

e.
$$\frac{(x-9)^2}{81} + \frac{(y+2)^2}{56} = 1$$

____ 10.   Find the center, vertices and foci of the hyperbola.

$$\frac{y^2}{36} - \frac{x^2}{49} = 1$$

a. Center: $(0,0)$
    Vertices: $(0,\pm 6)$
    Foci: $\left(0, \pm\sqrt{85}\right)$

b. Center: $(0,0)$
    Vertices: $(\pm 7,0)$
    Foci: $\left(\pm\sqrt{85},0\right)$

c. Center: $(0,0)$
    Vertices: $(0,7)$
    Foci: $\left(0,\sqrt{85}\right)$

d. Center: $(0,0)$
    Vertices: $(7,0)$
    Foci: $\left(\pm\sqrt{85},0\right)$

e. Center: $(0,0)$
    Vertices: $(\pm 7,0)$
    Foci: $\left(\sqrt{85},0\right)$

____ 11.   Select the graph of the equation as a circle, a parabola, an ellipse, or a hyperbola.

$$y^2 + 6x + 2y + 25 = 0$$

a. Hyperbola
b. Parabola
c. Circle
d. Ellipse
e. None of the above

_____ 12. The $x'y'$-coordinate system has been rotated θ degrees from the xy-coordinate system. The coordinates of a point in the xy-coordinate system are given. Find the coordinates of the point in the rotated coordinate system.

$\theta = 30°$, $(2,4)$

a. $\left(\dfrac{3-\sqrt{2}}{2}, \dfrac{2\sqrt{3}+1}{2} \right)$

b. $\left(\sqrt{3}-2, 2\sqrt{3}-1 \right)$

c. $\left(\sqrt{3}+2, 2\sqrt{3}+1 \right)$

d. $\left(\sqrt{3}+2, 2\sqrt{3}-1 \right)$

e. $\left(\dfrac{3-\sqrt{2}}{2}, \dfrac{2\sqrt{3}+3}{2} \right)$

_____ 13. Use the discriminant to classify the graph.

$x^2 + xy + 10y^2 + x + y - 10 = 0$

a. The graph is a parabola.
b. The graph is a hyperbola.
c. The graph is a line.
d. The graph is a ellipse or circle.
e. The graph is a cone.

_____ 14. Eliminate the parameter and write the corresponding rectangular equation whose graph represents the curve.

$x = \dfrac{1}{5}t$

$y = t^2$

a. $y = 5x^2$

b. $y = -25x^2$

c. $y = 25x^2$

d. $y = x^2$

e. $y = -5x^2$

_____   15.   Find a set of parametric equations for the rectangular equation.

$$t = 8 - x$$

$$y = \frac{1}{x}$$

a.
$$x = 8 - t, \; y = \frac{-1}{(t - 8)}$$

b.
$$x = t - 8, \; y = \frac{1}{(t + 8)}$$

c.
$$x = 8 + t, \; y = \frac{1}{(-t + 8)}$$

d.
$$x = 8 + t, \; y = \frac{1}{(t - 8)}$$

e.
$$x = t - 8, \; y = \frac{-1}{(t + 8)}$$

_____   16.   A projectile is launched at a height of h feet above the ground at an angle of θ with the horizontal. The initial velocity is v_0 feet per second, and the path of the projectile is modeled by the parametric equations

$$x = \left(v_0 \cos \theta \right) t \; \text{ and } \; y = h + \left(v_0 \sin \theta \right) t - 16 t^2.$$

Select the correct graph of the path of a projectile launched from ground level at the value of θ and v_0.

$\theta = 15°, \; v_0 = 80$ feet per second

a.

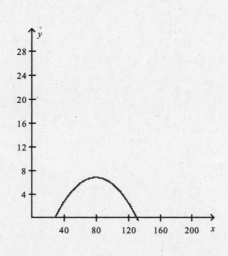

d.

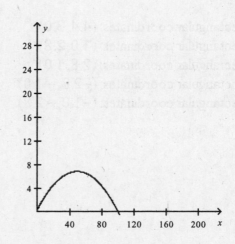

b.

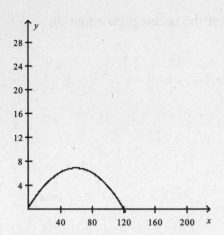

e.

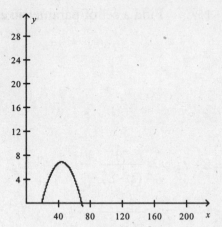

c.

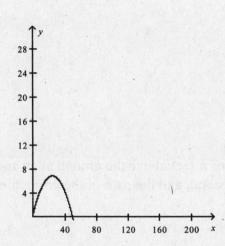

____ 17.   A point in polar coordinates is given. Convert the point to rectangular coordinates. Round your answers to one decimal places.

$(-3, 4.36)$

a.   Rectangular coordinates: $(4.4, 3.0)$
b.   Rectangular coordinates: $(1.0, 2.8)$
c.   Rectangular coordinates: $(2.8, 1.0)$
d.   Rectangular coordinates: $(-2.8, -1.0)$
e.   Rectangular coordinates: $(-1.0, -2.8)$

_____ 18.   Convert the rectangular equation to polar form. Assume $a > 0$.

$y = 1$

a. $r = \sec \theta$
b. $r = \cot \theta$
c. $r = \sin \theta$
d. $r = \cos \theta$
e. $r = \csc \theta$

_____ 19.   Convert the polar equation to rectangular form.

$r = 10 \cos 2\theta$

a. $\left(x^2 + y^2\right)^3 = 100\left(x^2 - y^2\right)^3$

b. $\left(x^2 + y^2\right)^3 = 10\left(x^2 - y^2\right)^2$

c. $\left(x^2 + y^2\right)^2 = 100\left(x^2 - y^2\right)^2$

d. $\left(x^2 + y^2\right)^3 = 100\left(x^2 - y^2\right)^2$

e. $\left(x^2 + y^2\right)^3 = 10\left(x^2 - y^2\right)^3$

_____   20.   Select the graph of the polar equation using symmetry, zeros, maximum *r*-values, and any

other additional points.

$$r = -\frac{3\pi}{8}$$

a.   Symmetric with respect to $\theta = \frac{\pi}{2}$, polar

axis, pole

Circle with radius $\frac{3\pi}{8}$

d.   Symmetric with respect to $\theta = \frac{\pi}{2}$, polar

axis, pole

Circle with radius $\frac{3\pi}{8}$

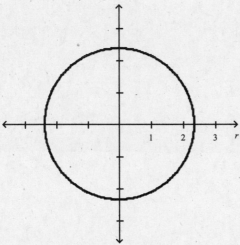
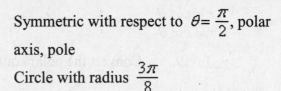

b.   Symmetric with respect to $\theta = \frac{\pi}{2}$, polar

axis, pole

Circle with radius $\frac{3\pi}{8}$

e.   Symmetric with respect to $\theta = \frac{\pi}{2}$, polar

axis, pole

Circle with radius $\frac{3\pi}{8}$

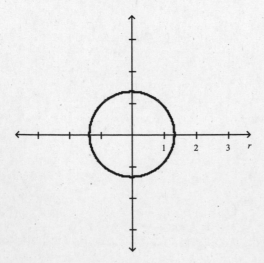
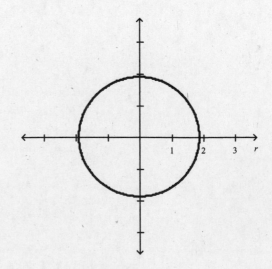

c.   Symmetric with respect to $\theta = \dfrac{\pi}{2}$, polar

axis, pole

Circle with radius $\dfrac{3\pi}{8}$

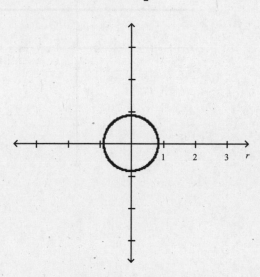

___ 21.   Select the graph of the equation.

$$r = 5\sec\left(\theta - \dfrac{\pi}{2}\right)$$

a.

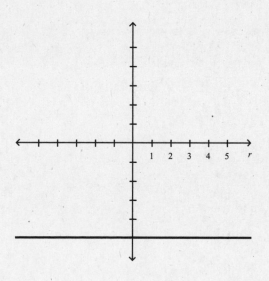

d.

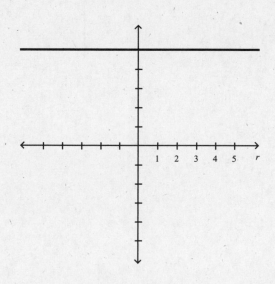

b.

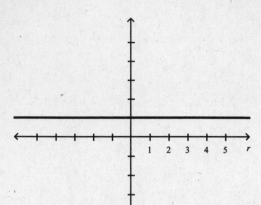

e.

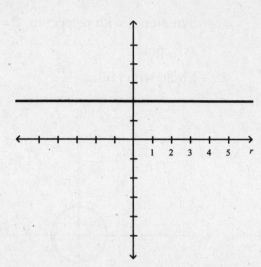

c.

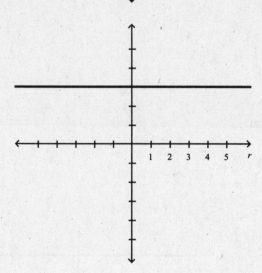

_____   22.   Select the correct graph of the polar equation. Find an interval for θ for which the graph is traced *only once*.

$r^2 = 4\sin 2\theta$

a.

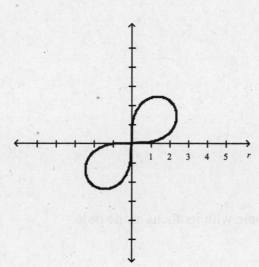

$0 \leq \theta < \pi$

b.

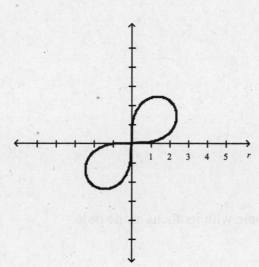

$0 \leq \theta < \pi$

d.

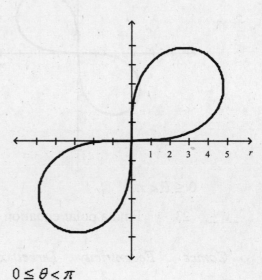

$0 \leq \theta < \pi$

e.

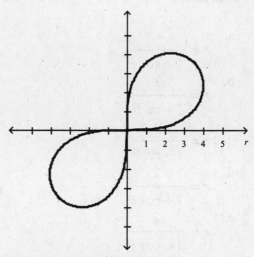

$0 \leq \theta < \pi$

c.

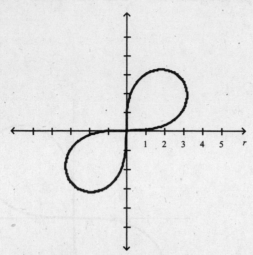

$0 \le \theta < \pi$

_____ 23.   Find a polar equation of the conic with its focus at the pole.

Conics	Eccentricity	Directrix
Parabola	$e = 1$	$x = -2$

a. $r = \dfrac{-2}{1 - \cos \theta}$

b. $r = \dfrac{2}{1 + \sin \theta}$

c. $r = \dfrac{2}{1 - \sin \theta}$

d. $r = \dfrac{2}{1 + \cos \theta}$

e. $r = \dfrac{2}{1 - \cos \theta}$

_____ 24.   Select the polar equation of graph.

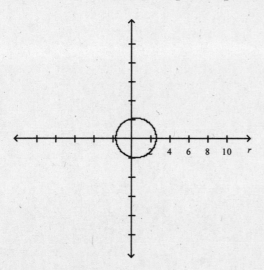

a. $\dfrac{8}{4+\cos\theta}$

b. $\dfrac{8}{4-\cos\theta}$

c. $\dfrac{1}{4-\cos\theta}$

d. $\dfrac{8}{4-\sin\theta}$

e. $\dfrac{8}{4+\sin\theta}$

_____ 25.   Find a polar equation of the conic with its focus at the pole.

Conics   *Vertex or vertices*

Parabola $(6, \pi)$

a. $\dfrac{12}{1 - \sin \theta}$

b. $\dfrac{12}{1 + \cos \theta}$

c. $\dfrac{12}{1 + \sin \theta}$

d. $\dfrac{-12}{1 - \sin \theta}$

e. $\dfrac{12}{1 - \cos \theta}$

Ch 10 Form B
Answer Section

1.	ANS:	C	PTS:	1	REF:	10.1.12
2.	ANS:	C	PTS:	1	REF:	10.1.41
3.	ANS:	C	PTS:	1	REF:	10.1.60a
4.	ANS:	C	PTS:	1	REF:	10.2.14
5.	ANS:	D	PTS:	1	REF:	10.2.40
6.	ANS:	E	PTS:	1	REF:	10.2.73a
7.	ANS:	A	PTS:	1	REF:	10.3.10
8.	ANS:	A	PTS:	1	REF:	10.3.31a
9.	ANS:	D	PTS:	1	REF:	10.3.28
10.	ANS:	A	PTS:	1	REF:	10.4.11
11.	ANS:	B	PTS:	1	REF:	10.4.63
12.	ANS:	D	PTS:	1	REF:	10.5.8
13.	ANS:	D	PTS:	1	REF:	10.5.50a
14.	ANS:	C	PTS:	1	REF:	10.6.9b
15.	ANS:	A	PTS:	1	REF:	10.6.47b
16.	ANS:	D	PTS:	1	REF:	10.6.62a
17.	ANS:	B	PTS:	1	REF:	10.7.28
18.	ANS:	E	PTS:	1	REF:	10.7.72
19.	ANS:	D	PTS:	1	REF:	10.7.104
20.	ANS:	D	PTS:	1	REF:	10.8.26
21.	ANS:	D	PTS:	1	REF:	10.8.78d
22.	ANS:	B	PTS:	1	REF:	10.8.63
23.	ANS:	E	PTS:	1	REF:	10.9.39
24.	ANS:	B	PTS:	1	REF:	10.9.10
25.	ANS:	E	PTS:	1	REF:	10.9.47

Ch 10 Form C

____ 1. Find the inclination θ (in degrees) of the line with a slope of m. Round your answer to one decimal places.

$$m = \frac{3}{4}$$

a. $\theta \approx 38.9°$
b. $\theta \approx 34.9°$
c. $\theta \approx 36.9°$
d. $\theta \approx 37.9°$
e. $\theta \approx 35.9°$

____ 2. Find the angle θ (in radians and degrees) between the lines. Round your answer to four decimal places for radians and round your answer to one decimal places for degree.

$$6x - 8y = 8$$

$$6x + 8y = 7$$

a. $\theta \approx 1.2870\,\text{radians} \approx 74.7°$
b. $\theta \approx 1.2870\,\text{radians} \approx 71.7°$
c. $\theta \approx 1.2870\,\text{radians} \approx 73.7°$
d. $\theta \approx 1.2870\,\text{radians} \approx 72.7°$
e. $\theta \approx 1.2870\,\text{radians} \approx 75.7°$

_____ 3.   A straight road rises with an inclination of 0.15 radian from the horizontal (see figure). Find the slope of the road and the change in elevation (x) over a two-mile stretch of the road. Round your answer to four decimal places for the m round your answers to nearest whole number for change in elevation.

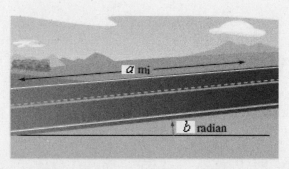

$a = 2, b = 0.15$

a. $m \approx 0.1511$

  $x \approx 1,579 \text{ feet}$

b. $m \approx 0.1511$

  $x \approx 1,577 \text{ feet}$

c. $m \approx 0.1511$

  $x \approx 1,576 \text{ feet}$

d. $m \approx 0.1511$

  $x \approx 1,580 \text{ feet}$

e. $m \approx 0.1511$

  $x \approx 1,578 \text{ feet}$

_____ 4.   Find the standard form of the equation of the parabola with the given characteristic and vertex at the origin.

Focus: $\left(-\dfrac{1}{2}, 0 \right)$

a. $y^2 = -2x$

b. $x^2 = 2y$

c. $y^2 = 3x$

d. $x^2 = -2y$

e. $y^2 = 2x$

_____ 5.   Find the vertex, focus, and directrix of the parabola.

$$\left(x+\frac{3}{2}\right)^2 = 4(y-1)$$

a.
Vertex: $\left(-\frac{3}{2},1\right)$; Focus: $\left(-\frac{3}{2},2\right)$; Directrix: $y = 0$

b.
Vertex: $\left(-\frac{3}{2},2\right)$; Focus: $\left(-\frac{3}{2},2\right)$; Directrix: $y = 1$

c.
Vertex: $\left(-\frac{3}{2},2\right)$; Focus: $\left(-\frac{3}{2},1\right)$; Directrix: $y = 0$

d.
Vertex: $\left(-\frac{3}{2},1\right)$; Focus: $\left(-\frac{3}{2},2\right)$; Directrix: $y = 1$

e.
Vertex: $\left(-\frac{3}{2},1\right)$; Focus: $\left(-\frac{3}{2},1\right)$; Directrix: $y = 1$

_____ 6.   Find the standard form of the equation of the parabola and determine the coordinates of the focus.

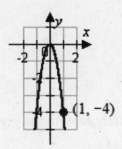

a. $x^2 = -4y$ focus: $\left(0,-\frac{1}{4}\right)$

b. $x^2 = -\frac{1}{16}y$ focus: $\left(0,-\frac{1}{16}\right)$

c. $x^2 = -4y$ focus: $(0,-4)$

d. $x^2 = -\frac{1}{4}y$ focus: $\left(0,-\frac{1}{4}\right)$

e. $x^2 = -\frac{1}{4}y$ focus: $\left(0,-\frac{1}{16}\right)$

_____ 7.   Find the standard form of the equation of the ellipse with the given characteristics and center at the origin.

Vertices: $(0, \pm 6)$; Foci: $(0, \pm 2)$

a. $\dfrac{x^2}{32} + \dfrac{y^2}{36} = 1$

b. $\dfrac{x^2}{6} + \dfrac{y^2}{2} = 1$

c. $\dfrac{x^2}{36} + \dfrac{y^2}{4} = 1$

d. $\dfrac{x^2}{36} - \dfrac{y^2}{32} = 1$

e. $\dfrac{x^2}{4} + \dfrac{y^2}{32} = 1$

_____ 8.   Select the graph of the conic.

$\dfrac{x^2}{9} + \dfrac{y^2}{9} = 1$

a.

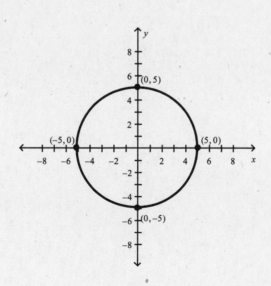

d.

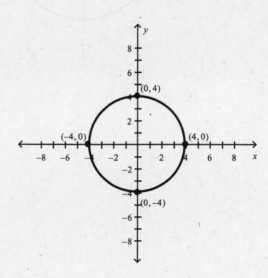

b.

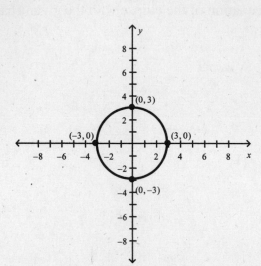

e.

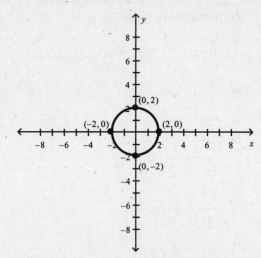

c.

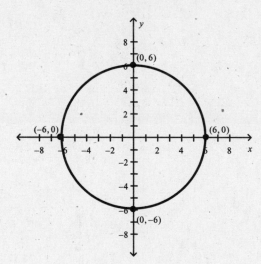

_____ 9.   Identify the conic by writing the equation in standard form.

$10y^2 - 20x^2 + 60y + 160x - 255 = 0$

a.
$$\frac{(y-3)^2}{\dfrac{149}{5}} + \frac{(x-4)^2}{\dfrac{149}{10}} = 1; \text{ ellipse}$$

b.
$$\frac{(y+3)^2}{\dfrac{97}{2}} - \frac{(x-4)^2}{\dfrac{97}{4}} = 1; \text{ hyperbola}$$

c.
$$\frac{(y-3)^2}{\dfrac{5}{2}} - \frac{(x-4)^2}{\dfrac{5}{4}} = 1; \text{ hyperbola}$$

d.
$$\frac{(y+3)^2}{\dfrac{5}{2}} - \frac{(x-4)^2}{\dfrac{5}{4}} = 1; \text{ hyperbola}$$

e.
$$\frac{(y+3)^2}{\dfrac{149}{5}} + \frac{(x-4)^2}{\dfrac{149}{10}} = 1; \text{ ellipse}$$

_____ 10.   Find the center, vertices and foci of the hyperbola.

$$\frac{y^2}{4} - \frac{x^2}{1} = 1$$

a.   Center: $(0,0)$
Vertices: $(0,\pm 2)$
Foci: $(0,\pm\sqrt{5})$

b.   Center: $(0,0)$
Vertices: $(\pm 2,0)$
Foci: $(0,\pm\sqrt{5})$

c.   Center: $(1,1)$
Vertices: $(\pm 2,0)$
Foci: $(\pm\sqrt{5},\ 0)$

d.   Center: $(4,1)$
Vertices: $(0,\pm 2)$
Foci: $(0,\pm\sqrt{5})$

e.   Center: $(0,0)$
Vertices: $(\pm 2,0)$
Foci: $(\pm\sqrt{5},\ 0)$

_____ 11.   Select the graph of the equation as a circle, a parabola, an ellipse, or a hyperbola.

$$25x^2 + 5y^2 + 5x - 27y + 58 = 0$$

a. Hyperbola
b. Circle
c. Ellipse
d. Parabola
e. None of the above

_____ 12.   Rotate the axes to eliminate the xy-term in the equation. Then write the equation in standard form.

$$xy + 4 = 0$$

a.
$$\frac{\left(y'\right)^2}{4} - \frac{\left(x'\right)^2}{4} = 1$$

b.
$$\frac{\left(y'\right)^2}{8} - \frac{\left(x'\right)^2}{4} = 1$$

c.
$$\frac{\left(y'\right)^2}{8} - \frac{\left(x'\right)^2}{8} = 1$$

d.
$$\frac{\left(y'\right)^2}{4} - \frac{\left(x'\right)^2}{8} = 1$$

e.
$$\frac{\left(y'\right)^2}{8} + \frac{\left(x'\right)^2}{8} = 1$$

_____ 13. Select the graph of degenerate conic.

$$16x^2 - 32xy + 16y^2 = 0$$

a.

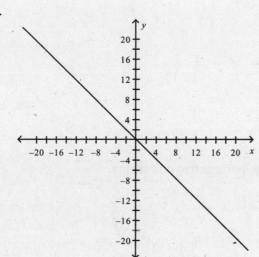

d.

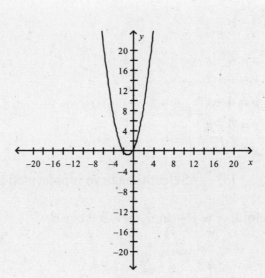

b.

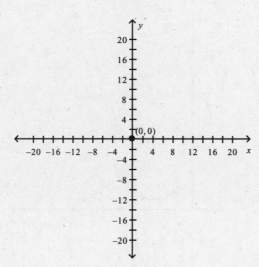

(0, 0)

e.

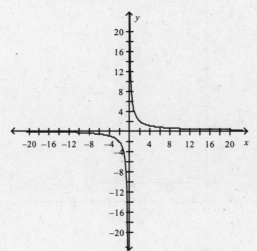

c.

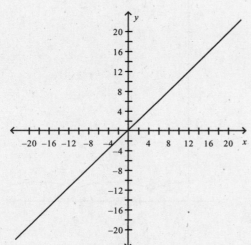

_____   14.   Eliminate the parameter and write the corresponding rectangular equation whose graph represents the curve.

$x = \sqrt{t}$
$y = 4 - t$

a. $y = 4 - x$
b. $y = 4 + x$
c. $y = 4 + x^2$
d. $y = 4 - x^2$
e. $y = \sqrt{x}$

_____   15.   Select the curve represented by the parametric equations.

Cycloid: $x = \theta + \sin \theta$, $y = 3 - \cos \theta$

a.

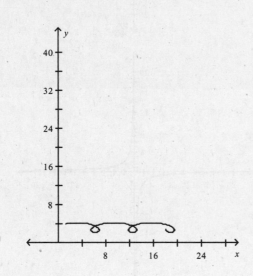

d.

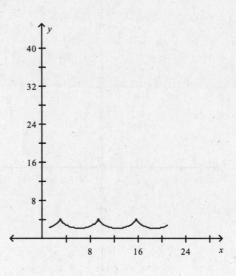

b.

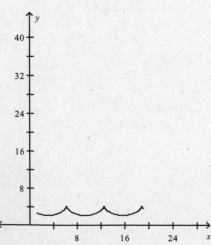

e.

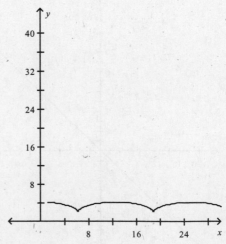

c.

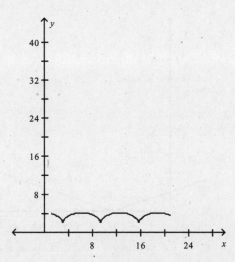

_____ 16. Select the curve represented by the parametric equations.

$x = 3(t+1)$
$y = |t-3|$

a.

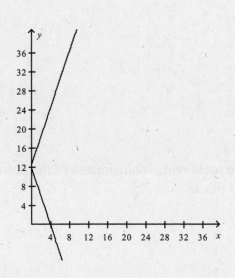

d.

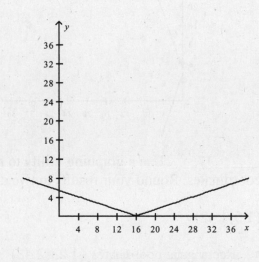

b.

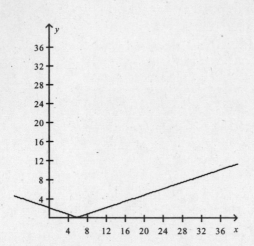

e.

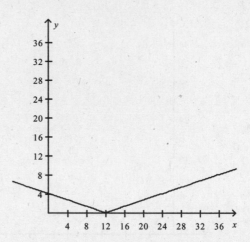

c.

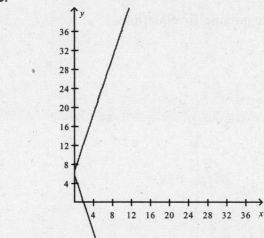

_____ 17.   Use a graphing utility to find the rectangular coordinates of the point given in polar coordinates. Round your results to two decimal places.

$(1.5, 1.42)$

a.   Rectangular coordinates: $(1.23, 2.48)$
b.   Rectangular coordinates: $(1.5, 1.42)$
c.   Rectangular coordinates: $(0.23, 1.48)$
d.   Rectangular coordinates: $(2.48, 1.23)$
e.   Rectangular coordinates: $(1.48, 0.23)$

____   18.   Convert the rectangular equation to polar form. Assume $a > 0$.

$xy = 17$

a. $r^2 = 17 \sec 2\theta$
b. $r^2 = 34 \csc 2\theta$
c. $r^2 = 34 \cos 2\theta$
d. $r^2 = 17 \csc 2\theta$
e. $r^2 = 34 \sec 2\theta$

____   19.   Describe the graph of the polar equation and find the corresponding rectangular equation. Select the correct graph.

$r = 5$

a.   The graph of the polar equation consists of all points that are five units from the pole.
$x^2 + y^2 = -25$

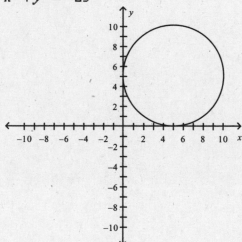

d.   The graph of the polar equation consists of all points that are five units from the pole.
$x^2 + y^2 = 25$

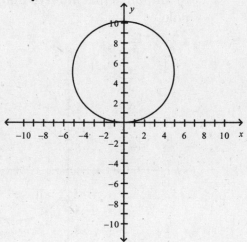

b. The graph of the polar equation consists of all points that are five units from the pole.
$$x^2 + y^2 = 25$$

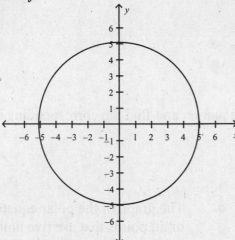

e. The graph of the polar equation consists of all points that are five units from the pole.
$$x^2 + y^2 = 5$$

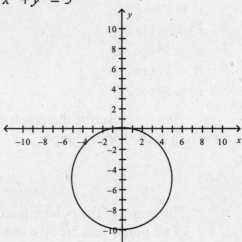

c. The graph of the polar equation consists of all points that are five units from the pole.
$$x^2 + y^2 = 5$$

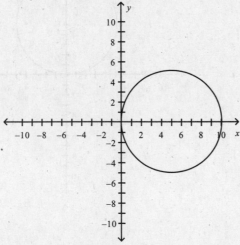

_____ 20.   Select the graph of the polar equation using symmetry, zeros, maximum *r*-values, and any
other additional points.

$r = (1 - \cos\theta)$

a.   Symmetric with respect to polar axis
   $|r| = 2$ when $\theta = \pi$

   $r = 0$ when $\theta = 0$

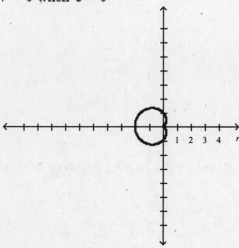

d.   Symmetric with respect to polar axis
   $|r| = 2$ when $\theta = \pi$

   $r = 0$ when $\theta = 0$

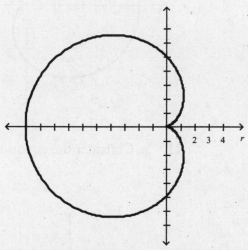

b.   Symmetric with respect to polar axis
   $|r| = 2$ when $\theta = \pi$

   $r = 0$ when $\theta = 0$

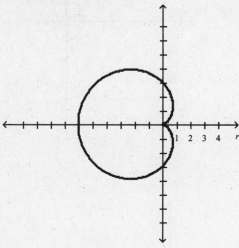

e.   Symmetric with respect to polar axis
   $|r| = 2$ when $\theta = \pi$

   $r = 0$ when $\theta = 0$

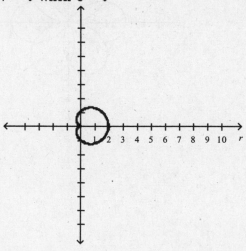

c.   Symmetric with respect to polar axis

$|r| = 2$ when $\theta = \pi$

$r = 0$ when $\theta = 0$

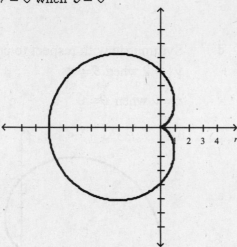

_____   21.   Consider the equation $r = 5 \sin k\theta$. Select the correct graph of the equation for $k = 1.5$.

a.

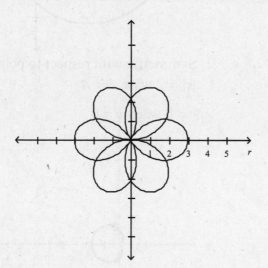

d.

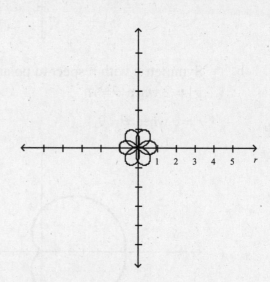

b.

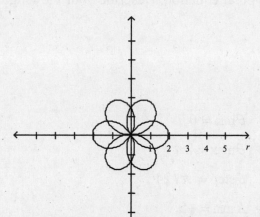

e.

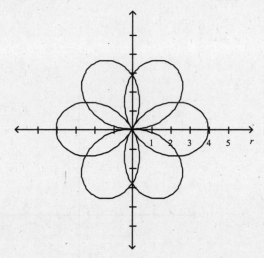

c.

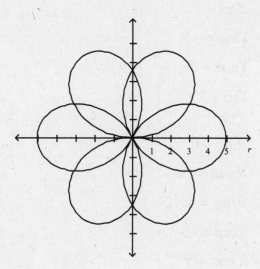

_____ 22.   Select the correct graph of the polar equation. Describe your viewing window.

$r = -\dfrac{9}{2}$

a.

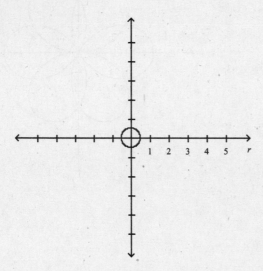

$\theta\,\text{min} = 0$

$\theta\,\text{max} = 2\pi$

$\theta\,\text{step} = \pi/24$

$X\,\text{min} = -5$

$X\,\text{max} = 5$

$X\,\text{scl} = 1$

$Y\,\text{min} = -5$

$Y\,\text{max} = 5$

$Y\,\text{scl} = 1$

b.

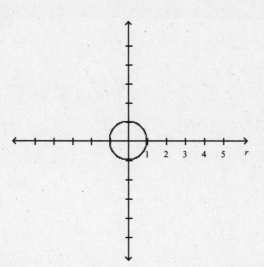

$\theta\,\text{min} = 0$

$\theta\,\text{max} = 2\pi$

$\theta\,\text{step} = \pi/24$

$X\,\text{min} = -5$

$X\,\text{max} = 5$

$X\,\text{scl} = 1$

$Y\,\text{min} = -5$

$Y\,\text{max} = 5$

$Y\,\text{scl} = 1$

c.

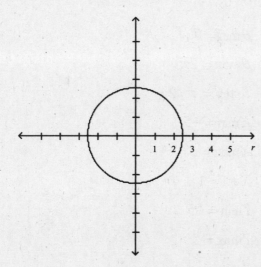

$\theta\min = 0$

$\theta\max = 2\pi$

$\theta\,\text{step} = \pi/24$

$X\min = -5$

$X\max = 5$

$X\text{scl} = 1$

$Y\min = -5$

$Y\max = 5$

$Y\text{scl} = 1$

d.

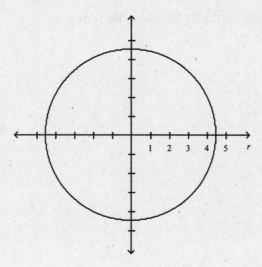

$\theta\min = 0$

$\theta\max = 2\pi$

$\theta\,\text{step} = \pi/24$

$X\min = -5$

$X\max = 5$

$X\text{scl} = 1$

$Y\min = -5$

$Y\max = 5$

$Y\text{scl} = 1$

e.

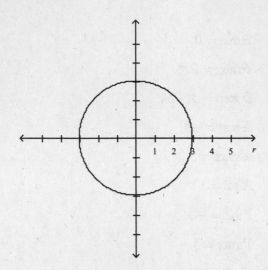

$\theta\,\text{min} = 0$

$\theta\,\text{max} = 2\pi$

$\theta\,\text{step} = \pi/24$

$X\text{min} = -5$

$X\text{max} = 5$

$X\text{scl} = 1$

$Y\text{min} = -5$

$Y\text{max} = 5$

$Y\text{scl} = 1$

_____ 23. Find a polar equation of the conic with its focus at the pole.

Conics	Eccentricity	Directrix
Hyperbola	$e = 4$	$x = 1$

a. $r = \dfrac{4}{1 + \cos\theta}$

b. $r = \dfrac{4}{1 + 4\cos\theta}$

c. $r = \dfrac{-4}{1 - \cos\theta}$

d. $r = \dfrac{4}{1 - \sin\theta}$

e. $r = \dfrac{4}{1 + 4\sin\theta}$

_____ 24.   Select the polar equation with graph.

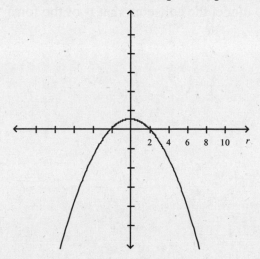

a. $\dfrac{2}{1-\sin\theta}$

b. $\dfrac{2}{1+\cos\theta}$

c. $\dfrac{2}{1+\sin\theta}$

d. $\dfrac{-2}{1-\cos\theta}$

e. $\dfrac{2}{1-\cos\theta}$

_____ 25.   The Roman Coliseum is an elliptical amphitheater measuring approximately 186 meters long and 150 meters wide. Find an equation to model the coliseum that is of the form

$$\frac{x^2}{a^2} + \frac{y^2}{b^2} = 1.$$

a.
$$\frac{x^2}{5625} + \frac{y^2}{8649} = 1$$

b.
$$\frac{x^2}{8649} + \frac{y^2}{5625} = 1$$

c.
$$\frac{x^2}{8649} + \frac{y^2}{5625} = 0$$

d.
$$\frac{x^2}{186^2} + \frac{y^2}{150^2} = 1$$

e.
$$\frac{x^2}{5625} + \frac{y^2}{8649} = 0$$

Ch 10 Form C
Answer Section

1.	ANS:	C	PTS:	1	REF:	10.1.17
2.	ANS:	C	PTS:	1	REF:	10.1.44
3.	ANS:	E	PTS:	1	REF:	10.1.65
4.	ANS:	A	PTS:	1	REF:	10.2.22
5.	ANS:	A	PTS:	1	REF:	10.2.42
6.	ANS:	E	PTS:	1	REF:	10.2.19
7.	ANS:	A	PTS:	1	REF:	10.3.14
8.	ANS:	B	PTS:	1	REF:	10.3.32f
9.	ANS:	D	PTS:	1	REF:	10.3.49
10.	ANS:	A	PTS:	1	REF:	10.4.14
11.	ANS:	C	PTS:	1	REF:	10.4.65
12.	ANS:	C	PTS:	1	REF:	10.5.13a
13.	ANS:	C	PTS:	1	REF:	10.5.53
14.	ANS:	D	PTS:	1	REF:	10.6.12b
15.	ANS:	D	PTS:	1	REF:	10.6.50
16.	ANS:	E	PTS:	1	REF:	10.6.15a
17.	ANS:	C	PTS:	1	REF:	10.7.33
18.	ANS:	B	PTS:	1	REF:	10.7.75
19.	ANS:	B	PTS:	1	REF:	10.7.109
20.	ANS:	A	PTS:	1	REF:	10.8.29
21.	ANS:	C	PTS:	1	REF:	10.8.81a
22.	ANS:	D	PTS:	1	REF:	10.8.50
23.	ANS:	B	PTS:	1	REF:	10.9.43
24.	ANS:	C	PTS:	1	REF:	10.9.13
25.	ANS:	B	PTS:	1	REF:	10.9.66a

Ch 10 Form D

_____ 1.   Find the inclination θ (in degrees) of the line with a slope of m. Round your answer to one decimal places.

$$m = \frac{2}{3}$$

a. $\theta \approx 33.7^\circ$
b. $\theta \approx 35.7^\circ$
c. $\theta \approx 31.7^\circ$
d. $\theta \approx 34.7^\circ$
e. $\theta \approx 32.7^\circ$

_____ 2.   Find the angle θ (in radians and degrees) between the lines. Round your answer to four decimal places for radians and round your answer to one decimal places for degree.

$$5x - 7y = 13$$

$$5x + 7y = 6$$

a. $\theta \approx 1.2405\ \text{radians} \approx 72.1^\circ$
b. $\theta \approx 1.2405\ \text{radians} \approx 71.1^\circ$
c. $\theta \approx 1.2405\ \text{radians} \approx 73.1^\circ$
d. $\theta \approx 1.2405\ \text{radians} \approx 69.1^\circ$
e. $\theta \approx 1.2405\ \text{radians} \approx 70.1^\circ$

_____   3.   A straight road rises with an inclination of 0.15 radian from the horizontal (see figure). Find the slope of the road and the change in elevation (x) over a three-mile stretch of the road. Round your answer to four decimal places for the m round your answers to nearest whole number for change in elevation.

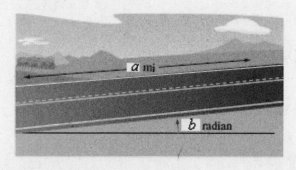

$a = 3, b = 0.15$

a. $m \approx 0.1511$

   $x \approx 2,369$ feet

b. $m \approx 0.1511$

   $x \approx 2,368$ feet

c. $m \approx 0.1511$

   $x \approx 2,366$ feet

d. $m \approx 0.1511$

   $x \approx 2,365$ feet

e. $m \approx 0.1511$

   $x \approx 2,367$ feet

_____   4.   Find the standard form of the equation of the parabola with the given characteristic and vertex at the origin.

Focus: $\left(-\dfrac{1}{8}, 0\right)$

a. $x^2 = \dfrac{1}{2}y$

b. $y^2 = \dfrac{1}{2}x$

c. $x^2 = -\dfrac{1}{2}y$

d. $y^2 = 7x$

e. $y^2 = -\dfrac{1}{2}x$

_____ 5. Find the vertex, focus, and directrix of the parabola.

$$\left(x + \frac{3}{2}\right)^2 = 8(y - 1)$$

a.
Vertex: $\left(-\frac{3}{2}, 1\right)$; Focus: $\left(-\frac{3}{2}, 3\right)$; Directrix: $y = 1$

b.
Vertex: $\left(-\frac{3}{2}, 3\right)$; Focus: $\left(-\frac{3}{2}, 3\right)$; Directrix: $y = 1$

c.
Vertex: $\left(-\frac{3}{2}, 1\right)$; Focus: $\left(-\frac{3}{2}, 1\right)$; Directrix: $y = 1$

d.
Vertex: $\left(-\frac{3}{2}, 3\right)$; Focus: $\left(-\frac{3}{2}, 1\right)$; Directrix: $y = -1$

e.
Vertex: $\left(-\frac{3}{2}, 1\right)$; Focus: $\left(-\frac{3}{2}, 3\right)$; Directrix: $y = -1$

_____ 6. Find the standard form of the equation of the parabola and determine the coordinates of the focus.

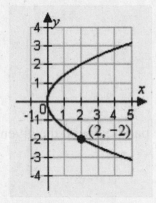

a.
$x = \frac{1}{2}y^2$ focus: $(2, 0)$

b.
$x = 2y^2$ focus: $(2, 0)$

c.
$y^2 = \frac{1}{2}x$ focus: $\left(\frac{1}{2}, 0\right)$

d.
$y^2 = 2x$ focus: $\left(\frac{1}{2}, 0\right)$

e.
$y^2 = \frac{1}{2}x$ focus: $(2, 0)$

_____ 7.   Find the standard form of the equation of the ellipse with the given characteristics and center at the origin.

Vertices: $(0, \pm 8)$; Foci: $(0, \pm 4)$

a. $\dfrac{x^2}{16} + \dfrac{y^2}{48} = 1$

b. $\dfrac{x^2}{64} - \dfrac{y^2}{48} = 1$

c. $\dfrac{x^2}{8} + \dfrac{y^2}{4} = 1$

d. $\dfrac{x^2}{64} + \dfrac{y^2}{16} = 1$

e. $\dfrac{x^2}{48} + \dfrac{y^2}{64} = 1$

_____ 8.   Select the graph of the conic.

$\dfrac{x^2}{16} + \dfrac{y^2}{16} = 1$

a.

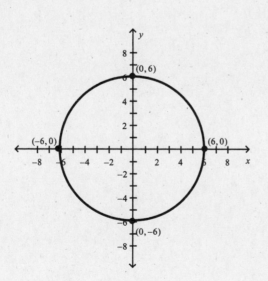

d.

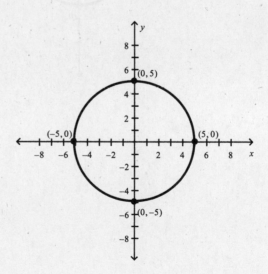

b.

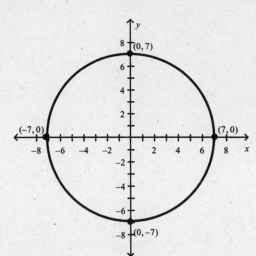

e.

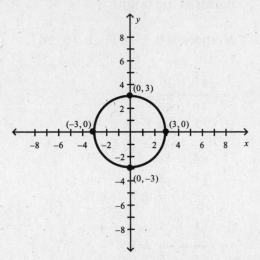

c.

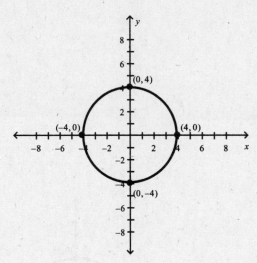

_____ 9.   Identify the conic by writing the equation in standard form.

$18y^2 - 20x^2 - 144y - 160x - 47 = 0$

a.
$$\frac{(y-4)^2}{\frac{17}{18}} + \frac{(x+4)^2}{\frac{17}{20}} = 1; \text{ ellipse}$$

b.
$$\frac{(y+4)^2}{\frac{5}{6}} - \frac{(x+4)^2}{\frac{3}{4}} = 1; \text{ hyperbola}$$

c.
$$\frac{(y-4)^2}{\frac{79}{18}} - \frac{(x+4)^2}{\frac{79}{20}} = 1; \text{ hyperbola}$$

d.
$$\frac{(y+4)^2}{\frac{17}{18}} + \frac{(x+4)^2}{\frac{17}{20}} = 1; \text{ ellipse}$$

e.
$$\frac{(y-4)^2}{\frac{5}{6}} - \frac{(x+4)^2}{\frac{3}{4}} = 1; \text{ hyperbola}$$

_____ 10.   Find the center, vertices and foci of the hyperbola.

$$\frac{y^2}{4} - \frac{x^2}{1} = 1$$

a. Center: $(1,1)$
    Vertices: $(\pm 2, 0)$
    Foci: $(\pm\sqrt{5}, \ 0)$
b. Center: $(0,0)$
    Vertices: $(\pm 2, 0)$
    Foci: $(0, \pm\sqrt{5})$
c. Center: $(4,1)$
    Vertices: $(0, \pm 2)$
    Foci: $(0, \pm\sqrt{5})$
d. Center: $(0,0)$
    Vertices: $(0, \pm 2)$
    Foci: $(0, \pm\sqrt{5})$
e. Center: $(0,0)$
    Vertices: $(\pm 2, 0)$
    Foci: $(\pm\sqrt{5}, \ 0)$

_____ 11.   Select the graph of the equation as a circle, a parabola, an ellipse, or a hyperbola.

$$4x^2 + 7y^2 + 6x - 28y + 55 = 0$$

a. Parabola
b. Circle
c. Hyperbola
d. Ellipse
e. None of the above

_____ 12.   Rotate the axes to eliminate the xy-term in the equation. Then write the equation in standard form.

$$xy + 5 = 0$$

a.
$$\frac{\left(y'\right)^2}{10} - \frac{\left(x'\right)^2}{5} = 1$$

b.
$$\frac{\left(y'\right)^2}{10} + \frac{\left(x'\right)^2}{10} = 1$$

c.
$$\frac{\left(y'\right)^2}{5} - \frac{\left(x'\right)^2}{10} = 1$$

d.
$$\frac{\left(y'\right)^2}{5} - \frac{\left(x'\right)^2}{5} = 1$$

e.
$$\frac{\left(y'\right)^2}{10} - \frac{\left(x'\right)^2}{10} = 1$$

_____ 13. Select the graph of degenerate conic.

$$4x^2 - 8xy + 4y^2 = 0$$

a.

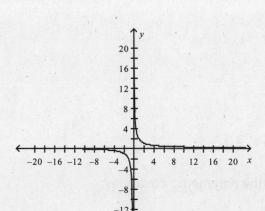

d.

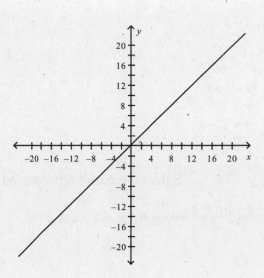

b.

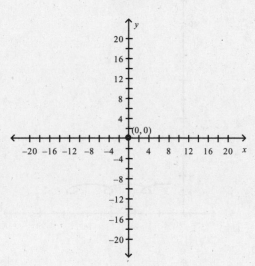

e.

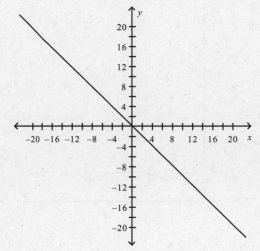

c.

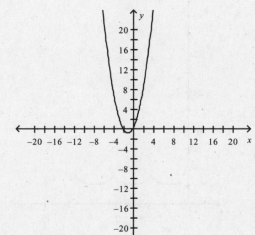

____ 14. Eliminate the parameter and write the corresponding rectangular equation whose graph represents the curve.

$x = \sqrt{t}$
$y = 2 - t$

a. $y = 2 + x^2$
b. $y = \sqrt{x}$
c. $y = 2 + x$
d. $y = 2 - x$
e. $y = 2 - x^2$

____ 15. Select the curve represented by the parametric equations.

Cycloid: $x = \theta + \sin\theta$, $y = 5 - \cos\theta$

a.

d.

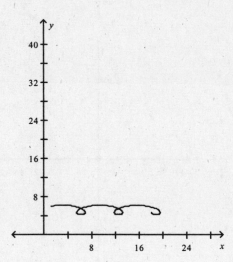

b.

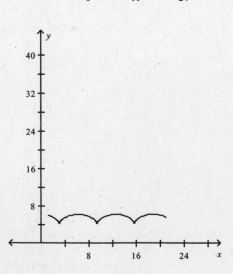

e.

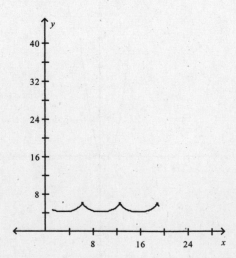

c.

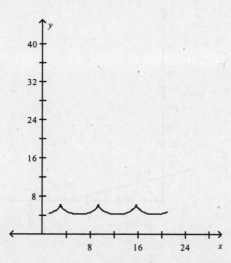

_____ 16.   Select the curve represented by the parametric equations.

$x = 4(t + 1)$
$y = |t - 4|$

a.

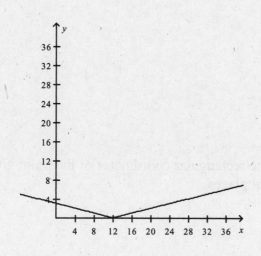

d.

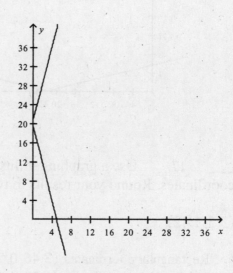

b.

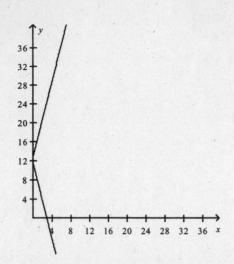

e.

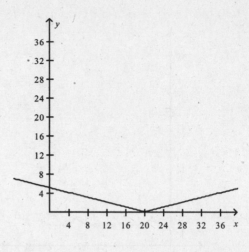

c.

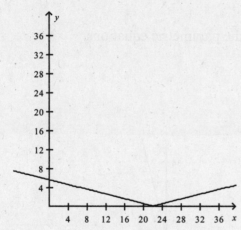

_____ 17.   Use a graphing utility to find the rectangular coordinates of the point given in polar coordinates. Round your results to two decimal places.

$(3.5, 1.42)$

a.   Rectangular coordinates: $(3.46, 0.53)$
b.   Rectangular coordinates: $(1.53, 4.46)$
c.   Rectangular coordinates: $(4.46, 1.53)$
d.   Rectangular coordinates: $(0.53, 3.46)$
e.   Rectangular coordinates: $(3.5, 1.42)$

_____ 18.   Convert the rectangular equation to polar form. Assume $a > 0$.

$xy = 12$

a. $r^2 = 24\csc 2\theta$
b. $r^2 = 24\sec 2\theta$
c. $r^2 = 12\csc 2\theta$
d. $r^2 = 24\cos 2\theta$
e. $r^2 = 12\sec 2\theta$

_____ 19.   Describe the graph of the polar equation and find the corresponding rectangular equation. Select the correct graph.

$r = 3$

a.   The graph of the polar equation consists of all points that are three units from the pole.

$x^2 + y^2 = 9$

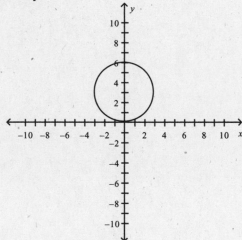

d.   The graph of the polar equation consists of all points that are three units from the pole.

$x^2 + y^2 = 3$

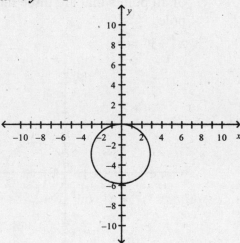

b. The graph of the polar equation consists of all points that are three units from the pole.

$x^2 + y^2 = -9$

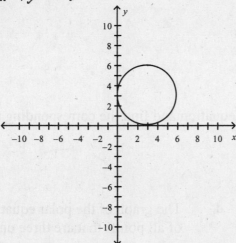

e. The graph of the polar equation consists of all points that are three units from the pole.

$x^2 + y^2 = 9$

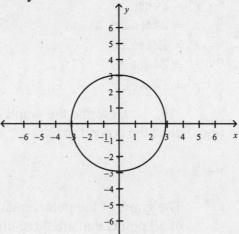

c. The graph of the polar equation consists of all points that are three units from the pole.

$x^2 + y^2 = 3$

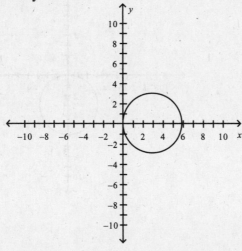

_____ 20.   Select the graph of the polar equation using symmetry, zeros, maximum *r*-values, and any

other additional points.

$r = 2(1 - \cos \theta)$

a.   Symmetric with respect to polar axis
       $|r| = 4$ when $\theta = \pi$

       $r = 0$ when $\theta = 0$

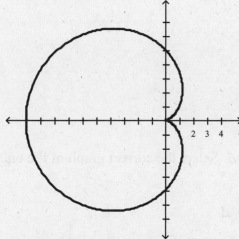

d.   Symmetric with respect to polar axis
       $|r| = 4$ when $\theta = \pi$

       $r = 0$ when $\theta = 0$

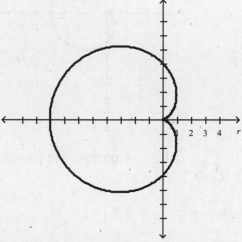

b.   Symmetric with respect to polar axis
       $|r| = 4$ when $\theta = \pi$

       $r = 0$ when $\theta = 0$

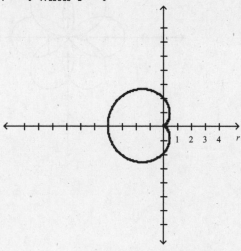

e.   Symmetric with respect to polar axis
       $|r| = 4$ when $\theta = \pi$

       $r = 0$ when $\theta = 0$

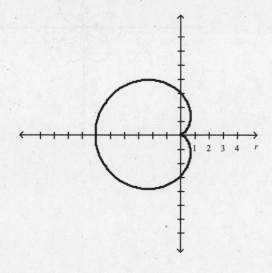

c.   Symmetric with respect to polar axis
      $|r| = 4$ when $\theta = \pi$

      $r = 0$ when $\theta = 0$

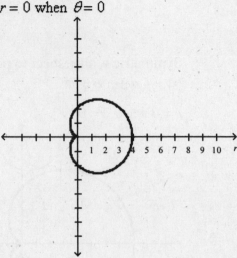

_____   21.   Consider the equation $r = 5 \sin k\theta$. Select the correct graph of the equation for $k = 1.5$.

a.

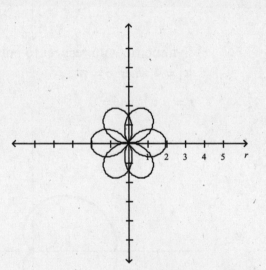

d.

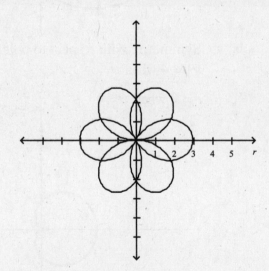

b.

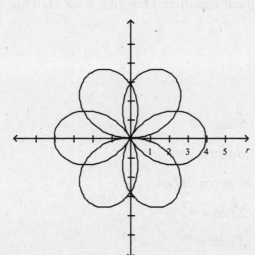

e.

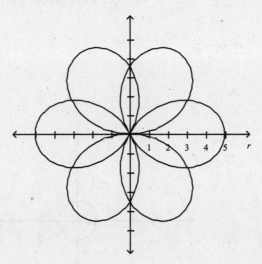

c.

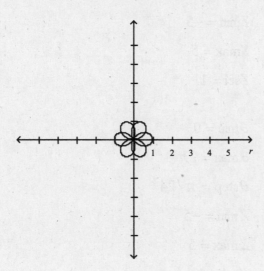

_____ 22.   Select the correct graph of the polar equation. Describe your viewing window.

$$r = -\frac{7}{5}$$

a.

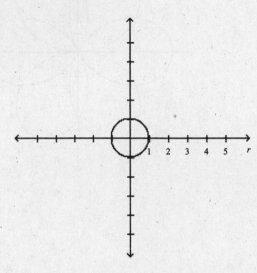

$\theta\,\text{min} = 0$

$\theta\,\text{max} = 2\pi$

$\theta\,\text{step} = \pi/24$

$X\,\text{min} = -5$

$X\,\text{max} = 5$

$X\,\text{scl} = 1$

$Y\,\text{min} = -5$

$Y\,\text{max} = 5$

$Y\,\text{scl} = 1$

b.

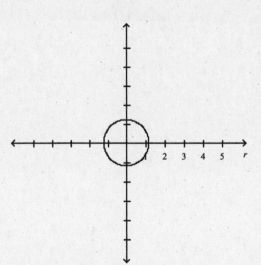

$\theta\,\text{min} = 0$

$\theta\,\text{max} = 2\pi$

$\theta\,\text{step} = \pi/24$

$X\,\text{min} = -5$

$X\,\text{max} = 5$

$X\,\text{scl} = 1$

$Y\,\text{min} = -5$

$Y\,\text{max} = 5$

$Y\,\text{scl} = 1$

c.

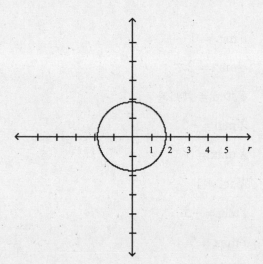

$\theta\min = 0$

$\theta\max = 2\pi$

$\theta\text{step} = \pi/24$

$X\min = -5$

$X\max = 5$

$X\text{scl} = 1$

$Y\min = -5$

$Y\max = 5$

$Y\text{scl} = 1$

d.

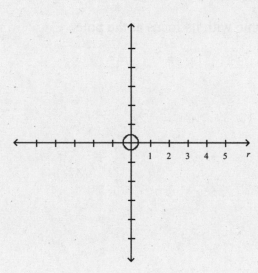

$\theta\min = 0$

$\theta\max = 2\pi$

$\theta\text{step} = \pi/24$

$X\min = -5$

$X\max = 5$

$X\text{scl} = 1$

$Y\min = -5$

$Y\max = 5$

$Y\text{scl} = 1$

e.

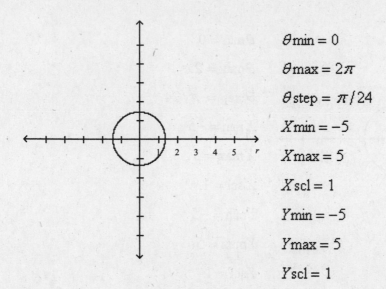

$\theta\min = 0$

$\theta\max = 2\pi$

$\theta\,\text{step} = \pi/24$

$X\min = -5$

$X\max = 5$

$X\mathrm{scl} = 1$

$Y\min = -5$

$Y\max = 5$

$Y\mathrm{scl} = 1$

_____ 23. Find a polar equation of the conic with its focus at the pole.

Conics	Eccentricity	Directrix
Hyperbola	$e = 4$	$x = 1$

a. $r = \dfrac{-4}{1 - \cos\theta}$

b. $r = \dfrac{4}{1 + 4\sin\theta}$

c. $r = \dfrac{4}{1 - \sin\theta}$

d. $r = \dfrac{4}{1 + \cos\theta}$

e. $r = \dfrac{4}{1 + 4\cos\theta}$

____   24.   Select the polar equation with graph.

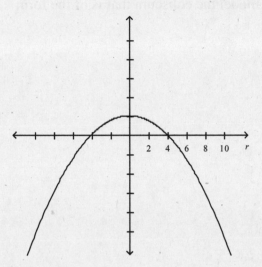

a. $\dfrac{4}{1 - \sin \theta}$

b. $\dfrac{4}{1 - \cos \theta}$

c. $\dfrac{4}{1 + \sin \theta}$

d. $\dfrac{-4}{1 - \cos \theta}$

e. $\dfrac{4}{1 + \cos \theta}$

_____ 25. The Roman Coliseum is an elliptical amphitheater measuring approximately 180 meters long and 158 meters wide. Find an equation to model the coliseum that is of the form

$$\frac{x^2}{a^2} + \frac{y^2}{b^2} = 1.$$

a. $\dfrac{x^2}{8100} + \dfrac{y^2}{6241} = 0$

b. $\dfrac{x^2}{6241} + \dfrac{y^2}{8100} = 1$

c. $\dfrac{x^2}{180^2} + \dfrac{y^2}{158^2} = 1$

d. $\dfrac{x^2}{8100} + \dfrac{y^2}{6241} = 1$

e. $\dfrac{x^2}{6241} + \dfrac{y^2}{8100} = 0$

Ch 10 Form D
Answer Section

1.	ANS: A	PTS: 1	REF:	10.1.17
2.	ANS: B	PTS: 1	REF:	10.1.44
3.	ANS: E	PTS: 1	REF:	10.1.65
4.	ANS: E	PTS: 1	REF:	10.2.22
5.	ANS: E	PTS: 1	REF:	10.2.42
6.	ANS: D	PTS: 1	REF:	10.2.19
7.	ANS: E	PTS: 1	REF:	10.3.14
8.	ANS: C	PTS: 1	REF:	10.3.32f
9.	ANS: E	PTS: 1	REF:	10.3.49
10.	ANS: D	PTS: 1	REF:	10.4.14
11.	ANS: D	PTS: 1	REF:	10.4.65
12.	ANS: E	PTS: 1	REF:	10.5.13a
13.	ANS: D	PTS: 1	REF:	10.5.53
14.	ANS: E	PTS: 1	REF:	10.6.12b
15.	ANS: C	PTS: 1	REF:	10.6.50
16.	ANS: E	PTS: 1	REF:	10.6.15a
17.	ANS: D	PTS: 1	REF:	10.7.33
18.	ANS: A	PTS: 1	REF:	10.7.75
19.	ANS: E	PTS: 1	REF:	10.7.109
20.	ANS: B	PTS: 1	REF:	10.8.29
21.	ANS: E	PTS: 1	REF:	10.8.81a
22.	ANS: E	PTS: 1	REF:	10.8.50
23.	ANS: E	PTS: 1	REF:	10.9.43
24.	ANS: C	PTS: 1	REF:	10.9.13
25.	ANS: D	PTS: 1	REF:	10.9.66a

Ch 10 Form E

____ 1.   Find the inclination θ (in radians and degrees) of the line passing through the points. Round your answer to four decimal places for radians and round your answer to one decimal places for degree.

$(0, 150), (30, 0)$

a. $\theta \approx 1.7682\,\text{radians} \approx 103.3°$
b. $\theta \approx 1.7682\,\text{radians} \approx 99.3°$
c. $\theta \approx 1.7682\,\text{radians} \approx 102.3°$
d. $\theta \approx 1.7682\,\text{radians} \approx 101.3°$
e. $\theta \approx 1.7682\,\text{radians} \approx 100.3°$

____ 2.   Find the distance between the point and the line. Round your answer to four decimal places.

Point   Line

$(6, 7)$ $7x + y = 1$

a. $d \approx 6.7882$
b. $d \approx 9.7882$
c. $d \approx 7.7882$
d. $d \approx 8.7882$
e. $d \approx 5.7882$

____ 3.   A moving conveyor is built so that it rises 7 meter for each 9 meters of horizontal travel.   Find the inclination of the conveyor. Round your answers to one decimal place.

a. $\theta \approx 39.9°$
b. $\theta \approx 36.9°$
c. $\theta \approx 38.9°$
d. $\theta \approx 37.9°$
e. $\theta \approx 35.9°$

_____ 4. Find the standard form of the equation of the parabola with the given characteristic and vertex at the origin.

Directrix: $x = -4$

a. $y^2 = 16x$
b. $y^2 = x$
c. $y^2 = -16x$
d. $x^2 = 16y$
e. $x^2 = -16y$

_____ 5. Find the standard form of the equation of the parabola with the given characteristics.

Vertex: $(1, 3)$; directrix: $y = -2$

a. $(y-1)^2 = 3(x-3)$
b. $(x-1)^2 = -20(y-3)$
c. $(y-1)^2 = -20(x-3)$
d. $(x-1)^2 = 3(y-3)$
e. $(x-1)^2 = 20(y-3)$

_____ 6. Find the vertex and focus of the parabola.
$x^2 - 36y = 0$
a. vertex: $(0, 0)$ focus: $(0, -9)$
b. vertex: $(0, 0)$ focus: $(0, 9)$
c. vertex: $(9, 0)$ focus: $(0, 0)$
d. vertex: $(-9, 0)$ focus: $(0, 0)$
e. vertex: $(0, 0)$ focus: $(9, 0)$

_____ 7.   Find the standard form of the equation of the ellipse with the given characteristics.

Vertices: $(0,2),(8,2)$; minor axis of length 6.

a.
$$\frac{(x+4)^2}{16}+\frac{(y+2)^2}{9}=1$$

b.
$$\frac{(x-4)^2}{16}+\frac{(y-2)^2}{9}=1$$

c.
$$\frac{(x+4)^2}{16}+\frac{(y-2)^2}{9}=1$$

d.
$$\frac{(x-4)^2}{16}+\frac{(y+2)^2}{9}=1$$

e.
$$\frac{(x-4)^2}{16}-\frac{(y-2)^2}{9}=1$$

_____ 8.   A semielliptical arch over a tunnel for a one-way road through a mountain has a major axis
of 52 feet and a height at the center of 18 feet. Find an equation of the semielliptical arch

a.
$$\frac{x^2}{324}-\frac{y^2}{676}=1$$

b.
$$\frac{x^2}{676}-\frac{y^2}{324}=1$$

c.
$$\frac{x^2}{676}+\frac{y^2}{324}=1$$

d.
$$\frac{x^2}{52}+\frac{y^2}{676}=1$$

e.
$$\frac{x^2}{324}+\frac{y^2}{676}=1$$

_____ 9.   Find the center and vertices of the ellipse.

$$x^2 + 9y^2 + 16x - 54y + 136 = 0$$

a. center: (3, –8)   vertices: (0, –8), (6, –8)
b. center: (–8, 3)   vertices: (–11, 3), (–5, 3)
c. center: (8, –3)   vertices: (7, –3), (9, –3)
d. center: (8, –3)   vertices: (5, –3), (11, –3)
e. center: (–8, 3)   vertices: (–9, 3), (–7, 3)

_____ 10.   Find the standard form of the equation of the hyperbola with the given characteristics and center at the origin.

Vertices: $(0, \pm 18)$; asymptotes: $y = \pm 9x$

a. $\dfrac{41x^2}{13,122} + \dfrac{41y^2}{162} = 1$

b. $\dfrac{41y^2}{13,122} - \dfrac{41x^2}{162} = 1$

c. $\dfrac{41y^2}{13,122} + \dfrac{41x^2}{162} = 1$

d. $\dfrac{13,122x^2}{41} - \dfrac{41y^2}{162} = 1$

e. $\dfrac{41x^2}{13,122} - \dfrac{41y^2}{162} = 1$

_____ 11.   Identify the equation as a circle, a parabola, an ellipse, or a hyperbola.

$$4x^2 - 4y^2 - 4x + 6y + 17 = 0$$

a. Circle
b. Hyperbola
c. Ellipse
d. Parabola
e. None of the above

_____ 12. Use a graphing utility to graph the conic. Determine the angle θ through which the axes are rotated.

$x^2 + 2xy + y^2 = 25$

a. $\theta = \dfrac{\pi}{4}$ or $45°$, $y = -x \pm \sqrt{25}$

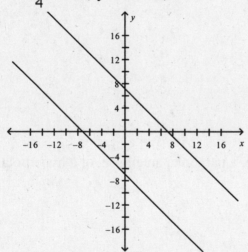

d. $\theta = \dfrac{\pi}{4}$ or $45°$, $y = -x \pm \sqrt{25}$

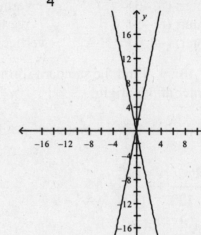

b. $\theta = \dfrac{\pi}{4}$ or $45°$, $y = -x \pm \sqrt{25}$

e. $\theta = \dfrac{\pi}{4}$ or $45°$, $y = -x \pm \sqrt{25}$

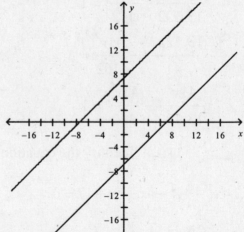

c.
$$\theta = \frac{\pi}{4} \text{ or } 45°, \quad y = -x \pm \sqrt{25}$$

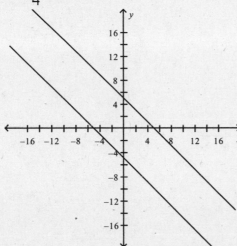

_____ 13.   Find any points of intersection of the graphs algebraically.

$$-x^2 + y^2 + 3x - 7y + 12 = 0$$

$$x^2 + y^2 - 3x - 7y + 12 = 0$$

a.   The points of intersection are $(3,3)$ and $(4,4)$.
b.   The points of intersection are $(-3,-3)$ and $(3,4)$.
c.   The points of intersection are $(4,4)$ and $(4,4)$.
d.   The points of intersection are $(3,3)$ and $(3,4)$.
e.   The points of intersection are $(4,4)$ and $(-4,-4)$.

_____ 14.   Eliminate the parameter and write the corresponding rectangular equation whose graph represents the curve.

$$x = 5(t+1)$$
$$y = |t - 5|$$

a.
$$y = \left| \frac{x}{6} - 5 \right|$$

b.
$$y = \left| \frac{x}{5} + 6 \right|$$

c. $y = |t - 6|$

d.
$$y = \left| \frac{x}{5} - 6 \right|$$

e. $y = |t + 6|$

_____ 15.   Select the parametric equations matching with the following graph.

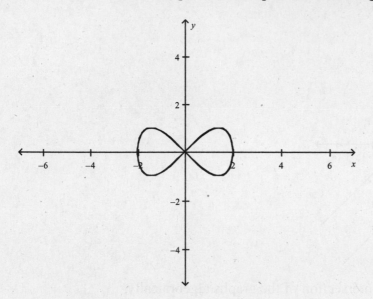

a.   Lissajous curve: $x = 2\sin\theta$, $y = \cos 2\theta$
b.   Lissajous curve: $x = 2\cos\theta$, $y = 2\sin 2\theta$
c.   Lissajous curve: $x = 2\sin\theta$, $y = \cos\theta$
d.   Lissajous curve: $x = 2\cos\theta$, $y = \sin 2\theta$
e.   Lissajous curve: $x = 2\cos 2\theta$, $y = \sin 2\theta$

_____ 16.   Eliminate the parameter and write the corresponding rectangular equation whose graph represents the curve.

$x = 3\cos\theta$
$y = 4\sin\theta$

a.
$$\frac{x^2}{9} + \frac{y^2}{16} = 1$$

b.
$$\frac{x^2}{9} - \frac{y^2}{16} = 1$$

c.
$$y = \frac{x}{4}$$

d.
$$\frac{x^2}{16} + \frac{y^2}{9} = 1$$

e.
$$y = \frac{x}{3}$$

_____ 17.   Use a graphing utility to find the rectangular coordinates of the point given in polar coordinates. Round your results to two decimal places.

$(7.2, -1.8)$

a. Rectangular coordinates: $(-1.64, -7.01)$
b. Rectangular coordinates: $(-7.01, -1.64)$
c. Rectangular coordinates: $(-6.01, -0.64)$
d. Rectangular coordinates: $(-8.00, -3.40)$
e. Rectangular coordinates: $(-0.64, -6.01)$

_____ 18.   Convert the polar equation to rectangular form.

$r = 4 \sin \theta$

a. $x^2 + y^2 - 4y = 0$
b. $x^2 + y^2 + 4x = 0$
c. $x^2 + y^2 - 4x = 0$
d. $x^2 + y^2 + 4y = 0$
e. $x^2 + y^2 - 4 = 0$

_____ 19.   Describe the graph of the polar equation and find the corresponding rectangular equation. Select the correct graph.

$r = 5 \csc \theta$

a. The graph of the polar equation is not evident by simple inspection. Convert to rectangular form first.

$y + 5 = 0$

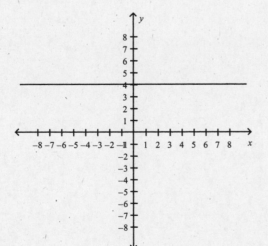

d. The graph of the polar equation is not evident by simple inspection. Convert to rectangular form first.

$y - 5 = 0$

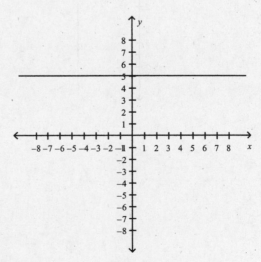

b. The graph of the polar equation is not evident by simple inspection. Convert to rectangular form first.

$y - 4 = 0$

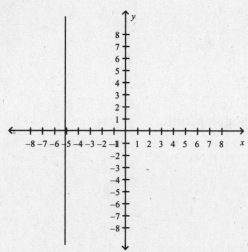

e. The graph of the polar equation is not evident by simple inspection. Convert to rectangular form first.

$y - 6 = 0$

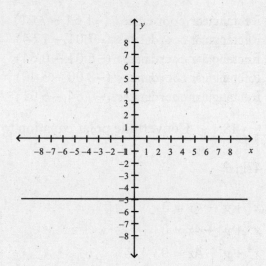

c. The graph of the polar equation is not evident by simple inspection. Convert to rectangular form first.

$y - 7 = 0$

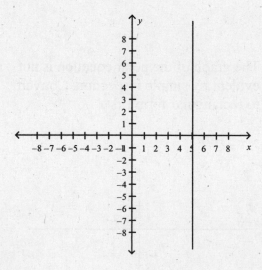

_____   20.   Select the graph of the polar equation using symmetry, zeros, maximum r-values, and any
other additional points.

$r = 1 - 5\sin\theta$

a.
Symmetric with respect to $\theta = \dfrac{\pi}{2}$

$|r| = 6$ when $\theta = \dfrac{3\pi}{2}$

$r = 0$ when $\theta = \dfrac{\pi}{6}, \dfrac{5\pi}{6}$

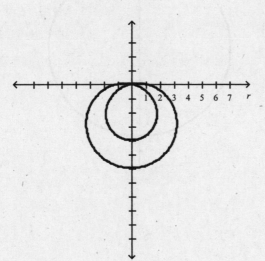

d.
Symmetric with respect to $\theta = \dfrac{\pi}{2}$

$|r| = 6$ when $\theta = \dfrac{3\pi}{2}$

$r = 0$ when $\theta = \dfrac{\pi}{6}, \dfrac{5\pi}{6}$

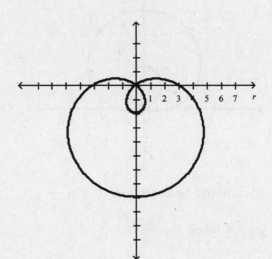

b. Symmetric with respect to $\theta = \dfrac{\pi}{2}$

$|r| = 6$ when $\theta = \dfrac{3\pi}{2}$

$r = 0$ when $\theta = \dfrac{\pi}{6}, \dfrac{5\pi}{6}$

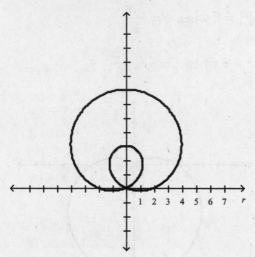

e. Symmetric with respect to $\theta = \dfrac{\pi}{2}$

$|r| = 6$ when $\theta = \dfrac{3\pi}{2}$

$r = 0$ when $\theta = \dfrac{\pi}{6}, \dfrac{5\pi}{6}$

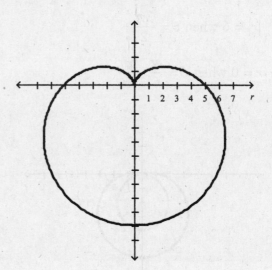

c. Symmetric with respect to $\theta = \dfrac{\pi}{2}$

$|r| = 6$ when $\theta = \dfrac{3\pi}{2}$

$r = 0$ when $\theta = \dfrac{\pi}{6}, \dfrac{5\pi}{6}$

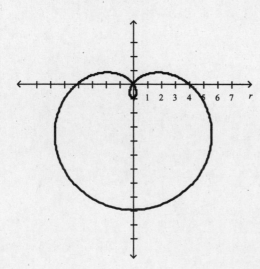

_____   21.   Select the correct graph of the polar equation. Find an interval for θ for which the graph is traced *only once*.

$$r = 4\cos\left(\frac{3\theta}{2}\right)$$

a.

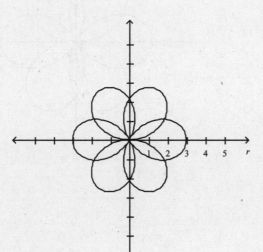

$$0 \le \theta < 4\pi$$

d.

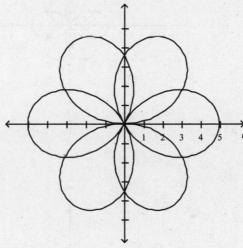

$$0 \le \theta < 4\pi$$

b.

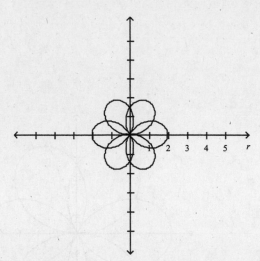

$0 \le \theta < 4\pi$

e.

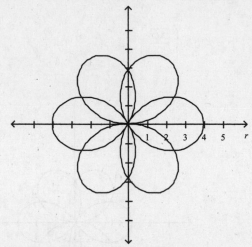

$0 \le \theta < 4\pi$

c.

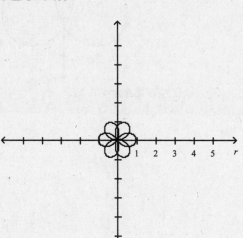

$0 \le \theta < 4\pi$

_____ 22.   Select the correct graph of the polar equation. Describe your viewing window.

$r = 2 \csc \theta + 6$

a.

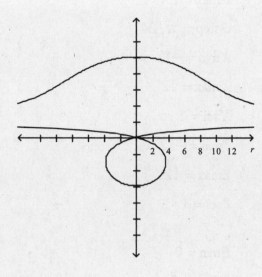

$\theta \min = 0$

$\theta \max = 2\pi$

$\theta \text{step} = \pi/24$

$X \min = -12$

$X \max = 12$

$X \text{scl} = 2$

$Y \min = -12$

$Y \max = 12$

$Y \text{scl} = 2$

b.

$\theta \min = 0$

$\theta \max = 2\pi$

$\theta \text{step} = \pi/24$

$X \min = -12$

$X \max = 12$

$X \text{scl} = 2$

$Y \min = -12$

$Y \max = 12$

$Y \text{scl} = 2$

c.

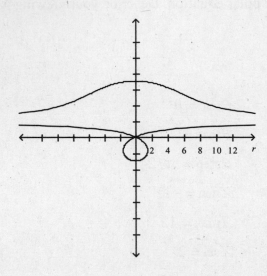

$\theta\min = 0$

$\theta\max = 2\pi$

$\theta\,\text{step} = \pi/24$

$X\min = -12$

$X\max = 12$

$X\text{scl} = 1$

$Y\min = -12$

$Y\max = 12$

$Y\text{scl} = 1$

d.

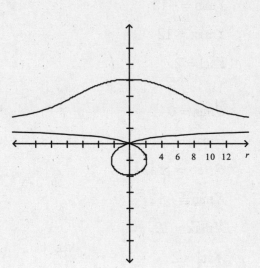

$\theta\min = 0$

$\theta\max = 2\pi$

$\theta\,\text{step} = \pi/24$

$X\min = -12$

$X\max = 12$

$X\text{scl} = 2$

$Y\min = -12$

$Y\max = 12$

$Y\text{scl} = 2$

e.

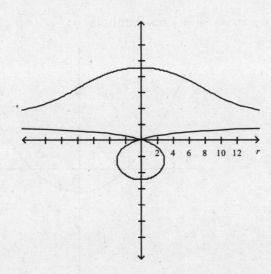

$\theta\min = 0$

$\theta\max = 2\pi$

$\theta\,\text{step} = \pi/24$

$X\min = -12$

$X\max = 12$

$X\,\text{scl} = 2$

$Y\min = -12$

$Y\max = 12$

$Y\,\text{scl} = 2$

_____ 23.   Identify the conic and select its correct graph.

$$r = \frac{5}{1+\cos\theta}$$

a. $e = 1 \Rightarrow$ Parabola

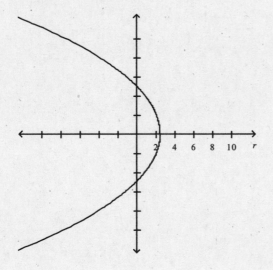

d. $e = 1 \Rightarrow$ Parabola

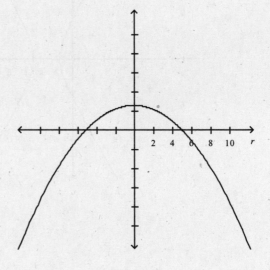

b. $e = 1 \Rightarrow$ Parabola

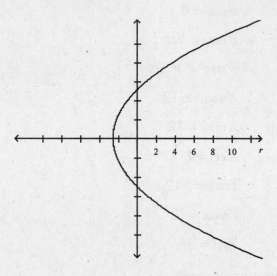

e. $e = 1 \Rightarrow$ Parabola

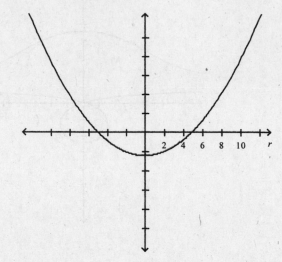

c. $e = 2 \Rightarrow$ Hyperabola

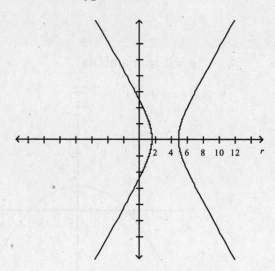

_____ 24. By using a graphing utility select the correct graph of the polar equation. Identify the graph.

$$\frac{11}{11 + 16 \sin \theta}$$

a.

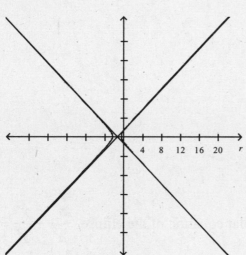

$e = \dfrac{16}{11} > 1 \Rightarrow$ Hyperabola

d.

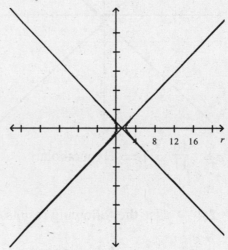

$e = \dfrac{16}{11} > 1 \Rightarrow$ Hyperabola

b.

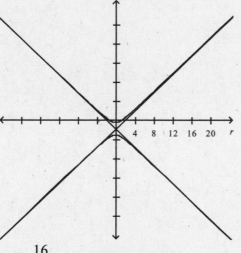

$e = \dfrac{16}{11} > 1 \Rightarrow$ Hyperabola

e.

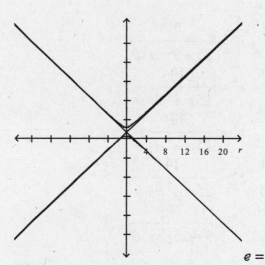

$e =$

$\dfrac{16}{11} > 1 \Rightarrow$ Hyperabola

c.

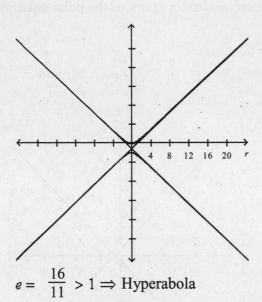

$$e = \frac{16}{11} > 1 \Rightarrow \text{Hyperabola}$$

_____ 25.   Use the following results the polar equation of the ellipse $\dfrac{x^2}{a^2} - \dfrac{y^2}{b^2} = 1$ is

$$r^2 = \frac{-b^2}{1 - e^2 \cos^2 \theta}$$ to write the polar form of the equation of the conic $\dfrac{x^2}{9} - \dfrac{y^2}{16} = 1.$

a. $r^2 = \dfrac{144}{25 + 9\cos^2 \theta}$

b. $r^2 = \dfrac{144}{25\cos^2 \theta - 9}$

c. $r^2 = \dfrac{144}{25\cos^2 \theta + 9}$

d. $r^2 = \dfrac{-144}{25\cos^2 \theta + 9}$

e. $r^2 = \dfrac{144}{9 - 25\cos^2 \theta}$

Ch 10 Form E
Answer Section

1.	ANS:	D	PTS:	1	REF:	10.1.26	
2.	ANS:	A	PTS:	1	REF:	10.1.53	
3.	ANS:	D	PTS:	1	REF:	10.1.68b	
4.	ANS:	A	PTS:	1	REF:	10.2.27	
5.	ANS:	E	PTS:	1	REF:	10.2.58	
6.	ANS:	B	PTS:	1	REF:	10.2.37	
7.	ANS:	B	PTS:	1	REF:	10.3.21	
8.	ANS:	C	PTS:	1	REF:	10.3.63b	
9.	ANS:	B	PTS:	1	REF:	10.3.44	
10.	ANS:	B	PTS:	1	REF:	10.4.33	
11.	ANS:	B	PTS:	1	REF:	10.4.66	
12.	ANS:	C	PTS:	1	REF:	10.5.27a	
13.	ANS:	D	PTS:	1	REF:	10.5.57	
14.	ANS:	D	PTS:	1	REF:	10.6.15b	
15.	ANS:	D	PTS:	1	REF:	10.6.57	
16.	ANS:	A	PTS:	1	REF:	10.6.18b	
17.	ANS:	A	PTS:	1	REF:	10.7.36	
18.	ANS:	A	PTS:	1	REF:	10.7.85	
19.	ANS:	D	PTS:	1	REF:	10.7.118	
20.	ANS:	A	PTS:	1	REF:	10.8.35	
21.	ANS:	E	PTS:	1	REF:	10.8.61	
22.	ANS:	D	PTS:	1	REF:	10.8.58	
23.	ANS:	A	PTS:	1	REF:	10.9.18	
24.	ANS:	E	PTS:	1	REF:	10.9.33	
25.	ANS:	B	PTS:	1	REF:	10.9.77	

Ch 10 Form F

____ 1.   Find the inclination θ (in radians and degrees) of the line passing through the points. Round your answer to four decimal places for radians and round your answer to one decimal places for degree.

$(0, 100), (40, 0)$

a. $\theta \approx 1.9513$ radians $\approx 109.8°$
b. $\theta \approx 1.9513$ radians $\approx 110.8°$
c. $\theta \approx 1.9513$ radians $\approx 112.8°$
d. $\theta \approx 1.9513$ radians $\approx 113.8°$
e. $\theta \approx 1.9513$ radians $\approx 111.8°$

____ 2.   Find the distance between the point and the line. Round your answer to four decimal places.

Point   *Line*

$(3, 4)$ $4x + y = 1$

a. $d \approx 5.6380$
b. $d \approx 2.6380$
c. $d \approx 3.6380$
d. $d \approx 6.6380$
e. $d \approx 4.6380$

____ 3.   A moving conveyor is built so that it rises 1 meter for each 3 meters of horizontal travel. Find the inclination of the conveyor. Round your answers to one decimal place.

a. $\theta \approx 18.4°$
b. $\theta \approx 19.4°$
c. $\theta \approx 17.4°$
d. $\theta \approx 20.4°$
e. $\theta \approx 16.4°$

_____   4.   Find the standard form of the equation of the parabola with the given characteristic and vertex at the origin.

Directrix: $x = -5$

a. $y^2 = -20x$

b. $x^2 = 20y$

c. $y^2 = x$

d. $x^2 = -20y$

e. $y^2 = 20x$

_____   5.   Find the standard form of the equation of the parabola with the given characteristics.

Vertex: $(1, 3)$; directrix: $y = -2$

a. $(y - 1)^2 = -20(x - 3)$

b. $(x - 1)^2 = 3(y - 3)$

c. $(x - 1)^2 = -20(y - 3)$

d. $(x - 1)^2 = 20(y - 3)$

e. $(y - 1)^2 = 3(x - 3)$

_____   6.   Find the vertex and focus of the parabola.

$x^2 + 20y = 0$

a. vertex: $(-5, 0)$ focus: $(0, 0)$

b. vertex: $(5, 0)$ focus: $(0, 0)$

c. vertex: $(0, 0)$ focus: $(0, 5)$

d. vertex: $(0, 0)$ focus: $(-5, 0)$

e. vertex: $(0, 0)$ focus: $(0, -5)$

_____ 7.   Find the standard form of the equation of the ellipse with the given characteristics.

Vertices: $(0,2),(10,2)$; minor axis of length 6.

a.
$$\frac{(x-5)^2}{25}+\frac{(y-2)^2}{9}=1$$

b.
$$\frac{(x+5)^2}{25}+\frac{(y-2)^2}{9}=1$$

c.
$$\frac{(x-5)^2}{25}-\frac{(y-2)^2}{9}=1$$

d.
$$\frac{(x+5)^2}{25}+\frac{(y+2)^2}{9}=1$$

e.
$$\frac{(x-5)^2}{25}+\frac{(y+2)^2}{9}=1$$

_____ 8.   A semielliptical arch over a tunnel for a one-way road through a mountain has a major axis
of 60 feet and a height at the center of 20 feet. Find an equation of the semielliptical arch

a.
$$\frac{x^2}{900}-\frac{y^2}{400}=1$$

b.
$$\frac{x^2}{900}+\frac{y^2}{400}=1$$

c.
$$\frac{x^2}{400}-\frac{y^2}{900}=1$$

d.
$$\frac{x^2}{60}+\frac{y^2}{900}=1$$

e.
$$\frac{x^2}{400}+\frac{y^2}{900}=1$$

_____   9.   Find the center and vertices of the ellipse.

$$x^2 + 9y^2 + 18x - 144y + 648 = 0$$

a. center: (−9, 8)   vertices: (−12, 8), (−6, 8)
b. center: (−9, 8)   vertices: (−10, 8), (−8, 8)
c. center: (8, −9)   vertices: (5, −9), (11, −9)
d. center: (9, −8)   vertices: (8, −8), (10, −8)
e. center: (9, −8)   vertices: (6, −8), (12, −8)

_____   10.   Find the standard form of the equation of the hyperbola with the given characteristics and center at the origin.

Vertices: $(0, \pm 18)$; asymptotes: $y = \pm 9x$

a. $$\dfrac{41x^2}{13,122} - \dfrac{41y^2}{162} = 1$$

b. $$\dfrac{41x^2}{13,122} + \dfrac{41y^2}{162} = 1$$

c. $$\dfrac{41y^2}{13,122} - \dfrac{41x^2}{162} = 1$$

d. $$\dfrac{41y^2}{13,122} + \dfrac{41x^2}{162} = 1$$

e. $$\dfrac{13,122x^2}{41} - \dfrac{41y^2}{162} = 1$$

_____   11.   Identify the equation as a circle, a parabola, an ellipse, or a hyperbola.

$$9x^2 - 4y^2 - 4x + 6y + 18 = 0$$

a. Ellipse
b. Hyperbola
c. Parabola
d. Circle
e. None of the above

_____ 12. Use a graphing utility to graph the conic. Determine the angle θ through which the axes are rotated.

$x^2 + 2xy + y^2 = 10$

a. $\theta = \dfrac{\pi}{4}$ or $45°$, $y = -x \pm \sqrt{10}$

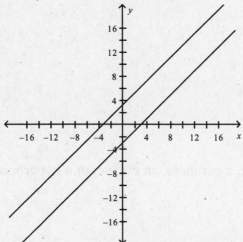

d. $\theta = \dfrac{\pi}{4}$ or $45°$, $y = -x \pm \sqrt{10}$

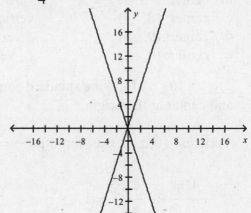

b. $\theta = \dfrac{\pi}{4}$ or $45°$, $y = -x \pm \sqrt{10}$

e. $\theta = \dfrac{\pi}{4}$ or $45°$, $y = -x \pm \sqrt{10}$

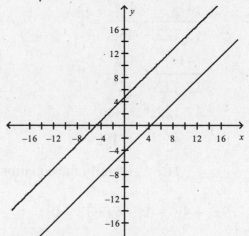

c.

$$\theta = \frac{\pi}{4} \text{ or } 45°, \; y = -x \pm \sqrt{10}$$

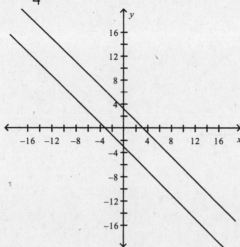

_____ 13.   Find any points of intersection of the graphs algebraically.

$$-x^2 + y^2 + 3x - 7y + 12 = 0$$

$$x^2 + y^2 - 3x - 7y + 12 = 0$$

a. The points of intersection are $(4, 4)$ and $(4, 4)$.
b. The points of intersection are $(3, 3)$ and $(3, 4)$.
c. The points of intersection are $(4, 4)$ and $(-4, -4)$.
d. The points of intersection are $(-3, -3)$ and $(3, 4)$.
e. The points of intersection are $(3, 3)$ and $(4, 4)$.

_____ 14.   Eliminate the parameter and write the corresponding rectangular equation whose graph represents the curve.

$$x = 2(t + 1)$$
$$y = |t - 2|$$

a.
$$y = \left| \frac{x}{3} - 2 \right|$$

b. $y = |t + 3|$

c. $y = |t - 3|$

d.
$$y = \left| \frac{x}{2} - 3 \right|$$

e.
$$y = \left| \frac{x}{2} + 3 \right|$$

_____   15.   Select the parametric equations matching with the following graph.

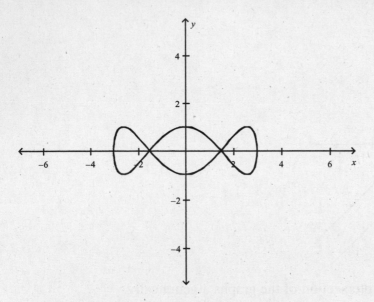

a.   Lissajous curve: $x = 3\sin\theta,\ y = \cos\theta$
b.   Lissajous curve: $x = 3\cos\theta,\ y = 3\sin 3\theta$
c.   Lissajous curve: $x = 3\cos\theta,\ y = \sin 3\theta$
d.   Lissajous curve: $x = 3\cos 3\theta,\ y = \sin 3\theta$
e.   Lissajous curve: $x = 3\sin\theta,\ y = \cos 3\theta$

_____   16.   Eliminate the parameter and write the corresponding rectangular equation whose graph represents the curve.

$x = 3\cos\theta$
$y = 5\sin\theta$

a.
$$y = \frac{x}{5}$$

b.
$$y = \frac{x}{3}$$

c.
$$\frac{x^2}{9} - \frac{y^2}{25} = 1$$

d.
$$\frac{x^2}{9} + \frac{y^2}{25} = 1$$

e.
$$\frac{x^2}{25} + \frac{y^2}{9} = 1$$

_____   17.   Use a graphing utility to find the rectangular coordinates of the point given in polar coordinates. Round your results to two decimal places.

$(7.6, -4.2)$

a. Rectangular coordinates: $(6.62, -3.73)$
b. Rectangular coordinates: $(-8.80, -1.20)$
c. Rectangular coordinates: $(7.62, -2.73)$
d. Rectangular coordinates: $(-2.73, 7.62)$
e. Rectangular coordinates: $(-3.73, 6.62)$

_____   18.   Convert the polar equation to rectangular form.

$r = 9 \sin \theta$

a. $x^2 + y^2 - 9y = 0$
b. $x^2 + y^2 - 9x = 0$
c. $x^2 + y^2 + 9x = 0$
d. $x^2 + y^2 - 9 = 0$
e. $x^2 + y^2 + 9y = 0$

_____   19.   Describe the graph of the polar equation and find the corresponding rectangular equation. Select the correct graph.

$r = 5 \csc \theta$

a. The graph of the polar equation is not evident by simple inspection. Convert to rectangular form first.

$y - 7 = 0$

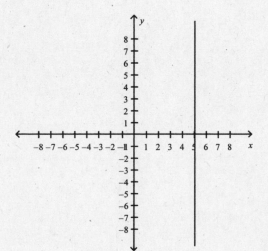

d. The graph of the polar equation is not evident by simple inspection. Convert to rectangular form first.

$y - 4 = 0$

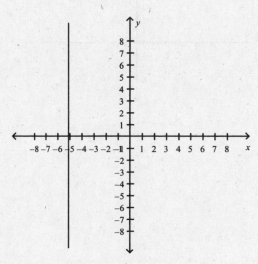

b. The graph of the polar equation is not evident by simple inspection. Convert to rectangular form first.

$$y + 5 = 0$$

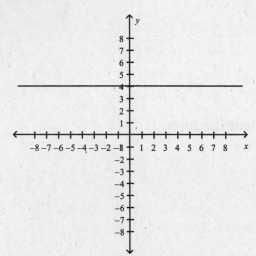

e. The graph of the polar equation is not evident by simple inspection. Convert to rectangular form first.

$$y - 5 = 0$$

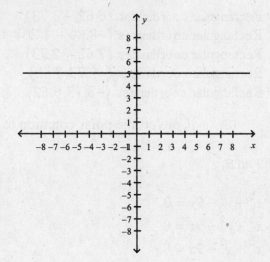

c. The graph of the polar equation is not evident by simple inspection. Convert to rectangular form first.

$$y - 6 = 0$$

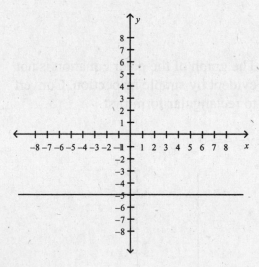

_____   20.   Select the graph of the polar equation using symmetry, zeros, maximum r-values, and any
other additional points.

$r = 3 - 5 \sin \theta$

a.
Symmetric with respect to $\theta = \dfrac{\pi}{2}$

$|r| = 8$ when $\theta = \dfrac{3\pi}{2}$

$r = 0$ when $\theta = \dfrac{\pi}{6}, \dfrac{5\pi}{6}$

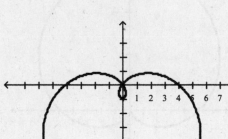

d.
Symmetric with respect to $\theta = \dfrac{\pi}{2}$

$|r| = 8$ when $\theta = \dfrac{3\pi}{2}$

$r = 0$ when $\theta = \dfrac{\pi}{6}, \dfrac{5\pi}{6}$

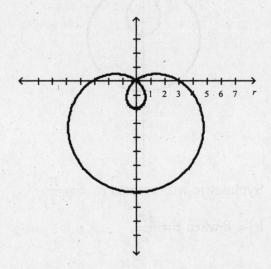

b. Symmetric with respect to $\theta = \dfrac{\pi}{2}$

$|r| = 8$ when $\theta = \dfrac{3\pi}{2}$

$r = 0$ when $\theta = \dfrac{\pi}{6}, \dfrac{5\pi}{6}$

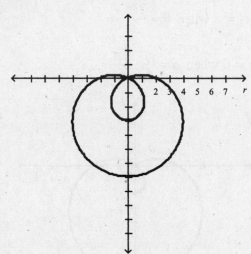

e. Symmetric with respect to $\theta = \dfrac{\pi}{2}$

$|r| = 8$ when $\theta = \dfrac{3\pi}{2}$

$r = 0$ when $\theta = \dfrac{\pi}{6}, \dfrac{5\pi}{6}$

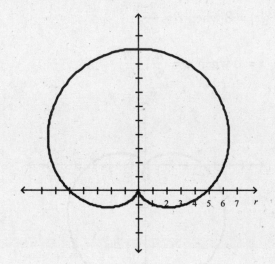

c. Symmetric with respect to $\theta = \dfrac{\pi}{2}$

$|r| = 8$ when $\theta = \dfrac{3\pi}{2}$

$r = 0$ when $\theta = \dfrac{\pi}{6}, \dfrac{5\pi}{6}$

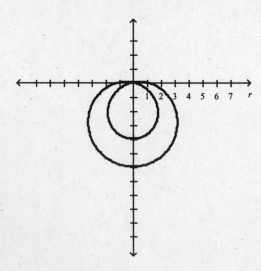

_____ 21. Select the correct graph of the polar equation. Find an interval for θ for which the graph is traced *only once*.

$$r = 2\cos\left(\frac{3\theta}{2}\right)$$

a.

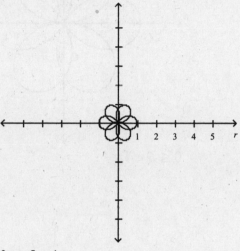

$$0 \le \theta < 4\pi$$

d.

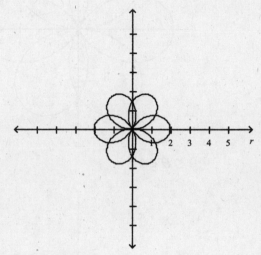

$$0 \le \theta < 4\pi$$

b.

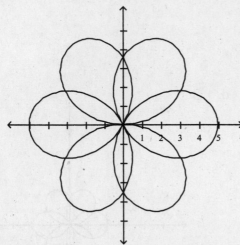

$0 \le \theta < 4\pi$

e.

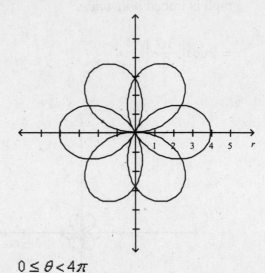

$0 \le \theta < 4\pi$

c.

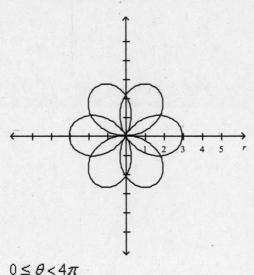

$0 \le \theta < 4\pi$

_____ 22.   Select the correct graph of the polar equation. Describe your viewing window.

$r = 2 \csc \theta + 8$

a.

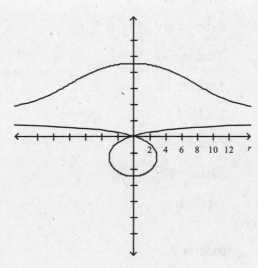

$\theta \min = 0$

$\theta \max = 2\pi$

$\theta \text{step} = \pi/24$

$X \min = -12$

$X \max = 12$

$X \text{scl} = 2$

$Y \min = -12$

$Y \max = 12$

$Y \text{scl} = 2$

b.

$\theta \min = 0$

$\theta \max = 2\pi$

$\theta \text{step} = \pi/24$

$X \min = -12$

$X \max = 12$

$X \text{scl} = 2$

$Y \min = -12$

$Y \max = 12$

$Y \text{scl} = 2$

c.

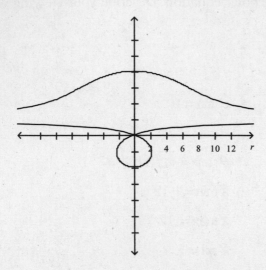

$\theta\min = 0$

$\theta\max = 2\pi$

$\theta\,\text{step} = \pi/24$

$X\min = -12$

$X\max = 12$

$X\,\text{scl} = 1$

$Y\min = -12$

$Y\max = 12$

$Y\,\text{scl} = 1$

d.

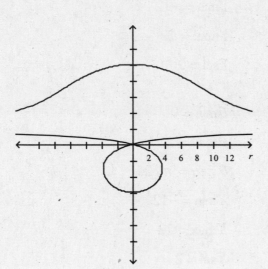

$\theta\min = 0$

$\theta\max = 2\pi$

$\theta\,\text{step} = \pi/24$

$X\min = -12$

$X\max = 12$

$X\,\text{scl} = 2$

$Y\min = -12$

$Y\max = 12$

$Y\,\text{scl} = 2$

e.

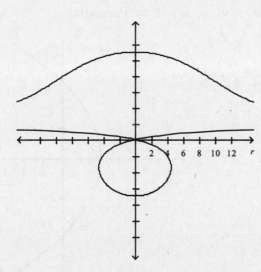

$\theta \min = 0$

$\theta \max = 2\pi$

$\theta \text{step} = \pi / 24$

$X \min = -12$

$X \max = 12$

$X \text{scl} = 2$

$Y \min = -12$

$Y \max = 12$

$Y \text{scl} = 2$

_____ 23.   Identify the conic and select its correct graph.

$$r = \frac{8}{1 + \cos \theta}$$

a. $e = 2 \Rightarrow$ Hyperabola

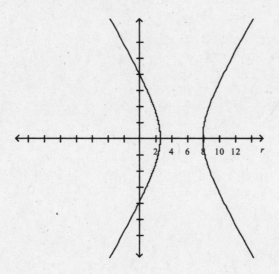

d. $e = 1 \Rightarrow$ Parabola

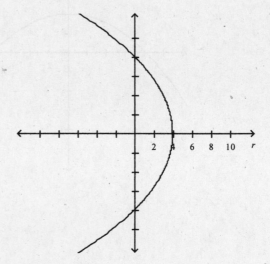

b. $e = 1 \Rightarrow$ Parabola

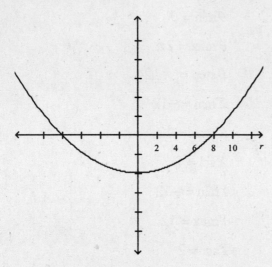

e. $e = 1 \Rightarrow$ Parabola

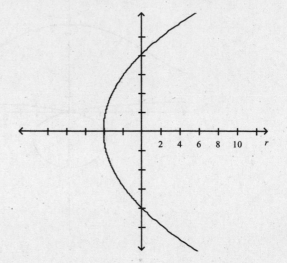

c. $e = 1 \Rightarrow$ Parabola

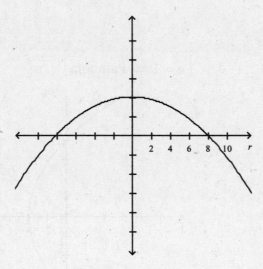

_____ 24.   By using a graphing utility select the correct graph of the polar equation. Identify the graph.

$$\frac{12}{12 + 18 \sin \theta}$$

a.

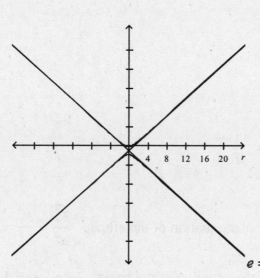

> 1 ⟹ Hyperabola

d.

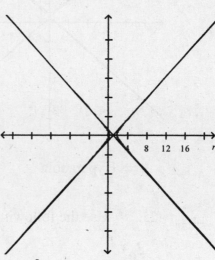

$e = \dfrac{3}{2}$ > 1 ⟹ Hyperabola

b.

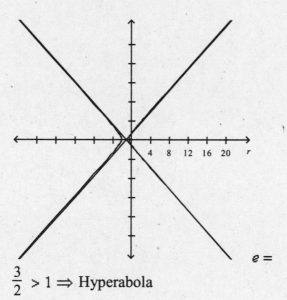

$\dfrac{3}{2}$ > 1 ⟹ Hyperabola

e.

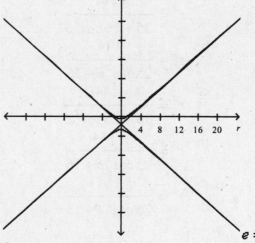

$\dfrac{3}{2}$ > 1 ⟹ Hyperabola

c.

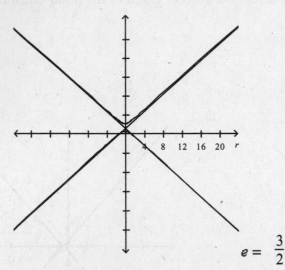

$$e = \frac{3}{2}$$

$> 1 \Rightarrow$ Hyperabola

_____ 25. Use the following results the polar equation of the ellipse $\dfrac{x^2}{a^2} - \dfrac{y^2}{b^2} = 1$ is

$r^2 = \dfrac{-b^2}{1 - e^2 \cos^2 \theta}$ to write the polar form of the equation of the conic $\dfrac{x^2}{16} - \dfrac{y^2}{9} = 1.$

a. $r^2 = \dfrac{144}{25 + 16 \cos^2 \theta}$

b. $r^2 = \dfrac{144}{25 \cos^2 \theta - 16}$

c. $r^2 = \dfrac{144}{16 - 25 \cos^2 \theta}$

d. $r^2 = \dfrac{-144}{25 \cos^2 \theta + 16}$

e. $r^2 = \dfrac{144}{25 \cos^2 \theta + 16}$

Ch 10 Form F
Answer Section

1.	ANS:	E	PTS:	1	REF:	10.1.26
2.	ANS:	C	PTS:	1	REF:	10.1.53
3.	ANS:	A	PTS:	1	REF:	10.1.68b
4.	ANS:	E	PTS:	1	REF:	10.2.27
5.	ANS:	D	PTS:	1	REF:	10.2.58
6.	ANS:	E	PTS:	1	REF:	10.2.37
7.	ANS:	A	PTS:	1	REF:	10.3.21
8.	ANS:	B	PTS:	1	REF:	10.3.63b
9.	ANS:	A	PTS:	1	REF:	10.3.44
10.	ANS:	C	PTS:	1	REF:	10.4.33
11.	ANS:	B	PTS:	1	REF:	10.4.66
12.	ANS:	C	PTS:	1	REF:	10.5.27a
13.	ANS:	B	PTS:	1	REF:	10.5.57
14.	ANS:	D	PTS:	1	REF:	10.6.15b
15.	ANS:	C	PTS:	1	REF:	10.6.57
16.	ANS:	D	PTS:	1	REF:	10.6.18b
17.	ANS:	E	PTS:	1	REF:	10.7.36
18.	ANS:	A	PTS:	1	REF:	10.7.85
19.	ANS:	E	PTS:	1	REF:	10.7.118
20.	ANS:	D	PTS:	1	REF:	10.8.35
21.	ANS:	D	PTS:	1	REF:	10.8.61
22.	ANS:	D	PTS:	1	REF:	10.8.58
23.	ANS:	D	PTS:	1	REF:	10.9.18
24.	ANS:	C	PTS:	1	REF:	10.9.33
25.	ANS:	B	PTS:	1	REF:	10.9.77

Ch 11 Form A

_____ 1.   Find the coordinates of the point.

The point is located six units behind the yz-plane, seven units to the right of the xz-plane, and eight units above the xy-plane.

a. $x = -6,\ y = 7,\ z = 8$
b. $x = -6,\ y = 7,\ z = -6$
c. $x = 7,\ y = 7,\ z = 8$
d. $x = 7,\ y = -6,\ z = -6$
e. $x = 6,\ y = 7,\ z = 8$

_____ 2.   Determine the octant(s) in which (x,y,z) is located so that the condition(s) is (are) satisfied.

$y < -5$

a. Octant II
b. Octants II, IV, VI, VIII
c. Octants I, II, III
d. Octants I, II, III, IV
e. Octants III, IV, VII, or VIII

_____ 3.   Find the distance between the points.

$(5, -5, 0), (0, 4, -5)$

a. $\sqrt{131}$ units
b. $3\sqrt{15}$ units
c. $\sqrt{134}$ units
d. $\sqrt{133}$ units
e. $2\sqrt{33}$ units

_____ 4.   Determine whether the triangle is a right triangle, an isosceles triangle, or neither.

$(-7, 5, 8), (3, 6, 4), (2, -4, 8)$

a. Neither Isosceles nor Right
b. Isosceles triangle
c. Right triangle
d. Right triangle and isosceles triangle

_____ 5.   Find the midpoint of the line segment joining the points.

$(-3, 5, 2), (7, -5, 3)$

a. $(2, 0, \frac{5}{2})$

b. $(0, \frac{5}{2}, 2)$

c. $(\frac{5}{2}, 0, 2)$

d. $(0, 2, -\frac{5}{2})$

e. $(\frac{5}{2}, 2, 0)$

_____ 6.   Assume that Earth is a sphere with a radius of 4300 miles. The center of Earth is placed at the origin of a three-dimensional coordinate system. What is the equation of the sphere?

a. $2x^2 + 2y^2 + 2z^2 = (4300)^2$

b. $2x^2 + y^2 + z^2 = (4300)^2$

c. $x^2 + y^2 + z^2 = (4300)^2$

d. $x^2 + y^2 + 2z^2 = (4300)^2$

e. $x^2 + 2y^2 + z^2 = (4300)^2$

_____ 7.   Find the vector z, given $\mathbf{u} = \langle -1, 3, 5 \rangle$, $\mathbf{v} = \langle 1, -5, -5 \rangle$.

$\mathbf{u} + \mathbf{v} + \mathbf{z} = 0$

a. $\mathbf{z} = \langle 0, 2, 0 \rangle$

b. $\mathbf{z} = \langle 0, 2, 5 \rangle$

c. $\mathbf{z} = \langle 25, 2, 0 \rangle$

d. $\mathbf{z} = \langle 2, 0, 0 \rangle$

e. $\mathbf{z} = \langle 25, 0, 2 \rangle$

_____ 8.　　Find the magnitude of **v**.

Initial point: $(0,-1,0)$
Terminal point: $(1,5,-5)$

a.　$\|\mathbf{v}\| = \sqrt{37}$
b.　$\|\mathbf{v}\| = \sqrt{61}$
c.　$\|\mathbf{v}\| = \sqrt{62}$
d.　$\|\mathbf{v}\| = \sqrt{26}$
e.　$\|\mathbf{v}\| = \sqrt{38}$

_____ 9.　　Find the angle θ between the vectors. Round your answer to two decimal places.

$\mathbf{u} = 10\mathbf{i} + 40\mathbf{j}$

$\mathbf{v} = -3\mathbf{j} + 8\mathbf{k}$

a.　$\theta \approx 110.92°$
b.　$\theta \approx 107.92°$
c.　$\theta \approx 111.92°$
d.　$\theta \approx 108.92°$
e.　$\theta \approx 109.92°$

_____ 10.　　Find a unit vector in the direction of the vector described below.
　　Initial point: $(0, 3, -9)$
　　Terminal point: $(-6, -2, 0)$

a.　$\langle -6,-5,9 \rangle$

b.　$2\sqrt{5}\langle -6,-5,9 \rangle$

c.　$\sqrt{142}\langle -6,-5,9 \rangle$

d.　$\dfrac{1}{\sqrt{142}}\langle -6,-5,9 \rangle$

e.　$\dfrac{1}{2\sqrt{5}}\langle -6,-5,9 \rangle$

_____ 11.   Find the dot product of **u** and **v**.

$\mathbf{u} = \langle -7,-1,8 \rangle, \mathbf{v} = \langle 0,8,2 \rangle$

a. 8

b. $\langle 0,-8,16 \rangle$

c. -24

d. $\langle -7,7,10 \rangle$

e. 10

_____ 12.   Determine whether **u** and **v** are parallel, orthogonal, or neither.

$\mathbf{u} = \langle -2,8,4 \rangle, \mathbf{v} = \langle 9,1,-1 \rangle$

a. parallel

b. neither

c. orthogonal

_____ 13.   Use the vectors **u** and **v** to find $\mathbf{v} \times \mathbf{u}$.

$\mathbf{u} = 5\mathbf{i} - \mathbf{j} + 6\mathbf{k} \quad \mathbf{v} = 4\mathbf{i} + 4\mathbf{j} - \mathbf{k}$

a. $\mathbf{v} \times \mathbf{u} = -23\mathbf{i} + 29\mathbf{j} + 24\mathbf{k}$

b. $\mathbf{v} \times \mathbf{u} = 23\mathbf{i} - 29\mathbf{j} - 24\mathbf{k}$

c. $\mathbf{v} \times \mathbf{u} = 29\mathbf{i} - 23\mathbf{j} + 24\mathbf{k}$

d. $\mathbf{v} \times \mathbf{u} = 23\mathbf{i} - 29\mathbf{j} + 24\mathbf{k}$

e. $\mathbf{v} \times \mathbf{u} = 23\mathbf{i} + 29\mathbf{j} - 24\mathbf{k}$

_____ 14. Find $\mathbf{u} \times \mathbf{v}$ and show that it is orthogonal to both $\mathbf{u}$ and $\mathbf{v}$.

$\mathbf{u} = -\mathbf{i} + \mathbf{k}$

$\mathbf{v} = \mathbf{j} - 4\mathbf{k}$

a. $\mathbf{u} \times \mathbf{v} = \mathbf{i} - 4\mathbf{j} - \mathbf{k}$

$(\mathbf{u} \times \mathbf{v}) \cdot \mathbf{u} = 0$

$(\mathbf{u} \times \mathbf{v}) \cdot \mathbf{v} = 0$

b. $\mathbf{u} \times \mathbf{v} = -\mathbf{i} - 4\mathbf{j} - \mathbf{k}$

$(\mathbf{u} \times \mathbf{v}) \cdot \mathbf{u} = 0$

$(\mathbf{u} \times \mathbf{v}) \cdot \mathbf{v} = 0$

c. $\mathbf{u} \times \mathbf{v} = -\mathbf{i} + 4\mathbf{j} + \mathbf{k}$

$(\mathbf{u} \times \mathbf{v}) \cdot \mathbf{u} = 0$

$(\mathbf{u} \times \mathbf{v}) \cdot \mathbf{v} = 0$

d. $\mathbf{u} \times \mathbf{v} = \mathbf{i} - 4\mathbf{j} + \mathbf{k}$

$(\mathbf{u} \times \mathbf{v}) \cdot \mathbf{u} = 0$

$(\mathbf{u} \times \mathbf{v}) \cdot \mathbf{v} = 0$

e. $\mathbf{u} \times \mathbf{v} = -\mathbf{i} - 4\mathbf{j} + \mathbf{k}$

$(\mathbf{u} \times \mathbf{v}) \cdot \mathbf{u} = 0$

$(\mathbf{u} \times \mathbf{v}) \cdot \mathbf{v} = 0$

_____ 15. Find the area of the parallelogram that has the vectors as adjacent sides.

$\mathbf{u} = -4\mathbf{i} + 8\mathbf{j} + 12\mathbf{k}$

$\mathbf{v} = 8\mathbf{i} + 5\mathbf{j} + 13\mathbf{k}$

a. Area $= 2\sqrt{5981}$ square units

b. Area $= 4\sqrt{1931}$ square units

c. Area $= 2\sqrt{7229}$ square units

d. Area $= 2\sqrt{542}$ square units

e. Area $= 4\sqrt{1049}$ square units

_____ 16.   Use the triple scalar product to find the volume of the parallelepiped having adjacent edges **u**, **v**, and **w**.

$$\mathbf{u} = 3\mathbf{i} + 3\mathbf{j}$$

$$\mathbf{v} = 3\mathbf{j} + 3\mathbf{k}$$

$$\mathbf{w} = 3\mathbf{i} + 3\mathbf{k}$$

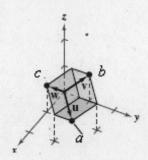

$$a = (3,3,0), b = (0,3,3), c = (3,0,3)$$

   a.   Volume = 55 cubic units
   b.   Volume = 53   cubic units
   c.   Volume = 54 cubic units
   d.   Volume = 52 cubic units
   e.   Volume = 56 cubic units

____ 17.   Both the magnitude and direction of the force on a crankshaft change as the crank-shaft rotates. Vectors representing the position of the crank and the force are

$$V = 0.12\left(-\cos 30°\,j - \sin 30°\,k\right)$$ and $F = -1000k$ respectively. The magnitude of the torque on the crank is given by $\|V \times F\|$, find the magnitude of the torque on the crank shaft using the position and data shown in the figure.

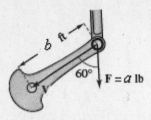

$a = 1000,\ b = 0.12$

a. $120\sqrt{3}$ ft-lb
b. $60\sqrt{2}$ ft-lb
c. $1000\sqrt{3}$ ft-lb
d. $60\sqrt{3}$ ft-lb
e. $120\sqrt{2}$ ft-lb

____ 18.   Use the vectors u and v to find $u \cdot (u \times v)$.

$$u = 7i - j + 8k \qquad v = 6i + 6j - k$$

a. $u \cdot (u \times v) = 12$
b. $u \cdot (u \times v) = -11$
c. $u \cdot (u \times v) = 11$
d. $u \cdot (u \times v) = -12$
e. $u \cdot (u \times v) = 0$

____ 19.   Find the area of the parallelogram that has the vectors as adjacent sides.
$$u = -2i + j + 5k, \quad v = 4i - 3j - 3k$$
a. $\sqrt{26}$
b. $2\sqrt{86}$
c. 86
d. 11
e. 1

_____　20.　　Find a set of parametric equations for the line through the point and parallel to the specified vector or line. (For each line, write the direction numbers as integers.)

Point: $(1, 0, 1)$
Parallel to: $x = 3 + 5t, y = 5 - 5t, z = -7 + 5t$

a.　Parametric equations: $x = -5t, y = 1 + 5t, z = 1 + 5t$
b.　Parametric equations: $x = -5t, y = 1 + 5t, z = 1 + 5t$
c.　Parametric equations: $x = 1 + 5t, y = -5t, z = 1 + 5t$
d.　Parametric equations: $x = 1 + 5t, y = 1 + 5t, z = -5t$
e.　Parametric equations: $x = 1 + 5t, y = 1 + 5t, z = -5t$

_____　21.　　Find the general form of the equation of the plane passing through the point and perpendicular to the specified vector or line.

Point: $(7, 4, 2)$
Perpendicular to: $\mathbf{n} = -3\mathbf{i} + \mathbf{j} - 6\mathbf{k}$

a.　$3x + y - 6z + 29 = 0$
b.　$-3x - y - 6z - 29 = 0$
c.　$-3x - y - 6z + 29 = 0$
d.　$-3x + y - 6z + 29 = 0$
e.　$-3x + y - 6z - 29 = 0$

_____　22.　　Find a set of symmetric equations of the line that passes through the given points.

$(-4, 6, 14), (1, -4, 16)$

a.　$\dfrac{x+4}{-10} = \dfrac{y-6}{2} = \dfrac{z-14}{5}$

b.　$\dfrac{x+4}{5} = \dfrac{y-6}{-10} = \dfrac{z-14}{2}$

c.　$\dfrac{x-4}{5} = \dfrac{y+6}{-10} = \dfrac{z+14}{2}$

d.　$\dfrac{x-4}{5} = \dfrac{y-6}{-10} = \dfrac{z-14}{2}$

e.　$\dfrac{x+4}{5} = \dfrac{y+6}{-10} = \dfrac{z+14}{2}$

_____   23.   Find a set of parametric equations of the line.

Passes through $(3,-6,-4)$ and is parallel to $\mathbf{v} = \langle 7, -4, 5 \rangle$.

a. $x = 3 + 7t$

$y = -6 - 4t$

$z = -4 + 5t$

b. $x = 3 - 7t$

$y = -6 - 4t$

$z = -4 - 5t$

c. $x = 3 + 7t$

$y = -6 - 4t$

$z = -4 - 5t$

d. $x = 3 + 7t$

$y = -6 + 4t$

$z = -4 + 5t$

e. $x = 3 - 7t$

$y = -6 - 4t$

$z = -4 + 5t$

_____   24.   Determine whether the planes are parallel, orthogonal, or neither.

$2x - y - 3z = -5$

$-2x - 6y - z = 3$

a. neither

b. parallel

c. orthogonal

____   25.   Find the general form of the equation of the plane passing through the three points.

$(0,0,0), (6,7,8), (-4,5,5)$

a. $-5x + 62y - 58z = 0$
b. $-5x + 62y + 58z = 0$
c. $-5x - 58y + 62z = 0$
d. $-5x - 62y - 58z = 0$
e. $-5x - 62y + 58z = 0$

Ch 11 Form A
Answer Section

1.	ANS:	A	PTS:	1	REF:	11.1.17
2.	ANS:	E	PTS:	1	REF:	11.1.24
3.	ANS:	A	PTS:	1	REF:	11.1.34
4.	ANS:	B	PTS:	1	REF:	11.1.41
5.	ANS:	A	PTS:	1	REF:	11.1.51
6.	ANS:	C	PTS:	1	REF:	11.1.78a
7.	ANS:	A	PTS:	1	REF:	11.2.18
8.	ANS:	C	PTS:	1	REF:	11.2.28
9.	ANS:	E	PTS:	1	REF:	11.2.37
10.	ANS:	D	PTS:	1	REF:	11.2.9c
11.	ANS:	A	PTS:	1	REF:	11.2.31
12.	ANS:	B	PTS:	1	REF:	11.2.41
13.	ANS:	B	PTS:	1	REF:	11.3.12
14.	ANS:	B	PTS:	1	REF:	11.3.29
15.	ANS:	B	PTS:	1	REF:	11.3.40
16.	ANS:	C	PTS:	1	REF:	11.3.55
17.	ANS:	D	PTS:	1	REF:	11.3.62
18.	ANS:	E	PTS:	1	REF:	11.3.19
19.	ANS:	B	PTS:	1	REF:	11.3.39
20.	ANS:	C	PTS:	1	REF:	11.4.10a
21.	ANS:	D	PTS:	1	REF:	11.4.23
22.	ANS:	B	PTS:	1	REF:	11.4.13b
23.	ANS:	A	PTS:	1	REF:	11.4.45
24.	ANS:	A	PTS:	1	REF:	11.4.39
25.	ANS:	E	PTS:	1	REF:	11.4.27

Ch 11 Form B

_____ 1.   Find the coordinates of the point.

The point is located five units behind the *yz*-plane, six units to the right of the *xz*-plane, and seven units above the *xy*-plane.

a. $x = -5, \ y = 6, \ z = 7$
b. $x = -5, \ y = 6, \ z = -5$
c. $x = 5, \ y = 6, \ z = 7$
d. $x = 6, \ y = -5, \ z = -5$
e. $x = 6, \ y = 6, \ z = 7$

_____ 2.   Determine the octant(s) in which (x, y, z) is located so that the condition(s) is (are) satisfied.

$y < -2$

a. Octant II
b. Octants I, II, III
c. Octants I, II, III, IV
d. Octants III, IV, VII, or VIII
e. Octants II, IV, VI, VIII

_____ 3.   Find the distance between the points.

$(4, -5, 0), (0, 6, -2)$

a. $\sqrt{143}$ units
b. $\sqrt{145}$ units
c. $\sqrt{142}$ units
d. 12 units
e. $\sqrt{141}$ units

_____ 4.   Determine whether the triangle is a right triangle, an isosceles triangle, or neither.

$(3, -6, 7), (2, 6, 1), (8, -6, 2)$

a. Right triangle and isosceles triangle
b. Neither Isosceles nor Right
c. Isosceles triangle
d. Right triangle

_____ 5.   Find the midpoint of the line segment joining the points.

$(-2,8,4),(9,-5,4)$

a. $(4, \dfrac{3}{2}, \dfrac{7}{2})$

b. $(\dfrac{7}{2}, \dfrac{3}{2}, 4)$

c. $(\dfrac{3}{2}, \dfrac{7}{2}, -4)$

d. $(4, \dfrac{7}{2}, \dfrac{3}{2})$

e. $(\dfrac{3}{2}, 4, \dfrac{7}{2})$

_____ 6.   Assume that Earth is a sphere with a radius of 4100 miles. The center of Earth is placed at the origin of a three-dimensional coordinate system. What is the equation of the sphere?

a. $2x^2 + 2y^2 + 2z^2 = (4100)^2$
b. $x^2 + y^2 + z^2 = (4100)^2$
c. $2x^2 + y^2 + z^2 = (4100)^2$
d. $x^2 + 2y^2 + z^2 = (4100)^2$
e. $x^2 + y^2 + 2z^2 = (4100)^2$

_____ 7.   Find the vector **z**, given $\mathbf{u} = \langle -1,3,9 \rangle$, $\mathbf{v} = \langle 1,-9,-9 \rangle$.

$\mathbf{u} + \mathbf{v} + \mathbf{z} = 0$

a. $\mathbf{z} = \langle 45,6,0 \rangle$

b. $\mathbf{z} = \langle 0,6,9 \rangle$

c. $\mathbf{z} = \langle 6,0,0 \rangle$

d. $\mathbf{z} = \langle 0,6,0 \rangle$

e. $\mathbf{z} = \langle 45,0,6 \rangle$

____   8.   Find the magnitude of **v**.

Initial point: $(0, -1, 0)$
Terminal point: $(1, 3, -3)$

a. $\| \mathbf{v} \| = \sqrt{26}$
b. $\| \mathbf{v} \| = \sqrt{17}$
c. $\| \mathbf{v} \| = \sqrt{10}$
d. $\| \mathbf{v} \| = 3\sqrt{2}$
e. $\| \mathbf{v} \| = 5$

____   9.   Find the angle θ between the vectors. Round your answer to two decimal places.

$\mathbf{u} = 12\mathbf{i} + 48\mathbf{j}$

$\mathbf{v} = -5\mathbf{j} + 10\mathbf{k}$

a. $\theta \approx 117.71°$
b. $\theta \approx 115.71°$
c. $\theta \approx 116.71°$
d. $\theta \approx 114.71°$
e. $\theta \approx 113.71°$

____   10.   Find a unit vector in the direction of the vector described below.
Initial point: $(8, 4, -2)$
Terminal point: $(-7, 3, 9)$

a. $\sqrt{347} \left\langle -15, -1, 11 \right\rangle$

b. $\left\langle -15, -1, 11 \right\rangle$

c. $\dfrac{1}{\sqrt{347}} \left\langle -15, -1, 11 \right\rangle$

d. $\dfrac{1}{3\sqrt{3}} \left\langle -15, -1, 11 \right\rangle$

e. $3\sqrt{3} \left\langle -15, -1, 11 \right\rangle$

____   11.   Find the dot product of **u** and **v**.
$\mathbf{u} = \left\langle 4, -1, 9 \right\rangle, v = \left\langle -2, -5, -9 \right\rangle$

a. $\left\langle 2, -6, 0 \right\rangle$

b. $\left\langle -8, 5, -81 \right\rangle$

c. -84
d. -4
e. 78

_____   12.   Determine whether **u** and **v** are parallel, orthogonal, or neither.

$\mathbf{u} = \langle 4, -3, -8 \rangle, \, v = \langle -6, 6, 4 \rangle$

a. orthogonal
b. neither
c. parallel

_____   13.   Use the vectors **u** and **v** to find $\mathbf{v} \times \mathbf{u}$.

$\mathbf{u} = 4\mathbf{i} - \mathbf{j} + 5\mathbf{k} \quad \mathbf{v} = 3\mathbf{i} + 3\mathbf{j} - \mathbf{k}$

a. $\mathbf{v} \times \mathbf{u} = 14\mathbf{i} - 19\mathbf{j} - 15\mathbf{k}$
b. $\mathbf{v} \times \mathbf{u} = 14\mathbf{i} + 19\mathbf{j} - 15\mathbf{k}$
c. $\mathbf{v} \times \mathbf{u} = -14\mathbf{i} + 19\mathbf{j} + 15\mathbf{k}$
d. $\mathbf{v} \times \mathbf{u} = 19\mathbf{i} - 14\mathbf{j} + 15\mathbf{k}$
e. $\mathbf{v} \times \mathbf{u} = 14\mathbf{i} - 19\mathbf{j} + 15\mathbf{k}$

_____   14.   Find $\mathbf{u} \times \mathbf{v}$ and show that it is orthogonal to both **u** and **v**.

$\mathbf{u} = -\mathbf{i} + \mathbf{k}$

$\mathbf{v} = \mathbf{j} - 7\mathbf{k}$

a. $\mathbf{u} \times \mathbf{v} = \mathbf{i} - 7\mathbf{j} - \mathbf{k}$

   $(\mathbf{u} \times \mathbf{v}) \cdot \mathbf{u} = 0$

   $(\mathbf{u} \times \mathbf{v}) \cdot \mathbf{v} = 0$
b. $\mathbf{u} \times \mathbf{v} = \mathbf{i} - 7\mathbf{j} + \mathbf{k}$

   $(\mathbf{u} \times \mathbf{v}) \cdot \mathbf{u} = 0$

   $(\mathbf{u} \times \mathbf{v}) \cdot \mathbf{v} = 0$
c. $\mathbf{u} \times \mathbf{v} = -\mathbf{i} + 7\mathbf{j} + \mathbf{k}$

   $(\mathbf{u} \times \mathbf{v}) \cdot \mathbf{u} = 0$

   $(\mathbf{u} \times \mathbf{v}) \cdot \mathbf{v} = 0$
d. $\mathbf{u} \times \mathbf{v} = -\mathbf{i} - 7\mathbf{j} - \mathbf{k}$

   $(\mathbf{u} \times \mathbf{v}) \cdot \mathbf{u} = 0$

   $(\mathbf{u} \times \mathbf{v}) \cdot \mathbf{v} = 0$
e. $\mathbf{u} \times \mathbf{v} = -\mathbf{i} - 7\mathbf{j} + \mathbf{k}$

   $(\mathbf{u} \times \mathbf{v}) \cdot \mathbf{u} = 0$

   $(\mathbf{u} \times \mathbf{v}) \cdot \mathbf{v} = 0$

_____   15.   Find the area of the parallelogram that has the vectors as adjacent sides.

$u = -5i + 10j + 15k$

$v = 10i + 6j + 16k$

a.   Area = $2\sqrt{1315}$ square units

b.   Area = $10\sqrt{409}$ square units

c.   Area = $\sqrt{69730}$ square units

d.   Area = $30\sqrt{83}$ square units

e.   Area = $\sqrt{57930}$ square units

_____   16.   Use the triple scalar product to find the volume of the parallelepiped having adjacent edges $u, v,$ and w.

$u = 5i + 5j$

$v = 5j + 5k$

$w = 5i + 5k$

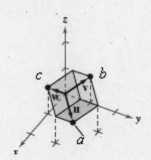

$a = (5,5,0), b = (0,5,5), c = (5,0,5)$

a.   Volume = 248 cubic units

b.   Volume = 250 cubic units

c.   Volume = 249   cubic units

d.   Volume = 252 cubic units

e.   Volume = 251 cubic units

_____   17.   Both the magnitude and direction of the force on a crankshaft change as the crank-shaft rotates. Vectors representing the position of the crank and the force are

$V = 0.22\left(-\cos 30° j - \sin 30° k\right)$ and $F = -2000k$ respectively. The magnitude of the torque on the

crank is given by $\|V \times F\|$, find the magnitude of the torque on the crank shaft using the position and data shown in the figure.

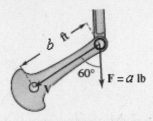

$a = 2000, b = 0.22$

a. $2000\sqrt{3}$ ft-lb
b. $440\sqrt{2}$ ft-lb
c. $220\sqrt{2}$ ft-lb
d. $440\sqrt{3}$ ft-lb
e. $220\sqrt{3}$ ft-lb

_____   18.   Use the vectors **u** and **v** to find $u \cdot (u \times v)$.

$u = 6i - j + 7k \quad v = 5i + 5j - k$

a. $u \cdot (u \times v) = 10$
b. $u \cdot (u \times v) = 0$
c. $u \cdot (u \times v) = 9$
d. $u \cdot (u \times v) = -9$
e. $u \cdot (u \times v) = -10$

_____   19.   Find the area of the parallelogram that has the vectors as adjacent sides.
$u = 3i - 5j + 3k, \quad v = i - 3j + 5k$
a. $\sqrt{33}$
b.   26
c.   2
d.   18
e. $4\sqrt{26}$

_____   20.   Find a set of parametric equations for the line through the point and parallel to the specified vector or line. (For each line, write the direction numbers as integers.)

Point: $(1,0,1)$
Parallel to: $x = 3+7t, y = 5-5t, z = -7+3t$

a.   Parametric equations: $x = 1+7t, y = -5t, z = 1+3t$
b.   Parametric equations: $x = 1+7t, y = 1+3t, z = -5t$
c.   Parametric equations: $x = 1+3t, y = 1+7t, z = -5t$
d.   Parametric equations: $x = -5t, y = 1+7t, z = 1+3t$
e.   Parametric equations: $x = -5t, y = 1+3t, z = 1+7t$

_____   21.   Find the general form of the equation of the plane passing through the point and perpendicular to the specified vector or line.

Point: $(4,7,6)$
Perpendicular to: $\mathbf{n} = -4\mathbf{i}+\mathbf{j}-5\mathbf{k}$

a. $4x+y-5z+39 = 0$
b. $-4x+y-5z+39 = 0$
c. $-4x-y-5z-39 = 0$
d. $-4x+y-5z-39 = 0$
e. $-4x-y-5z+39 = 0$

_____   22.   Find a set of symmetric equations of the line that passes through the given points.

$(-2,8,15),(1,-2,16)$

a. $\dfrac{x+2}{3} = \dfrac{y-8}{-10} = \dfrac{z-15}{1}$

b. $\dfrac{x+2}{-10} = \dfrac{y-8}{1} = \dfrac{z-15}{3}$

c. $\dfrac{x+2}{3} = \dfrac{y+8}{-10} = \dfrac{z+15}{1}$

d. $\dfrac{x-2}{3} = \dfrac{y+8}{-10} = \dfrac{z+15}{1}$

e. $\dfrac{x-2}{3} = \dfrac{y-8}{-10} = \dfrac{z-15}{1}$

____ 23.   Find a set of parametric equations of the line.

Passes through $(3,-5,-5)$ and is parallel to $\mathbf{v} = \langle 4,-6,2 \rangle$.

a. $x = 3 - 4t$

$y = -5 - 6t$

$z = -5 - 2t$

b. $x = 3 + 4t$

$y = -5 - 6t$

$z = -5 + 2t$

c. $x = 3 + 4t$

$y = -5 + 6t$

$z = -5 + 2t$

d. $x = 3 + 4t$

$y = -5 - 6t$

$z = -5 - 2t$

e. $x = 3 - 4t$

$y = -5 - 6t$

$z = -5 + 2t$

____ 24.   Determine whether the planes are parallel, orthogonal, or neither.
$5x + 2y + 2z = -2$
$-5x - 6y + 2z = -2$
a. parallel
b. neither
c. orthogonal

____   25.   Find the general form of the equation of the plane passing through the three points.

$(0,0,0)$, $(2,3,4)$,$(-6,7,7)$

a. $-7x - 32y + 38z = 0$
b. $-7x + 38y - 32z = 0$
c. $-7x + 38y + 32z = 0$
d. $-7x - 38y + 32z = 0$
e. $-7x - 38y - 32z = 0$

Ch 11 Form B
Answer Section

1.	ANS:	A	PTS:	1	REF:	11.1.17
2.	ANS:	D	PTS:	1	REF:	11.1.24
3.	ANS:	E	PTS:	1	REF:	11.1.34
4.	ANS:	C	PTS:	1	REF:	11.1.41
5.	ANS:	B	PTS:	1	REF:	11.1.51
6.	ANS:	B	PTS:	1	REF:	11.1.78a
7.	ANS:	D	PTS:	1	REF:	11.2.18
8.	ANS:	A	PTS:	1	REF:	11.2.28
9.	ANS:	B	PTS:	1	REF:	11.2.37
10.	ANS:	C	PTS:	1	REF:	11.2.9c
11.	ANS:	C	PTS:	1	REF:	11.2.31
12.	ANS:	B	PTS:	1	REF:	11.2.41
13.	ANS:	A	PTS:	1	REF:	11.3.12
14.	ANS:	D	PTS:	1	REF:	11.3.29
15.	ANS:	D	PTS:	1	REF:	11.3.40
16.	ANS:	B	PTS:	1	REF:	11.3.55
17.	ANS:	E	PTS:	1	REF:	11.3.62
18.	ANS:	B	PTS:	1	REF:	11.3.19
19.	ANS:	E	PTS:	1	REF:	11.3.39
20.	ANS:	A	PTS:	1	REF:	11.4.10a
21.	ANS:	B	PTS:	1	REF:	11.4.23
22.	ANS:	A	PTS:	1	REF:	11.4.13b
23.	ANS:	B	PTS:	1	REF:	11.4.45
24.	ANS:	B	PTS:	1	REF:	11.4.39
25.	ANS:	D	PTS:	1	REF:	11.4.27

Ch 11 Form C

_____ 1.   Determine whether **u** and **v** are parallel, orthogonal, or neither.

$\mathbf{u} = \langle 4,-3,-8 \rangle, v = \langle -6,6,4 \rangle$

a. orthogonal
b. neither
c. parallel

_____ 2.   Find the coordinates of the point.

The point is located seven units in front of the yz-plane, two units to the left of the xz-plane, and one units below the xy-plane.

a. $x = 7,\ y = -2,\ z = 7$
b. $x = -2,\ y = 7,\ z = 7$
c. $x = 7,\ y = -2,\ z = -1$
d. $x = -2,\ y = 7,\ z = -1$
e. $x = -2,\ y = -2,\ z = -1$

_____ 3.   Determine the octant(s) in which (x,y,z) is located so that the condition(s) is (are) satisfied.

$xy < -3$

a. Octant II
b. Octants I, II, III, IV
c. Octants II, IV, VI, VIII
d. Octants II, VI, VIII
e. Octants I, II, III

_____ 4.   Find the distance between the points.

$(8,-7,5),(-4,-1,5)$

a. $\sqrt{182}$ units
b. $6\sqrt{5}$ units
c. $\sqrt{181}$ units
d. $\sqrt{183}$ units
e. $2\sqrt{46}$ units

_____ 5.   Determine whether the triangle is a right triangle, an isosceles triangle, or neither.

$(8,4,6),(10,2,5),(6,6,5)$

a. Isosceles triangle
b. Right triangle
c. Neither Isosceles nor Right

_____ 6.   Find the midpoint of the line segment joining the points.

$(5,-1,4),(5,-2,-1)$

a. $(\frac{3}{2}, 5, -\frac{3}{2})$

b. $(-\frac{3}{2}, \frac{3}{2}, 5)$

c. $(\frac{3}{2}, -\frac{3}{2}, 5)$

d. $(5, -\frac{3}{2}, \frac{3}{2})$

e. $(-\frac{3}{2}, 5, \frac{3}{2})$

_____ 7.   Use the relationship $(x_2,y_2,z_2) = (2x_m - x_1, 2y_m - y_1, 2z_m - z_1)$ to find the coordinates of the endpoint of a line segment if the coordinates of the other endpoint and the midpoint are $(3,0,2)$ and $(3,6,7)$, respectively.

a. $(3,12,-12)$
b. $(3,12,12)$
c. $(-3,-12,-12)$
d. $(-3,12,12)$
e. $(3,-12,12)$

_____ 8.   Find the magnitude of **v**.

$\mathbf{v} = \langle 6,7,6 \rangle$

a. $\|\mathbf{v}\| = 11$
b. $\|\mathbf{v}\| = \sqrt{87}$
c. $\|\mathbf{v}\| = \sqrt{85}$
d. $\|\mathbf{v}\| = \sqrt{123}$
e. $\|\mathbf{v}\| = 6\sqrt{2}$

_____ 9.   Find a unit vector in the direction of **u**

$\mathbf{u} = 10\mathbf{i} + 5\mathbf{j} - \mathbf{k}$

a.
$$\frac{\mathbf{u}}{\|\mathbf{u}\|} = \frac{\sqrt{126}}{126}\left(10\mathbf{i} + 5\mathbf{j} - \mathbf{k}\right)$$

b.
$$\frac{\mathbf{u}}{\|\mathbf{u}\|} = -\frac{126\sqrt{126}}{126}\left(10\mathbf{i} + 5\mathbf{j} + \mathbf{k}\right)$$

c.
$$\frac{\mathbf{u}}{\|\mathbf{u}\|} = -\frac{\sqrt{126}}{126}\left(10\mathbf{i} + 5\mathbf{j} - \mathbf{k}\right)$$

d.
$$\frac{\mathbf{u}}{\|\mathbf{u}\|} = \frac{\sqrt{126}}{126}\left(10\mathbf{i} + 5\mathbf{j} + \mathbf{k}\right)$$

e.
$$\frac{\mathbf{u}}{\|\mathbf{u}\|} = \frac{126\sqrt{126}}{126}\left(10\mathbf{i} + 5\mathbf{j} - \mathbf{k}\right)$$

_____ 10.   Find the angle θ between the vectors. Round your answer to two decimal places.

$\mathbf{u} = 13\mathbf{j} - 30\mathbf{k}$

$\mathbf{v} = 15\mathbf{i} - 10\mathbf{k}$

a. $\theta \approx 61.40°$
b. $\theta \approx 57.40°$
c. $\theta \approx 60.40°$
d. $\theta \approx 58.40°$
e. $\theta \approx 59.40°$

_____ 11.   Find the vector **z**, given $\mathbf{u} = \langle 8, -7, -9 \rangle$ and $\mathbf{v} = \langle -8, -2, 5 \rangle$, and $\mathbf{w} = \langle 56, 13, -80 \rangle$.
$3\mathbf{u} - 5\mathbf{v} + 4\mathbf{z} = \mathbf{w}$
a. $\langle 2, -6, -7 \rangle$

b. $\langle -1, -6, -6 \rangle$

c. $\langle 6, -2, -7 \rangle$

d. $\langle -8, 24, -28 \rangle$

e. $\langle -2, 6, -7 \rangle$

_____ 12. Find the angle between the vectors **u** and **v.** Express your answer in degrees and round to the nearest tenth of a degree.

u = –2**i** –3**j** –3**k**,   **v** = –2**i** –2**j** –7**k**

a. 41.2°

b. 61.1°

c. 48.8°

d. 28.9°

e. 90°

_____ 13. Use the vectors **u** and **v** to find $\mathbf{v} \times (\mathbf{u} \times \mathbf{u})$.

$$\mathbf{u} = 6\mathbf{i} - \mathbf{j} + 7\mathbf{k} \quad \mathbf{v} = 5\mathbf{i} + 5\mathbf{j} - \mathbf{k}$$

a. $\mathbf{v} \times (\mathbf{u} \times \mathbf{u}) = -10$

b. $\mathbf{v} \times (\mathbf{u} \times \mathbf{u}) = 0$

c. $\mathbf{v} \times (\mathbf{u} \times \mathbf{u}) = 9$

d. $\mathbf{v} \times (\mathbf{u} \times \mathbf{u}) = -9$

e. $\mathbf{v} \times (\mathbf{u} \times \mathbf{u}) = 10$

_____ 14. Find $\mathbf{u} \times \mathbf{v}$ and show that it is orthogonal to both $\mathbf{u}$ and $\mathbf{v}$.

$\mathbf{u} = \mathbf{i} - 2\mathbf{k}$

$\mathbf{v} = -\mathbf{j} + \mathbf{k}$

a. $\mathbf{u} \times \mathbf{v} = 2\mathbf{i} - \mathbf{j} - \mathbf{k}$

$(\mathbf{u} \times \mathbf{v}) \cdot \mathbf{u} = 0$

$(\mathbf{u} \times \mathbf{v}) \cdot \mathbf{v} = 0$

b. $\mathbf{u} \times \mathbf{v} = -2\mathbf{i} + \mathbf{j} + \mathbf{k}$

$(\mathbf{u} \times \mathbf{v}) \cdot \mathbf{u} = 0$

$(\mathbf{u} \times \mathbf{v}) \cdot \mathbf{v} = 0$

c. $\mathbf{u} \times \mathbf{v} = -2\mathbf{i} - \mathbf{j} + \mathbf{k}$

$(\mathbf{u} \times \mathbf{v}) \cdot \mathbf{u} = 0$

$(\mathbf{u} \times \mathbf{v}) \cdot \mathbf{v} = 0$

d. $\mathbf{u} \times \mathbf{v} = -2\mathbf{i} + \mathbf{j} - \mathbf{k}$

$(\mathbf{u} \times \mathbf{v}) \cdot \mathbf{u} = 0$

$(\mathbf{u} \times \mathbf{v}) \cdot \mathbf{v} = 0$

e. $\mathbf{u} \times \mathbf{v} = -2\mathbf{i} - \mathbf{j} - \mathbf{k}$

$(\mathbf{u} \times \mathbf{v}) \cdot \mathbf{u} = 0$

$(\mathbf{u} \times \mathbf{v}) \cdot \mathbf{v} = 0$

_____ 15. Find the area of the parallelogram that has the vectors as adjacent sides.

$\mathbf{u} = \langle 14, 14, -16 \rangle$

$\mathbf{v} = \langle 14, 0, 16 \rangle$

a. Area $= 4\sqrt{14,959}$ square units
b. Area $= 28\sqrt{271}$ square units
c. Area $= 2\sqrt{217}$ square units
d. Area $= 84\sqrt{41}$ square units
e. Area $= 4\sqrt{2,443}$ square units

_____   16.   Use the triple scalar product to find the volume of the parallelepiped having adjacent edges **u**, **v**, and **w**.

$$\mathbf{u} = \langle 9, 9, 0 \rangle$$

$$\mathbf{v} = \langle 0, 0, -9 \rangle$$

$$\mathbf{w} = \langle 9, 0, 9 \rangle$$

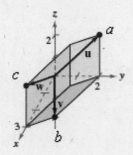

$$a = (9, 9, 0), \; b = (0, 0, -9), \; c = (9, 0, 9)$$

a.   Volume = 730   cubic units
b.   Volume = 733 cubic units
c.   Volume = 731 cubic units
d.   Volume = 729 cubic units
e.   Volume = 732 cubic units

_____ 17.   Find $\mathbf{u} \times \mathbf{v}$ and show that it is orthogonal to both $\mathbf{u}$ and $\mathbf{v}$.

$$\mathbf{u} = \langle 3, -1, 4 \rangle \quad \mathbf{v} = \langle 2, 2, -1 \rangle$$

a. $\mathbf{u} \times \mathbf{v} = \langle 7, -11, 8 \rangle$

    $(\mathbf{u} \times \mathbf{v}) \cdot \mathbf{u} = 0$

    $(\mathbf{u} \times \mathbf{v}) \cdot \mathbf{v} = 0$

b. $\mathbf{u} \times \mathbf{v} = \langle -7, 11, 8 \rangle$

    $(\mathbf{u} \times \mathbf{v}) \cdot \mathbf{u} = 0$

    $(\mathbf{u} \times \mathbf{v}) \cdot \mathbf{v} = 0$

c. $\mathbf{u} \times \mathbf{v} = \langle 7, 11, 8 \rangle$

    $(\mathbf{u} \times \mathbf{v}) \cdot \mathbf{u} \neq 0$

    $(\mathbf{u} \times \mathbf{v}) \cdot \mathbf{v} \neq 0$

d. $\mathbf{u} \times \mathbf{v} = \langle -7, 11, -8 \rangle$

    $(\mathbf{u} \times \mathbf{v}) \cdot \mathbf{u} = 0$

    $(\mathbf{u} \times \mathbf{v}) \cdot \mathbf{v} = 0$

e. $\mathbf{u} \times \mathbf{v} = \langle 7, -11, -8 \rangle$

    $(\mathbf{u} \times \mathbf{v}) \cdot \mathbf{u} = 0$

    $(\mathbf{u} \times \mathbf{v}) \cdot \mathbf{v} = 0$

_____   18.   Verify that the points are the vertices of a parallelogram.

$A(5,5,5), B(6,7,8), C(10,9,6), D(11,11,9)$

a. $\overrightarrow{AB} = \langle 1,2,3 \rangle$ is parallel to $\overrightarrow{AC} = \langle 5,4,1 \rangle$.

   $\overrightarrow{BD} = \langle 5,4,1 \rangle$ is parallel to $\overrightarrow{CD} = \langle 1,2,3 \rangle$.

   Opposites are parallel and same length. So ABCD form a parallelogram.

b. $\overrightarrow{AB} = \langle 1,2,3 \rangle$ is not parallel to $\overrightarrow{AC} = \langle 5,4,1 \rangle$.

   $\overrightarrow{BD} = \langle 5,4,1 \rangle$ is not parallel to $\overrightarrow{CD} = \langle 1,2,3 \rangle$.

   Opposites are not parallel and do not have same length. So ABCD form a parallelogram.

c. $\overrightarrow{AB} = \langle 1,2,3 \rangle$ is not parallel to $\overrightarrow{CD} = \langle 1,2,3 \rangle$.

   $\overrightarrow{BD} = \langle 5,4,1 \rangle$ is not parallel to $\overrightarrow{AC} = \langle 5,4,1 \rangle$.

   Opposites are not parallel and same length. So ABCD form a parallelogram.

d. $\overrightarrow{AB} = \langle 1,2,3 \rangle$ is perpendicular to $\overrightarrow{CD} = \langle 1,2,3 \rangle$.

   $\overrightarrow{BD} = \langle 5,4,1 \rangle$ is perpendicular to $\overrightarrow{AC} = \langle 5,4,1 \rangle$.

   Opposites are perpendicular and same length. So ABCD form a parallelogram.

e. $\overrightarrow{AB} = \langle 1,2,3 \rangle$ is parallel to $\overrightarrow{CD} = \langle 1,2,3 \rangle$.

   $\overrightarrow{BD} = \langle 5,4,1 \rangle$ is parallel to $\overrightarrow{AC} = \langle 5,4,1 \rangle$.

   Opposites are parallel and same length. So ABCD form a parallelogram.

_____   19.   Find the area of the triangle with the given vertices.
$(5, -1, 2), (7, -4, -2), (2, -6, 3)$

a. $\dfrac{3\sqrt{110}}{2}$

b. $\dfrac{3\sqrt{110}}{4}$

c. 0

d. $3\sqrt{110}$

e. 5

_____ 20.   Find a set of symmetric equations for the line through the point and parallel to the specified vector or line.

Point: $(3, -6, 1)$

Parallel to: $\mathbf{v} = \langle 7, -3, -10 \rangle$

a.
  Symmetric equations: $\dfrac{x-3}{7} = \dfrac{y+6}{-3} = \dfrac{z-1}{-10}$

b.
  Symmetric equations: $\dfrac{x-3}{-10} = \dfrac{y+6}{7} = \dfrac{z-1}{-3}$

c.
  Symmetric equations: $\dfrac{x-3}{7} = \dfrac{y-6}{-3} = \dfrac{z+1}{-10}$

d.
  Symmetric equations: $\dfrac{x+3}{7} = \dfrac{y-6}{-3} = \dfrac{z-1}{-10}$

e.
  Symmetric equations: $\dfrac{x-3}{-3} = \dfrac{y+6}{-10} = \dfrac{z-1}{7}$

_____ 21.   Find the general form of the equation of the plane passing through the point and perpendicular to the specified vector or line.

Point: $(3, 0, 0)$

Perpendicular to: $x = 3 - t, y = 2 - 5t, z = 4 + t$

a. $-x - 5y - z - 3 = 0$
b. $-x - 5y + z = 0$
c. $-x - 5y - z + 3 = 0$
d. $-x - 5y + z + 3 = 0$
e. $-x - 5y + z - 3 = 0$

_____ 22.   Find the general form of the equation of the plane with the given characteristics.

Passes through $(8, 4, 4)$ and is parallel to the yz-plane

a. $x = 0$
b. $-8x = 0$
c. $x + 8 = 0$
d. $8x = 0$
e. $x - 8 = 0$

_____ 23. Find the general form of the equation of the plane passing through the point and perpendicular to the specified line. [Be sure to reduce the coefficients in your answer to lowest terms by dividing out any common factor.]

$$(-3, 8, -4), \begin{array}{l} x = 3 + t \\ y = -1 - 3t \\ z = -6 + 3t \end{array}$$

a. $3x - 8y + 4z + 39 = 0$
b. $3x - 8y + 4z - 39 = 0$
c. $x - 3y + 3z - 39 = 0$
d. $x - 3y + 3z + 39 = 0$
e. $x - 3y + 3z = 0$

_____ 24. Determine whether the planes are parallel, orthogonal, or neither.
$5x - 2y - 4z = 6$
$-15x + 6y + 12z = -16$

a. orthogonal
b. parallel
c. neither

_____ 25. Determine whether the planes are parallel, orthogonal, or neither.

$x - 4y - z = 3$

$2x - 8y - 2z = -7$

a. Neither
b. Orthogonal
c. Parallel

Ch 11 Form C
Answer Section

1.	ANS:	B	PTS:	1	REF:	11.2.41
2.	ANS:	C	PTS:	1	REF:	11.1.18
3.	ANS:	C	PTS:	1	REF:	11.1.25
4.	ANS:	B	PTS:	1	REF:	11.1.35
5.	ANS:	A	PTS:	1	REF:	11.1.42
6.	ANS:	D	PTS:	1	REF:	11.1.52
7.	ANS:	B	PTS:	1	REF:	11.1.86
8.	ANS:	A	PTS:	1	REF:	11.2.19
9.	ANS:	A	PTS:	1	REF:	11.2.29a
10.	ANS:	E	PTS:	1	REF:	11.2.38
11.	ANS:	E	PTS:	1	REF:	11.2.16
12.	ANS:	D	PTS:	1	REF:	11.2.38
13.	ANS:	B	PTS:	1	REF:	11.3.14
14.	ANS:	E	PTS:	1	REF:	11.3.30
15.	ANS:	D	PTS:	1	REF:	11.3.42
16.	ANS:	D	PTS:	1	REF:	11.3.57
17.	ANS:	B	PTS:	1	REF:	11.3.21
18.	ANS:	E	PTS:	1	REF:	11.3.44a
19.	ANS:	A	PTS:	1	REF:	11.3.48
20.	ANS:	A	PTS:	1	REF:	11.4.6b
21.	ANS:	D	PTS:	1	REF:	11.4.25
22.	ANS:	E	PTS:	1	REF:	11.4.32
23.	ANS:	D	PTS:	1	REF:	11.4.25
24.	ANS:	B	PTS:	1	REF:	11.4.40
25.	ANS:	C	PTS:	1	REF:	11.4.40

Ch 11 Form D

_____   1.   Determine whether **u** and **v** are parallel, orthogonal, or neither.
$\mathbf{u} = \langle -2, -3, 3 \rangle, \mathbf{v} = \langle 7, 2, 9 \rangle$
a.   neither
b.   parallel
c.   orthogonal

_____   2.   Find the coordinates of the point.

The point is located seven units in front of the yz-plane, two units to the left of the xz-plane, and one units below the xy-plane.

a. $x = -2, y = -2, z = -1$
b. $x = -2, y = 7, z = -1$
c. $x = 7, y = -2, z = 7$
d. $x = 7, y = -2, z = -1$
e. $x = -2, y = 7, z = 7$

_____   3.   Determine the octant(s) in which (x, y, z) is located so that the condition(s) is (are) satisfied.

$xy < -2$

a.   Octants I, II, III
b.   Octants II, IV, VI, VIII
c.   Octants II, VI, VIII
d.   Octants I, II, III, IV
e.   Octant II

_____   4.   Find the distance between the points.

$(7, -7, 1), (-1, -5, 7)$

a. $6\sqrt{3}$ units
b. $\sqrt{107}$ units
c. $2\sqrt{26}$ units
d. $\sqrt{105}$ units
e. $\sqrt{106}$ units

_____ 5.   Determine whether the triangle is a right triangle, an isosceles triangle, or neither.

$(8,4,4),(10,2,3),(6,6,3)$

a. Neither Isosceles nor Right
b. Isosceles triangle
c. Right triangle

_____ 6.   Find the midpoint of the line segment joining the points.

$(7,-4,3),(7,-5,-2)$

a. $(7, -\dfrac{9}{2}, \dfrac{1}{2})$

b. $(-\dfrac{9}{2}, \dfrac{1}{2}, 7)$

c. $(\dfrac{1}{2}, 7, -\dfrac{9}{2})$

d. $(\dfrac{1}{2}, -\dfrac{9}{2}, 7)$

e. $(-\dfrac{9}{2}, 7, \dfrac{1}{2})$

_____ 7.   Use the relationship $\left(x_2, y_2, z_2\right) = \left(2x_m - x_1, 2y_m - y_1, 2z_m - z_1\right)$ to find the coordinates of the endpoint of a line segment if the coordinates of the other endpoint and the midpoint are $(4,0,1)$ and $(3,6,4)$, respectively.

a. $(2, -12, 7)$
b. $(2, 12, -7)$
c. $(-2, 12, 7)$
d. $(-2, -12, -7)$
e. $(2, 12, 7)$

_____ 8.   Find the magnitude of **v**.

$\mathbf{v} = \langle 8, 9, 8 \rangle$

a. $\| \mathbf{v} \| = \sqrt{211}$
b. $\| \mathbf{v} \| = \sqrt{145}$
c. $\| \mathbf{v} \| = \sqrt{209}$
d. $\| \mathbf{v} \| = 8\sqrt{2}$
e. $\| \mathbf{v} \| = 7\sqrt{3}$

____ 9.   Find a unit vector in the direction of **u**

$$\mathbf{u} = 7\mathbf{i} + 2\mathbf{j} - \mathbf{k}$$

a.
$$\frac{\mathbf{u}}{\|\mathbf{u}\|} = \frac{54\sqrt{54}}{54}(7\mathbf{i} + 2\mathbf{j} - \mathbf{k})$$

b.
$$\frac{\mathbf{u}}{\|\mathbf{u}\|} = -\frac{54\sqrt{54}}{54}(7\mathbf{i} + 2\mathbf{j} + \mathbf{k})$$

c.
$$\frac{\mathbf{u}}{\|\mathbf{u}\|} = -\frac{\sqrt{54}}{54}(7\mathbf{i} + 2\mathbf{j} - \mathbf{k})$$

d.
$$\frac{\mathbf{u}}{\|\mathbf{u}\|} = \frac{\sqrt{54}}{54}(7\mathbf{i} + 2\mathbf{j} + \mathbf{k})$$

e.
$$\frac{\mathbf{u}}{\|\mathbf{u}\|} = \frac{\sqrt{54}}{54}(7\mathbf{i} + 2\mathbf{j} - \mathbf{k})$$

____ 10.   Find the angle θ between the vectors. Round your answer to two decimal places.

$$\mathbf{u} = 14\mathbf{j} - 32\mathbf{k}$$

$$\mathbf{v} = 16\mathbf{i} - 11\mathbf{k}$$

a. $\theta \approx 57.73°$
b. $\theta \approx 59.73°$
c. $\theta \approx 58.73°$
d. $\theta \approx 56.73°$
e. $\theta \approx 60.73°$

____ 11.   Find the vector **z**, given $\mathbf{u} = \langle 7, 8, -5 \rangle$ and $\mathbf{v} = \langle -9, 7, -2 \rangle$, and $\mathbf{w} = \langle -39, 6, 9 \rangle$.
$$-\mathbf{u} + 4\mathbf{v} + 2\mathbf{z} = \mathbf{w}$$

a. $\langle -7, 2, 6 \rangle$

b. $\langle 4, -14, 12 \rangle$

c. $\langle 3, 7, 7 \rangle$

d. $\langle 2, -7, 6 \rangle$

e. $\langle -2, 7, 6 \rangle$

____   12.   Find the angle between the vectors **u** and **v.** Express your answer in degrees and round to the nearest tenth of a degree.

u = –2**i** –7**j** –4**k**,   **v** = 5**i** 8**j** 5**k**

a. 165.9°
b. 90°
c. 44.1°
d. 75.9°
e. 45.9°

____   13.   Use the vectors **u** and **v** to find $\mathbf{v} \times (\mathbf{u} \times \mathbf{u})$.

$\mathbf{u} = 5\mathbf{i} - \mathbf{j} + 6\mathbf{k}$ $\mathbf{v} = 4\mathbf{i} + 4\mathbf{j} - \mathbf{k}$

a. $\mathbf{v} \times (\mathbf{u} \times \mathbf{u}) = 7$
b. $\mathbf{v} \times (\mathbf{u} \times \mathbf{u}) = -7$
c. $\mathbf{v} \times (\mathbf{u} \times \mathbf{u}) = -8$
d. $\mathbf{v} \times (\mathbf{u} \times \mathbf{u}) = 0$
e. $\mathbf{v} \times (\mathbf{u} \times \mathbf{u}) = 8$

_____ 14.   Find $\mathbf{u} \times \mathbf{v}$ and show that it is orthogonal to both $\mathbf{u}$ and $\mathbf{v}$.

$\mathbf{u} = \mathbf{i} - 5\mathbf{k}$

$\mathbf{v} = -\mathbf{j} + \mathbf{k}$

a. $\mathbf{u} \times \mathbf{v} = -5\mathbf{i} - \mathbf{j} + \mathbf{k}$

$(\mathbf{u} \times \mathbf{v}) \cdot \mathbf{u} = 0$

$(\mathbf{u} \times \mathbf{v}) \cdot \mathbf{v} = 0$

b. $\mathbf{u} \times \mathbf{v} = -5\mathbf{i} - \mathbf{j} - \mathbf{k}$

$(\mathbf{u} \times \mathbf{v}) \cdot \mathbf{u} = 0$

$(\mathbf{u} \times \mathbf{v}) \cdot \mathbf{v} = 0$

c. $\mathbf{u} \times \mathbf{v} = -5\mathbf{i} + \mathbf{j} + \mathbf{k}$

$(\mathbf{u} \times \mathbf{v}) \cdot \mathbf{u} = 0$

$(\mathbf{u} \times \mathbf{v}) \cdot \mathbf{v} = 0$

d. $\mathbf{u} \times \mathbf{v} = 5\mathbf{i} - \mathbf{j} - \mathbf{k}$

$(\mathbf{u} \times \mathbf{v}) \cdot \mathbf{u} = 0$

$(\mathbf{u} \times \mathbf{v}) \cdot \mathbf{v} = 0$

e. $\mathbf{u} \times \mathbf{v} = -5\mathbf{i} + \mathbf{j} - \mathbf{k}$

$(\mathbf{u} \times \mathbf{v}) \cdot \mathbf{u} = 0$

$(\mathbf{u} \times \mathbf{v}) \cdot \mathbf{v} = 0$

_____ 15.   Find the area of the parallelogram that has the vectors as adjacent sides.

$\mathbf{u} = \langle 10, 10, -12 \rangle$

$\mathbf{v} = \langle 10, 0, 12 \rangle$

a. Area $= 2\sqrt{16,930}$ square units

b. Area $= 2\sqrt{115}$ square units

c. Area $= 20\sqrt{155}$ square units

d. Area $= 20\sqrt{205}$ square units

e. Area $= 2\sqrt{2,590}$ square units

_____ 16.   Use the triple scalar product to find the volume of the parallelepiped having adjacent edges **u**, **v**, and **w**.

$$\mathbf{u} = \langle 5, 5, 0 \rangle$$

$$\mathbf{v} = \langle 0, 0, -5 \rangle$$

$$\mathbf{w} = \langle 5, 0, 5 \rangle$$

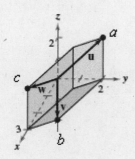

$$a = (5, 5, 0), b = (0, 0, -5), c = (5, 0, 5)$$

a.   Volume = 125 cubic units
b.   Volume = 129 cubic units
c.   Volume = 127 cubic units
d.   Volume = 128 cubic units
e.   Volume = 126   cubic units

_____ 17.   Find $\mathbf{u} \times \mathbf{v}$ and show that it is orthogonal to both $\mathbf{u}$ and $\mathbf{v}$.

$$\mathbf{u} = \langle 5, -1, 6 \rangle \quad \mathbf{v} = \langle 4, 4, -1 \rangle$$

a. $\mathbf{u} \times \mathbf{v} = \langle 23, -29, -24 \rangle$

   $(\mathbf{u} \times \mathbf{v}) \cdot \mathbf{u} = 0$

   $(\mathbf{u} \times \mathbf{v}) \cdot \mathbf{v} = 0$

b. $\mathbf{u} \times \mathbf{v} = \langle -23, 29, 24 \rangle$

   $(\mathbf{u} \times \mathbf{v}) \cdot \mathbf{u} = 0$

   $(\mathbf{u} \times \mathbf{v}) \cdot \mathbf{v} = 0$

c. $\mathbf{u} \times \mathbf{v} = \langle -23, 29, -24 \rangle$

   $(\mathbf{u} \times \mathbf{v}) \cdot \mathbf{u} = 0$

   $(\mathbf{u} \times \mathbf{v}) \cdot \mathbf{v} = 0$

d. $\mathbf{u} \times \mathbf{v} = \langle 23, -29, 24 \rangle$

   $(\mathbf{u} \times \mathbf{v}) \cdot \mathbf{u} = 0$

   $(\mathbf{u} \times \mathbf{v}) \cdot \mathbf{v} = 0$

e. $\mathbf{u} \times \mathbf{v} = \langle 23, 29, 24 \rangle$

   $(\mathbf{u} \times \mathbf{v}) \cdot \mathbf{u} \neq 0$

   $(\mathbf{u} \times \mathbf{v}) \cdot \mathbf{v} \neq 0$

_____   18.   Verify that the points are the vertices of a parallelogram.

$A(5,5,5), B(6,7,8), C(10,9,6), D(11,11,9)$

a. $\overrightarrow{AB} = \langle 1,2,3 \rangle$ is perpendicular to $\overrightarrow{CD} = \langle 1,2,3 \rangle$.

$\overrightarrow{BD} = \langle 5,4,1 \rangle$ is perpendicular to $\overrightarrow{AC} = \langle 5,4,1 \rangle$.

Opposites are perpendicular and same length. So ABCD form a parallelogram.

b. $\overrightarrow{AB} = \langle 1,2,3 \rangle$ is not parallel to $\overrightarrow{CD} = \langle 1,2,3 \rangle$.

$\overrightarrow{BD} = \langle 5,4,1 \rangle$ is not parallel to $\overrightarrow{AC} = \langle 5,4,1 \rangle$.

Opposites are not parallel and same length. So ABCD form a parallelogram.

c. $\overrightarrow{AB} = \langle 1,2,3 \rangle$ is parallel to $\overrightarrow{CD} = \langle 1,2,3 \rangle$.

$\overrightarrow{BD} = \langle 5,4,1 \rangle$ is parallel to $\overrightarrow{AC} = \langle 5,4,1 \rangle$.

Opposites are parallel and same length. So ABCD form a parallelogram.

d. $\overrightarrow{AB} = \langle 1,2,3 \rangle$ is not parallel to $\overrightarrow{AC} = \langle 5,4,1 \rangle$.

$\overrightarrow{BD} = \langle 5,4,1 \rangle$ is not parallel to $\overrightarrow{CD} = \langle 1,2,3 \rangle$.

Opposites are not parallel and do not have same length. So ABCD form a parallelogram.

e. $\overrightarrow{AB} = \langle 1,2,3 \rangle$ is parallel to $\overrightarrow{AC} = \langle 5,4,1 \rangle$.

$\overrightarrow{BD} = \langle 5,4,1 \rangle$ is parallel to $\overrightarrow{CD} = \langle 1,2,3 \rangle$.

Opposites are parallel and same length. So ABCD form a parallelogram.

_____   19.   Find the area of the triangle with the given vertices.
$(5, 1, 5), (4, -1, 9), (6, -4, 3)$

a.   1

b. $\dfrac{\sqrt{629}}{4}$

c. $\dfrac{\sqrt{629}}{2}$

d.   0

e. $\sqrt{629}$

_____ 20.   Find a set of symmetric equations for the line through the point and parallel to the specified vector or line.

Point: $(7, -6, 3)$

Parallel to: $\mathbf{v} = \langle 3, -6, -6 \rangle$

a.
Symmetric equations: $\dfrac{x+7}{3} = \dfrac{y-6}{-6} = \dfrac{z-3}{-6}$

b.
Symmetric equations: $\dfrac{x-7}{-6} = \dfrac{y+6}{3} = \dfrac{z-3}{-6}$

c.
Symmetric equations: $\dfrac{x-7}{-6} = \dfrac{y+6}{-6} = \dfrac{z-3}{3}$

d.
Symmetric equations: $\dfrac{x-7}{3} = \dfrac{y+6}{-6} = \dfrac{z-3}{-6}$

e.
Symmetric equations: $\dfrac{x-7}{3} = \dfrac{y-6}{-6} = \dfrac{z+3}{-6}$

_____ 21.   Find the general form of the equation of the plane passing through the point and perpendicular to the specified vector or line.

Point: $(2, 0, 0)$

Perpendicular to: $x = 3 - t, y = 2 - 2t, z = 4 + t$

a. $-x - 2y - z + 2 = 0$
b. $-x - 2y + z + 2 = 0$
c. $-x - 2y - z - 2 = 0$
d. $-x - 2y + z - 2 = 0$
e. $-x - 2y + z = 0$

_____ 22.   Find the general form of the equation of the plane with the given characteristics.

Passes through $(3, 2, 3)$ and is parallel to the yz-plane

a. $x - 3 = 0$
b. $x + 3 = 0$
c. $x = 0$
d. $3x = 0$
e. $-3x = 0$

_____   23.   Find the general form of the equation of the plane passing through the point and perpendicular to the specified line. [Be sure to reduce the coefficients in your answer to lowest terms by dividing out any common factor.]

$$x = 3 - 4t$$

$$(-5, -4, -2),\ y = -6 + 5t$$

$$z = -6 - 2t$$

a. $4x - 5y + 2z - 4 = 0$
b. $5x + 4y + 2z + 4 = 0$
c. $5x + 4y + 2z - 4 = 0$
d. $4x - 5y + 2z + 4 = 0$
e. $4x - 5y + 2z = 0$

_____   24.   Determine whether the planes are parallel, orthogonal, or neither.

$$x + y + 4z = 3$$
$$-3x - 3y - 12z = -7$$

a.   neither
b.   orthogonal
c.   parallel

_____   25.   Determine whether the planes are parallel, orthogonal, or neither.

$$x - 9y - z = 2$$

$$5x - 45y - 5z = -7$$

a.   Parallel
b.   Orthogonal
c.   Neither

Ch 11 Form D
Answer Section

1.	ANS:	A	PTS:	1	REF:	11.2.41
2.	ANS:	D	PTS:	1	REF:	11.1.18
3.	ANS:	B	PTS:	1	REF:	11.1.25
4.	ANS:	C	PTS:	1	REF:	11.1.35
5.	ANS:	B	PTS:	1	REF:	11.1.42
6.	ANS:	A	PTS:	1	REF:	11.1.52
7.	ANS:	E	PTS:	1	REF:	11.1.86
8.	ANS:	C	PTS:	1	REF:	11.2.19
9.	ANS:	E	PTS:	1	REF:	11.2.29a
10.	ANS:	C	PTS:	1	REF:	11.2.38
11.	ANS:	D	PTS:	1	REF:	11.2.16
12.	ANS:	A	PTS:	1	REF:	11.2.38
13.	ANS:	D	PTS:	1	REF:	11.3.14
14.	ANS:	B	PTS:	1	REF:	11.3.30
15.	ANS:	D	PTS:	1	REF:	11.3.42
16.	ANS:	A	PTS:	1	REF:	11.3.57
17.	ANS:	B	PTS:	1	REF:	11.3.21
18.	ANS:	C	PTS:	1	REF:	11.3.44a
19.	ANS:	C	PTS:	1	REF:	11.3.48
20.	ANS:	D	PTS:	1	REF:	11.4.6b
21.	ANS:	B	PTS:	1	REF:	11.4.25
22.	ANS:	A	PTS:	1	REF:	11.4.32
23.	ANS:	D	PTS:	1	REF:	11.4.25
24.	ANS:	C	PTS:	1	REF:	11.4.40
25.	ANS:	A	PTS:	1	REF:	11.4.40

Ch 11 Form E

_____ 1.   Determine whether the planes are parallel, orthogonal, or neither.
$x + y + 4z = 3$
$-3x - 3y - 12z = -7$
a. neither
b. orthogonal
c. parallel

_____ 2.   Find the coordinates of the point.

The point is located in the yz-plane, one unit to the right of the xz-plane, and three units above the xy-plane.

a. $x = 3,\ y = 0,\ z = 3$
b. $x = 1,\ y = 1,\ z = 3$
c. $x = 1,\ y = 0,\ z = 3$
d. $x = 0,\ y = 1,\ z = 1$
e. $x = 0,\ y = 1,\ z = 3$

_____ 3.   Find the distance between the points.

$(0,0,0), (5,2,6)$

a. 65 units
b. 67 units
c. $\sqrt{65}$ units
d. $\sqrt{67}$ units
e. $\sqrt{66}$ units

_____ 4.   Find the lengths of the sides of the triangle with the indicated vertices.

$(0,0,2), (-3,4,2), (0,4,0)$

a. $d1 = 2\sqrt{5},\ d2 = 2\sqrt{5},\ d3 = \sqrt{13}$
b. $d1 = 5,\ d2 = 2\sqrt{5},\ d3 = 5$
c. $d1 = 5,\ d2 = 2\sqrt{5},\ d3 = \sqrt{13}$
d. $d1 = 5,\ d2 = 5,\ d3 = \sqrt{13}$
e. $d1 = \sqrt{13},\ d2 = 2\sqrt{5},\ d3 = \sqrt{13}$

_____   5.   Find the midpoint of the line segment joining the points.

$(5, 5, -3), (2, 2, 2)$

a. $(-\dfrac{7}{2}, \dfrac{7}{2}, -\dfrac{1}{2})$

b. $(-\dfrac{1}{2}, -\dfrac{7}{2}, \dfrac{7}{2})$

c. $(\dfrac{7}{2}, -\dfrac{1}{2}, \dfrac{7}{2})$

d. $(-\dfrac{1}{2}, \dfrac{7}{2}, \dfrac{7}{2})$

e. $(\dfrac{7}{2}, \dfrac{7}{2}, -\dfrac{1}{2})$

_____   6.   Find the standard form of the equation of the sphere with the given characteristics.

Center: $(-1, 1, 5)$; radius: 5

a. $(x+1)^2 + (y+1)^2 + (z+5)^2 = 25$

b. $(x-1)^2 - (y-1)^2 - (z-5)^2 = 25$

c. $(x+1)^2 - (y+1)^2 - (z+5)^2 = 25$

d. $(x+1)^2 + (y-1)^2 + (z-5)^2 = 25$

e. $(x-1) + (y-1) + (z-5) = 25$

_____   7.   Determine the octant(s) in which (x,y,z) is located so that the conditions are satisfied.
$x > 0, y > 0, z > 0$
a.   octant V
b.   octant I
c.   octant III
d.   octant I or octant II
e.   octant VIII

____   8.   Find the magnitude of **v**.

$$\mathbf{v} = \langle 1, -5, 10 \rangle$$

a. $\| \mathbf{v} \| = 10\sqrt{2}$
b. $\| \mathbf{v} \| = 8\sqrt{2}$
c. $\| \mathbf{v} \| = 3\sqrt{14}$
d. $\| \mathbf{v} \| = 5\sqrt{5}$
e. $\| \mathbf{v} \| = 5\sqrt{2}$

____   9.   Find a unit vector in the direction of **u**.

$$\mathbf{u} = -3\mathbf{i} + 5\mathbf{j} + 10\mathbf{k}$$

a.
$$\frac{\mathbf{u}}{\| \mathbf{u} \|} = \frac{\sqrt{134}}{134}\left(-3\mathbf{i} + 5\mathbf{j} + 10\mathbf{k}\right)$$

b.
$$\frac{\mathbf{u}}{\| \mathbf{u} \|} = -\frac{\sqrt{134}}{134}\left(-3\mathbf{i} + 5\mathbf{j} + 10\mathbf{k}\right)$$

c.
$$\frac{\mathbf{u}}{\| \mathbf{u} \|} = \frac{\sqrt{134}}{134}\left(3\mathbf{i} + 5\mathbf{j} + 10\mathbf{k}\right)$$

d.
$$\frac{\mathbf{u}}{\| \mathbf{u} \|} = \frac{134\sqrt{134}}{134}\left(-3\mathbf{i} + 5\mathbf{j} + 10\mathbf{k}\right)$$

e.
$$\frac{\mathbf{u}}{\| \mathbf{u} \|} = -\frac{134\sqrt{134}}{134}\left(-3\mathbf{i} + 5\mathbf{j} + 10\mathbf{k}\right)$$

____   10.   The vector **v** and its initial point are given. Find the terminal point.

$$\mathbf{v} = \langle 6, -1, -1 \rangle$$

Initial point: $(10, -6, 5)$

a.   Terminal point is $(16, -7, 4)$.
b.   Terminal point is $(4, -7, 16)$.
c.   Terminal point is $(16, 4, -7)$.
d.   Terminal point is $(-7, 16, 4)$.
e.   Terminal point is $(4, 16, -7)$.

____ 11.   Find the magnitude of the vector **v** described below.

Initial point: $(-6, -3, -6)$

Terminal point: $(-1, 9, -4)$

a. $\sqrt{173}$

b. 19

c. $2\sqrt{173}$

d. -11

e. $\sqrt{19}$

____ 12.   Determine whether **u** and **v** are parallel, orthogonal, or neither.

$\mathbf{u} = \langle 8, -4, 7 \rangle, \mathbf{v} = \langle 40, -20, 35 \rangle$

a. neither

b. parallel

c. orthogonal

____ 13.   Use vectors to determine whether the points are collinear.

$(7, 5, -3), (2, 3, -4), (3, 2, -5)$

a. not collinear

b. collinear

____ 14.   Use the vectors **u** and **v** to find $\mathbf{u} \times (-\mathbf{v})$.

$\mathbf{u} = 5\mathbf{i} - \mathbf{j} + 6\mathbf{k} \quad \mathbf{v} = 4\mathbf{i} + 4\mathbf{j} - \mathbf{k}$

a. $\mathbf{u} \times (-\mathbf{v}) = 23\mathbf{i} - 29\mathbf{j} - 24\mathbf{k}$

b. $\mathbf{u} \times (-\mathbf{v}) = 23\mathbf{i} + 29\mathbf{j} - 24\mathbf{k}$

c. $\mathbf{u} \times (-\mathbf{v}) = 29\mathbf{i} - 23\mathbf{j} + 24\mathbf{k}$

d. $\mathbf{u} \times (-\mathbf{v}) = 23\mathbf{i} - 29\mathbf{j} + 24\mathbf{k}$

e. $\mathbf{u} \times (-\mathbf{v}) = 23\mathbf{i} + 29\mathbf{j} + 24\mathbf{k}$

____ 15.   Find the area of the parallelogram that has the vectors as adjacent sides.

$\mathbf{u} = 5\mathbf{k}$

$\mathbf{v} = 5\mathbf{i} + 5\mathbf{k}$

a. Area = 28 square units

b. Area = 29 square units

c. Area = 25 square units

d. Area = 27 square units

e. Area = 26 square units

_____ 16. Find the triple scalar product.

$$\mathbf{u} = \langle 2, 0, 3 \rangle, \ \mathbf{v} = \langle 0, 4, 0 \rangle, \ \mathbf{w} = \langle 0, 0, 6 \rangle$$

a. $\mathbf{u} \cdot (\mathbf{v} \times \mathbf{w}) = 50$
b. $\mathbf{u} \cdot (\mathbf{v} \times \mathbf{w}) = 48$
c. $\mathbf{u} \cdot (\mathbf{v} \times \mathbf{w}) = 47$
d. $\mathbf{u} \cdot (\mathbf{v} \times \mathbf{w}) = 46$
e. $\mathbf{u} \cdot (\mathbf{v} \times \mathbf{w}) = 49$

_____ 17. Find the volume of the parallelepiped with the given vertices.

$$A(0,0,0), B(6,0,0), C(6,-4,5), D(0,-4,5), E(6,7,5), F(0,7,5), G(0,5,8), H(6,5,8)$$

a. Volume = 331 cubic units
b. Volume = 332 cubic units
c. Volume = 329 cubic units
d. Volume = 330 cubic units
e. Volume = 328 cubic units

_____ 18. Find $\mathbf{u} \times \mathbf{v}$ and show that it is orthogonal to both $\mathbf{u}$ and $\mathbf{v}$.

$$\mathbf{u} = \langle 11, 1, 12 \rangle \quad \mathbf{v} = \langle 10, -10, -1 \rangle$$

a.
$$\mathbf{u} \times \mathbf{v} = \langle -119, 131, -120 \rangle$$

$$(\mathbf{u} \times \mathbf{v}) \cdot \mathbf{u} = 0$$

$$(\mathbf{u} \times \mathbf{v}) \cdot \mathbf{v} = 0$$

b.
$$\mathbf{u} \times \mathbf{v} = \langle 119, -131, 120 \rangle$$

$$(\mathbf{u} \times \mathbf{v}) \cdot \mathbf{u} = 0$$

$$(\mathbf{u} \times \mathbf{v}) \cdot \mathbf{v} = 0$$

c.
$$\mathbf{u} \times \mathbf{v} = \langle 119, -131, -120 \rangle$$

$$(\mathbf{u} \times \mathbf{v}) \cdot \mathbf{u} = 0$$

$$(\mathbf{u} \times \mathbf{v}) \cdot \mathbf{v} = 0$$

d.
$$\mathbf{u} \times \mathbf{v} = \langle 119, 131, -120 \rangle$$

$$(\mathbf{u} \times \mathbf{v}) \cdot \mathbf{u} = 0$$

$$(\mathbf{u} \times \mathbf{v}) \cdot \mathbf{v} = 0$$

e.
$$\mathbf{u} \times \mathbf{v} = \langle -119, 131, 120 \rangle$$

$$(\mathbf{u} \times \mathbf{v}) \cdot \mathbf{u} \neq 0$$

$$(\mathbf{u} \times \mathbf{v}) \cdot \mathbf{v} \neq 0$$

_____ 19. Find $\mathbf{u} \times \mathbf{v}$.

$\mathbf{u} = 4\mathbf{i} + \mathbf{j} - 3\mathbf{k}, \quad \mathbf{v} = -3\mathbf{i} + 5\mathbf{j} + \mathbf{k}$

a. -10

b. $-12\mathbf{i} + 5\mathbf{j} - 3\mathbf{k}$

c. $16\mathbf{i} - 5\mathbf{j} + 23\mathbf{k}$

d. -20

e. $16\mathbf{i} + 5\mathbf{j} + 23\mathbf{k}$

_____ 20. Find the triple scalar product $\mathbf{u} \cdot (\mathbf{v} \times \mathbf{w})$ for the vectors

$\mathbf{u} = 9\mathbf{i} - 7\mathbf{j} - 3\mathbf{k}, \quad \mathbf{v} = -6\mathbf{i} + \mathbf{j} - 5\mathbf{k}, \quad \mathbf{w} = 2\mathbf{i} + 8\mathbf{j} - 9\mathbf{k}$

a. 0

b. -19

c. -877

d. 877

e. -299

_____   21.   Find a set of symmetric equations for the line through the point and parallel to the specified vector or line.

Point: $(-6, 0, 6)$
Parallel to: $\mathbf{v} = 5\mathbf{i} + 5\mathbf{j} - 5\mathbf{k}$

a.
   Symmetric equations: $\dfrac{x-6}{5} = \dfrac{y}{5} = \dfrac{z-6}{-5}$

b.
   Symmetric equations: $\dfrac{x+6}{5} = \dfrac{y}{5} = \dfrac{z-6}{-5}$

c.
   Symmetric equations: $\dfrac{x+6}{5} = \dfrac{y}{-5} = \dfrac{z-6}{5}$

d.
   Symmetric equations: $\dfrac{x+6}{5} = \dfrac{y}{5} = \dfrac{z+6}{-5}$

e.
   Symmetric equations: $\dfrac{x-6}{5} = \dfrac{y}{5} = \dfrac{z+6}{-5}$

_____   22.   Find a set of parametric equations of the line that passes through the given points.

$(6, 0, 3), (1, 6, -5)$

a. $x = 6 - 5t, y = 6t, z = -3 - 8t$
b. $x = 6 - 5t, y = -6t, z = 3 - 8t$
c. $x = 6 - 5t, y = 6t, z = 3 - 8t$
d. $x = -6 - 5t, y = -6t, z = 3 - 8t$
e. $x = -6 - 5t, y = 6t, z = -3 - 8t$

_____   23.   Find a set of parametric equations of the line.

Passes through $(-2, 6, 5)$ and is parallel to the xy-plane and the yz-plane

a. $x = -2$

$y = 6$

$z = 5 - t$

b. $x = -2 + t$

$y = 6$

$z = 5$

c. $x = -2 + t$

$y = 6 + t$

$z = 5$

d. $x = -2$

$y = 6 + t$

$z = 5$

e. $x = -2$

$y = 6$

$z = 5 + t$

_____   24.   Find the general form of the equation of the plane with the given characteristics.
The plane passes through the point $(-2, -3, -5)$ and is parallel to the yz-plane.
a. $x + y + z = -10$
b. $y = -3$
c. $z = -5$
d. $y + z = -8$
e. $x = -2$

_____ 25.   Find the angle between the two planes.

$6x - 7y + 8z = 9$

$x + y - z = 6$

a.   65.8°
b.   67.8°
c.   66.8°
d.   64.8°
e.   63.8°

Ch 11 Form E
Answer Section

1.	ANS:	C	PTS:	1	REF:	11.4.40
2.	ANS:	E	PTS:	1	REF:	11.1.20
3.	ANS:	C	PTS:	1	REF:	11.1.27
4.	ANS:	C	PTS:	1	REF:	11.1.37
5.	ANS:	E	PTS:	1	REF:	11.1.46
6.	ANS:	D	PTS:	1	REF:	11.1.54
7.	ANS:	B	PTS:	1	REF:	11.1.21
8.	ANS:	C	PTS:	1	REF:	11.2.21
9.	ANS:	A	PTS:	1	REF:	11.2.30a
10.	ANS:	A	PTS:	1	REF:	11.2.52
11.	ANS:	A	PTS:	1	REF:	11.2.27
12.	ANS:	B	PTS:	1	REF:	11.2.39
13.	ANS:	A	PTS:	1	REF:	11.2.48
14.	ANS:	A	PTS:	1	REF:	11.3.17
15.	ANS:	C	PTS:	1	REF:	11.3.37
16.	ANS:	B	PTS:	1	REF:	11.3.52
17.	ANS:	D	PTS:	1	REF:	11.3.59
18.	ANS:	D	PTS:	1	REF:	11.3.22
19.	ANS:	E	PTS:	1	REF:	11.3.11
20.	ANS:	D	PTS:	1	REF:	11.3.55
21.	ANS:	B	PTS:	1	REF:	11.4.8b
22.	ANS:	C	PTS:	1	REF:	11.4.11a
23.	ANS:	D	PTS:	1	REF:	11.4.42
24.	ANS:	E	PTS:	1	REF:	11.4.32
25.	ANS:	D	PTS:	1	REF:	11.4.47a

Ch 11 Form F

_____   1.   Determine whether the planes are parallel, orthogonal, or neither.
$x + 4y - 4z = 1$
$-3x - 12y + 12z = -1$
a.   parallel
b.   orthogonal
c.   neither

_____   2.   Find the coordinates of the point.

The point is located in the yz-plane, four unit to the right of the xz-plane, and six units above the xy-plane.

a. $x = 0,\ y = 4,\ z = 4$
b. $x = 4,\ y = 4,\ z = 6$
c. $x = 0,\ y = 4,\ z = 6$
d. $x = 4,\ y = 0,\ z = 6$
e. $x = 6,\ y = 0,\ z = 6$

_____   3.   Find the distance between the points.

$(0,0,0), (6,3,7)$

a. $\sqrt{96}$ units
b.   94 units
c. $\sqrt{94}$ units
d. $\sqrt{95}$ units
e.   96 units

_____   4.   Find the lengths of the sides of the triangle with the indicated vertices.

$(0,0,2), (-5,5,5), (0,5,0)$

a. $d1 = \sqrt{59},\ d2 = \sqrt{29},\ d3 = 5\sqrt{2}$
b. $d1 = 5\sqrt{2},\ d2 = \sqrt{29},\ d3 = 5\sqrt{2}$
c. $d1 = \sqrt{29},\ d2 = \sqrt{29},\ d3 = 5\sqrt{2}$
d. $d1 = \sqrt{59},\ d2 = \sqrt{29},\ d3 = \sqrt{59}$
e. $d1 = \sqrt{59},\ d2 = \sqrt{59},\ d3 = 5\sqrt{2}$

_____ 5.   Find the midpoint of the line segment joining the points.

$(5,5,-1),(1,1,1)$

a. $(0, -3, 3)$
b. $(3, 3, 0)$
c. $(3, 0, 3)$
d. $(0, 3, 3)$
e. $(-3, 3, 0)$

_____ 6.   Find the standard form of the equation of the sphere with the given characteristics.

Center: $(-6, 2, 3)$; radius: 3

a. $(x+6)^2+(y-2)^2+(z-3)^2=9$

b. $(x+6)^2+(y+2)^2+(z+3)^2=9$

c. $(x+6)^2-(y+2)^2-(z+3)^2=9$

d. $(x-6)+(y-2)+(z-3)=9$

e. $(x-6)^2-(y-2)^2-(z-3)^2=9$

_____ 7.   Determine the octant(s) in which (x,y,z) is located so that the conditions are satisfied.
$x > 0, y < 0, z > 0$
a. octant VI
b. octant I or octant II
c. octant I
d. octant IV
e. octant V

_____ 8.   Find the magnitude of **v**.

$\mathbf{v} = \langle 1, -8, 16 \rangle$

a. $\| \mathbf{v} \| = 8\sqrt{5}$
b. $\| \mathbf{v} \| = 8\sqrt{2}$
c. $\| \mathbf{v} \| = \sqrt{323}$
d. $\| \mathbf{v} \| = 16\sqrt{2}$
e. $\| \mathbf{v} \| = \sqrt{321}$

____ 9.   Find a unit vector in the direction of **u**.

$$\mathbf{u} = -6\mathbf{i} + 8\mathbf{j} + 16\mathbf{k}$$

a.
$$\frac{\mathbf{u}}{\|\mathbf{u}\|} = \frac{\sqrt{356}}{356}\left(-6\mathbf{i} + 8\mathbf{j} + 16\mathbf{k}\right)$$

b.
$$\frac{\mathbf{u}}{\|\mathbf{u}\|} = -\frac{\sqrt{356}}{356}\left(-6\mathbf{i} + 8\mathbf{j} + 16\mathbf{k}\right)$$

c.
$$\frac{\mathbf{u}}{\|\mathbf{u}\|} = \frac{356\sqrt{356}}{356}\left(-6\mathbf{i} + 8\mathbf{j} + 16\mathbf{k}\right)$$

d.
$$\frac{\mathbf{u}}{\|\mathbf{u}\|} = \frac{\sqrt{356}}{356}\left(6\mathbf{i} + 8\mathbf{j} + 16\mathbf{k}\right)$$

e.
$$\frac{\mathbf{u}}{\|\mathbf{u}\|} = -\frac{356\sqrt{356}}{356}\left(-6\mathbf{i} + 8\mathbf{j} + 16\mathbf{k}\right)$$

____ 10.   The vector **v** and its initial point are given. Find the terminal point.

$$\mathbf{v} = \left\langle 5, -1, -1 \right\rangle$$

Initial point: $(8, -5, 4)$

a. Terminal point is $(13, 3, -6)$.
b. Terminal point is $(3, -6, 13)$.
c. Terminal point is $(-6, 13, 3)$.
d. Terminal point is $(3, 13, -6)$.
e. Terminal point is $(13, -6, 3)$.

____ 11.   Find the magnitude of the vector **v** described below.
    Initial point: $(-3, 4, 1)$
    Terminal point: $(-5, -2, 1)$
a. $2\sqrt{2}$
b. 8
c. $2\sqrt{10}$
d. $4\sqrt{10}$
e. -4

_____ 12. Determine whether **u** and **v** are parallel, orthogonal, or neither.

$\mathbf{u} = \langle -5, -9, -1 \rangle, \mathbf{v} = \langle -10, -18, -2 \rangle$

a. parallel
b. orthogonal
c. neither

_____ 13. Use vectors to determine whether the points are collinear.

$(1, 6, -1), (5, 2, -4), (0, 11, -9)$

a. not collinear
b. collinear

_____ 14. Use the vectors **u** and **v** to find $\mathbf{u} \times (-\mathbf{v})$.

$\mathbf{u} = 4\mathbf{i} - \mathbf{j} + 5\mathbf{k} \quad \mathbf{v} = 3\mathbf{i} + 3\mathbf{j} - \mathbf{k}$

a. $\mathbf{u} \times (-\mathbf{v}) = 14\mathbf{i} - 19\mathbf{j} + 15\mathbf{k}$
b. $\mathbf{u} \times (-\mathbf{v}) = 14\mathbf{i} - 19\mathbf{j} - 15\mathbf{k}$
c. $\mathbf{u} \times (-\mathbf{v}) = 14\mathbf{i} + 19\mathbf{j} - 15\mathbf{k}$
d. $\mathbf{u} \times (-\mathbf{v}) = 19\mathbf{i} - 14\mathbf{j} + 15\mathbf{k}$
e. $\mathbf{u} \times (-\mathbf{v}) = 14\mathbf{i} + 19\mathbf{j} + 15\mathbf{k}$

_____ 15. Find the area of the parallelogram that has the vectors as adjacent sides.

$\mathbf{u} = 6\mathbf{k}$

$\mathbf{v} = 6\mathbf{i} + 6\mathbf{k}$

a. Area = 36 square units
b. Area = 38 square units
c. Area = 39 square units
d. Area = 37 square units
e. Area = 40 square units

_____ 16. Find the triple scalar product.

$\mathbf{u} = \langle 8, 0, 9 \rangle, \mathbf{v} = \langle 0, 10, 0 \rangle, \mathbf{w} = \langle 0, 0, 18 \rangle$

a. $\mathbf{u} \cdot (\mathbf{v} \times \mathbf{w}) = 1,442$
b. $\mathbf{u} \cdot (\mathbf{v} \times \mathbf{w}) = 1,439$
c. $\mathbf{u} \cdot (\mathbf{v} \times \mathbf{w}) = 1,440$
d. $\mathbf{u} \cdot (\mathbf{v} \times \mathbf{w}) = 1,438$
e. $\mathbf{u} \cdot (\mathbf{v} \times \mathbf{w}) = 1,441$

_____   17.   Find the volume of the parallelepiped with the given vertices.

$A(0,0,0), B(3,0,0), C(3,-1,2), D(0,-1,2), E(3,4,2), F(0,4,2), G(0,2,5), H(3,2,5)$

a.   Volume = 30 cubic units
b.   Volume = 29 cubic units
c.   Volume = 31 cubic units
d.   Volume = 32 cubic units
e.   Volume = 28 cubic units

_____   18.   Find $\mathbf{u} \times \mathbf{v}$ and show that it is orthogonal to both $\mathbf{u}$ and $\mathbf{v}$.

$\mathbf{u} = \langle 9, 1, 10 \rangle \quad \mathbf{v} = \langle 8, -8, -1 \rangle$

a. $\mathbf{u} \times \mathbf{v} = \langle 79, -89, -80 \rangle$

$(\mathbf{u} \times \mathbf{v}) \cdot \mathbf{u} = 0$

$(\mathbf{u} \times \mathbf{v}) \cdot \mathbf{v} = 0$

b. $\mathbf{u} \times \mathbf{v} = \langle -79, 89, -80 \rangle$

$(\mathbf{u} \times \mathbf{v}) \cdot \mathbf{u} = 0$

$(\mathbf{u} \times \mathbf{v}) \cdot \mathbf{v} = 0$

c. $\mathbf{u} \times \mathbf{v} = \langle -79, 89, 80 \rangle$

$(\mathbf{u} \times \mathbf{v}) \cdot \mathbf{u} \neq 0$

$(\mathbf{u} \times \mathbf{v}) \cdot \mathbf{v} \neq 0$

d. $\mathbf{u} \times \mathbf{v} = \langle 79, -89, 80 \rangle$

$(\mathbf{u} \times \mathbf{v}) \cdot \mathbf{u} = 0$

$(\mathbf{u} \times \mathbf{v}) \cdot \mathbf{v} = 0$

e. $\mathbf{u} \times \mathbf{v} = \langle 79, 89, -80 \rangle$

$(\mathbf{u} \times \mathbf{v}) \cdot \mathbf{u} = 0$

$(\mathbf{u} \times \mathbf{v}) \cdot \mathbf{v} = 0$

_____   19.   Find **u** × **v**.

u = –4**i** – 6**j** – 7**k**,   **v** = –7**i** + 5**j** – **k**

a. 65
b. 41**i** – 45**j** – 62**k**
c. 5
d. 41**i** + 45**j** – 62**k**
e. 28**i** – 30**j** + 7**k**

_____   20.   Find the triple scalar product **u** · (**v** × **w**) for the vectors

u = **i** – 7**j** + **k**,   **v** = 2**i** – 2**j** + 8**k**,   **w** = –8**i** + 5**j** + 2**k**

a. –426
b. 0
c. 426
d. 70
e. –526

_____   21.   Find a set of symmetric equations for the line through the point and parallel to the specified vector or line.

Point: $(-3, 0, 2)$
Parallel to: **v** = 7**i** + 3**j** – 3**k**

a.
Symmetric equations: $\dfrac{x+3}{7} = \dfrac{y}{3} = \dfrac{z+2}{-3}$

b.
Symmetric equations: $\dfrac{x-3}{7} = \dfrac{y}{3} = \dfrac{z+2}{-3}$

c.
Symmetric equations: $\dfrac{x+3}{7} = \dfrac{y}{-3} = \dfrac{z-2}{3}$

d.
Symmetric equations: $\dfrac{x-3}{7} = \dfrac{y}{3} = \dfrac{z-2}{-3}$

e.
Symmetric equations: $\dfrac{x+3}{7} = \dfrac{y}{3} = \dfrac{z-2}{-3}$

_____   22.   Find a set of parametric equations of the line that passes through the given points.

$(6, 0, 6), (1, 4, -4)$

a. $x = -6 - 5t, y = 4t, z = -6 - 10t$
b. $x = 6 - 5t, y = 4t, z = 6 - 10t$
c. $x = 6 - 5t, y = -4t, z = 6 - 10t$
d. $x = 6 - 5t, y = 4t, z = -6 - 10t$
e. $x = -6 - 5t, y = -4t, z = 6 - 10t$

_____   23.   Find a set of parametric equations of the line.

Passes through $(-6, 7, 2)$ and is parallel to the xy-plane and the yz-plane

a. $x = -6 + t$

$y = 7$

$z = 2$

b. $x = -6$

$y = 7$

$z = 2 + t$

c. $x = -6$

$y = 7$

$z = 2 - t$

d. $x = -6 + t$

$y = 7 + t$

$z = 2$

e. $x = -6$

$y = 7 + t$

$z = 2$

_____   24.   Find the general form of the equation of the plane with the given characteristics.
The plane passes through the point $(4, -1, -7)$ and is parallel to the yz-plane.
a. $y + z = -8$
b. $x = 4$
c. $x + y + z = -4$
d. $y = -1$
e. $z = -7$

____   25.   Find the angle between the two planes.

$5x - 6y + 7z = 8$

$x + y - z = 4$

a. 65.9°
b. 62.9°
c. 64.9°
d. 63.9°
e. 66.9°

Ch 11 Form F
Answer Section

1.	ANS:	A	PTS: 1	REF:	11.4.40
2.	ANS:	C	PTS: 1	REF:	11.1.20
3.	ANS:	C	PTS: 1	REF:	11.1.27
4.	ANS:	A	PTS: 1	REF:	11.1.37
5.	ANS:	B	PTS: 1	REF:	11.1.46
6.	ANS:	A	PTS: 1	REF:	11.1.54
7.	ANS:	D	PTS: 1	REF:	11.1.21
8.	ANS:	E	PTS: 1	REF:	11.2.21
9.	ANS:	A	PTS: 1	REF:	11.2.30a
10.	ANS:	E	PTS: 1	REF:	11.2.52
11.	ANS:	C	PTS: 1	REF:	11.2.27
12.	ANS:	A	PTS: 1	REF:	11.2.39
13.	ANS:	A	PTS: 1	REF:	11.2.48
14.	ANS:	B	PTS: 1	REF:	11.3.17
15.	ANS:	A	PTS: 1	REF:	11.3.37
16.	ANS:	C	PTS: 1	REF:	11.3.52
17.	ANS:	A	PTS: 1	REF:	11.3.59
18.	ANS:	E	PTS: 1	REF:	11.3.22
19.	ANS:	D	PTS: 1	REF:	11.3.11
20.	ANS:	C	PTS: 1	REF:	11.3.55
21.	ANS:	E	PTS: 1	REF:	11.4.8b
22.	ANS:	B	PTS: 1	REF:	11.4.11a
23.	ANS:	E	PTS: 1	REF:	11.4.42
24.	ANS:	B	PTS: 1	REF:	11.4.32
25.	ANS:	D	PTS: 1	REF:	11.4.47a

Ch 12 Form A

_____   1.   Select the correct graph for the following function using a graphing utility.

$$f(x) = \frac{x-1}{x^2+5x-6}$$

a.

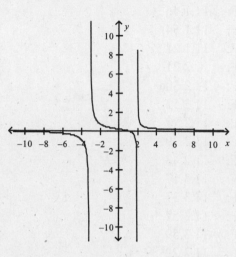

d.

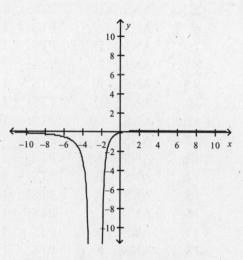

b.

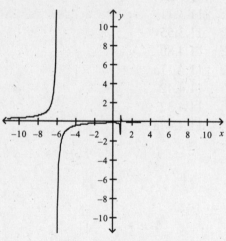

e.

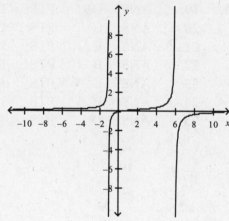

c.

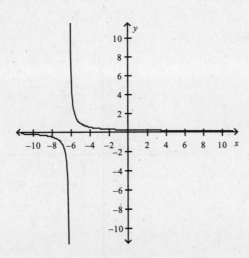

_____ 2.   Select the correct graph for the following function using a graphing utility.

$$f(x) = \frac{e^{5x} - 1}{5x}$$

a.

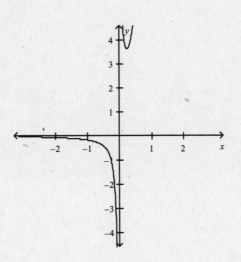

d.

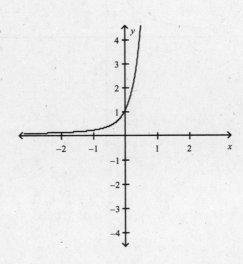

b.

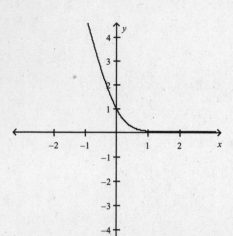

e.

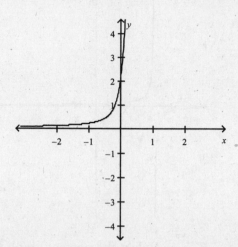

c.

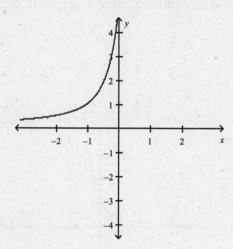

_____   3.   Select the correct graph for the following function using a graphing utility. Determine whether the limit exists or not.

$$f(x) = \frac{\sqrt{x+8}-4}{x-6}, \quad \lim_{x \to 6} f(x)$$

a.

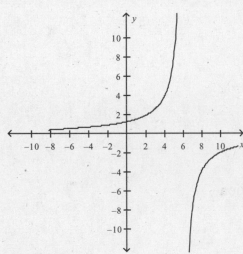

$$\lim_{x \to 6} f(x) = 8$$

d.

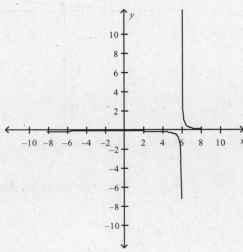

$$\lim_{x \to 6} f(x) = 0$$

b.

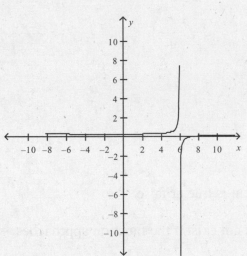

$$\lim_{x \to 6} f(x) \text{ does not exist}$$

e.

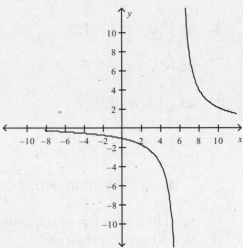

$$\lim_{x \to 6} f(x) = 4$$

c.

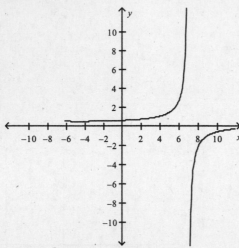

$\lim\limits_{x \to 6} f(x)$ does not exist

_____ 4. Find the limit by direct substitution.

$$\lim\limits_{x \to 5} \left(10 - x^2 \right)$$

a. $\lim\limits_{x \to 5} \left(10 - x^2 \right) = \infty$

b. $\lim\limits_{x \to 5} \left(10 - x^2 \right) = 15$

c. $\lim\limits_{x \to 5} \left(10 - x^2 \right) = 5$

d. $\lim\limits_{x \to 5} \left(10 - x^2 \right) = 35$

e. $\lim\limits_{x \to 5} \left(10 - x^2 \right) = -15$

_____ 5. Determine whether the statement is true or false.

The limit of a function as x approaches c does not exist if the function approaches -5 from the left of c and 5 from the right of c.

a. False
b. True

_____ 6.   Find the limit (if it exists). Use a graphing utility to verify your result graphically.

$$\lim_{x \to 5} \frac{x-5}{x^2-25}$$

a. $\lim_{x \to 5} \frac{x-5}{x^2-25} = \frac{1}{10}$

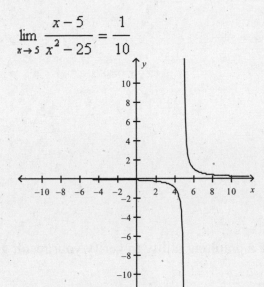

d. $\lim_{x \to 5} \frac{x-5}{x^2-25} = \frac{1}{25}$

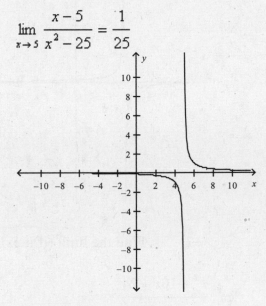

b. $\lim_{x \to 5} \frac{x-5}{x^2-25} = \frac{1}{5}$

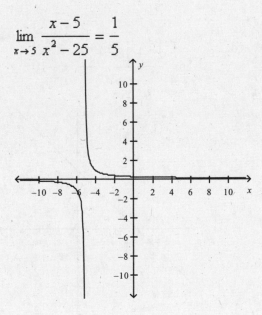

e. $\lim_{x \to 5} \frac{x-5}{x^2-25} = \frac{1}{10}$

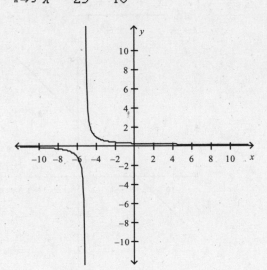

c.

$$\lim_{x \to 5} \frac{x-5}{x^2-25} = \frac{1}{25}$$

7.   Find the limit (if it exists). Use a graphing utility to verify your result graphically.

$$\lim_{x \to -4} \frac{x^2+10x+24}{x+4}$$

a.

$$\lim_{x \to -4} \frac{x^2+10x+24}{x+4} = 24$$

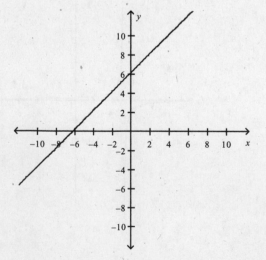

d.

$$\lim_{x \to -4} \frac{x^2+10x+24}{x+4} = -10$$

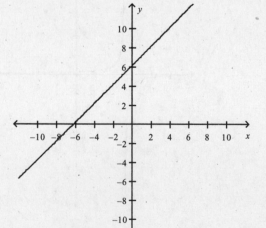

b.

$$\lim_{x \to -4} \frac{x^2 + 10x + 24}{x+4} = -2$$

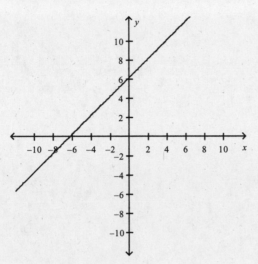

e.

$$\lim_{x \to -4} \frac{x^2 + 10x + 24}{x+4} = 25$$

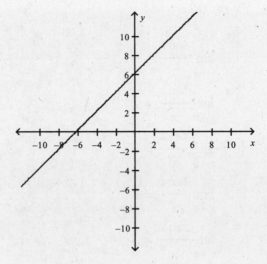

c.

$$\lim_{x \to -4} \frac{x^2 + 10x + 24}{x+4} = 2$$

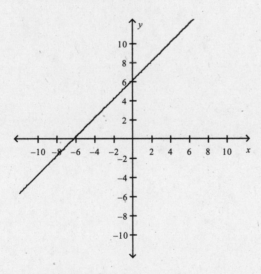

_____ 8.   Approximate the limit accurate to three decimal places.

$$\lim_{x \to 0} \frac{\tan x}{x}$$

a. $\lim\limits_{x \to 0} \dfrac{\tan x}{x} = -1$

b. $\lim\limits_{x \to 0} \dfrac{\tan x}{x} = 2$

c. $\lim\limits_{x \to 0} \dfrac{\tan x}{x} = -3$

d. $\lim\limits_{x \to 0} \dfrac{\tan x}{x} = 1$

e. $\lim\limits_{x \to 0} \dfrac{\tan x}{x} = 3$

_____ 9.   Find $\lim\limits_{h \to 0} \dfrac{f(x+h) - f(x)}{h}$.

$$f(x) = \sqrt{x - 2}$$

a. $\lim\limits_{h \to 0} \dfrac{f(x+h) - f(x)}{h} = \dfrac{1}{2\sqrt{x-1}}$

b. $\lim\limits_{h \to 0} \dfrac{f(x+h) - f(x)}{h} = -\dfrac{1}{2\sqrt{x-2}}$

c. $\lim\limits_{h \to 0} \dfrac{f(x+h) - f(x)}{h} = \dfrac{1}{2\sqrt{x-4}}$

d. $\lim\limits_{h \to 0} \dfrac{f(x+h) - f(x)}{h} = -\dfrac{1}{2\sqrt{x-4}}$

e. $\lim\limits_{h \to 0} \dfrac{f(x+h) - f(x)}{h} = \dfrac{1}{2\sqrt{x-2}}$

_____ 10. Find the limit (if it exists). Round your answer to four decimal places.

$$\lim_{z \to 0} \frac{\sqrt{7-z} - \sqrt{7}}{z}$$

a.
$$\lim_{z \to 0} \frac{\sqrt{7-z} - \sqrt{7}}{z} \approx 0.1890$$

b.
$$\lim_{z \to 0} \frac{\sqrt{7-z} - \sqrt{7}}{z} \approx -0.3780$$

c.
$$\lim_{z \to 0} \frac{\sqrt{7-z} - \sqrt{7}}{z} \approx 0.3780$$

d.
$$\lim_{z \to 0} \frac{\sqrt{7-z} - \sqrt{7}}{z} \approx -0.1890$$

e.
$$\lim_{z \to 0} \frac{\sqrt{7-z} - \sqrt{7}}{z} \approx 5.2915$$

_____ 11. Use the limit process to find the slope of the graph of the function at the specified point. Use a graphing utility to confirm your result.

$$g(x) = x^2 - 8x, \qquad (7, -7)$$

a. $m = -7$
b. $m = 7$
c. $m = -6$
d. $m = 6$
e. $m = 8$

_____   12.   Find a formula for the slope of the graph of f at the point $(x, f(x))$. Then use it to find the slope at the given point.

$f(x) = x^3$, $(1, 1)$

a. $m = -3x^2$
     At $(1, 1)$, $m = 3$

b. $m = -3x^2$
     At $(1, 1)$, $m = -3$

c. $m = x^2$
     At $(1, 1)$, $m = -3$

d. $m = 3x$
     At $(1, 1)$, $m = 3$

e. $m = 3x^2$
     At $(1, 1)$, $m = 3$

_____   13.   Select a graph of the function and the tangent line at the point $(1, f(1))$.

$f(x) = x^2 - 4$

a.

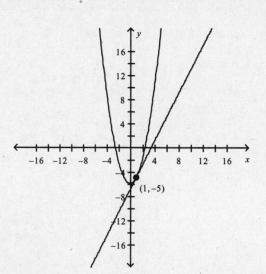

d.

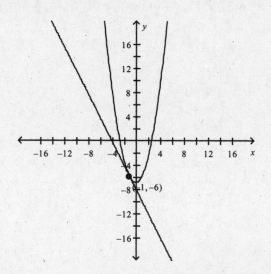

b.

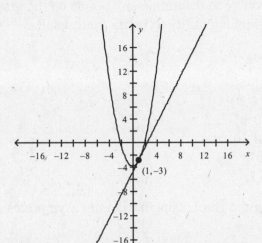

e.

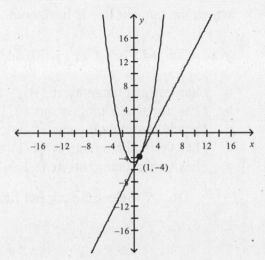

c.

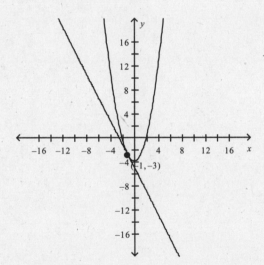

_____ 14.   Find the derivative of the function.

$$f(x) = \sqrt{x - 6}$$

a. $\dfrac{18}{x^4}$

b. $\dfrac{1}{2\sqrt{x+6}}$

c. $2x + 6$

d. $\dfrac{1}{2\sqrt{x-6}}$

e. $-\dfrac{1}{2\sqrt{x+6}}$

_____   15.   Use the function and its derivative to determine any points on the graph of f at which the tangent line is horizontal. Use a graphing utility to verify your results.

$$f(x) = 5x^6 + 6x^5, \quad f'(x) = 30x^5 + 30x^4$$

a. f has vertical tangents at $(-1, -1)$ and $(0, 0)$.
b. f has horizontal tangents at $(1, 1)$ and $(0, 0)$.
c. f has horizontal tangents at $(-1, -1)$ and $(0, 0)$.
d. f has vertical tangents at $(1, 1)$ and $(0, 0)$.
e. f has vertical tangents at $(-1, -1)$ and $(1, 1)$.

_____   16.   Select the correct function for the graph using horizontal asymptotes as aids.

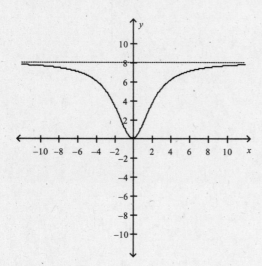

a. $\dfrac{5x^2}{x^2 + 8}$

b. $\dfrac{8x^2}{x^2 - 5}$

c. $\dfrac{x^2}{x^2 - 5}$

d. $\dfrac{x^2}{x^2 + 5}$

e. $\dfrac{8x^2}{x^2 + 5}$

_____ 17.   Find the limit (if it exists).

$$\lim_{x \to \infty} \left(\frac{5 - 14x}{x + 5} \right)$$

a. 14
b. −14
c. 5
d. −5
e. Does not exist

_____ 18.   Find the limit (if it exists).

$$\lim_{x \to -\infty} \frac{7}{3}x - \frac{6}{x^2}$$

a. −7
b. −3
c. 7
d. 0
e. Does not exist

_____ 19.   Select the correct graph of the following function.

$$f(x) = 4\left(4x - \sqrt{16x^2 + x} \right)$$

a.

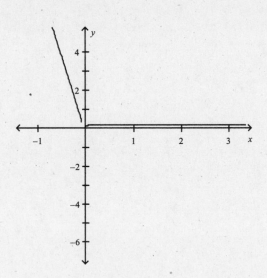

d.

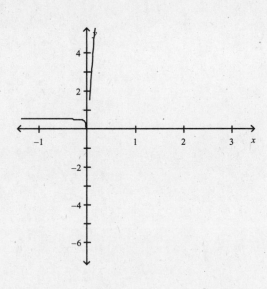

b.

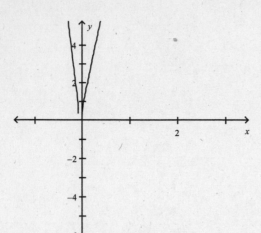

e.

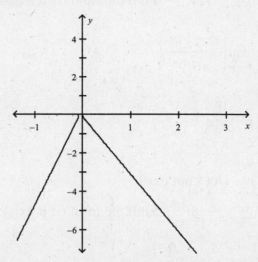

c.

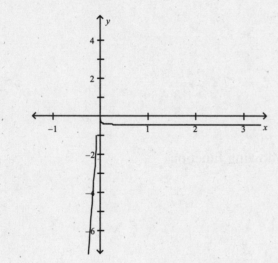

_____ 20.   The average typing speed S (in words per minute) for a student after t weeks of lessons is given by

$$S = \frac{130t^2}{63+t^2}, t > 0.$$

What is the limit of S as t approaches infinity?

a.
$$\lim_{t \to \infty} \frac{130t^2}{63+t^2} = \frac{1}{63}$$

b.
$$\lim_{t \to \infty} \frac{130t^2}{63+t^2} = 63$$

c.
$$\lim_{t \to \infty} \frac{130t^2}{63+t^2} = 0$$

d.
$$\lim_{t \to \infty} \frac{130t^2}{63+t^2} = 130$$

e.   Does not exist

_____ 21.   Evaluate the sum using the summation formula and property.

$$\sum_{i=1}^{60} 2.$$

a.   110
b.   100
c.   120
d.   130
e.   140

_____ 22.   Rewrite the sum as a rational function $S(n)$.

$$\sum_{i=1}^{n} \frac{i}{n^5}$$

a. $S(n) = \dfrac{n+1}{2n^7}$

b. $S(n) = \dfrac{n+1}{2n^6}$

c. $S(n) = \dfrac{n+1}{2n^4}$

d. $S(n) = \dfrac{n+1}{2n^8}$

e. $S(n) = \dfrac{n+1}{2n^5}$

_____ 23.   Complete the table using the function $f(x)$, over the specified interval $[a,b]$ to approximate the area of the region bounded by the graph of $y = f(x)$, the x-axis, and the vertical lines $x = a$ and $x = b$ using the indicated number of rectangles. Then find the exact area as $n \to \infty$.

n	4	8	20	50	100	∞
Approximate area						

Function	Interval

$$f(x) = x^2 + 8 \qquad [4,6]$$

(Round the answer to four decimal places.)

a.

n	4	8	20	50	100	∞
Approximate area	72.75	69.1875	67.67	67.0672	66.8668	200

b.

n	4	8	20	50	100	∞
Approximate area	75.75	69.1875	67.67	67.0672	66.8668	200

c.

n	4	8	20	50	100	∞
Approximate area	71.75	69.1875	67.67	67.0672	66.8668	66.6667

d.

n	4	8	20	50	100	∞
Approximate area	73.75	69.1875	67.67	67.0672	66.8668	200

e.

n	4	8	20	50	100	∞
Approximate area	74.75	69.1875	67.67	67.0672	66.8668	200

_____ 24.   Use the limit process to find the area of the region between the graph of the function and the
x-axis over the specified interval.

Function	Interval
$g(x) = 70 - x^3$	$[1,4]$

a. $A = \dfrac{1413}{4}$ square units

b. $A = \dfrac{603}{2}$ square units

c. $A = \dfrac{999}{4}$ square units

d. $A = 198$ square units

e. $A = \dfrac{585}{4}$ square units

_____ 25.   Determine whether the statement is true or false.

The sum of the first n positive integers is $n(n+1)/2$.

a. True
b. False

Ch 12 Form A
Answer Section

1.	ANS: C	PTS: 1	REF: 12.1.13
2.	ANS: D	PTS: 1	REF: 12.1.23
3.	ANS: B	PTS: 1	REF: 12.1.42
4.	ANS: E	PTS: 1	REF: 12.1.49
5.	ANS: B	PTS: 1	REF: 12.1.69
6.	ANS: E	PTS: 1	REF: 12.2.9
7.	ANS: C	PTS: 1	REF: 12.2.12
8.	ANS: D	PTS: 1	REF: 12.2.43
9.	ANS: E	PTS: 1	REF: 12.2.74
10.	ANS: D	PTS: 1	REF: 12.2.22
11.	ANS: D	PTS: 1	REF: 12.3.9
12.	ANS: E	PTS: 1	REF: 12.3.18a
13.	ANS: B	PTS: 1	REF: 12.3.23
14.	ANS: D	PTS: 1	REF: 12.3.37
15.	ANS: C	PTS: 1	REF: 12.3.64
16.	ANS: E	PTS: 1	REF: 12.4.5
17.	ANS: B	PTS: 1	REF: 12.4.14
18.	ANS: E	PTS: 1	REF: 12.4.24
19.	ANS: C	PTS: 1	REF: 12.4.37b
20.	ANS: D	PTS: 1	REF: 12.4.54a
21.	ANS: C	PTS: 1	REF: 12.5.5
22.	ANS: C	PTS: 1	REF: 12.5.14a
23.	ANS: C	PTS: 1	REF: 12.5.34
24.	ANS: E	PTS: 1	REF: 12.5.44
25.	ANS: A	PTS: 1	REF: 12.5.51

Ch 12 Form B

_____ 1.   Select the correct graph for the following function using a graphing utility.

$$f(x) = \frac{x-1}{x^2 + 2x - 3}$$

a.

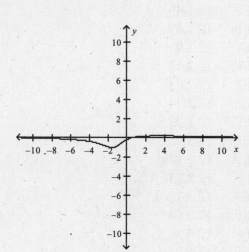

d.

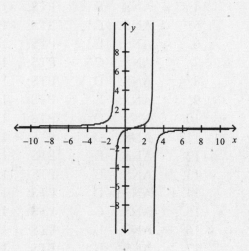

b.

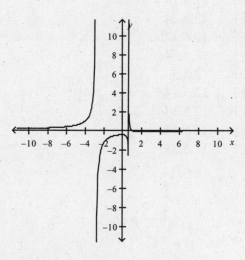

e.

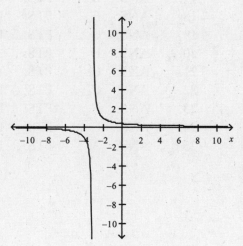

c.

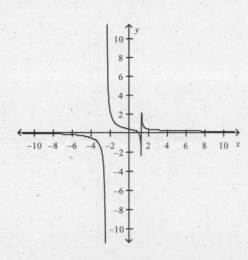

_____ 2.   Select the correct graph for the following function using a graphing utility.

$$f(x) = \frac{e^{8x} - 1}{8x}$$

a.

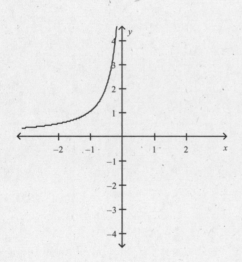

d.

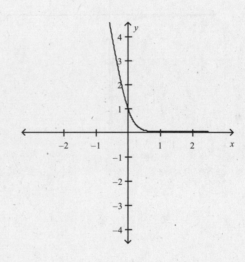

b.

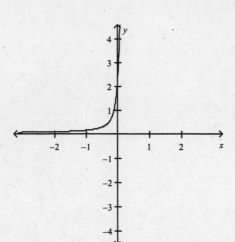

e.

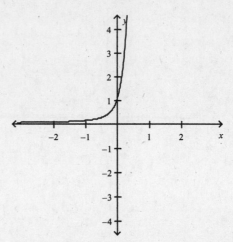

c.

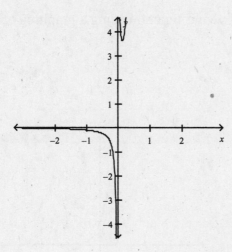

_____ 3. Select the correct graph for the following function using a graphing utility. Determine whether the limit exists or not.

$$f(x) = \frac{\sqrt{x+4} - 6}{x - 5}, \quad \lim_{x \to 5} f(x)$$

a.

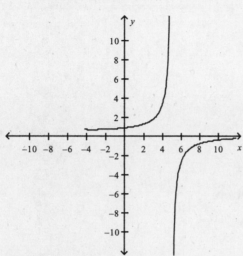

$\lim_{x \to 5} f(x)$ does not exist

d.

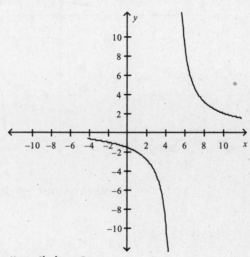

$\lim_{x \to 5} f(x) = 6$

b.

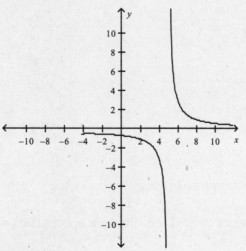

$\lim_{x \to 5} f(x) = 0$

e.

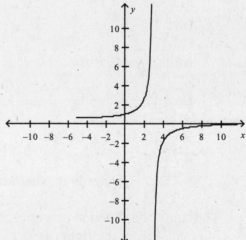

$\lim_{x \to 5} f(x)$ does not exist

c.

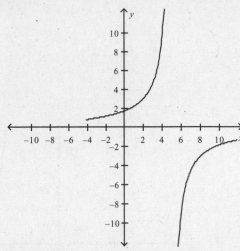

$$\lim_{x \to 5} f(x) = 4$$

_____ 4.   Find the limit by direct substitution.

$$\lim_{x \to 4} \left(15 - x^2 \right)$$

a. $\lim\limits_{x \to 4} \left(15 - x^2 \right) = 31$

b. $\lim\limits_{x \to 4} \left(15 - x^2 \right) = -1$

c. $\lim\limits_{x \to 4} \left(15 - x^2 \right) = \infty$

d. $\lim\limits_{x \to 4} \left(15 - x^2 \right) = 19$

e. $\lim\limits_{x \to 4} \left(15 - x^2 \right) = 11$

_____ 5.   Determine whether the statement is true or false.

The limit of a function as x approaches c does not exist if the function approaches -4 from the left of c and 4 from the right of c.

a.   False
b.   True

_____ 6.   Find the limit (if it exists). Use a graphing utility to verify your result graphically.

$$\lim_{x \to 4} \frac{x-4}{x^2-16}$$

a. $$\lim_{x \to 4} \frac{x-4}{x^2-16} = \frac{1}{16}$$

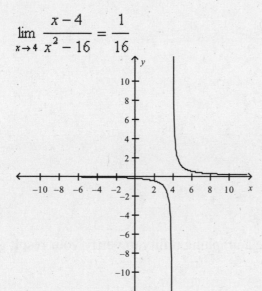

d. $$\lim_{x \to 4} \frac{x-4}{x^2-16} = \frac{1}{4}$$

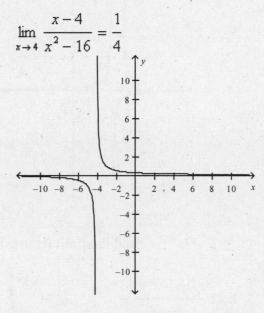

b. $$\lim_{x \to 4} \frac{x-4}{x^2-16} = \frac{1}{8}$$

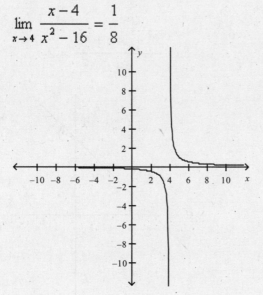

e. $$\lim_{x \to 4} \frac{x-4}{x^2-16} = \frac{1}{8}$$

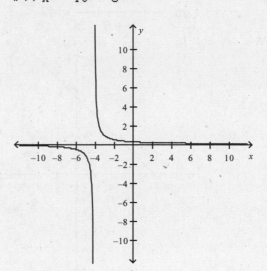

c.

$$\lim_{x \to 4} \frac{x-4}{x^2-16} = \frac{1}{16}$$

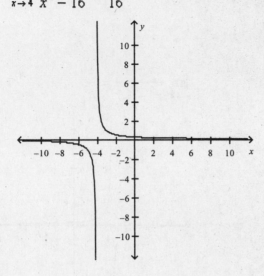

_____ 7.   Find the limit (if it exists). Use a graphing utility to verify your result graphically.

$$\lim_{x \to -6} \frac{x^2 + 14x + 48}{x+6}$$

a.

$$\lim_{x \to -6} \frac{x^2 + 14x + 48}{x+6} = 49$$

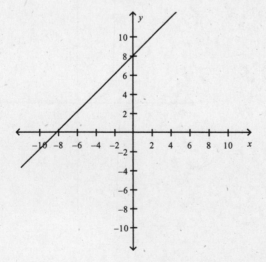

d.

$$\lim_{x \to -6} \frac{x^2 + 14x + 48}{x+6} = 2$$

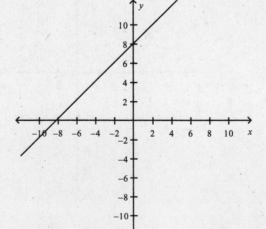

b.
$$\lim_{x \to -6} \frac{x^2 + 14x + 48}{x + 6} = -14$$

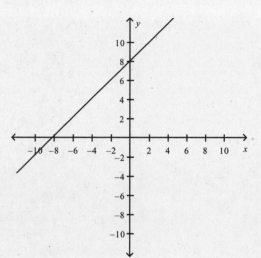

e.
$$\lim_{x \to -6} \frac{x^2 + 14x + 48}{x + 6} = -2$$

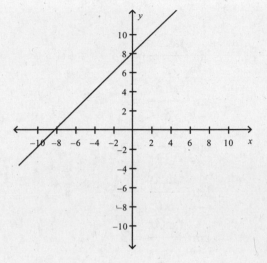

c.
$$\lim_{x \to -6} \frac{x^2 + 14x + 48}{x + 6} = 48$$

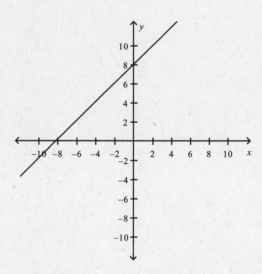

_____ 8.   Approximate the limit accurate to three decimal places.

$$\lim_{x \to 0} \frac{\tan 3x}{x}$$

a. $\lim_{x \to 0} \dfrac{\tan 3x}{x} = -3$

b. $\lim_{x \to 0} \dfrac{\tan 3x}{x} = 4$

c. $\lim_{x \to 0} \dfrac{\tan 3x}{x} = 5$

d. $\lim_{x \to 0} \dfrac{\tan 3x}{x} = -5$

e. $\lim_{x \to 0} \dfrac{\tan 3x}{x} = 3$

_____ 9.   Find $\lim_{h \to 0} \dfrac{f(x+h)-f(x)}{h}$.

$$f(x) = \sqrt{x - 2}$$

a. $\lim_{h \to 0} \dfrac{f(x+h)-f(x)}{h} = -\dfrac{1}{2\sqrt{x-4}}$

b. $\lim_{h \to 0} \dfrac{f(x+h)-f(x)}{h} = \dfrac{1}{2\sqrt{x-2}}$

c. $\lim_{h \to 0} \dfrac{f(x+h)-f(x)}{h} = \dfrac{1}{2\sqrt{x-1}}$

d. $\lim_{h \to 0} \dfrac{f(x+h)-f(x)}{h} = -\dfrac{1}{2\sqrt{x-2}}$

e. $\lim_{h \to 0} \dfrac{f(x+h)-f(x)}{h} = \dfrac{1}{2\sqrt{x-4}}$

_____ 10.   Find the limit (if it exists). Round your answer to four decimal places.

$$\lim_{z \to 0} \frac{\sqrt{5-z} - \sqrt{5}}{z}$$

a.
$$\lim_{z \to 0} \frac{\sqrt{5-z} - \sqrt{5}}{z} \approx -0.2236$$

b.
$$\lim_{z \to 0} \frac{\sqrt{5-z} - \sqrt{5}}{z} \approx 4.4721$$

c.
$$\lim_{z \to 0} \frac{\sqrt{5-z} - \sqrt{5}}{z} \approx 0.4472$$

d.
$$\lim_{z \to 0} \frac{\sqrt{5-z} - \sqrt{5}}{z} \approx 0.2236$$

e.
$$\lim_{z \to 0} \frac{\sqrt{5-z} - \sqrt{5}}{z} \approx -0.4472$$

_____ 11.   Use the limit process to find the slope of the graph of the function at the specified point. Use a graphing utility to confirm your result.

$$g(x) = x^2 - 10x, \qquad (9, -9)$$

a. $m = 9$

b. $m = -8$

c. $m = 10$

d. $m = -9$

e. $m = 8$

_____ 12.   Find a formula for the slope of the graph of f at the point $\left(x, f(x)\right)$. Then use it to find the slope at the given point.

$$f(x) = x^3, \qquad (3, 27)$$

a. $m = x^2$
    At $(3, 27)$, $m = -27$

b. $m = 3x$
    At $(3, 27)$, $m = 27$

c. $m = -3x^2$
    At $(3, 27)$, $m = -27$

d. $m = -3x^2$
    At $(3, 27)$, $m = 27$

e. $m = 3x^2$
    At $(3, 27)$, $m = 27$

_____ 13.   Select a graph of the function and the tangent line at the point $\left(1, f(1)\right)$.

$$f(x) = x^2 - 5$$

a.

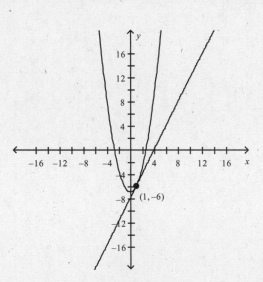

d.

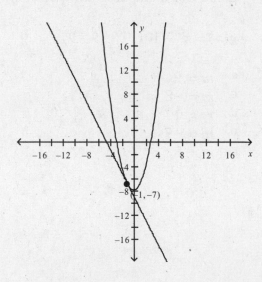

b.

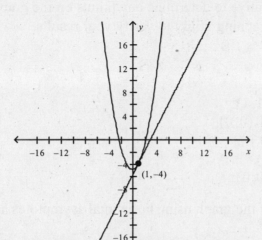

$(1, -4)$

e.

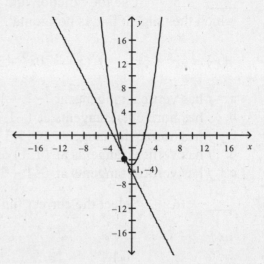

$(-1, -4)$

c.

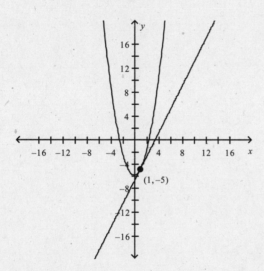

$(1, -5)$

_____ 14.   Find the derivative of the function.

$$f(x) = \sqrt{x - 8}$$

a. $\dfrac{1}{2\sqrt{x - 8}}$

b. $\dfrac{1}{2\sqrt{x + 8}}$

c. $-\dfrac{1}{2\sqrt{x + 8}}$

d. $2x + 8$

e. $\dfrac{24}{x^4}$

_____ 15.   Use the function and its derivative to determine any points on the graph of f at which the tangent line is horizontal. Use a graphing utility to verify your results.

$$f(x) = 5x^6 + 6x^5, \quad f'(x) = 30x^5 + 30x^4$$

a. f has vertical tangents at $(-1, -1)$ and $(1, 1)$.
b. f has horizontal tangents at $(-1, -1)$ and $(0, 0)$.
c. f has horizontal tangents at $(1, 1)$ and $(0, 0)$.
d. f has vertical tangents at $(1, 1)$ and $(0, 0)$.
e. f has vertical tangents at $(-1, -1)$ and $(0, 0)$.

_____ 16.   Select the correct function for the graph using horizontal asymptotes as aids.

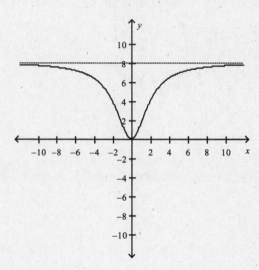

a. $\dfrac{x^2}{x^2 + 4}$

b. $\dfrac{4x^2}{x^2 + 8}$

c. $\dfrac{8x^2}{x^2 + 4}$

d. $\dfrac{x^2}{x^2 - 4}$

e. $\dfrac{8x^2}{x^2 - 4}$

_____ 17.   Find the limit (if it exists).

$$\lim_{x \to \infty} \left(\frac{1 - 8x}{x + 2} \right)$$

a.   −1
b.   −8
c.   1
d.   8
e.   Does not exist

_____ 18.   Find the limit (if it exists).

$$\lim_{x \to -\infty} \frac{4}{7} x - \frac{8}{x^2}$$

a.   −4
b.   Does not exist
c.   −7
d.   0
e.   4

_____ 19.   Select the correct graph of the following function.

$$f(x) = 2 \left(6x - \sqrt{36x^2 + x} \right)$$

a.

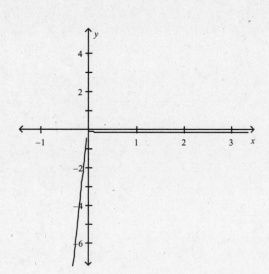

d.

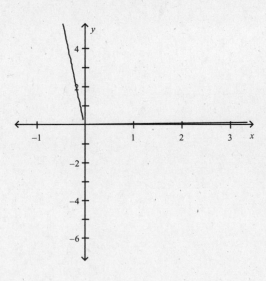

b.

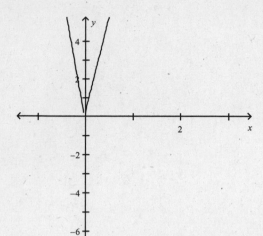

c.

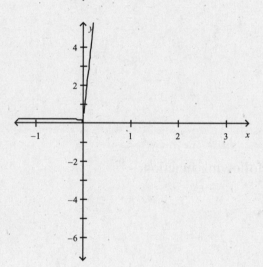

e.

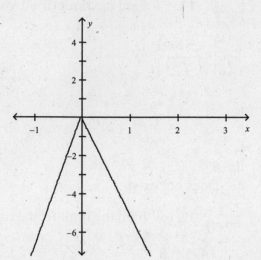

_____ 20.   The average typing speed S (in words per minute) for a student after t weeks of lessons is given by

$$S = \frac{120t^2}{67+t^2}, t > 0.$$

What is the limit of S as t approaches infinity?

a.
$$\lim_{t \to \infty} \frac{120t^2}{67+t^2} = \frac{1}{67}$$

b.
$$\lim_{t \to \infty} \frac{120t^2}{67+t^2} = 67$$

c.
$$\lim_{t \to \infty} \frac{120t^2}{67+t^2} = 0$$

d.   Does not exist

e.
$$\lim_{t \to \infty} \frac{120t^2}{67+t^2} = 120$$

_____ 21.   Evaluate the sum using the summation formula and property.

$$\sum_{i=1}^{60} 3$$

a.   160
b.   190
c.   170
d.   200
e.   180

_____ 22.   Rewrite the sum as a rational function $S(n)$.

$$\sum_{i=1}^{n} \frac{i}{n^2}$$

a. $S(n) = \dfrac{n+1}{2n}$

b. $S(n) = \dfrac{n+1}{2n^3}$

c. $S(n) = \dfrac{n+1}{2n^4}$

d. $S(n) = \dfrac{n+1}{2n^2}$

e. $S(n) = \dfrac{n+1}{2n^5}$

_____ 23. Complete the table using the function $f(x)$, over the specified interval $[a,b]$ to approximate the area of the region bounded by the graph of $y = f(x)$, the x-axis, and the vertical lines $x = a$ and $x = b$ using the indicated number of rectangles. Then find the exact area as $n \to \infty$.

n	4	8	20	50	100	∞
Approximate area						

Function   Interval

$f(x) = x^2 + 3$ $[4,6]$

(Round the answer to four decimal places.)

a.

n	4	8	20	50	100	∞
Approximate area	61.75	59.1875	57.67	57.0672	56.8668	56.6667

b.

n	4	8	20	50	100	∞
Approximate area	63.75	59.1875	57.67	57.0672	56.8668	170

c.

n	4	8	20	50	100	∞
Approximate area	62.75	59.1875	57.67	57.0672	56.8668	170

d.

n	4	8	20	50	100	∞
Approximate area	65.75	59.1875	57.67	57.0672	56.8668	170

e.

n	4	8	20	50	100	∞
Approximate area	64.75	59.1875	57.67	57.0672	56.8668	170

_____ 24. Use the limit process to find the area of the region between the graph of the function and the
x-axis over the specified interval.

Function   Interval

$g(x) = 67 - x^3$ $[1,4]$

a.
$A = \dfrac{945}{4}$ square units

b.
$A = \dfrac{1143}{4}$ square units

c.
$A = \dfrac{1341}{4}$ square units

d.
$A = \dfrac{549}{4}$ square units

e.
$A = \dfrac{747}{4}$ square units

_____ 25. Determine whether the statement is true or false.

The sum of the first n positive integers is $n^2(n+1)^2/4$.

a. False
b. True

Ch 12 Form B
Answer Section

1.	ANS:	E	PTS:	1	REF:	12.1.13
2.	ANS:	E	PTS:	1	REF:	12.1.23
3.	ANS:	A	PTS:	1	REF:	12.1.42
4.	ANS:	B	PTS:	1	REF:	12.1.49
5.	ANS:	B	PTS:	1	REF:	12.1.69
6.	ANS:	E	PTS:	1	REF:	12.2.9
7.	ANS:	D	PTS:	1	REF:	12.2.12
8.	ANS:	E	PTS:	1	REF:	12.2.43
9.	ANS:	B	PTS:	1	REF:	12.2.74
10.	ANS:	A	PTS:	1	REF:	12.2.22
11.	ANS:	E	PTS:	1	REF:	12.3.9
12.	ANS:	E	PTS:	1	REF:	12.3.18a
13.	ANS:	B	PTS:	1	REF:	12.3.23
14.	ANS:	A	PTS:	1	REF:	12.3.37
15.	ANS:	B	PTS:	1	REF:	12.3.64
16.	ANS:	C	PTS:	1	REF:	12.4.5
17.	ANS:	B	PTS:	1	REF:	12.4.14
18.	ANS:	B	PTS:	1	REF:	12.4.24
19.	ANS:	A	PTS:	1	REF:	12.4.37b
20.	ANS:	E	PTS:	1	REF:	12.4.54a
21.	ANS:	E	PTS:	1	REF:	12.5.5
22.	ANS:	A	PTS:	1	REF:	12.5.14a
23.	ANS:	A	PTS:	1	REF:	12.5.34
24.	ANS:	D	PTS:	1	REF:	12.5.44
25.	ANS:	A	PTS:	1	REF:	12.5.51

Ch 12 Form C

_____ 1.   Select the correct graph for the following function using a graphing utility.

$$f(x) = \frac{\sqrt{1-x}-7}{x+48}$$

a.

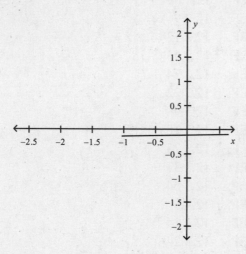

d.

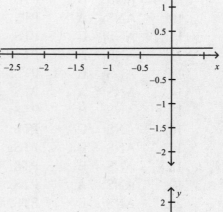

b.

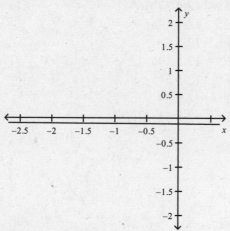

e.

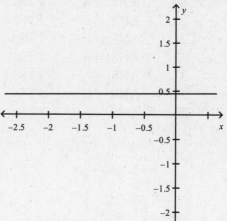

c.

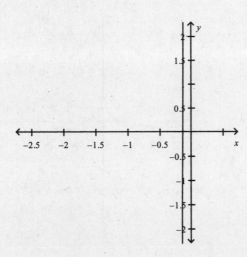

_____ 2.   Select the correct graph for the following function using a graphing utility.

$$f(x) = \frac{\ln\left(x^4\right)}{x - 6}$$

a.

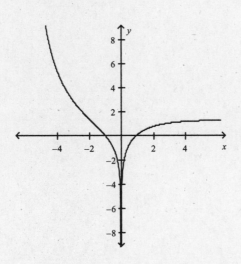

d.

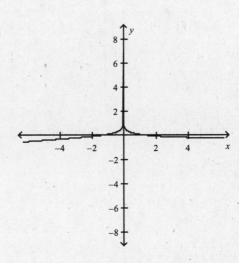

b.

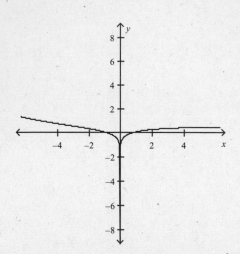

e.

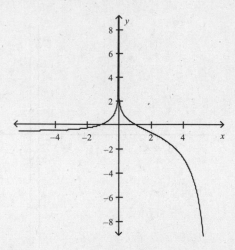

c.

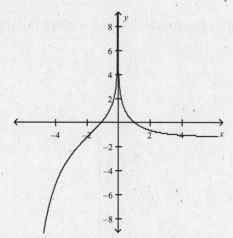

_____ 3.　　　Use the given information to evaluate the limit.

$$\lim_{x \to c} f(x) = 2, \ \lim_{x \to c} g(x) = 7$$
$$\lim_{x \to c} \left[f(x) + g(x) \right]$$

a.　$\lim_{x \to c} \left[f(x) + g(x) \right] = 11$

b.　$\lim_{x \to c} \left[f(x) + g(x) \right] = 2$

c.　$\lim_{x \to c} \left[f(x) + g(x) \right] = 9$

d.　$\lim_{x \to c} \left[f(x) + g(x) \right] = 10$

e.　$\lim_{x \to c} \left[f(x) + g(x) \right] = 7$

_____ 4.   Find the limit by direct substitution.

$$\lim_{x \to -5} \left(\frac{12x}{x^2 + 1} \right)$$

a. $$\lim_{x \to -5} \left(\frac{12x}{x^2 + 1} \right) = \infty$$

b. $$\lim_{x \to -5} \left(\frac{12x}{x^2 + 1} \right) = -\frac{30}{13}$$

c. $$\lim_{x \to -5} \left(\frac{12x}{x^2 + 1} \right) = \frac{57}{26}$$

d. $$\lim_{x \to -5} \left(\frac{12x}{x^2 + 1} \right) = -\frac{26}{57}$$

e. $$\lim_{x \to -5} \left(\frac{12x}{x^2 + 1} \right) = \frac{13}{30}$$

_____ 5.

Use the graph to find

$$\lim_{x \to 3} \frac{4x^2 - 36}{x - 3}$$

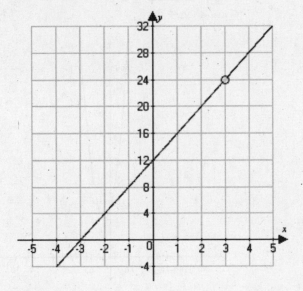

a. ∞

b. 24

c. 0

d. 12

e. limit does not exist

_____ 6.   Find the limit (if it exists). Use a graphing utility to verify your result graphically.

$$\lim_{a \to -4} \frac{a^3 + 64}{a + 4}$$

a.
$$\lim_{a \to -4} \frac{a^3 + 64}{a + 4} = -48$$

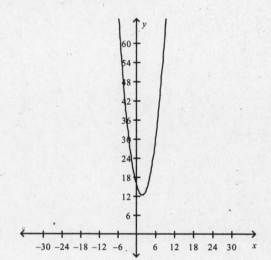

d.
$$\lim_{a \to -4} \frac{a^3 + 64}{a + 4} = 16$$

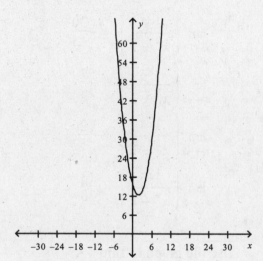

b.
$$\lim_{a \to -4} \frac{a^3 + 64}{a + 4} = 48$$

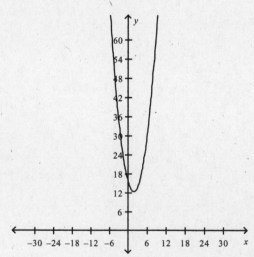

e.
$$\lim_{a \to -4} \frac{a^3 + 64}{a + 4} = -64$$

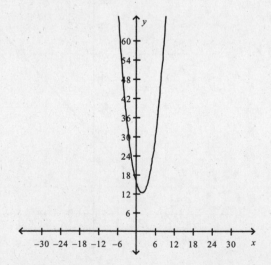

c.

$$\lim_{a \to -4} \frac{a^3 + 64}{a + 4} = 64$$

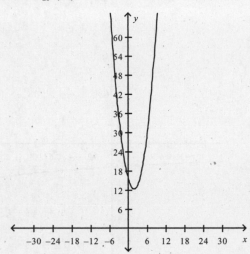

_____ 7.   Find the limit (if it exists). Use a graphing utility to verify your result graphically.

$$\lim_{x \to 0} \frac{\dfrac{1}{x-4} + \dfrac{1}{4}}{x}$$

a.

$$\lim_{x \to 0} \frac{\dfrac{1}{x-4} + \dfrac{1}{4}}{x} = \frac{1}{4}$$

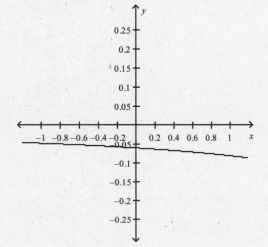

d.

$$\lim_{x \to 0} \frac{\dfrac{1}{x-4} + \dfrac{1}{4}}{x} = \frac{1}{20}$$

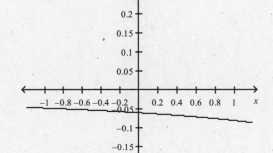

b.

$$\lim_{x \to 0} \frac{\dfrac{1}{x-4} + \dfrac{1}{4}}{x} = -\frac{1}{16}$$

e.

$$\lim_{x \to 0} \frac{\dfrac{1}{x-4} + \dfrac{1}{4}}{x} = -\frac{1}{20}$$

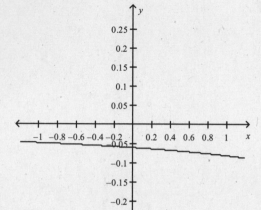

c.

$$\lim_{x \to 0} \frac{\dfrac{1}{x-4} + \dfrac{1}{4}}{x} = \frac{1}{16}$$

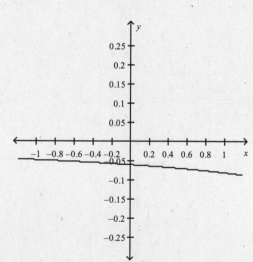

_____ 8. Algebraically evaluate the limit (if it exists) by the appropriate technique(s).

$$\lim_{x \to 5^+} \frac{5-x}{25-x^2}$$

a. $\lim_{x \to 5^+} \frac{5-x}{25-x^2} = \frac{1}{12}$

b. $\lim_{x \to 5^+} \frac{5-x}{25-x^2} = -\frac{1}{12}$

c. $\lim_{x \to 5^+} \frac{5-x}{25-x^2} = \frac{1}{11}$

d. $\lim_{x \to 5^+} \frac{5-x}{25-x^2} = \frac{1}{10}$

e. $\lim_{x \to 5^+} \frac{5-x}{25-x^2} = -\frac{1}{10}$

_____ 9. Find $\lim_{h \to 0} \frac{f(x+h)-f(x)}{h}$.

$$f(x) = \frac{1}{x+3}$$

a. $\lim_{h \to 0} \frac{f(x+h)-f(x)}{h} = \frac{-3}{(x+3)^2}$

b. $\lim_{h \to 0} \frac{f(x+h)-f(x)}{h} = \frac{1}{(x+3)^{-2}}$

c. $\lim_{h \to 0} \frac{f(x+h)-f(x)}{h} = \frac{3}{(x+3)^2}$

d. $\lim_{h \to 0} \frac{f(x+h)-f(x)}{h} = \frac{-1}{(x+3)^2}$

e. $\lim_{h \to 0} \frac{f(x+h)-f(x)}{h} = \frac{-1}{(x+3)^{-2}}$

____ 10.   Find $\lim\limits_{t \to 5} \dfrac{t^3 - 125}{t - 5}$.

a. 50
b. 5
c. limit does not exist
d. 15
e. 75

____ 11.   Use the limit process to find the slope of the graph of the function at the specified point. Use a graphing utility to confirm your result.

$$g(x) = \dfrac{25}{x}, \qquad (5,5)$$

a. $m = -1$
b. $m = 25$
c. $m = -5$
d. $m = 5$
e. $m = -25$

_____ 12. Find a formula for the slope of the graph of f at the point $(x, f(x))$. Then use it to find the slope at the given point.

$$f(x) = \frac{1}{x+4}, \qquad \left(-2, \frac{1}{2}\right)$$

a. $$m = \frac{1}{(x+4)^2}$$

At $\left(-2, \frac{1}{2}\right)$, $m = -\frac{1}{4}$

b. $$m = \frac{1}{(x+4)^2}$$

At $\left(-2, \frac{1}{2}\right)$, $m = \frac{1}{4}$

c. $$m = -\frac{1}{(x+4)^2}$$

At $\left(-2, \frac{1}{2}\right)$, $m = \frac{1}{4}$

d. $$m = -\frac{1}{(x+4)^2}$$

At $\left(-2, \frac{1}{2}\right)$, $m = -\frac{1}{4}$

e. $$m = -\frac{1}{(x+4)}$$

At $\left(-2, \frac{1}{2}\right)$, $m = -\frac{1}{4}$

_____ 13. Find the derivative of the function.

$$f(x) = -7$$

a. -7
b. 7
c. $-7x$
d. 0
e. $7x$

_____   14.   Find the derivative of the function.

$$f(x) = \frac{1}{\sqrt{x - 14}}$$

a. $\dfrac{1}{2(x - 14)^{\frac{3}{2}}}$

b. $\dfrac{1}{2(x + 14)^{\frac{3}{2}}}$

c. $\dfrac{1}{(x + 14)^2}$

d. $\dfrac{1}{2\sqrt{x - 14}}$

e. $-\dfrac{1}{2(x - 14)^{\frac{3}{2}}}$

_____   15.   Use the limit process to find the slope of the graph of $\sqrt{x + 17}$ at $(8, 5)$.

a. $\dfrac{1}{10}$

b. ∞

c. the slope is undefined at this point

d. 5

e. $\dfrac{1}{5}$

_____ 16. Select the correct function for the graph using horizontal asymptotes as aids.

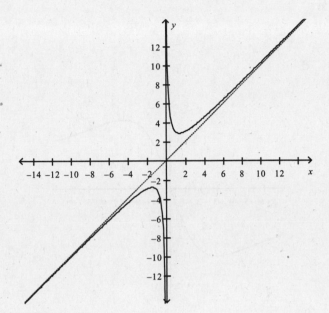

a. $x + \dfrac{2}{x^2}$

b. $x - \dfrac{2}{x}$

c. $2 - \dfrac{1}{x}$

d. $x + \dfrac{2}{x}$

e. $2 + \dfrac{1}{x^2}$

_____ 17. Find the limit (if it exists).

$$\lim_{t \to \infty} \frac{t^2}{t+4}$$

a. $-\dfrac{1}{4}$

b. 0

c. 4

d. $\dfrac{1}{4}$

e. Does not exist

_____ 18.   Select the correct graph of   the following function.

$$y = \frac{x^2}{x^2 + 8}$$

a.

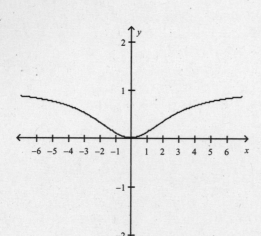

d.

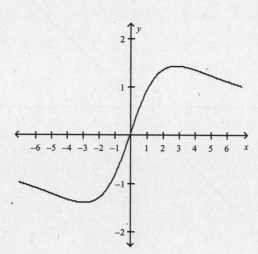

b.

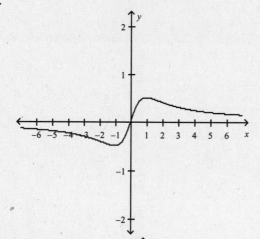

e.

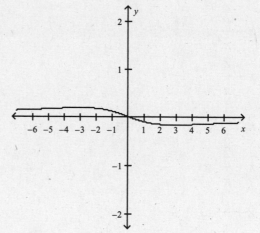

c.

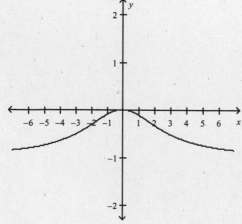

_____   19.   Find the limit of the sequence (if it exists).

$$a_n = \frac{4n}{n^2 + 8}$$

a. $\lim\limits_{n \to \infty} a_n = 0$

b. $\lim\limits_{n \to \infty} a_n = 4$

c. $\lim\limits_{n \to \infty} a_n = 8$

d. $\lim\limits_{n \to \infty} a_n = -4$

e.   Does not exist

_____   20.   Use asymptotes to match

$$f(x) = \frac{3x^2}{x^2 + 2}$$

with its graph.

a.

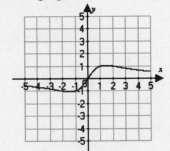

b.

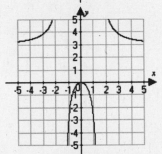

c.

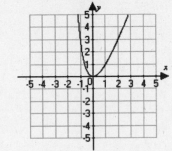

d.

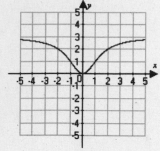

e.

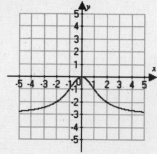

_____ 21.   Evaluate the sum using the summation formula and property.

$$\sum_{k=1}^{20} \left(k^3 + 2 \right)$$

a. 44,040
b. 44,340
c. 44,240
d. 43,940
e. 44,140

_____ 22.   Find $\lim\limits_{n \to \infty} S(n)$.

$$\sum_{i=1}^{n} \frac{i^3}{n^4}$$

a.
$$\lim_{n \to \infty} S(n) = \frac{1}{7}$$

b.
$$\lim_{n \to \infty} S(n) = \frac{1}{6}$$

c.
$$\lim_{n \to \infty} S(n) = \frac{1}{4}$$

d.
$$\lim_{n \to \infty} S(n) = \frac{1}{5}$$

e.
$$\lim_{n \to \infty} S(n) = \frac{1}{8}$$

_____ 23.   Use the limit process to find the area of the region between the graph of the function and the
x-axis over the specified interval.

Function   *Interval*

$f(x) = 3x + 2$ $[0, 2]$

a. $A = 14$ square units
b. $A = 13$ square units
c. $A = 12$ square units
d. $A = 10$ square units
e. $A = 11$ square units

_____   24.   Use $S(n)$ to complete the table.

n	10^0	10^1	10^2	10^3	10^4
$S(n)$					

$$\sum_{i=1}^{n} \frac{3}{n^3}\left(1+i^2\right)$$

(Round the answer to 5 decimal places.)

a.

n	10^0	10^1	10^2	10^3	10^4
$S(n)$	6	1.185	1.01535	1.0015	1.00015

b.

n	10^0	10^1	10^2	10^3	10^4
$S(n)$	1.00015	1.0015	1.01535	1.185	6

c.

n	10^0	10^1	10^2	10^3	10^4
$S(n)$	0	1	2	3	4

d.

n	10^0	10^1	10^2	10^3	10^4
$S(n)$	10	1.185	1.01535	1.0015	1.00015

e.

n	10^0	10^1	10^2	10^3	10^4
$S(n)$	10	100	1,000	10,000	100,000

_____   25.   Evaluate

$$\sum_{j=1}^{25}\left(j^3-4j^2\right)$$

using the summation formulas and properties.
a.   105,621
b.   105,525
c.   103,125
d.   105,625
e.   83,525

Ch 12 Form C
Answer Section

1.	ANS:	B	PTS:	1	REF:	12.1.16
2.	ANS:	E	PTS:	1	REF:	12.1.26
3.	ANS:	C	PTS:	1	REF:	12.1.45b
4.	ANS:	B	PTS:	1	REF:	12.1.55
5.	ANS:	B	PTS:	1	REF:	12.1.30
6.	ANS:	B	PTS:	1	REF:	12.2.16
7.	ANS:	B	PTS:	1	REF:	12.2.30
8.	ANS:	D	PTS:	1	REF:	12.2.50c
9.	ANS:	D	PTS:	1	REF:	12.2.77
10.	ANS:	E	PTS:	1	REF:	12.2.15
11.	ANS:	A	PTS:	1	REF:	12.3.13
12.	ANS:	D	PTS:	1	REF:	12.3.19b
13.	ANS:	D	PTS:	1	REF:	12.3.30
14.	ANS:	E	PTS:	1	REF:	12.3.41
15.	ANS:	A	PTS:	1	REF:	12.3.16
16.	ANS:	D	PTS:	1	REF:	12.4.8
17.	ANS:	E	PTS:	1	REF:	12.4.17
18.	ANS:	A	PTS:	1	REF:	12.4.30
19.	ANS:	A	PTS:	1	REF:	12.4.40
20.	ANS:	D	PTS:	1	REF:	12.4.5
21.	ANS:	E	PTS:	1	REF:	12.5.9
22.	ANS:	C	PTS:	1	REF:	12.5.14c
23.	ANS:	D	PTS:	1	REF:	12.5.38
24.	ANS:	A	PTS:	1	REF:	12.5.15b
25.	ANS:	E	PTS:	1	REF:	12.5.12

Ch 12 Form D

_____ 1.   Select the correct graph for the following function using a graphing utility.

$$f(x) = \frac{\sqrt{1-x} - 3}{x+8}$$

a.

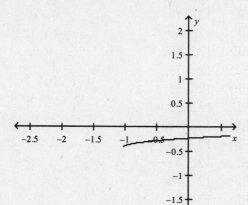

d.

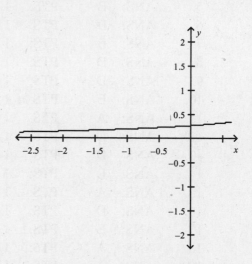

b.

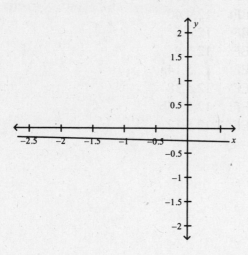

e.

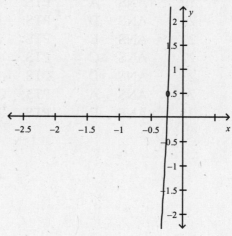

c.

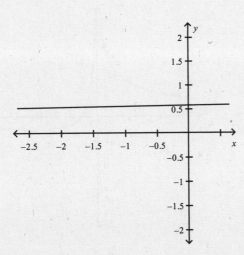

_____ 2.   Select the correct graph for the following function using a graphing utility.

$$f(x) = \frac{\ln\left(x^2\right)}{x-1}$$

a.

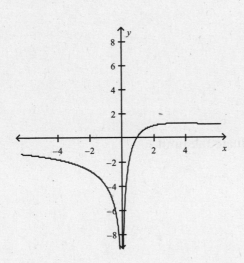

d.

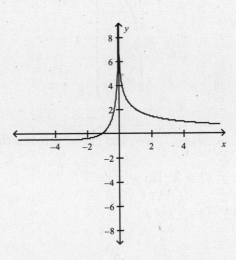

b.

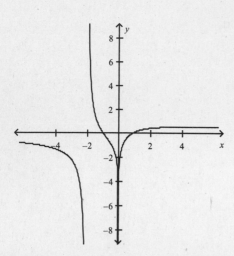

e.

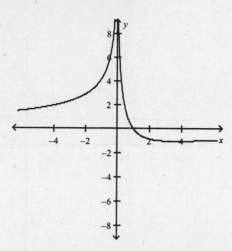

c.

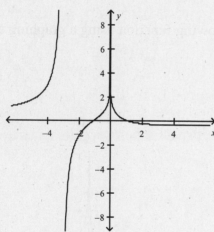

_____   3.   Use the given information to evaluate the limit.

$$\lim_{x \to c} f(x) = 5, \ \lim_{x \to c} g(x) = 7$$

$$\lim_{x \to c} \left[f(x) + g(x) \right]$$

a. $\lim_{x \to c} \left[f(x) + g(x) \right] = 7$

b. $\lim_{x \to c} \left[f(x) + g(x) \right] = 5$

c. $\lim_{x \to c} \left[f(x) + g(x) \right] = 14$

d. $\lim_{x \to c} \left[f(x) + g(x) \right] = 12$

e. $\lim_{x \to c} \left[f(x) + g(x) \right] = 13$

_____ 4.   Find the limit by direct substitution.

$$\lim_{x \to -3} \left(\frac{4x}{x^2 + 1} \right)$$

a.
$$\lim_{x \to -3} \left(\frac{4x}{x^2 + 1} \right) = \frac{5}{6}$$

b.
$$\lim_{x \to -3} \left(\frac{4x}{x^2 + 1} \right) = -\frac{10}{9}$$

c.
$$\lim_{x \to -3} \left(\frac{4x}{x^2 + 1} \right) = \infty$$

d.
$$\lim_{x \to -3} \left(\frac{4x}{x^2 + 1} \right) = -\frac{6}{5}$$

e.
$$\lim_{x \to -3} \left(\frac{4x}{x^2 + 1} \right) = \frac{9}{10}$$

_____ 5.

Use the graph to find

$$\lim_{x \to 4} \frac{5x^2 - 80}{x - 4}$$

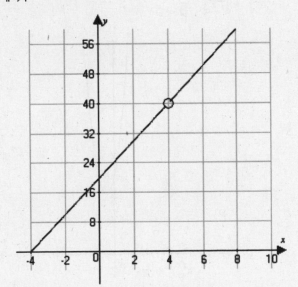

a.   0

b.   20

c.   40

d. ∞

e.   limit does not exist

_____ 6.   Find the limit (if it exists). Use a graphing utility to verify your result graphically.

$$\lim_{a \to -5} \frac{a^3 + 125}{a + 5}$$

a.
$$\lim_{a \to -5} \frac{a^3 + 125}{a + 5} = -75$$

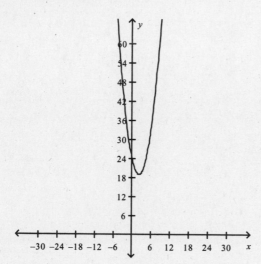

d.
$$\lim_{a \to -5} \frac{a^3 + 125}{a + 5} = 75$$

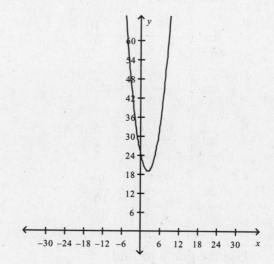

b.
$$\lim_{a \to -5} \frac{a^3 + 125}{a + 5} = 125$$

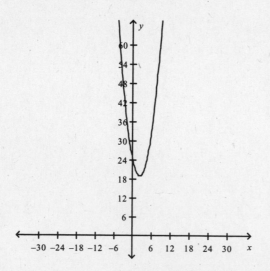

e.
$$\lim_{a \to -5} \frac{a^3 + 125}{a + 5} = -125$$

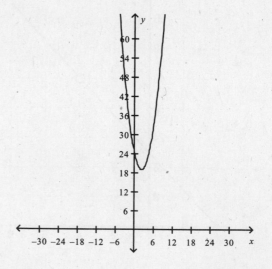

c.

$$\lim_{a \to -5} \frac{a^3 + 125}{a + 5} = 25$$

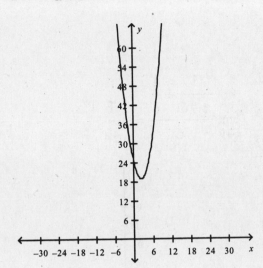

_____ 7.   Find the limit (if it exists). Use a graphing utility to verify your result graphically.

$$\lim_{x \to 0} \frac{\dfrac{1}{x-6} + \dfrac{1}{6}}{x}$$

a. $\lim_{x \to 0} \dfrac{\dfrac{1}{x-6} + \dfrac{1}{6}}{x} = -\dfrac{1}{36}$

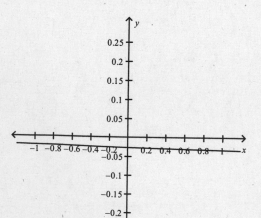

d. $\lim_{x \to 0} \dfrac{\dfrac{1}{x-6} + \dfrac{1}{6}}{x} = -\dfrac{1}{42}$

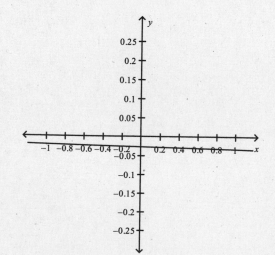

b. $\lim_{x \to 0} \dfrac{\dfrac{1}{x-6} + \dfrac{1}{6}}{x} = \dfrac{1}{36}$

e. $\lim_{x \to 0} \dfrac{\dfrac{1}{x-6} + \dfrac{1}{6}}{x} = \dfrac{1}{6}$

c.

$$\lim_{x \to 0} \frac{\dfrac{1}{x-6} + \dfrac{1}{6}}{x} = \frac{1}{42}$$

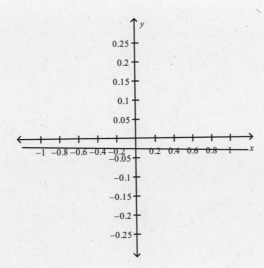

_____ 8. Algebraically evaluate the limit (if it exists) by the appropriate technique(s).

$$\lim_{x \to 5^+} \frac{5-x}{25-x^2}$$

a. $\displaystyle \lim_{x \to 5^+} \frac{5-x}{25-x^2} = -\frac{1}{12}$

b. $\displaystyle \lim_{x \to 5^+} \frac{5-x}{25-x^2} = \frac{1}{12}$

c. $\displaystyle \lim_{x \to 5^+} \frac{5-x}{25-x^2} = \frac{1}{11}$

d. $\displaystyle \lim_{x \to 5^+} \frac{5-x}{25-x^2} = -\frac{1}{10}$

e. $\displaystyle \lim_{x \to 5^+} \frac{5-x}{25-x^2} = \frac{1}{10}$

_____   9.   Find $\lim\limits_{h \to 0} \dfrac{f(x+h)-f(x)}{h}$.

$$f(x) = \dfrac{1}{x+3}$$

a. $\lim\limits_{h \to 0} \dfrac{f(x+h)-f(x)}{h} = \dfrac{3}{(x+3)^2}$

b. $\lim\limits_{h \to 0} \dfrac{f(x+h)-f(x)}{h} = \dfrac{-1}{(x+3)^{-2}}$

c. $\lim\limits_{h \to 0} \dfrac{f(x+h)-f(x)}{h} = \dfrac{1}{(x+3)^{-2}}$

d. $\lim\limits_{h \to 0} \dfrac{f(x+h)-f(x)}{h} = \dfrac{-1}{(x+3)^2}$

e. $\lim\limits_{h \to 0} \dfrac{f(x+h)-f(x)}{h} = \dfrac{-3}{(x+3)^2}$

_____   10.   Find $\lim\limits_{t \to 9} \dfrac{t^3 - 729}{t-9}$.

a. 243
b. 9
c. 162
d. limit does not exist
e. 27

_____   11.   Use the limit process to find the slope of the graph of the function at the specified point. Use a graphing utility to confirm your result.

$$g(x) = \dfrac{25}{x}, \qquad (5,5)$$

a. $m = 5$
b. $m = -5$
c. $m = -25$
d. $m = -1$
e. $m = 25$

_____   12.   Find a formula for the slope of the graph of f at the point $(x, f(x))$. Then use it to find the slope at the given point.

$$f(x) = \frac{1}{x+5}, \qquad \left(-2, \frac{1}{2}\right)$$

a. $m = \dfrac{1}{(x+5)^2}$

    At $\left(-2, \dfrac{1}{2}\right)$, $m = \dfrac{1}{9}$

b. $m = -\dfrac{1}{(x+5)^2}$

    At $\left(-2, \dfrac{1}{2}\right)$, $m = \dfrac{1}{9}$

c. $m = -\dfrac{1}{(x+5)^2}$

    At $\left(-2, \dfrac{1}{2}\right)$, $m = -\dfrac{1}{9}$

d. $m = -\dfrac{1}{(x+5)}$

    At $\left(-2, \dfrac{1}{2}\right)$, $m = -\dfrac{1}{9}$

e. $m = \dfrac{1}{(x+5)^2}$

    At $\left(-2, \dfrac{1}{2}\right)$, $m = -\dfrac{1}{9}$

_____   13.   Find the derivative of the function.

$$f(x) = -4$$

a. $-4x$
b. -4
c. $4x$
d. 4
e. 0

_____ 14.   Find the derivative of the function.

$$f(x) = \frac{1}{\sqrt{x} - 15}$$

a. $\dfrac{1}{2\sqrt{x} - 15}$

b. $\dfrac{1}{2(x+15)^{\frac{3}{2}}}$

c. $\dfrac{1}{(x+15)^2}$

d. $\dfrac{1}{2(x-15)^{\frac{3}{2}}}$

e. $-\dfrac{1}{2(x-15)^{\frac{3}{2}}}$

_____ 15.   Use the limit process to find the slope of the graph of $\sqrt{x+2}$ at (2, 2).

a. $\dfrac{1}{4}$

b.   the slope is undefined at this point

c.   2

d. $\dfrac{1}{2}$

e. ∞

_____ 16.   Select the correct function for the graph using horizontal asymptotes as aids.

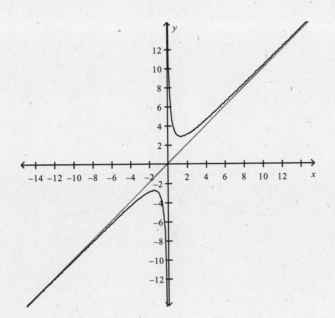

a. $x - \dfrac{2}{x}$

b. $x + \dfrac{2}{x}$

c. $2 + \dfrac{1}{x^2}$

d. $2 - \dfrac{1}{x}$

e. $x + \dfrac{2}{x^2}$

_____ 17.   Find the limit (if it exists).

$$\lim_{t \to \infty} \frac{t^2}{t+3}$$

a. 3

b. 0

c. Does not exist

d. $-\dfrac{1}{3}$

e. $\dfrac{1}{3}$

_____ 18.   Select the correct graph of the following function.

$$y = \frac{x^2}{x^2 + 6}$$

a.

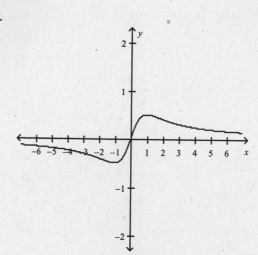

d.

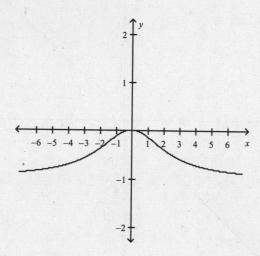

b.

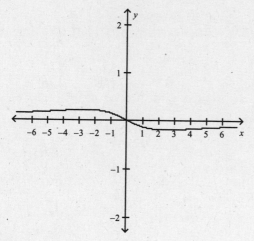

e.

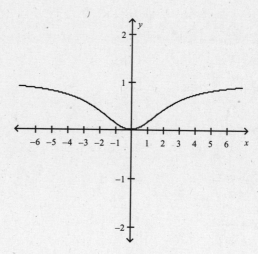

c.

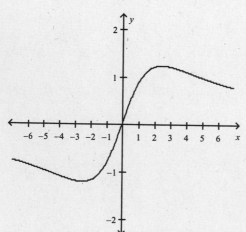

_____ 19.   Find the limit of the sequence (if it exists).

$$a_n = \frac{6n}{n^2 + 5}$$

a. $\lim_{n \to \infty} a_n = -6$

b. $\lim_{n \to \infty} a_n = 5$

c. $\lim_{n \to \infty} a_n = 0$

d.   Does not exist

e. $\lim_{n \to \infty} a_n = 6$

_____ 20.   Use asymptotes to match

$$f(x) = \frac{3x^2}{x^2 - 2}$$

with its graph.

a.

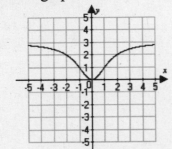

b.

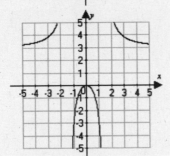

c.

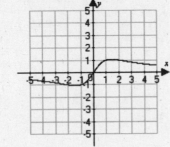

d.

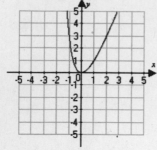

e.

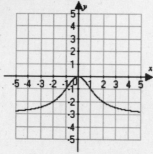

_____ 21.   Evaluate the sum using the summation formula and property.

$$\sum_{k-1}^{30}\left(k^3+9\right)$$

a. 216,595
b. 216,295
c. 216,395
d. 216,495
e. 216,695

_____ 22. Find $\lim\limits_{n \to \infty} S(n)$.

$$\sum_{i=1}^{n} \frac{i^3}{n^4}$$

a. $\lim\limits_{n \to \infty} S(n) = \dfrac{1}{6}$

b. $\lim\limits_{n \to \infty} S(n) = \dfrac{1}{8}$

c. $\lim\limits_{n \to \infty} S(n) = \dfrac{1}{7}$

d. $\lim\limits_{n \to \infty} S(n) = \dfrac{1}{5}$

e. $\lim\limits_{n \to \infty} S(n) = \dfrac{1}{4}$

_____ 23. Use the limit process to find the area of the region between the graph of the function and the
x-axis over the specified interval.

Function	Interval
$f(x) = 3x + 3$	$[0, 2]$

a. $A = 13$ square units
b. $A = 16$ square units
c. $A = 14$ square units
d. $A = 15$ square units
e. $A = 12$ square units

____   24.   Use $S(n)$ to complete the table.

n	8^0	8^1	8^2	8^3	8^4
$S(n)$					

$$\sum_{i-1}^{n} \frac{3}{n^3}\left(1+i^2\right)$$

(Round the answer to 5 decimal places.)

a.

n	8^0	8^1	8^2	8^3	8^4
$S(n)$	10	100	1,000	10,000	100,000

b.

n	8^0	8^1	8^2	8^3	8^4
$S(n)$	1.00037	1.00294	1.02429	1.24219	6

c.

n	8^0	8^1	8^2	8^3	8^4
$S(n)$	0	1	2	3	4

d.

n	8^0	8^1	8^2	8^3	8^4
$S(n)$	6	1.24219	1.02429	1.00294	1.00037

e.

n	8^0	8^1	8^2	8^3	8^4
$S(n)$	10	1.24219	1.02429	1.00294	1.00037

____   25.   Evaluate

$$\sum_{j-1}^{15}\left(j^3-5j^2\right)$$

using the summation formulas and properties.
a. 14,325
b. 14,400
c. 13,275
d. 14,395
e. 8,200

Ch 12 Form D
Answer Section

1.	ANS:	B	PTS:	1	REF:	12.1.16
2.	ANS:	D	PTS:	1	REF:	12.1.26
3.	ANS:	D	PTS:	1	REF:	12.1.45b
4.	ANS:	D	PTS:	1	REF:	12.1.55
5.	ANS:	C	PTS:	1	REF:	12.1.30
6.	ANS:	D	PTS:	1	REF:	12.2.16
7.	ANS:	A	PTS:	1	REF:	12.2.30
8.	ANS:	E	PTS:	1	REF:	12.2.50c
9.	ANS:	D	PTS:	1	REF:	12.2.77
10.	ANS:	A	PTS:	1	REF:	12.2.15
11.	ANS:	D	PTS:	1	REF:	12.3.13
12.	ANS:	C	PTS:	1	REF:	12.3.19b
13.	ANS:	E	PTS:	1	REF:	12.3.30
14.	ANS:	E	PTS:	1	REF:	12.3.41
15.	ANS:	A	PTS:	1	REF:	12.3.16
16.	ANS:	B	PTS:	1	REF:	12.4.8
17.	ANS:	C	PTS:	1	REF:	12.4.17
18.	ANS:	E	PTS:	1	REF:	12.4.30
19.	ANS:	C	PTS:	1	REF:	12.4.40
20.	ANS:	B	PTS:	1	REF:	12.4.5
21.	ANS:	D	PTS:	1	REF:	12.5.9
22.	ANS:	E	PTS:	1	REF:	12.5.14c
23.	ANS:	E	PTS:	1	REF:	12.5.38
24.	ANS:	D	PTS:	1	REF:	12.5.15b
25.	ANS:	E	PTS:	1	REF:	12.5.12

Ch 12 Form E

_____   1.   Select the correct graph for the following function using a graphing utility.

$$f(x) = \frac{\sin 3x}{3x}$$

a.

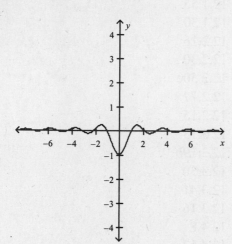

d.

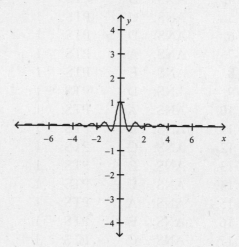

b.

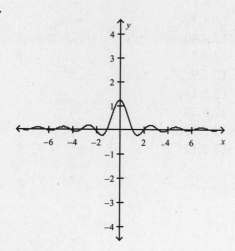

e.

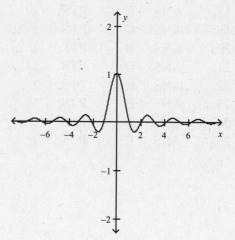

c.

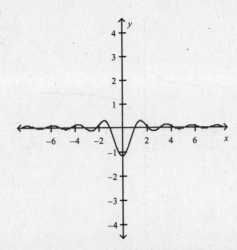

_____ 2. Select the correct graph for the following function using a graphing utility. Determine whether the limit exists or not.

$$f(x) = \frac{6}{2 + e^{1/x}}, \quad \lim_{x \to 0} f(x)$$

a.

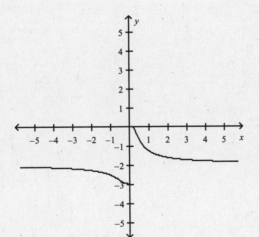

$$\lim_{x \to 0} f(x) = \ln 6$$

d.

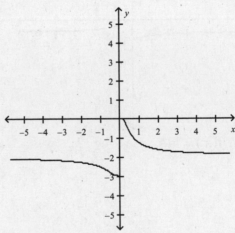

$$\lim_{x \to 0} f(x) \text{ does not exist.}$$

b.

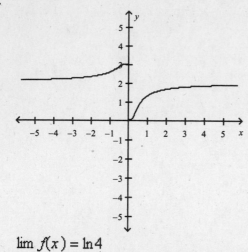

$$\lim_{x \to 0} f(x) = \ln 4$$

e.

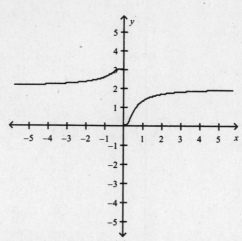

$$\lim_{x \to 0} f(x) \text{ does not exist.}$$

c.

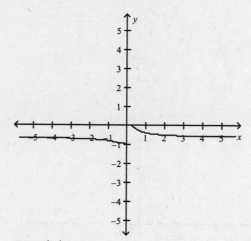

$$\lim_{x \to 0} f(x) = \ln 4.$$

_____ 3. Find $\lim\limits_{x \to 2} g(x)$.

$$g(x) = \frac{\sqrt{x^2 + 21}}{10x^2}$$

a. $\lim\limits_{x \to 2} g(x) = \infty$

b. $\lim\limits_{x \to 2} g(x) = \dfrac{1}{5}$

c. $\lim\limits_{x \to 2} g(x) = 8$

d. $\lim\limits_{x \to 2} g(x) = \dfrac{1}{8}$

e. $\lim\limits_{x \to 2} g(x) = 5$

_____ 4. Find the limit by direct substitution.

$$\lim_{x \to 24} \frac{\sqrt{x + 1}}{x - 15}$$

a. $\lim\limits_{x \to 24} \dfrac{\sqrt{x + 1}}{x - 15} = -\dfrac{5}{9}$

b. $\lim\limits_{x \to 24} \dfrac{\sqrt{x + 1}}{x - 15} = 3$

c. $\lim\limits_{x \to 24} \dfrac{\sqrt{x + 1}}{x - 15} = \infty$

d. $\lim\limits_{x \to 24} \dfrac{\sqrt{x + 1}}{x - 15} = \dfrac{5}{9}$

e. $\lim\limits_{x \to 24} \dfrac{\sqrt{x + 1}}{x - 15} = -3$

_____ 5.   Find

$$\lim_{x \to 5} \left[g(x) - f(x) \right]$$

for $f(x) = 4x^3$ and $g(x) = \dfrac{\sqrt{x^2 + 5}}{3x^2}$.

a. $\dfrac{\sqrt{30}}{75} - 500$

b. $\dfrac{\sqrt{6}}{3} - 500$

c. $\dfrac{20\sqrt{30}}{3}$

d. limit does not exist

e. $\dfrac{\sqrt{6}}{3} + 500$

_____   6.   Use the graph to determine the limit visually (if it exists). Then identify another function that

agrees with the given function at all but one point.

$$g(x) = \frac{x^3 - x}{x - 1}$$

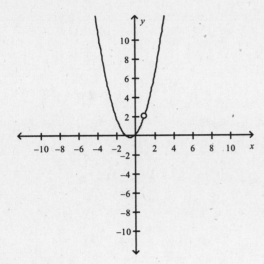

$$\lim_{x \to 1} g(x) = ?$$

a. $g_2(x) = x(x+1)$

$$\lim_{x \to 1} g(x) = 2$$

b. $g_2(x) = 3x^2 + 1$

$$\lim_{x \to 1} g(x) = 4$$

c. $g_2(x) = 3x^2 - 1$

$$\lim_{x \to 1} g(x) = 2$$

d. $g_2(x) = x(x-1)$

$$\lim_{x \to 1} g(x) = 0$$

e. $g_2(x) = x(x+1)$

$$\lim_{x \to 1} g(x) = -2$$

_____ 7.   Find the limit (if it exists).

$$\lim_{x \to \pi/2} \frac{3(\cos x - 1)}{\sin x}$$

a. $$\lim_{x \to \pi/2} \frac{3(\cos x - 1)}{\sin x} = -9$$

b. $$\lim_{x \to \pi/2} \frac{3(\cos x - 1)}{\sin x} = -3$$

c. $$\lim_{x \to \pi/2} \frac{3(\cos x - 1)}{\sin x} = 12$$

d. $$\lim_{x \to \pi/2} \frac{3(\cos x - 1)}{\sin x} = 9$$

e. $$\lim_{x \to \pi/2} \frac{3(\cos x - 1)}{\sin x} = 3$$

_____ 8.   Find $\lim_{h \to 0} \dfrac{f(x+h) - f(x)}{h}$.

$$f(x) = 7x + 1$$

a. $$\lim_{h \to 0} \frac{f(x+h) - f(x)}{h} = -8$$

b. $$\lim_{h \to 0} \frac{f(x+h) - f(x)}{h} = 7$$

c. $$\lim_{h \to 0} \frac{f(x+h) - f(x)}{h} = 6$$

d. $$\lim_{h \to 0} \frac{f(x+h) - f(x)}{h} = 8$$

e. $$\lim_{h \to 0} \frac{f(x+h) - f(x)}{h} = -7$$

_____ 9. Graphically approximate the limit (if it exists) by using a graphing utility to graph the function.

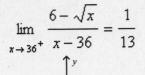
$$\lim_{x \to 36^+} \frac{6 - \sqrt{x}}{x - 36}$$

a.
$$\lim_{x \to 36^+} \frac{6 - \sqrt{x}}{x - 36} = \frac{1}{13}$$

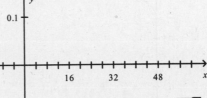

d.
$$\lim_{x \to 36^+} \frac{6 - \sqrt{x}}{x - 36} = -\frac{1}{12}$$

b.
$$\lim_{x \to 36^+} \frac{6 - \sqrt{x}}{x - 36} = \frac{1}{14}$$

e.
$$\lim_{x \to 36^+} \frac{6 - \sqrt{x}}{x - 36} = -\frac{1}{14}$$

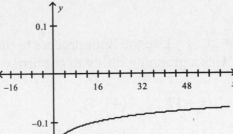

c.
$$\lim_{x \to 36^+} \frac{6 - \sqrt{x}}{x - 36} = \frac{1}{12}$$

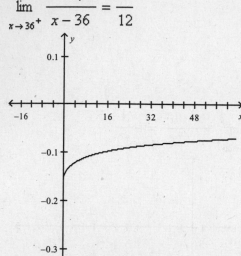

_____ 10.   Determine

$\lim_{x \to 1} f(x)$ where $f(x) = \begin{cases} 8 - x^2, & x \leq 1 \\ 3 - x, & x > 1 \end{cases}$

(if it exists) by evaluating the corresponding one-sided limits.
a.   limit does not exist
b.   2
c.   3
d.   7
e.   8

_____ 11.   Use the limit process to find the slope of the graph of the function at the specified point. Use a graphing utility to confirm your result.

$h(x) = \sqrt{x + 17}, \qquad (-1, 4)$

a. $m = -\dfrac{1}{8}$

b. $m = 16$

c. $m = \dfrac{1}{8}$

d. $m = -4$

e. $m = 4$

_____ 12. Find a formula for the slope of the graph of f at the point $\left(x, f(x)\right)$. Then use it to find the slope at the given point.

$$f(x) = \sqrt{x - 1}, \qquad (5, 2)$$

a. $m = \dfrac{1}{\sqrt{x - 1}}$

At $(5, 2)$, $m = \dfrac{1}{4}$

b. $m = \dfrac{1}{2\sqrt{x - 1}}$

At $(5, 2)$, $m = \dfrac{1}{4}$

c. $m = \dfrac{1}{2\sqrt{x - 1}}$

At $(5, 2)$, $m = -\dfrac{1}{4}$

d. $m = -\dfrac{1}{2\sqrt{x - 1}}$

At $(5, 2)$, $m = \dfrac{1}{4}$

e. $m = -\dfrac{1}{2\sqrt{x - 1}}$

At $(5, 2)$, $m = -\dfrac{1}{4}$

_____ 13. Find the derivative of the function.

$$f(x) = 4 - 3x^2$$

a. $-\dfrac{1}{3}$

b. $6x$

c. $\dfrac{1}{3}$

d. $-6x$

e. $3x$

_____   14.   Use the slope $m = 4$ to find an equation of the tangent line to the graph at the given point.

$f(x) = x^2 - 1, \ (2, 3)$

a. $y = 4x + 2$
b. $y = 4x - 5$
c. $y = 4x + 5$
d. $y = 4x - 2$
e. $y = 4x - 4$

_____   15.   Find a formula for the slope of the graph of $f(x) = \dfrac{2}{x+7}$.

a. $\dfrac{2}{(x+7)^2}$

b. $\dfrac{2}{x+7}$

c. $-\dfrac{1}{2(x+7)^2}$

d. $-\dfrac{2}{(x+7)^2}$

e. $-\dfrac{2}{x+7}$

_____   16.   Find the limit (if it exists).

$\lim\limits_{x \to \infty} \left(\dfrac{5-x}{5+x} \right)$

a.   5
b. -1
c.   1
d. -5
e.   Does not exist

_____   17.   Find the limit (if it exists).

$\lim\limits_{x \to -\infty} \dfrac{-\left(x^2 + 4\right)}{(2-x)^2}$

a.   2
b. -1
c.   1
d.   0
e.   Does not exist

_____ 18. Select correct graph of the following function.

$$y = 7 - \frac{4}{x^2}$$

a.

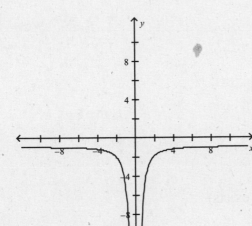

d.

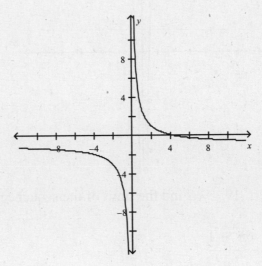

b.

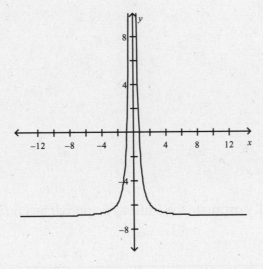

e.

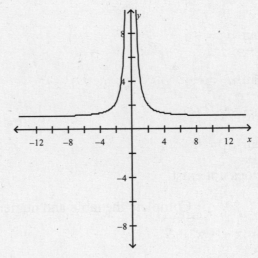

c.

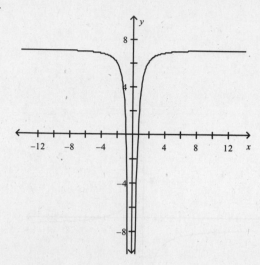

_____ 19.   Find the limit of the sequence (if it exists).

$$a_n = \frac{6n^2 + 1}{2n}$$

a. $\lim\limits_{n \to \infty} a_n = -6$

b. $\lim\limits_{n \to \infty} a_n = \frac{1}{2}$

c. $\lim\limits_{n \to \infty} a_n = 6$

d. $\lim\limits_{n \to \infty} a_n = 0$

e.   Does not exist

_____ 20.   Complete the table and numerically estimate the limit as x approaches infinity for
$f(x) = x - \sqrt{x^2 + 5}$.

x	10^0	10^1	10^2	10^3	10^4	10^5	10^6
$f(x)$							

a.   0
b.   limit does not exist
c.   5
d.   −5
e.   ∞

_____ 21. Evaluate the sum using the summation formula and property.

$$\sum_{j=1}^{10}\left(j^3 - 3j^2\right)$$

a. 1,970
b. 1,770
c. 2,070
d. 1,670
e. 1,870

____ 22.   Complete the table using the function $f(x)$, over the specified interval $[a,b]$ to approximate the area of the region bounded by the graph of $y = f(x)$, the x-axis, and the vertical lines $x = a$ and $x = b$ using the indicated number of rectangles. Then find the exact area as $n \to \infty$.

n	4	8	20	50	100	∞
Approximate area						

Function   Interval

$f(x) = 23 - 2x$ $[2,6]$

(Round the answer to two decimal places.)

a.

n	4	8	20	50	100	∞
Approximate area	57	58	59.2	59.68	59.84	60

b.

n	4	8	20	50	100	∞
Approximate area	60	58	59.2	59.68	59.84	60

c.

n	4	8	20	50	100	∞
Approximate area	58	58	59.2	59.68	59.84	60

d.

n	4	8	20	50	100	∞
Approximate area	56	58	59.2	59.68	59.84	60

e.

n	4	8	20	50	100	∞
Approximate area	59	58	59.2	59.68	59.84	60

_____ 23.   Use the limit process to find the area of the region between the graph of the function and the
x-axis over the specified interval.

   Function   *Interval*

$f(x) = 2 - x^2$ $[-1, 1]$

a.
$A = \dfrac{22}{3}$ square units

b.
$A = \dfrac{19}{3}$ square units

c.
$A = \dfrac{16}{3}$ square units

d.
$A = \dfrac{13}{3}$ square units

e.
$A = \dfrac{10}{3}$ square units

_____ 24.   Use $S(n)$ to complete the table.

n	8^0	8^1	8^2	8^3	8^4
$S(n)$					

$$\sum_{i=1}^{n} \left(\frac{i^2}{n^3} + \frac{2}{n} \right)\left(\frac{1}{n} \right)$$

(Round the answer to 5 decimal places.)

a.

n	8^0	8^1	8^2	8^3	8^4
$S(n)$	3	0.2998	0.03658	0.00456	0.00057

b.

n	8^0	8^1	8^2	8^3	8^4
$S(n)$	0.00057	0.00456	0.03658	0.2998	3

c.

n	8^0	8^1	8^2	8^3	8^4
$S(n)$	0	1	2	3	4

d.

n	8^0	8^1	8^2	8^3	8^4
$S(n)$	10	0.2998	0.03658	0.00456	0.00057

e.

n	8^0	8^1	8^2	8^3	8^4
$S(n)$	10	100	1,000	10,000	100,000

_____ 25. Approximate the area of the indicated region under the given curve using five rectangles.

$f(x) = 5 - x^2$

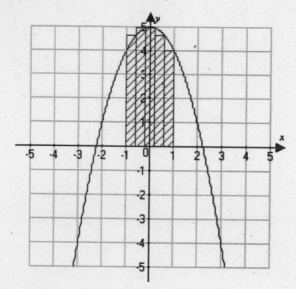

a. 4.83
b. 9.25
c. 5.48
d. 9.28
e. 4.64

Ch 12 Form E
Answer Section

1.	ANS:	E	PTS:	1	REF:	12.1.19
2.	ANS:	E	PTS:	1	REF:	12.1.37
3.	ANS:	D	PTS:	1	REF:	12.1.47b
4.	ANS:	D	PTS:	1	REF:	12.1.62
5.	ANS:	A	PTS:	1	REF:	12.1.47d
6.	ANS:	A	PTS:	1	REF:	12.2.7
7.	ANS:	B	PTS:	1	REF:	12.2.36
8.	ANS:	B	PTS:	1	REF:	12.2.71
9.	ANS:	D	PTS:	1	REF:	12.2.53a
10.	ANS:	A	PTS:	1	REF:	12.2.59
11.	ANS:	C	PTS:	1	REF:	12.3.16
12.	ANS:	B	PTS:	1	REF:	12.3.21a
13.	ANS:	D	PTS:	1	REF:	12.3.33
14.	ANS:	B	PTS:	1	REF:	12.3.43b
15.	ANS:	D	PTS:	1	REF:	12.3.19
16.	ANS:	B	PTS:	1	REF:	12.4.11
17.	ANS:	B	PTS:	1	REF:	12.4.21
18.	ANS:	C	PTS:	1	REF:	12.4.33
19.	ANS:	E	PTS:	1	REF:	12.4.44
20.	ANS:	A	PTS:	1	REF:	12.4.35
21.	ANS:	E	PTS:	1	REF:	12.5.12
22.	ANS:	D	PTS:	1	REF:	12.5.32
23.	ANS:	E	PTS:	1	REF:	12.5.41
24.	ANS:	A	PTS:	1	REF:	12.5.17b
25.	ANS:	D	PTS:	1	REF:	12.5.22

Ch 12 Form F

_____ 1.   Select the correct graph for the following function using a graphing utility.

$$f(x) = \frac{\sin 3x}{3x}$$

a.

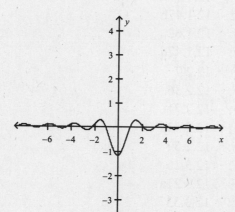

d.

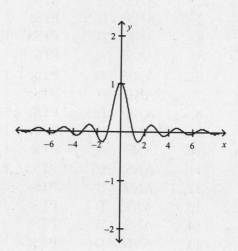

b.

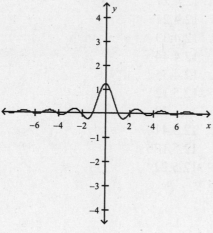

e.

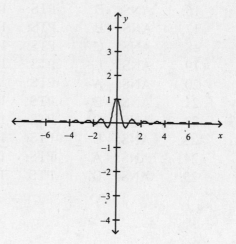

c.

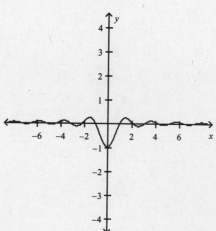

_____ 2.   Select the correct graph for the following function using a graphing utility. Determine whether the limit exists or not.

$$f(x) = \frac{8}{5 + e^{1/x}}, \quad \lim_{x \to 0} f(x)$$

a.

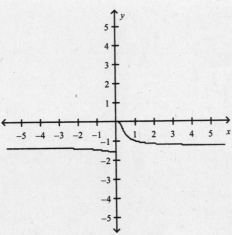

$$\lim_{x \to 0} f(x) \text{ does not exist.}$$

d.

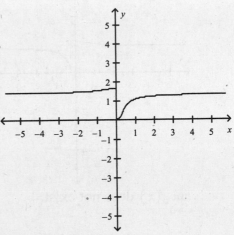

$$\lim_{x \to 0} f(x) = \ln 3$$

b.

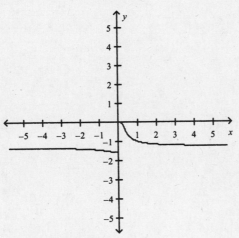

$$\lim_{x \to 0} f(x) = \ln 8$$

e.

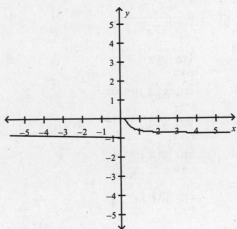

$$\lim_{x \to 0} f(x) = \ln 3.$$

c.

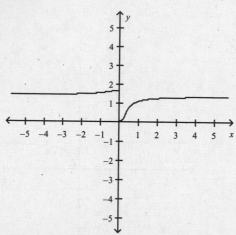

$$\lim_{x \to 0} f(x) \text{ does not exist.}$$

_____   3.   Find $\lim_{x \to 2} g(x)$.

$$g(x) = \frac{\sqrt{x^2 + 12}}{7x^2}$$

a. $\lim_{x \to 2} g(x) = \frac{1}{7}$

b. $\lim_{x \to 2} g(x) = \infty$

c. $\lim_{x \to 2} g(x) = 7$

d. $\lim_{x \to 2} g(x) = 4$

e. $\lim_{x \to 2} g(x) = \frac{1}{4}$